THE
KASHMIR SHAWL

Ladies' Library Association.

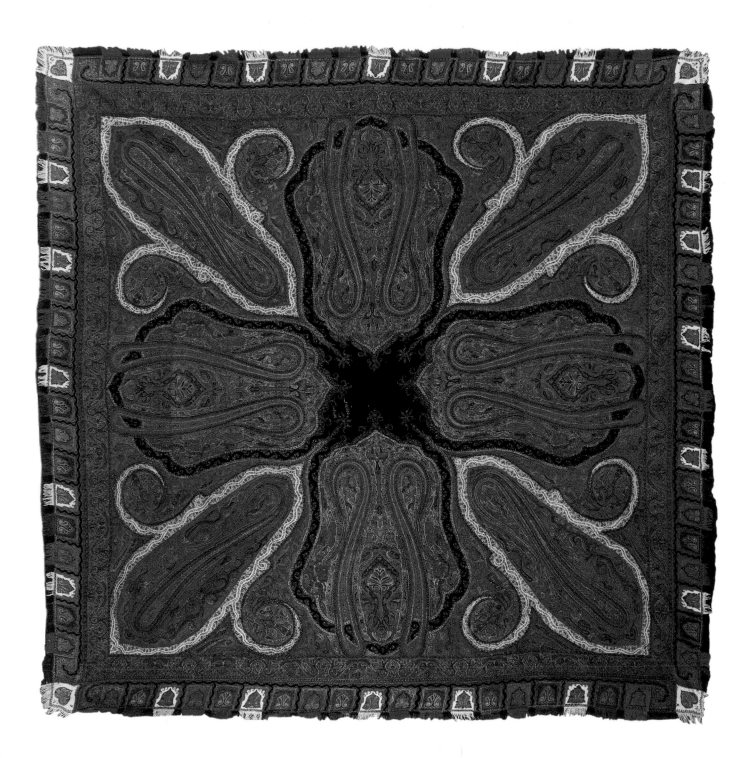

THE KASHMIR SHAWL

and its Indo-French Influence

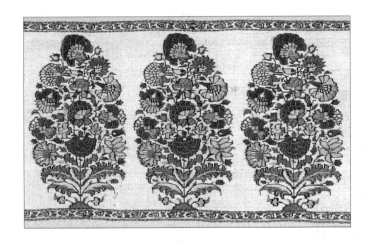

FRANK AMES

ANTIQUE COLLECTORS' CLUB

British Library Cataloguing-in-Publication Data
A catalogue record for this book is available from the British Library

Printed in England
by the Antique Collectors' Club Ltd., Woodbridge, Suffolk
on Consort Royal Era Satin paper
supplied by the Donside Paper Company, Aberdeen, Scotland

FRONTISPIECE: *Rumal, shoulder mantle, Dogra period, c.1870. See Plate 166.*

To My Parents

Shawl Routes of the Orient

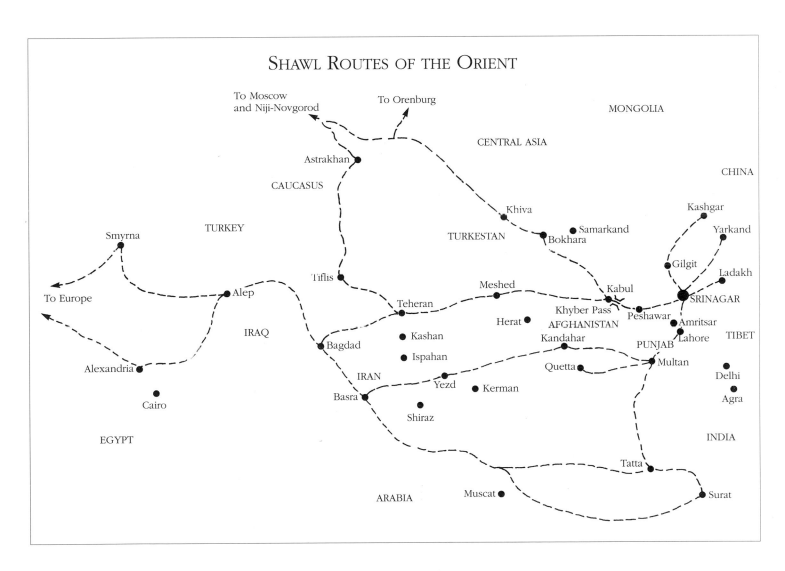

ANTIQUE COLLECTORS' CLUB

The Antique Collectors' Club was formed in 1966 and now has a five figure membership spread throughout the world. It publishes the only independently run monthly antiques magazine, *Antique Collecting*, which caters for those collectors who are interested in widening their knowledge of antiques, both by greater awareness of quality and by discussion of the factors which influence the price that is likely to be asked. The Antique Collectors' Club pioneered the provision of information on prices for collectors and the magazine still leads in the provision of detailed articles on a variety of subjects.

It was in response to the enormous demand for information on 'what to pay' that the price guide series was introduced in 1968 with the first edition of *The Price Guide to Antique Furniture* (completely revised 1978 and 1989), a book which broke new ground by illustrating the more common types of antique furniture, the sort that collectors could buy in shops and at auctions rather than the rare museum pieces which had previously been used (and still to a large extent are used) to make up the limited amount of illustrations in books published by commercial publishers. Many other price guides have followed, all copiously illustrated, and greatly appreciated by collectors for the valuable information they contain, quite apart from prices. The Antique Collectors' Club also publishes other books on antiques (including horology and art), garden history and architecture, and a full book list is available.

Club membership, open to all collectors, costs little. Members receive free of charge *Antique Collecting*, the Club's magazine (published ten times a year), which contains well-illustrated articles dealing with the practical aspects of collecting not normally dealt with by magazines. Prices, features of value, investment potential, fakes and forgeries are all given prominence in the magazine.

Among other facilities available to members are private buying and selling facilities and the opportunity to meet other collectors at their local antique collectors' clubs. There are over eighty in Britain and more than a dozen overseas. Members may also buy the Club's publications at special pre-publication prices.

As its motto implies, the Club is an organisation designed to help collectors get the most out of their hobby: it is informal and friendly and gives enormous enjoyment to all concerned.

For Collectors — By Collectors — About Collecting

THE ANTIQUE COLLECTORS' CLUB
5 CHURCH STREET, WOODBRIDGE, SUFFOLK IP12 1DS, ENGLAND

ACKNOWLEDGEMENTS

I am very grateful to the many persons who shared generously of their time, knowledge and enthusiasm in the production of this book, and I am deeply indebted to those private and public institutions who generously permitted the illustration of their shawls.

In France, great thanks are due to my friend Dr. Jim Williams whose unstinting help and expert advice on the initial organisation of the book was of invaluable assistance to me. Without Jim's vast knowledge of carpets and of things Oriental this project might never have seen the light of day; to Madame Krishna Riboud, president and founder of Association pour l'Etude et la Documentation des Textiles d'Asie (AEDTA), I am particularly thankful for the liberal access to her museum's rich holdings. AEDTA, under the efficient administration of Frédérique Delbecq, offered me a unique atmosphere for the study of Asian textiles in Paris; Madame Jacqueline Jacque, Musée de l'Impression sur Etoffes, Mulhouse; Madame Madeleine Delpierre, Musée de la Mode et du Costume, Paris; La Bibliothèque Nationale, Paris, and their excellent staff of librarians; Pierre Arizzoli Clementel and Evelyne Goudry, Musée Historique des Tissus, Lyon; Les Archives Nationales, Paris.

In London, Betty Tyers, Victoria and Albert Museum; M.J. Pollack, Indian Office Library; Meg Andrews, Sotheby's Belgravia; Anne Marie Benson, Phillips, Patricia Frost, Christie's South Kensington.

In the United States, Milton Sonday, Cooper Hewitt Museum; Richard Lanier, of the Asian Cultural Council, who introduced me to India's Museums; the Metropolitan Museum of Art; Lotus Stack, Minneapolis Institute of Arts; Yale University Art Gallery; Fine Arts Museum of San Francisco; Boston Museum of Fine Arts; Textile Museum, Washington, D.C.

In India, O.P. Tandon and Devaki Ahivasi, Bharat Kala Bhavan, Benaras, and Dr. Anand Krishna for having read the manuscript and his inspiring letter of send-off; Krishna Lal of the National Museum Delhi, who surmounted incredible difficulties of access to the museum's collection; Martand Singh, Calico Museum of Textiles, Ahmedabad; Dr. M.L. Nigam, Salor Jung Museum, Hyderabad; the Jagdish and Kamla Mittal Museum of Indian Art, Hyderabad; Sushil Kumar and his staff at the Indian Textile Company, Bombay; Dr. Karin Singh and Madame Shobha Nehru who graciously permitted me to view the 'toshakhana' of the Maharaja of Kashmir; Dr. Asok Kumar Das and Chandramani Singh of the Maharaja Sawai Man Singh II Museum, Jaipur; Sadashiv Gorakshkar, Prince of Wales Museum, Bombay; Vishnu Lall and Family, Agra; Dr. Bashir Ahmad Dar, Srinagar, for translation; Bapa, Bombay, for his encouragement and dynamic energy..

Warm regards and much appreciation to Lucien Arcache, Guillermo Arizcorreta (for the line drawings of shawl construction), Valery Beranstain, Anne Christine, Steven Cohen, Roseline Degrain, Jacqueline Daniel, Henri and Jacqueline Dumas, Francesca Galloway, Roland Gilles, Christian Grandin, Renate and Arthur Halpern, Tessa Hughes, Jack Ismidlian, Joan Lecoutour (for having read the manuscript), Monique Lévis-Strauss, Louis Lomüller, George Michel, Michel Spink, Jeff Spurr, Marie-Noëlle Sudre, Roben Tala and Gabriel Vial; to Joyce Ames and Eddie Fazio for their continued encouragement to see this project through; and to all my friends in Kashmir who brought me into intimate contact with their families, work and culture.

Lastly, very special thanks to Evelyne Chevallier for typing much of the manuscript and for accompanying me on several study trips to India. Her devoted help in assisting me during many of the photo sessions went far beyond the call of duty.

PHOTOGRAPHIC ACKNOWLEDGEMENTS

The author is deeply grateful to the following people, museums and institutions who have so generously contributed photographs and other documentation:

Meg Andrews, Bharany, Evelyne Chevallier, Rosaline Degrain, Tessa Hughes, Ganeshi Lall and Son, Susan Meller, Sotheby's, London, Marie Noëlle Sudre, Dr. Jim Williams, Roland Gilles, and many private collectors. A special thanks to Linda and Ralph Kaffel for the transparency of their rare Marasali rug (Colour Plate 38a) and to the Marie-Anne Krugier Collection for Colour Plates 46, 47, 48, 49, 101 and 103. And, lastly, deep gratitude to Dr. Martha B. Boyd for Colour Plates 53-58, 66-76, 77b, 79-97, 99a-h, 100a-h and Plate 61.

MUSEUMS AND INSTITUTIONS

Association pour l'Etude et la Documentation des Textiles d'Asie (A.E.D.T.A.), Krishna Riboud, President, Paris: Colour Plates 20, 21, 34a; Plates 23, 81, 161.
Bharat Kala Bhavan (Benaras Hindu University): Colour Plates 120, 121, 122, 127, 128, 137, 139, 140, 142, 144, 145, 147, 148, 149, 150, 158, 159, 160, 164, 162, 163, 164, 168, 169a, 173, 174, 190, 192, 205.
Bibliothèque Nationale, Paris: Plates 33, 34, 35, 37, 38, 39, 62, 63, 64, 65, 66, 67, 68.
Boston Museum of Fine Arts: Plates 83, 86, 105, 109a, 110, 112, 113, 114, 121, 122, 123, 125, 127, 138, 139, 146, 147, 149, 150, 151, 158, 165.
Calico Museum, Ahmedabad: Colour Plate 129; Plates 85, 88, 141, 143
Conservatoire National des Arts et Métiers, Paris: Colour Plate 189; Plates 53, 54, 58a, 58b.
Fine Arts Museum of San Francisco: Plate 167
Indian Office Library, London: Plate 23
Jagdish and Kamla Mittal Museum of Indian Art, Hyderabad: Colour Plate 123; Plate 119.
Louvre, Paris: Plate 15
Metropolitan Museum of Art, New York: Plates 26, 27, 27a, 28a-e, 57, 32a, 32b.
Musée de l'Impression sur Etoffes, Mulhouse: Plate 51 (Studio Basset).
Musées des Arts Décoratifs, Paris: Colour Plate 43; Plates 43, 44a, 44b, 48.
Musée Historique des Tissus, Lyon: Colour Plate 179; Plates 6, 52.
Musées de Nice; Plate 16
National Museum, Delhi: Colour Plates 135, 138, 165, 166, 170, 171, 173, 174; Plates 94, 98, 109.
The Textile Museum, Washington, D.C.: Colour Plate 116; Plates 32b, 87, 90, 110, 120.
The Victoria and Albert Museum, London: Plates 46, 60a, 80, 82, 84,89, 95, 96, 97, 100, 102, 104, 126, 133, 135, 143, 154, 155, 159, 160, 162, 168, 169.
Yale University Art Gallery, Connecticut: Plates 115, 153, 166.

Colour Photography: Studios James Lignier and Jean Claude Valette, Paris; Lynn Diane De Marco, New York; Christina Carter, New York (for Colour Plates 53-58, 66-76, 77b, 79-97, 99a-h, 100a-h and Plate 61); Patrick Goetelen, Geneva.

CONTENTS

PREFACE TO THE THIRD EDITION

The present edition represents a major leap forward and the reader will be happy to learn of the many new additions which have been incorporated since the publication of the first edition in 1986. By far the most significant is the profusion of marvellous colour plates (about 140), many of which replace the earlier black and white photographs which were used to illustrate the fabulous Mughal collection from the Bharat Kala Bhawan, Benaras.

Bridging the gap between the needs of the interested shawl public and those of the collector/historian is not an easy feat. We hope to have satisfied at least part of this need with the addition of a new chapter, 'British Shawls in the Indian Style', by the English scholar, Pamela Clabburn. In 'Manufacturing Techniques up to the Present Day' Peter Harris, a contemporary weaver from Ayton, Ontario with a keen and inquisitive eye, has written an illuminating analysis discussing the technicalities of the double-locked twill tapestry (kani) weave and how they were resolved by the Kashmiri weaver. Warm thanks to you both your for kind participation in this project.

The last decade has seen the discovery of a number of new traceable French shawls designs, either through auction, dealer or gallery sales, many of which are now in private collections scattered around the globe. However, an exciting new feature of the third edition can be found in Chapter 7, 'The French School of Shawl Design', in which about forty of some of the rarest and most beautiful signed and dated shawls are illustrated – all of which form the core of the vast U.S. private collection belonging to Martha B. Boyd, M.D. Besides the famous Nou-Rouz and Isphahan, many of them are from the brilliant hand of France's gifted nineteenth century shawl artist, Antony Berrus. Over the many enjoyable years I have known and worked with Dr. Boyd, I have found few collectors who could equal her vision, commitment and boundless energy. Dr. Boyd's generosity in offering to help illustrate this chapter brings to life a clearer picture of the immense creativity of the French shawl artist.

In the same chapter I have endeavoured to expand the profile on the character of Amédée Couder and his family, a man whose obscure life has roused my curiosity ever since I first discovered a full size shawl painting of his hanging in the National Conservatory of Industrial Arts, Paris, in 1980. Architect, industrial designer, writer, poet, Couder takes credit for some of the most innovative advances in early jacquard loom technology. Due to the importance of his architectural work, work that was also reflected in his shawl designs, several drawings from his architectural projects have also been included.

In 1955 John Irwin, then Assistant Keeper of the Indian Department of the Victoria and Albert Museum, published an unassuming yet groundbreaking monograph entitled 'Shawls'. In this seminal document, Mr. Irwin had blazed an important path for future historians of Indian and European 'Kashmir' shawls. Over forty years later the importance of this study still remains intact. In 1980 I happened to be just one of those obsessed persons who set out to tie the whole story into a more complete picture. When the first edition of this book appeared it was not without some apprehension; for in it I had advanced some rather bold theories and had established what I considered an important system of classification of the Kashmir shawl, i.e. Mughal Period, Afghan Period, Sikh Period and Dogra Period. Two years later, after its initial success, the second edition (1988) arrived, basically unchanged except for a few more colour plates and about fifteen new black and whites.

A subject so vast can never be completely covered in one volume. Time and expense have not permitted the weave analysis of the hundreds of illustrated shawls. Certainly, knowledge of how the wool or silk was spun, plied, knotted, etc. can be very helpful, and it is hoped that this book and the ideas presented herein will inspire future scholars to pursue new avenues of study.

Lastly, I would like to thank my publisher, Diana Steel, whose continuing support of this work over the years has made this present volume possible.

F. Ames, June 1997
Upper West Side, Manhattan

PREFACE TO THE 1986 EDITION

The idea of putting together a comprehensive book on the Kashmir shawl was first suggested to me by a good friend while I was vacationing on New York's Fire Island during the warm summer of 1979. It had been almost ten years since I first left the States and had taken up residence in Europe. Paris had become my 'plaque tournante' for what was soon to become an endless number of voyages to India.

But before setting foot in the Orient, I had already become keenly intrigued by the European 'Kashmir' shawl. Seeing them lying around in the auction rooms of Paris, London or New York, thrown into a heap in some obscure corner of the saleroom, I was continually struck by the richness of their colours and changing patterns, the ingenious combinations of which sometimes imitated the real Kashmir shawls so closely that it was impossible not to do a double take.

I have found the auction sale room a great place for learning about art and antiques. There, even the most casual viewer can enter into intimate contact with the rarest of objects, be they paintings, jewellery, rugs or sculpture, in a way impossible in a museum. Once sold they will probably sit in the coveted world of private collections, glassed enclosed museums or securely locked vaults. But before the hammer falls, there is an opportunity to hold in your own hands the precious piece which, except possibly through a published photograph, has for so long eluded the public's eye; a rare experience indeed. And even if one is not a connoisseur, there is always a powerful delight in being able to inspect the object briefly with a feigned and savoury expertise while others are forced to wait at the sidelines with bated breath wondering whether you've secretly condemned it as a fake or acclaimed it as a treasure.

Most fascinating of all is the chance of viewing an entire collection built up by one individual, a meaningful and homogeneous collection, reflecting the particular empathy and stamp of a single collector. Museums, dependent on the state for finance, find their budgets restricted and monies frequently inaccessible when the need arises thus preventing them from buying entire collections. Some institutions are more fortunate and make acquisitions through wealthy people who seek tax benefits. But in general an enormous amount of bureaucratic red-tape must be cut before an object becomes a new acquisition; the museums' collections suffer accordingly. In this respect a private citizen has much greater versatility. As new pieces come on to the art market which represent a more expressive aspect of the field in which he is interested, they can be used to replace earlier acquired pieces whose brilliance has waned, whereas rarely can a museum resell or exchange an object once it has been formally acquired.

After that warm summer, I found myself compulsively pursuing this project, tracing the boteh's slow, painstaking pictographic evolution. The world stood still while I forged the missing links in its chain of development.

As the 'canvas' of an expressive art medium, I began to discover that the Kashmir shawl, viewed in its earliest manifestations, harboured stylistic doors the keys to which remain frustratingly elusive. At the root of each Mughal flower lay a tiny trap door concealing another world; and crossing the threshold was as precarious as Alice's dreamworld pursuit after a pocket-watch rabbit. I suppose it is just this elusiveness which urges one continually to dig below the surface; to find the doors which will liberate from those great Oriental vaults of man's immortalised genius the missing links of spiritual antiquity, the lost horizons of an extinct art.

In India, outside the major collections of Benaras, Delhi and Calico, few shawls of importance exist. At the museum in Srinagar a few early nineteenth century pieces are on display, but the pitiful conditions in which they are kept will not assure them of a very long life. The Bharat Kala Bhawan is endowed with by far the richest collection, the greater portion of which has come down directly from the family of the Maharaja of Jaipur. It is said that, just after India's independence, the Maharani decided to do some palatial spring cleaning. Bundles of seventeenth and eighteenth century shawls were thrown out into the courtyard and sold on a first-come-first-served basis for a handful of rupees.

Things have changed a lot since then. During one of my recent trips to India I had found myself in a run-down section of Old Delhi where a dealer and I were haggling over what he considered to be a very rare object and needless to say his price was 'top quality' too. Without batting an eyelid, he snatches off his dusty shelf one of the latest western catalogues on the subject replete with glossy colour plates and points out a vaguely similar object that had just been exhibited at a well-known Western museum. This is what shopping is all about in India today.

If one wants to view the 'kani' techniques in operation one must go to Kanihama (twelve miles from Srinagar) where the government is making a vain attempt to revive the art. However, anybody who really appreciates the complexity of these tapestry weaves risks a terrible let-down. On the other hand the visitor will walk away rewarded by the even deeper understanding of the Herculean effort and patience that was invested in them years ago, and the fine-tuned system of a highly sophisticated division of labour where the skill of the weaver, dyer or spinner was as much hailed and sought after as gold. In craftsmanship the Kashmiri still possesses one of the greatest abilities in the world, but for Kashmir once again to flex its true artistic muscles the stimuli will have to come through private enterprise.

F. Ames, March 1986
Rue Sainte Apolline, Paris

INTRODUCTION

After many centuries, the Kashmir shawl still fires our imagination as an exotic souvenir of the Orient, representing a bygone and opulent era. The shawl's sudden migration in 1800 from Kashmir to Europe spawned important new developments in European design ideas, centring around one of the most ubiquitous motifs ever to come from the East: the 'buta' or 'boteh' as it is known in the West, a cone-like form that is commonly found on printed goods, on rugs, embroideries and many other textiles.

The present work attempts to define and classify the Kashmir shawl, analyses the wealth of images and symbolism found in its finely ornamented weave, and places its development within the context of the four major periods of Kashmir's history. Unlike many Near Eastern textiles which have a continuous and uninterrupted history, the Kashmir shawl remains unique as a weave which has not been produced in over a century; as a result, certain technical facets concerning its construction have almost completely disappeared, a fact which tends to intensify our perception of its mysterious beauty and illuminating colours.

Kashmir shawls, as a general rule, did not represent a folk art as did nomadic carpets, kilims, and Indian embroideries. They were made, rather, for an expanding commercial market ignorant of and far removed from the hardships experienced by the poor shawl weaver striving to support his family. The shawl may represent an expression of the weaver's art, but economic necessity was his probable motivation.

The Kashmiris were not part of a nomadic group and remained far removed from contact with the outside world. To this day their origins are still in dispute. Indeed some claim they are one of the lost tribes of Israel. Perhaps the natural beauty and tranquillity of the Kashmir valley, despite its many invaders, enabled the weavers to devote so much painstaking effort to one of the most difficult weaves in the history of textiles.

Kashmir, bordered by Chinese, Indian and Muslim territories, resisted for a long time before acquiescing to the teachings of the Sufi dervishes who brought the Islamic religion into the Kashmir valley in the eleventh century, and from this time Islam became a continual inspiration in the creation of designs. By the fourteenth century it was firmly implanted and declared a state religion. Medieval Kashmir witnessed numerous lootings by Turkish invaders until the Sultan dynasty was founded by Sultan Sham-ud-Din (1339-1342). A century later, Kashmir's art and culture flourished under Zain-ul-Abidin (1420-1470). Under his rule Persian replaced Sanskrit as the official language of government.

The English word 'shawl' is derived from the Persian 'shal'. In Oriental tradition, shal describes not only one particular article of clothing, but a whole range of fine woollen fabrics.

This book is only concerned with the woven, decorated shawl for which Kashmir has been famous. The appellation 'kani' shawl, as it is popularly known in Kashmir, originally meant simply a woven shawl, but during the course of time the term kani has taken on a more special significance and is defined as a type of weave in which the design is formed by the manipulation of small wooden sticks called 'tojis' which interlock their respective coloured threads as they complete each weft of the shawl. Traditionally the most valued shawls were composed of threads of delicate wool from the underbelly of the wild Tibetan mountain goat, the pattern being worked by the technique known to Western textile historians as 'twill tapestry'. These are the 'woven jewels' of Kashmir.

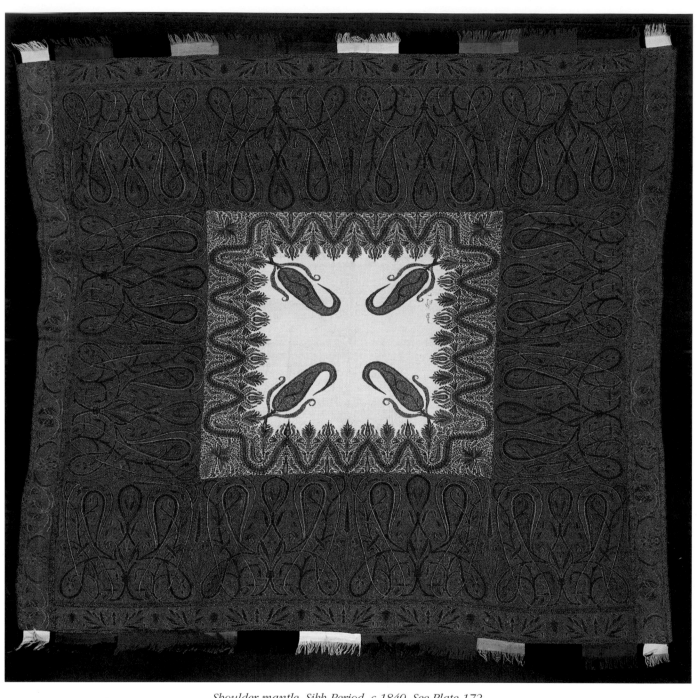

Shoulder mantle. Sikh Period, c.1840. See Plate 172

CHAPTER ONE
Classification of the Kashmir Shawl

The most striking fact about the history of Kashmir is that its people rose to great heights of art, culture and economic prosperity primarily when the impulses came from outside rather than from within. The Kashmir shawl developed over three hundred years, through four different periods of foreign political rule, during which Kashmir was ruled successively by the Mughals, the Afghans, the Sikhs, and the Dogras and the shawls illustrated in this book have been classified according to these four main periods.

It is impossible to speak of one 'great period' in the development of the Kashmir shawl; each culture brought its own unique contribution. The development of the Kashmir shawl is influenced directly by changing historical circumstances; it reflects times of peace and of war, of famine and prosperity, as well as changes in royal patronage.

In order to set the stage for the ornamentation of the Kashmir shawl this chapter provides a brief historical background of the four main periods. Detailed discussion of the evolution of the boteh is discussed in Chapter 4, again under the period headings. In this way the reader may gain a better insight from a narrative focused directly on elements of style rather than on one which attempts to combine historical facts with theories of artistic sensitivities. Nevertheless, and so that the basis of this system of classification may come into sharper focus, a few stylistic points are briefly discussed here to clarify the attribution of the shawls illustrated in this book.

It appears that the early Mughal period represents an important and prosperous moment for the kani shawl. At the time the Renaissance was flourishing in the West and the Orient too was experiencing great artistic achievements. However, there are no dated shawls of the Mughal period, and extant pieces attributable to the seventeenth century do not seem to date much earlier than the reign of Jehangir (1605-1627). His reign is important for our study because this is when the 'flowering plant' first appeared, a design of delicate beauty which had a great influence on future generations of shawl designs. But a word of caution is due here. Other contemporary patterns surely existed and probably enjoyed an equal popularity which should not be overlooked. Unfortunately, the dearth of early shawls inhibits any positive statements concerning concurrent schools of design. The situation becomes clearer in the eighteenth century, but it is not until the early nineteenth century that a firm overall picture of the multitudinous shawl patterns emerges. This is due, of course, not only to the numerous extant pieces available to us for examination from this period but also to pictorial references by Western painters.

The Kashmiri people suffered under their Afghan overlords and this is manifested in the more restrained expressiveness of many of the extant patterns. What was lost in the sensuous lines of the 'flowering plant' was gained in the regal stature of the more rigorous and hardy plant of the eighteenth century. Later on it was the outline shape of the boteh that reigned supreme, which the artist filled with a floral mosaic. As the curtain fell on the eighteenth century, Sikh power began to proliferate slowly throughout the Punjab and two decades later it engulfed Kashmir. A prelude to what would constitute distinct stylistic elements of the Sikh period becomes progressively apparent during this time. Because the effect of political change can be seen in the shawl's design, an attempt has been made here to classify the shawl according to whoever held power over Kashmir at the time of its manufacture.

No system of classification is foolproof and obviously certain imperfections are bound to arise. For example, one of the biggest problems was how to classify a shawl piece exhibiting design characteristics from one period (such as the spacing of the botehs) while it was probably woven during the course of another. In such cases the shawl is classified under the period in which it is thought to have been woven, with a sub-classification attributing style to a different period.

Of course in the long run, where certain examples proved difficult, an educated guess had to be made based on experience gained over many years in the study and handling of literally thousands of both rare and common specimens in public and private collections. This collation is the result of extensive fieldwork spanning three continents; the pieces have been chosen not only for their fine quality but also for the ways in which they document particular periods of styles (see An Illustrated Guide…, page 253).

ORIGIN OF THE KASHMIR SHAWL

The shoulder mantle or shawl had been in existence, in a variety of forms, from the most ancient times, serving as a staple and protective garment not only for the rich and noble but also and above all for the common people. In ancient Buddhist literature the shawl can be found among recorded inventories of woollen textiles, and its manufacture appears to have been a cottage industry in Kashmir as early as the eleventh century.

Doubt still persists, however, as to the actual beginnings of the kani shawl industry. At present there is no extant kani piece which may be said with certainty to predate the seventeenth century, in spite of the nineteenth century legend recorded by the Baron von Hugel who cites Zain-ul-Abidin's (1420-1470) enthusiastic encouragement of the arts of Kashmir. Nevertheless, the high degree of sophistication of the early seventeenth century fragments suggests that the shawl industry may have been in existence at least as early as the late sixteenth century.

A recently-found document[1] provides new evidence suggesting that indeed it may have been during either the fifteenth or sixteenth century that the industry first began. This document was written by the well-known shawl merchant of nineteenth century Kashmir, Hajji Mukhtar Shah. Mukhtar Shah, whose ancestors began working in the shawl trade in the seventeenth century, was painfully struck by its sudden demise during the 1870s, and, at the request of the eminent linguist G.W. Leitner, wrote a history tracing the early development of the industry which, he said, had given 'a lease on life to five lakh[2] souls'.

Mukhtar's treatise, like any Oriental document, should be interpreted with care, since it reflects a vision of time and history often different from that of Western thought. It provides a remarkable picture of the development of the weaving industry. Furthermore, conversations with present-day descendants of old weaving families bear out its arguments.

Mukhtar records that Kashmir came under the *de facto* domination of Mirza Haider Dughlat in 1540. Haider was born in 1500 in Tashghar at the Eastern end of Turkestan and was a first cousin to the great Mughal, Babur. At fifteen he left

1. Shah.
2. Five hundred thousand.

his cousin's protection to join the forces of Abu Said in Kashgar, whom he served for nineteen years. In those days the governments of Tibet, Ladakh and Kashmir were closely interrelated.

Mirza Haider Dughlat encouraged many of the industries originally introduced by Zain-ul-Abidin a hundred years earlier, and among the annual presents offered to him in tribute were a few rolls of very fine but crudely woven Ladakhi wool, called 'putto'. Woven from goat's wool, the cloth was softer and warmer than any yet manufactured in Kashmir, apparently because shawls, until then, were made only from sheep's wool. Mirza Haider felt that if this wool, called 'pashm', could be spun and woven by the expert craftsmen of Kashmir, perhaps an even better material could be produced.

According to Mukhtar, it was under the guidance of Haider's faithful adherent and cook, Naghz Beg, that a new industry was generated which induced the local people to develop the kani shawl technique. Beg, to whom Kashmir owes the kani shawl, instituted a thin instrument called a 'seekh' or spike, at each end of which different coloured yarns were placed. He also introduced a new feature of red and green spots in regular rows.[3] Following his death, shawl weavers continued developing the spike-shuttling method, using the double-colour scheme in various ways; generally white putto for men and red for women. Later, saffron yellow and indigo blue were also added.

The industry continued to flower, but, as Mukhtar points out, it was not until the Mughals' conquest of Kashmir in 1586 that the Kashmir shawl industry realised its full potential.

MUGHAL PERIOD (1586-1753)

The Mughals (also known as Moguls or Mongols), inhabitants of the vast steppe land of Central Asia, were a race of warlike nomads who conquered Northern India in the early part of the sixteenth century. Under Mughal rule Kashmir abandoned its antediluvian isolation, and its natural beauty attracted people from all over Asia. The Mughals instituted great building projects and a sound system of administration, and Kashmir enjoyed a brisk trade as part of the great highway of Central Asia.

Akbar, grandson of the great founder of the Mughal dynasty, Babur, ruled Kashmir for nineteen years. He abolished many of the religious persecutions and iniquities suffered by the people under the rule of the Turkish Sultans. He also took a personal interest in the manufacture of Kashmir's artefacts and paid special attention to the shawl industry, which he admired greatly.

His interest in religion and his tendency toward free thought and mysticism were known and admired throughout the world. Akbar's genius lay in the shrewd reconciliation of the often opposing forces of Hindu and Muslim philosophies. He successfully achieved this by establishing a cult of monarchy, presenting himself as a semi-divine ruler, whom it was a religious duty to obey and sacrilege to oppose. His son Jehangir, impressed by the nimbus or halo he observed in Western religious painting, sustained this idea of divine rule by featuring himself in paintings glorified by shimmering gold nimbuses of exaggerated dimensions. The powerful military force and 'divine' monarchal aura which reigned during this great period of regal opulence should be borne in mind when studying the remaining Mughal textiles handed down to us.

No other Mughal textiles used the kani technique. It was used, however, in

3. Sufi, pp. 563-564.

COLOUR PLATE 1.
Srinagar, capital of Kashmir, on the Jhelum River from the Zain-a-Kadal bridge.

COLOUR PLATE 2.
Wall decorations on the entrance to the Jama Majid, Lahore, 17th century.

COLOUR PLATE 4.
Fragment detail. Strikingly similar to Colour Plate 3, this well-known shawl bears all the characteristics of the Shah Jehan Mughal Period.

textiles of the Central Asian region and certain areas of Persia, especially in kilims, saddle bags and Soumak weaves. For example, the Bakhtiari tribes of Southern Persia produce a single faced weave just like the shawl, although without a twill and with the reverse side displaying a relief of ridges where the various colour areas join. Textiles of the kani technique were also woven by people of early Turkish origin, although weavings of this type are extremely rare, probably because they were not exported and served simply the utilitarian purposes of the nomadic tribes who wove them. Because of the scarcity of adept Kashmiri craftsmen, it is known that Akbar brought many weavers from the city of Andizhan, Eastern Turkestan (about 750km – 470 miles – north of Kashmir), down to Kashmir, and one inevitably speculates on whether the kani weave originated in these areas or in the Kashmir.

Akbar's keen interest in textiles is illustrated by the meticulous efforts undertaken to have them carefully arranged and preserved in the toshikana or imperial wardrobe. Textiles which had been offered to him as tribute, and various court commissioned pieces, shawls amongst them, were all labelled as to their date of entry, price, colour and weight.

Abul Fazl, his court chronicler, wrote that Akbar improved the shawl department by making a 'visual' improvement to the tus shawls. Tus was an extremely fine goat's wool which came from the wild ibex whose natural colour was brown, grey or white or various shades in between. The tus shawl was unrivalled for its lightness, warmth and softness; and it was generally dyed without altering its natural colour (see Wool, Chapter 3). Akbar experimented with various techniques in shawl dyeing and discovered that tus wool was impervious to the colour red.

Akbar went so far as to experiment with the dye colours and it is very possible that the refusal of the precious shah tus to take to a red dye had left him royally disappointed. Undaunted over the prospects of not being able to create an imperial-red Kashmir shawl, he busied himself over the etiquette of how the shawl should be donned, as one discovers in the *Ain-i-Akbari*. And here the succinct passage[4] is worth quoting as its analysis surely leaves us longing for more information: 'In former times, shawls were often brought from Kashmir. People folded them up in four folds and wore them for a very long time. Now-a-days they are generally worn without folds and merely thrown over the shoulder. His Majesty has commenced to wear them double, which looks very well.' Wearing them double surely represented a major fashion statement but this quote from Blochman's translation is not wholly clear and one should be careful about interpreting it as Akbar having two shawls stitched back to back and wearing them as a pair, as Irwin explains in his monograph. Only the word potara appears which means two warps. One thing is clear, there have been found more than a few period shawls sewn back to back as a pair, hence the name dochalla, so we know that the style did in fact exist. He also reports that Akbar increased the size of the Kashmir shawl so that it could be made into a complete suit.

George Forster, who visited Kashmir in 1783, was informed that during the Mughal period 40,000 looms were in operation (see Figure 1, page 41); of course not all of these were involved in the manufacture of kani shawls. Fazl cites one thousand workshops in Lahore alone, where mostly 'chirahs' (turbans) and 'fautahs' (loinbands) were made. These fabrics were known as 'mayan' and were made of silk and wool.

Following Akbar's death his son, Jehangir, succeeded to the throne. Jehangir had fallen in love with the natural beauty of Kashmir the day he paid his first visit to the Valley with his father in 1589. He described the incredible flora of the valley in his memoirs, *Tuzk-i-Jehangir*: 'The red rose, the violet, and the narcissus grow of themselves; in the fields there are all kinds of flowers and all sorts of sweet, scented herbs, more than can be calculated. In the soul-enchanting spring the hills and plains are filled with blossoms, the gates, the walls, the courts, the roofs are lighted up by the torches of banquet-adorning tulips.'

Kashmir became his favourite abode and he declared that he would rather be deprived of every other province of his mighty empire than lose Kashmir. In this connection Forster wrote: 'the interests of this province were so strongly favoured at the Mughal court that every complaint against its governors was attentively listened to, and any attempt to molest the people was restrained or punished. Under Jehangir's rule, Kashmir enjoyed one of its most prosperous periods.

Jehangir also writes about the shawls of Kashmir in his memoirs: 'The shawls of kashmir to which my father gave the name of "param-naram" are very famous; there is no need to praise them. Another kind is "narharma"; it is thicker than a shawl and soft. Another is 'darm': it is like a "jul-i-khirsak" and is put on a carpet. With the exception of shawls they make other woollen material better in Tibet. Though they bring the wool for the shawls from Tibet they do not make them there. The wool for the shawls comes from a goat which is peculiar to Tibet. In

4. *Ain-I-Akbari*, translated by H. Blochman, vol. I Calcutta, 1873, p. 92. The author is grateful to Rosemary Crill for her knowledge of the Persian language and her help in the review of this important passage in Abul Fazl's text. (See p. 10 of *Shawls*, 1955.)

Kashmir they weave the "pattu" shawl from wool, and sewing two shawls together they smooth them into a kind of "saqarlat" (broad-cloth) which is not bad for a raincoat.[5]

The Hindi name for shawls, 'param-naram', coined by Akbar continued, and it seems to have been given to an article regularly presented to the nobles. 'Narharma' means 'like a river', for the shawl had waves (maujdar) as a decorative feature (see Plate 94). Jehangir noted in his memoirs that he once presented to Mirza Raja Bhao Singh a special Kashmir shawl called a 'phup', derived from the sanskrit word 'pushpa', flower. We thus learn that the shawl, at that time, was ornamented with flowers.

Sir Thomas Roe, James I's ambassador to the Mughal court, was offered a gold shawl by the Governor of Surat in 1616. Decorative shawls such as these were apparently used as enticing bribes and this is mentioned in the early records of the English East India Trading Company. Roe, however, rejected the governor's offer, writing in his memoirs: 'and pressing me to take a gold "shal", I answered we were but newly friends; when I saw any constancy in his carriage and the money paid I would be more free with him yet I would receive no obligation.'[6]

Jehangir was succeeded in turn by his son, Shah Jehan, who ruled from 1627 to 1658. He took an even greater interest in the welfare of Kashmir than had his father. Among the Mughal rulers, Shah Jehan is remembered as a builder. His monumental constructions, like the Taj Mahal in Agra and the Red Forts in Agra and Delhi, testify to his unusually fine architectural taste, which synthesised several impulses: Hindu, Buddhist, and Persian.

The most coveted shawls during the Mughal period were often ornamented with precious metals. Manrique, a Spanish monk travelling in India in 1630, described fine shawls as having 'borders ornamented with fringes of gold, silver and silk thread. The princes and nobles wear them like cloaks, either muffling themselves up in them or else carrying them under their arms. These choice cloths are of white colour when they leave the loom but are afterwards dyed any hue desired and are ornamented with various coloured flowers and other kinds of decoration which make them very gay and showy.'

The remarks by this early traveller imply that embroidery was at that time used in shawl decoration. Had Manrique been speaking of the kani method, he would not have described it as having been removed from the loom. Curiously, no mention of 'tojis' (the wooden needles used in the kani weaving) nor any description of the intricacies and lengthy time required to weave the kani shawl is found in the writings left from the Mughal period. The descriptions focus on the uniqueness of the high quality wool (not necessarily Kashmiri wool) rather than on the techniques by which it was manufactured.

Aurangzeb came to the throne of his father, Shah Jehan, in the year 1658. With him the mighty Mughal empire founded by Babur and consolidated by Akbar and his two successors began to decline. Aurangzeb was a strict, orthodox Muslim, and his views and sentiments towards his Hindu subjects directly opposed those held by his predecessors. The great artistic tradition of Mughal India began to decline under Aurangzeb's regime.

François Bernier, the celebrated doctor, philosopher and traveller, spent twelve years in India as physician to Aurangzeb. He had the privilege of visiting Kashmir while accompanying Aurangzeb and of thus being the first Westerner ever to set foot in the 'enchanted land'. He contradicted Manrique's description regarding shawl decoration, saying that they were made with a 'sort of embroidery made on the loom'. These differences of observation are typical of Western travellers

5. Jehangir, vol. 2, pp. 147-148.
6. Irwin, 1973, p. 10.

COLOUR PLATE 5.
Fragment detail. 17th century. (See Colour Plate 124 for detailed description.)

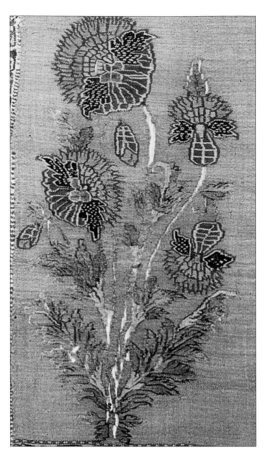

COLOUR PLATE 6.
Single buta detail, freely spaced, from large shoulder mantle, 17th century. (See Colour Plate 116 for detailed description.)

COLOUR PLATE 7.
Detail of shoulder mantle, mid-18th century. (See Colour Plate 140 for detailed description.)

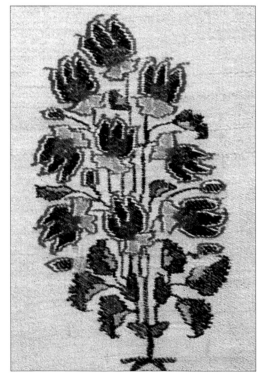

COLOUR PLATE 8.
Single buta detail, from large shoulder mantle, 17th century. (See Colour Plate 120 for details.).

COLOUR PLATE 9.
*Detail of shoulder mantle fragment, c.1700.
(See Colour Plate 143 for further details.)*

COLOUR PLATE 10.
*Detail of shoulder mantle, early 18th
century. (See Colour Plate 132 for detailed
description.)*

COLOUR PLATE 11.
View of the Taj Mahal, built by Shah Jehan.

COLOUR PLATE 12.
*Carved marble flowers from the Amber
Place, Jaipur, 17th century.*

whose knowledge of loom techniques was poor. Since Bernier actually visited Kashmir, where one could hardly escape the sight of weaving being performed, his observation is probably the more believable.

Bernier also described the shawl industry in some detail. 'Large quantities of shawls were manufactured which gave employment even to children,' he wrote. 'These shawls measured five by two and a half feet [152.4 by 76.2cm], were ornamented at both ends with a sort of embroidery made in the loom, a foot [30cm] in height. The Mughals and Indian men and women wore them in winter around their heads, passing them over the shoulders as a mantle. One sort was manufactured with the wool of the country and the other with the wool of the shawl goat of Tibet. The price of the tus shawl ranged from 50 to 150 rupees. Great pains were taken to manufacture similar shawls at Patna, Agra and Lahore but they lacked the delicate texture of Kashmir shawls.'[7]

Bernier also explained the ranks within the social and military hierarchy[8] in a letter to one Monseigneur Colbert and it appears highly possible that shawls reflected military rank, both through the variations in the 'boteh' patterns (see, for example, Plate 90 and Colour Plate 121), and through the actual colour of the shawl itself. The small number of extant Mughal pieces known does not offer enough evidence at present to comment definitively on the question of rank, with the exception of the pure white tus or tooch shawls reserved for the king alone and used by him as gifts for foreign dignitaries.

Part of the shawl trade with India during the Mughal and Afghan periods was carried out through the agency of the government. Most of the shawls, for instance, were taken by officials and sent to Delhi and Agra where some were presented to the Emperor and the rest sold to courtiers and the nobility. The Mughal emperors, during their many visits, were frequently followed by a horde of traders from Hindustan who purchased shawls and other artistic wares and sold them at a profit in the chief cities of India.

A new shawl design which caught the eye of an Emperor often found immediate popularity among his followers and the nobles of the court. Accordingly, when the Mughal ruler, Muhammud Shah (1720-1742), was presented with a shawl of a fascinating floral design, he ordered that 40,000 rupees-worth be supplied to him annually. No real description of the design remains but, nevertheless, the shawl came to be called, after the name of the emperor, 'Buta Muhammud Shahi'.[9]

As the Mughal kingdoms began to collapse and Kashmir came under Afghan rule, the shawl trade began to focus increasingly on the West, while the Indian market fell into decline. In spite of this change, the government of Hyderabad in the Deccan, under the rule of Nizzam'ul Mulk, continued to be a rich outlet for the Kashmir shawl where it remained the conventional dress of the nobles at court.

AFGHAN PERIOD (1753-1819)

The Afghan invasion in 1753 by Ahmad Shah Abdali put an end to the Mughal rule of Kashmir. Under the rule of the Afghans, the country was reduced to the lowest depths of penury and degradation, a slavery lasting for sixty-seven years. The Afghans' cruelty also threatened the life and property of all foreigners who had been residing in Kashmir. About ninety firms established by Hindu businessmen were closed down as their owners returned to their homeland,

7. Bernier, pp. 402-403.
8. At the top of the military ladder of command were the 'Omraha' or 'seigneurs', often foreign adventurers who advanced through the ranks and were rewarded with attractive salaries and titles. The titles signified the number of horses under their command, such as 'hazari', one thousand, 'do-hazari', two thousand, up to the maximum 'Duazdeh-hazari', or twelve thousand. Such honourable titles represented exalted positions and were created expressly to attract public attention. Under the Omrahs came the 'mansadbars' or cavaliers. Although they lacked the Omrahs' pomp and high status, they were nevertheless often able to ascend the ranks to eventually become Omrahs.
9. Koul, p. 37.

while nearly half the population of Kashmir left the terror-stricken land permanently. Nevertheless, shawl weaving continued during these difficult times and accounted for a significant portion of Kashmir's revenue. The shawl's popularity abroad resulted in a brisk trade.

Afghan's control of Kashmir represented just another provincial addition to an already vast empire carved out by Ahmad Shah Abdali. Ahmed Shah was chosen by the Afghan chiefs at Qandahar to be their leader. He thus inherited the incalculable treasures amassed by his predecessor Nadir Shah (assassinated 1747), including the famous Koh-i-nor diamond and the peacock throne taken as booty by the latter when he sacked Delhi in 1739. He assumed power over the eastern part of Nadir's empire, and Afghanistan took its place among the kingdoms of the world. His empire at one time extended from Herat, Meshed, Khurasan and Nishapur in the West to Multan, the Punjab and finally Delhi in the East.

Towards the end of the eighteenth century and during the time of Abdali's rule, the Qajar dynasty arose in Southern Persia bringing with it an increasingly strong patronage of the arts. This was something absent from the life-style of the warring Afghans. The oil paintings produced during the reign of Fath 'Ali Shah (1798-1834) and those just preceding his monarchy do not necessarily represent new sources of Kashmir design inspiration but they do provide images of bejewelled royalty, rich in sumptuous brocades, embroideries and Kashmir shawls. The importance of these Qajar paintings lies in their iconography and they represent some of the earliest known illustrations of Kashmir shawls and shawl designs. (For style development of the Kashmir shawl the reader is referred to Chapter 4, 'Symbolism and the Boteh'.)

The darkest period in Kashmir's history occurred during the regime of the Afghan governor Haji Dad Khan (1776-1783). He imposed a heavy tax on the shawl-weaving trade, and began the system of 'dagshawl' or excise-tax on shawls which later became such a burden for the poor shawl weavers that they even preferred death to the weaver's profession. Bamzai explains that the dagshawl system first developed out of the need by the state to seek more taxes than that which it already received through the usurious sale of saffron and grain.[10] In lieu of taxes from such produce, Haji Dad Khan taxed the weavers directly, who then numbered 12,000, with a small tax called 'Qasur-i-shali'. Subsequently, this too was abolished and a new *ad valorem* tax was imposed on every shawl manufactured. By 1813, when Azim Khan was the governor of Kashmir, the number of looms rose to 24,000. Azim brought back the forcible sale of grain to the weavers but kept the *ad valorem* tax. Thus the poor weaver was squeezed into debt. Invariably he had to borrow against future shawl sales in order to purchase his grain. In order to eat he had to weave.

Although Forster does not mention the dagshawl system *per se,* the high taxes accumulated by a shawl caused him to remark with a slight note of astonishment:

The price at the loom of an ordinary shawl is eight rupees, thence in proportional quality, it produces from fifteen to twenty; and I have seen a very fine piece sold at forty rupees the first cost. But the value of this commodity may be largely enhanced by the introduction of flowered work; and when you are informed that the sum of one hundred rupees is occasionally given for a shawl to the weaver, the half amount may be fairly ascribed to the ornaments.[11]

Statistics on the number of shawl looms in Kashmir at that time are not always

10. Bamzai, p. 489.
11. Ibid, p. 489, 490.

  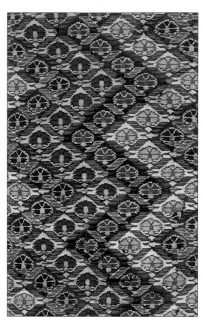

COLOUR PLATE 13.
Shawl palla detail, Afghan Period, late 18th century. (See Plate 111 for detailed description.)

COLOUR PLATE 14.
Shawl palla fragment. Afghan Period, late 18th century.

COLOUR PLATE 15.
Shawl or kani material. Buti pattern, late 18th century.

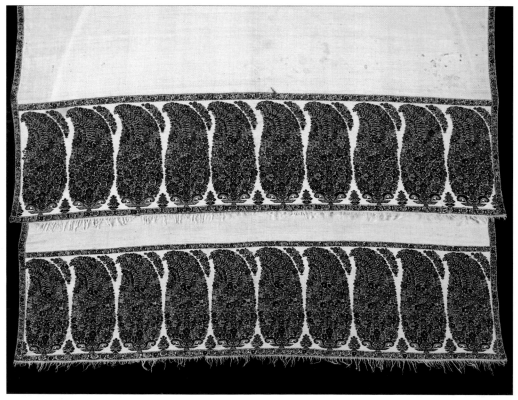

COLOUR PLATE 16.
Full shoulder mantle showing both pallas. A popular boteh style during the Napoléonic Period, late 18th century.

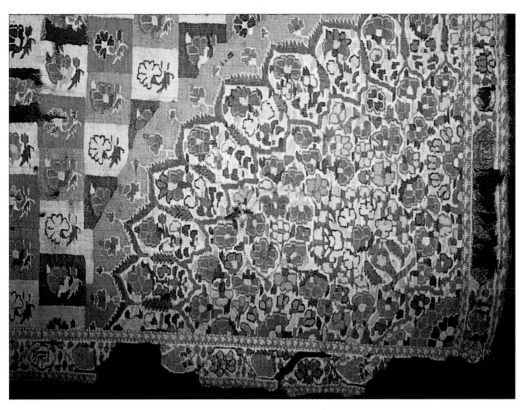

COLOUR PLATE 17.
Moon shawl detail showing typical Afghan Period features, late 18th century. (See Plate 112 for detailed description.)

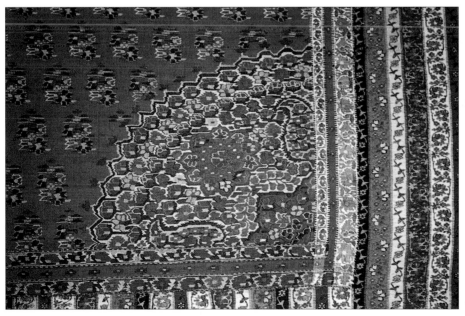

COLOUR PLATE 18.
Moon shawl detail similar in pattern to Colour Plate 14, c.1800. (See Colour Plate 182 for detailed description.)

COLOUR PLATE 19.
Shoulder mantle detail, late 18th century. (See Colour Plate 154 for detailed description.)

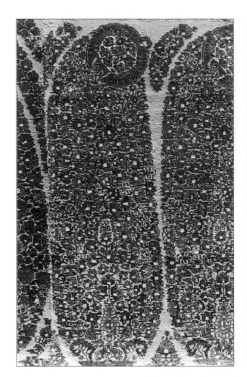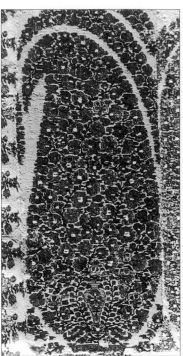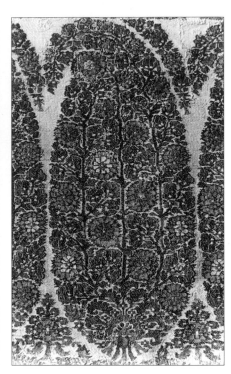

PLATE 1, a, b, and c.
Boteh details of Colour Plate 186. Afghan Period, c 1810.

reliable. Usually they were estimates received through word of mouth and they probably took into consideration all types of looms which were set up for shawl weaving. Our attention here is basically focused on the kani shawl and not on the plain or simple, undecorated shawl which served as the staple product (and still does) for both Kashmir's inhabitants and foreign markets. The kani shawl was made almost exclusively for the foreign market. This market is non-existent today although the Indian government is trying to revive the industry and there may be a maximum of fifty kani looms in operation now. Unfortunately, the product of today cannot compare with the level of art which was achieved over a hundred years ago – even among the most inferior kani shawls made then.

Although 23,000 looms were mentioned as being in operation in 1823, Richard Strachey provides a conflicting statistic in his 1812 report to the Bengal Civil Service. He estimates, in what appears to be a more precise manner, that 16,000 looms were operating in Srinagar and its surrounding area, and calculates that 80,000 kani shawls were made in the course of a year (see Figure l).

SIKH PERIOD (1819-1846)

Kashmir became a vital frontier region in the nineteenth century. With the advance of the British Empire to the north, Tsarist Russia into Asia towards the North-West, and the extension of the Chinese borders to Sinkiang, Kashmir occupied an important strategic area as the meeting place of three great empires. It was to become a centre of activity of various foreign agents engaged in collecting information on its geography, administrative set-up and defence.

The Sikhs were originally a religious sect, founded by Guru Nanak in the late sixteenth century. Among the peoples of India, they are marked by a distinctive religion and by intense devotion to their homeland, the Punjab. The Sikhs repudiated mosques and Hindu temples and taught the worship of God as Truth. They proclaimed the town of Amritsar as the centre of Sikhism and as a place of pilgrimage. Perhaps because of their conflict with the Mughals and Afghans, the Sikhs became superb soldiers and the sword evolved into a symbol of both spiritual and secular authority. Guru Govind Singh (1675-1708), the tenth and last guru, devised two sacraments in order to create the idea of Militant Brotherhood: the first a form of baptism with consecrated water stirred by a sword or dagger and the second the communal partaking of a mixture of flour, sugar and butter, which broke caste. The brotherhood created by these rites was called the 'Khalsa' or 'the Pure', and a member of the Khalsa observed the five Ks: i.e. his hair was unshaven, he wore a wooden comb in his hair, he had an iron bracelet on his wrist, he wore shorts and he carried a sword. In addition, the members of the brotherhood adopted the name of Singh or Lion.

The Sikhs became a military as well as a religious power. In 1799 the leader, Runjit Singh, captured the city of Lahore and became Raja. Twenty years later, in 1819, he forced the Afghans to relinquish their hold on Kashmir, and Runjit Singh became one of the greatest leaders of India during the period of transition between the fall of the Mughals and the establishment of the British Empire.

Travellers into the Punjab during the time of Runjit Singh were fascinated by the Sikh ruler. Those who had the rare opportunity of meeting him invariably recorded the interesting impressions they had felt. Runjit Singh was a short man with a terribly disfigured face ravaged in his youth by smallpox. In addition, he was blind in the left eye. The effect of this disability was awesomely enhanced due to the fact that his piercing right eye was unusually large (see Plate 2). His passion for horses was unequalled and his ability in swordsmanship was admired.

Sir Lepel Griffin, a Victorian biographer, on the other hand, wrote 'His moral being seemed at a superficial glance as dwarfed and distorted as its physical envelop. He was selfish, false and avaricious; grossly superstitious, shamelessly and openly drunken and debauched. In the respectable virtues he had no part; but in their default he was still great. With him, as with the most illustrious leaders of men, from Caesar and Alexander to Napoléon, intellectual strength was not allied to moral rectitude. He was great because he possessed the qualities without which the highest success cannot be attained. He was a born ruler with the natural genius of command. Men obeyed him by instinct and because they had no power to disobey. The control which he exercised over the whole Sikh people, nobles, priest and people, was the measure of his greatness.[12]

The Sikhs ruled for only twenty-seven years. During that period they were preoccupied with military expeditions and therefore devoted very little time and thought to ameliorating the sad condition of the people. Baron von Hugel, who visited Kashmir in 1836, wrote: 'the dreadful cruelties perpetrated by their earlier rulers who, for the smallest offence, punished them with the loss of their noses and ears, make the poor Kashmiri well satisfied with their present, comparatively mild government.'

Kashmir was frequently hit by natural calamities. In 1827 a severe earthquake caused a heavy loss of life and property. The tremors lasted for three months and, to make matters worse, an epidemic of cholera broke out. The number of dead was so great that there was not enough cloth to shroud the dead bodies. Just five years later, in 1832, a terrible snowstorm ruined the rice crops just before the

12. Archer, p. XX.

harvest, resulting in severe famine. Thousands died and thousands more emigrated to the Punjab plains of Northern India. The population of the Valley was reduced from eight to two lakhs.[13] Another famine devastated the region in 1838.

Few clues exist, at present, which might establish whether Sikh influence directly affected the style of the Kashmir shawl. It is true that its style underwent a vast, if not dramatic, transformation during the reign of the Sikhs but perhaps this was coincidental rather than that a valid association can be made between the Sikh way of life and the weaving industry (see Colour Plate 199).

Pictures from this period tell us little. Sikh portraiture occurred rather late, since Runjit Singh did not like to be painted, obviously because of his own personal appearance. There is no evidence that he liked or even encouraged the activities of painters. The first time he ever sat to an artist was in 1832, when he was visited by the Governor-General, Bentinck. In fact, he was amazed that the Europeans should attach importance to drawing at all. The Hungarian painter, Schoefft, illustrated a few shawls in paintings of the Sikh military court based on notes made in 1841. But here their prosaic uses as curtains and saddles do not directly further our knowledge of style.

Until the second quarter of the nineteenth century, no painting that is truly Sikh can be said to exist. Miniature painting as practised for the Mughals had expired

COLOUR PLATE 20b.
Detail of Colour Plate 199 showing daggers. Sikh Period.

COLOUR PLATE 20a.
Palla detail of long shawl. Sikh Period, c.1825. (See Colour Plate 37 for detailed description.)

13. A lakh equals one hundred thousand.

PLATE 2.
A drawing of Runjit Singh, described as 'King of Lahore'.

PLATE 3a.
Embroidered shawl, Sikh Period.

and it was only in the Punjab hills that artists painted for the local Rajput princes and their courts. A review of Sikh portraiture does not offer any revealing discovery about style or about the type of shawl preferred by the Sikhs. Neither is there any detail in other aspects of their paintings, including the boteh itself, which might be associated with some of the common motifs often found in contemporary shawls. Similarly, the contemporary Qajar paintings of Persia must be excluded although they show us that the Persian nobles, especially the women, admired the Kashmir shawl greatly.

The weaving industry was regulated by Runjit Singh's loyal governors who once attempted to entice the Maharaja to Kashmir, a region in which he never set foot. One day a silk carpet of extreme beauty was placed before him which depicted all the wonders of Kashmir's luscious gardens and rainbow colours. Overwhelmed by its magnificence, it is said that he literally threw himself on the carpet, and in rolling on its rich velour, Runjit Singh vicariously tasted the sweet pleasures of Kashmir.

The labour employed by the 'karkhandars', or proprietors, of weaving factories had begun to be regulated by the dagshawl system (see above) which was created under the Afghans. As taxes became heavier, the rich karkhandars found more and more ways to shift the burden on to the shoulders of the weavers. The proprietors complained that as soon as a man learned his work and some of the employer's trade secrets, he rose in value on the labour market, and every effort was made by his employer's rivals to secure his services. The practice of luring

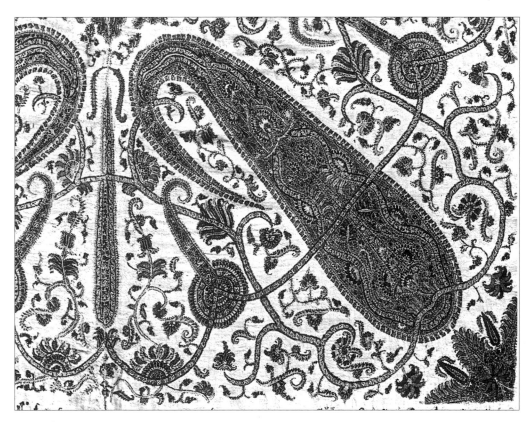

PLATE 3b.
Embroidered shawl, Sikh Period.

away a weaver was, therefore, made punishable by law. The weavers were now completely controlled by the karkhandars, a situation which amounted to little more than slavery. Furthermore, their survival was dependent on the allotment of rice that weavers were forced to purchase from the proprietors. The weaver, whether he worked or not, was obliged to pay.

These oppressive laws did not go unchallenged. Many weavers were said to have cut off their thumbs to escape the tyrannies of the karkhandars. The last Sikh governor, Sheikh Imam-ud-din, gave them a little relief in 1846 by setting the shawl weavers free from the bondage of the karkhandars. This revived the industry and during the rule of Gulab Singh there were 27,000 weavers working at 11,000 looms. But the wages paid to the workmen were miserably low and, moreover, in actual practice, the karkhandars managed somehow to keep the workmen under perpetual bondage.

Shawls manufactured in Kashmir during the Sikh regime were bought by Persian merchants and sent to Persia. Next came the Hindu bankers who bought them directly from the karkhandars and exported them to Lahore and Amritsar for Punjabi consumption. Runjit Singh distributed many of them as presents, as did several members of the Sikh hierarchy who imitated their ruler in their own small courts.

Jacquemont, a French botanist who travelled in Kashmir in the 1820s, pointed out that the officers under the Maharaja were careful to keep an agent in Kashmir to look after the shawls which were woven each year. This was obviously

necessary to assure that the goods be delivered to the Sikhs in spite of the strong European demand where clients were paying exorbitant prices.

According to Schoefft and the Russian prince, Soltykoff, the Sikhs probably made the Kashmir shawl more a part of their daily lives than their predecessors. 'The tents were doubled with Kashmir shawls', wrote the awestruck Soltykoff,

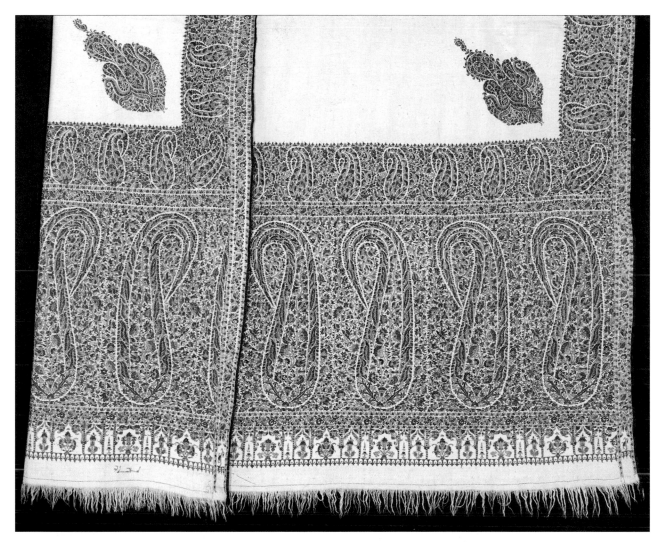

COLOUR PLATE 21.
A doruka or reversible shoulder mantle, single interlocked weave. Dogra Period, c.1865.

who entered Amritsar in 1842. 'We only walked on Kashmir shawls and while sitting down I perceived that all the alleys, ceilings and streets, as far as the eye could encompass were covered thusly of superb shawls – even the horses were prancing on them.[14]

During the reign of Maharaja Runjit Singh the Sikh interest in the shawl, and its symbol of the cone boteh, found expression in mural painting. The interior walls of the Golden Temple of Amritsar display a liberal use of the cone and bent cypress tree as purely decorative motifs. Apparently, it was not until about 1835 that the Maharaja was able to order the embellishment of the temple's interior. Another example is the 'baradari' or open pavilion of the Lahore Fort where Runjit Singh held court, and built possibly at the end of the eighteenth century. From what remains of the pavilion's mural, we can see a painted mihrab, the centre of which contains a large medallion on a sky-blue field in which prominent botehs appear 'floating' in scattered directions.

14. Soltykoff, p. 158.

PLATE 4, a, b, and c.
Details of a shawl with spectacular 'art deco' patterns. Sikh Period.

Plate 5.
*General Allard,
described as chief
commander of the
armies of the King of
Lahore.*

In contrast with the Afghan period, the shawl in the Sikh period, with its boldly sweeping curves, was more grandiose in design than ever before. It was a period of creativity unprecedented in the history of Kashmir, perhaps triggered by Runjit Singh's conquest of Kashmir in 1819, which had united it with the rest of the Punjab where his court was renowned for its splendour and magnificence.

Beautifully illustrating these ideas of pomp and grandeur is a vivid description by W.G. Archer:

As Western missions, travellers and explorers traversed the Punjab, visited the Sikh court or watched the Sikh cavalry riding and drilling, all succumbed to the glittering dazzle of their dress, their handsome appearance, their great beards and turbans, above all, to the sheer sensuousness of Sikh colour. Ranjit Singh himself might consciously affect a wilfully drab attire but his troops and courtiers exuded feverish brilliance. So strong a love for flashing, almost gaudy hues inevitably influenced the artist and it is hardly surprising that in

COLOUR PLATE 22.
Doruka with embroidered double interlocked weave. Dogra Period.

evoking the splendours of Ranjit's 'public image' they adopted a gay and dazzling palette. Confining pallid greens and misty blues to backgrounds, they employed colours as bold and loud as the great scarlet areas so common in certain types of Guler painting. Rich blues and deep greens, blazing orange-reds and piercing yellows imbued their portraits with clamant gusto and by a strident heightening of tones, gave the Sikh community a vivid impression of Sikh majesty.'[15]

This love of colour can be clearly seen in the shawl industry. During this great era shawl manufacturing transcended the mere decoration of a woollen ground and became the true vehicle of the technique of tapestry. At the same time the amli or embroidered shawl gained prominence. Although some authorities state that this technique began in about 1803, the shawl pieces themselves belie this theory. Up to now no embroidered pieccs have ever been seen which might show pre-Sikh characteristics. As a matter of fact, shawls woven before this period are devoid of any such amli technique; even the corners of the central field (matan) are undecorated.

During the Sikh period, although Kashmir was the centre of attraction for so many surrounding countries and provinces, each vying for a share of its com-

15. Archer, pp. 39-40.

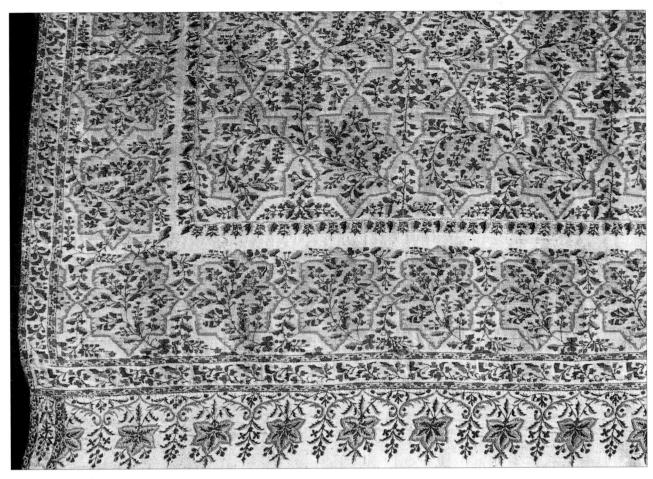

mercial activities, its weaving industry appeared to remain predominantly in the hands of Persian merchants. Jacquemont remarks that 'for the most part, Kashmir shawls were bought by a small number of very wealthy Persians who export them to their native country via Bombay and Bouchir.'

Alongside the strong presence of Persian shawl merchants and the markets they represented, there was also the presence of Europeans, engaged in the service of Runjit Singh. From this point on, Europeans were to play an increasingly important role in the kani shawl industry. Tales of Napoléon's military exploits were widely known and admired, particularly by a militaristic society whose symbol was the sword, and when two of his former generals, Allard and Ventura, rode into the camp of Runjit Singh in 1822, the Raja quickly recognised the advantage to be gained by having them in his army.

Other foreign officers followed: Colonel Henry Court, a French nobleman who later organised the French Legion, and Paolo de Avitable, an Italian by birth, whose dramatic career brought him to the governorship of Peshawar. But it is without doubt due to General Allard that the first direct link between Parisian shawl manufacturers and those of Kashmir was achieved.

Allard (see Plate 5) had been an aide-de-camp to Marshal Brune and, having

PLATE 6.
Kashmir shawl with Maltese cross, Sikh Period, c.1830. Except for a few details and the matan, this design is identical to one in a long shawl at the Yale University Art Gallery, with the Sacred Mountain pattern in the matan and sharp lunar crescents.

miraculously escaped death in 1815 following the fall of Napoléon, he sought refuge in Egypt before going on to Northern India. There he gained the confidence of the Sikh ruler; he organised his troops and ultimately became his 'conseiller intime'.[16]

Allard visited Paris in 1835, after an absence of twenty years. He spent about six months there and was received by King Louis Philippe (1830-1848) several times during the course of his stay.[17] He was the centre of attention of many shawl manufacturers, each attempting to entice him with various business propositions and to profit from his lucrative situation in Lahore and Kashmir. One businessman even proposed the importation of Kashmiri weavers and their looms.[18]

It is known that the General took advantage of at least one situation, with the prestigious firm of the Gagelin Shawl Company, who gave him instructions on

16. Cuvillier-Fleury,
Voyages et Voyageurs, pp.
294-5.
17. Expo 1867, illustré,
Poitevin, pp. 172-5.
18. Cuvillier-Fleury, *Notes
historiques...,* p. 89.

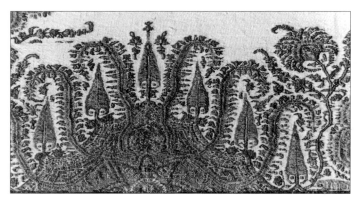

Plate 7, a and b.
Matan details from Colour Plate 37 of Sikh Period shawl.

'ways of *ameliorating* the Indian shawl industry'. On his return to Lahore he immediately arranged the export of eighty shawls chosen among 'the most beautiful fabrics of Kashmir and Lahore' and shortly afterwards, another very large collection of four hundred shawls was sent by his successor, General Ventura.[19]

Besides his status as commander of Runjit Singh's army, Allard was also appointed 'political agent of the French government at the court of Lahore' by Louis Philippe. He remained in close communication with French manufacturers and often sent the latest ideas in Kashmiri styles to Paris.[20] He also sent the Minister of Commerce in Paris the complete colour sample and warp-number designations stamped by the Syndicated Weavers' Corporation of Lahore. This proved very helpful to the wool spinners and shawl manufacturers of Paris.[21]

A few years after Allard's return to India, the nature of the instructions he received from Paris shawl manufacturers became apparent in a letter drafted by

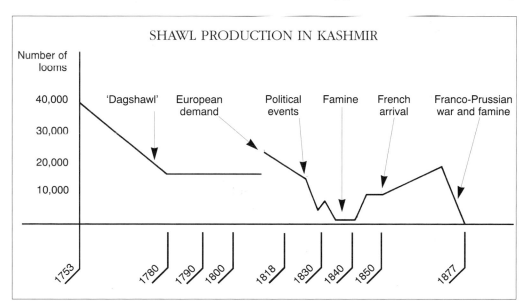

FIGURE 1.
A diagram showing Kashmir's shawl production based on statistics recorded by visitors to Kashmir during the 18th and 19th century. For monetary values recorded during the years 1850-1865 see Watson, appendix B.

19. Poitevin, op.cit.
20. Expo 1839 vol. 1 p. 145, J.L. Arnould received the public's admiration for a long shawl completely designed and coloured from a sketch sent by Allard from Lahore.
21. Deneirouse, *Traité*, p. 38.

the Corporation of Kashmiri Shawl Trade Experts. A French translation of the letter was found in the report of the 'Exposition des Produits de l'Industrie Française' in 1839. A further translation into English follows, hopefully still with some of its Persian flavour.

The weavers point out that a long shawl (dochalla) with large cones and borders, of the finest quality and sought after on the market can be constructed in the following manner: a pair of long shawls mounted on 32 looms can be woven within six or seven months and they would contain 20 seams. Now the question was: could a long shawl, unique (without a pair) be constructed on one loom without any seam in the body of the shawl.

It is for this reason that the Syndicated Experts Corporation of Long Shawl Manufacture has been convoked and after consultation, all things considered and weighed, they declare that if the shawl is established on two looms it is necessary that the warps and the wefts be of a superior quality to that of ordinary shawls and that in such case the design and colour mélange be in every way of rare perfection. Under these conditions a long shawl without seam would require three years to make during which time one would fear the alteration of colour and harm from insects.

The price of a shawl of commercial quality woven on 12 looms demanding

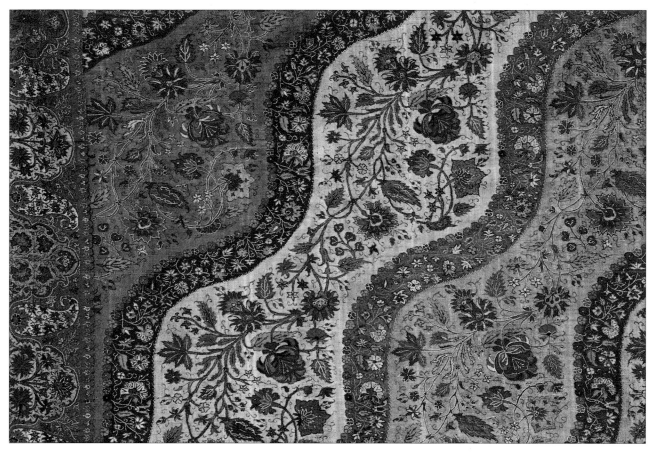

six or seven months of work would cost according to its beauty 1,200 to 2,000 rupees. Such is the information that we can submit to Mirza-Ahad.

Now from a common accord between the said manufacturers it is agreed that unless superior orders are given, the manufacture of a long shawl, in the best ateliers, will be based upon the following:

1. Four large cones, on four looms with head of large border on six looms.
2. The middle with the large border, scalloped edges and small exterior border on two looms.

In one word, in the centre of a unique shawl (without pair) there are always two seams the latter handled exclusively by the seamster (rafugar), who performs this task with a perfection impossible to perceive by the average person.

In these conditions a long shawl would require a full twelve months of work day and night. We will wait for orders from Mirza-Ahad before starting.

A square shawl with cones and open centre with large borders is made on four looms according to antique usage. On the demand of Mirza-Ahad, manufacturers have engaged themselves to make a square shawl (roumal) on one loom and this would require about eleven months of work.

Written in Persian and faithfully translated into French, First Secretary Interpreter to the King, (signed) Jouannin, Paris December 21, 1838.

The letter suggests that Allard's instructions involved the important and puzzling question of why the Kashmiri weavers were no longer producing shawls made in one piece (see Counterfeit or Kashmir, Chapter 6). This report confirms the weavers' intransigence against making such a shawl. Taxes on kani-woven shawl goods were extremely severe. As soon as a small piece of fabric was woven, the tax collector saw to it that it was cut from the loom and physically brought for public examination and taxed according to its quality.[22] The consequences of the dagshawl system were far-reaching and shawls were later on constructed by the patchwork method.

Although it has been assumed that the first French agents arrived in Kashmir about 1850,[23] it is now understood that the two generals, Allard and Ventura, were acting as agents as early as 1835, and they were probably responsible for the publication of Chavant's design book, 'Album du Cachemirien' by the Kashmiri editor Kel-Avak-Oghlou, in 1837. The album was composed of detailed tracings of Kashmir shawls and rug designs which appealed to French taste (see Chapter 7). The generals' desire at the time was not to impose French taste, but rather to ensure that French merchants were receiving an above-average and high quality product based on the tastes to which Parisian fashion had become most accustomed. They were also trying to break the monopoly of the East India Trading Company.

After the death of Allard, just a month after the report was written, Ventura picked up on both the military and business affairs left by his colleague. A year later in 1839 Runjit Singh also died but Ventura continued in the shawl-trade business. 'During the last 10 or 15 years', wrote Baron Schonberg, who was in Kashmir in the middle of the nineteenth century, 'a brisk trade in shawls has been greatly promoted through the influence of the French gentleman resident at Lahore, General Ventura. He took a very active interest in this trade and during some years kept an agent in Kashmir.'[24]

The Baron also refers to a Monsieur Francis Le Boeuf, whose name often appears scattered among the shawl literature of the early nineteenth century. Honigberger mentions him as a travelling companion to General Ventura.[25] But by far the clearest evidence of Le Boeuf's role in this highly competitive fashion industry lies in Hajji Mukhtar Shah's manuscript.

Le Boeuf established himself in the shawl business in Srinagar under the guidance of General Ventura. Mukhtar claims that he introduced 'designs of French taste' to the Kashmiri craft, and in particular the date of 1838 is mentioned for at least one special design. Unfortunately, this adds little to our knowledge since the date of many of Mukhtar's sketches is unknown. Nevertheless, it could be supposed that it was the 'bent-tip' boteh that was suggested by the sketches, in which the end of the boteh 'sprouted' another design device in the form of either a type of lance or a small thin cone, otherwise called 'buti-tip' cone (see Figure 29).

SHAWL ACTIVITIES IN THE PUNJAB

Even before the arrival of French generals in Lahore, repeated attempts had been made at establishing a prosperous shawl industry in the Punjab, but Lahore witnessed many sieges and wars and the emigrant weavers were frequently forced to flee back to their native lands. Sufi cites from an anonymous report dated 1820: 'A rich banker, Shoogun Chund, of a respectable establishment and treasurer to the residency, has within two years made up several shawls under his

22. Jacquemont, vol.3, p. 285.
23. Baden-Powell, p. 44.
24. Sufi, p. 567.
25. Honigberger, p. 92.

own personal supervision, getting material and workmen from Cashmere; but the expenses are much beyond the saleable value of the manufacture, nor is it equal in any respect to the kind of article made at Cashmere. The colour is particularly defective and this, it is said, is a particular property of Cashmere itself. No article washed [sic] even in its neighbourhood attains to the same superior perfection in this respect. Runjit Singh tried similarly to manufacture shawls at Lahore but failed just as Chund did.'[26]

Following the great 1834 famine in Kashmir, however, the centre of the shawl industry shifted to Amritsar in the Punjab plain. Amritsar specialised in embroidered shawls that copied the kani ones. The Kashmir weaving industry slowly recovered, yet there were still advantages in shipping the unfinished woven product to Amritsar for bleaching, additional embroidery, fringes and borders.

The beginning of the shawl industry in Amritsar was due possibly to English initiative. A report written by Richard Strachey on the manufacture of the kani shawl at Srinagar confirms that at the early date of 1812 in Amritsar 'shawls are better washed and packed than in Kashmir'. Strachey also travelled with Baron Elphinstone, as his secretary, when the Baron established an English embassy in Kabul. Elphinstone wrote in 1815 that 'Mr. Strachey made many inquiries on this subject and had some shawl stuffs made under his own inspection of wool procured at Amritsar. The manufacturers were pioneers belonging to the embassy and they worked in a common tent.[27]

During his trip through Hindustan in the years 1838-9, C.J. French confirmed the presence of a shawl industry in Amritsar. 'The local manufacturers are limited to coarse woollen and other stuffs, while some fine textures are produced by the loom under the superintendence and by the manual labour of the poor Cachemerians who, driven from their mountain homes, are forced to come hither for a livelihood, such as the tolerance of the Sikhs will allow them to earn. The unbleached shawls of Cashmere are frequently brought here for the express purpose of being dyed and having their borders put on, the work of embroidery being very successfully carried out in this town.'[28] Still, much of the bleaching work was abandoned and, as a result, Westward-bound shawl products were poorly finished and often went unwashed. Indeed, on some shawls found in western collections, bits of crusty rice paste can still be seen stuck between the woven fibres of the wool.

Other towns of the Punjab also developed their own 'Kashmir' shawl industry, due to the emigration of Kashmiri artisans who were forced to flee the Afghans. Jacquemont noted that 'since about 1810, Loudhiana has been the site of a new industry' employing 'over a thousand specialised workers and 400 looms', and in Islamabad there were '360 looms in activity as compared to 800 in the old days'.

While Lahore was still under Sikh rule the English government attempted to bring Kashmiri weavers to Loudhiana. According to the historian Sufi, 'a large bazaar was built for them and shops and houses were erected for workmen to feed the supply for England.'[29]

Apparently, in spite of the fact that such new industries were developing far from Kashmir, they were, nevertheless, closely supervised. The eighteen-day walk to, say, Loudhiana, was frequently undertaken so that Srinagar's merchants could assure the smooth production of their products.

This carefully guarded control of the weavers might have annoyed the English and prevented them from controlling the manufacture or distribution of the shawl. The French of course were very influential in this domain, due to the presence of Allard and Ventura, and it appears that the first half of the nineteenth

26. Sufi, p. 567.
27. Elphinstone, p. 508.
28. French, p. 72.
29. Sufi, p. 567.

45

COLOUR PLATE 26.
Doruka woven in double interlocked method with embroidery.

century was marked by a continuous economic tug-of-war between the two colonial powers, each trying to establish its own separate shawl industry, independent from Srinagar.

THE DOGRA PERIOD (1846-1877)

With the death of Runjit Singh in 1839 the Punjab fell into a state of anarchy. By 1844 many foreign officers and residents, previously engaged in the service of the Maharaja, had wisely left the area for fear of losing both life and property. It was not until the British, after a fierce battle against the Sikhs, consolidated their domination of India that Kashmir came within their direct sphere of influence. The Dogra[30] prince, Raja Gulab Singh, was given the rule of the Kingdom of Kashmir by the British under the Treaty of Lahore in 1846.

Conditions prevailing in Kashmir at this time were deplorable. Baron Schönberg, who visited the valley, gave a sad picture of the people:

> The artisans and the weavers of shawls were in…miserable condition. The daily wage of a shawl weaver was 4 annas (16 annas to the rupee) of which half was taken by the governor in taxes and for the remaining 2 annas he was paid in kind…from the government depot at a higher price than that prevailing in the open market. A shawl weaver was forbidden to change his employer, the Karkhandar.

30. 'Dogra' is a corruption of the sanskrit 'Dogirath', meaning two lakes. The name was originally applied to the inhabitants of the Jammu province.

46

Colour Plate 27.
Doruka-dorunga, completely reversible, single interlocked weave with ground colour change.
Detail shows fragment folded over to demonstrate the invisibility of the workmanship.

The weavers' endurance reached its limit and on 6 June 1847 they assembled and went on strike. In their demands to the Maharaja they asked for a permit to emigrate in a body to the Punjab. The threat was a success and the Maharaja conceded that the weaver should now be paid only according to the actual work found on the loom and could change his employer at will. However, it was not long before the weavers again fell slave to the oppressive tax system. In fact, the account left to us by the American visitor John Ireland tells us that the system

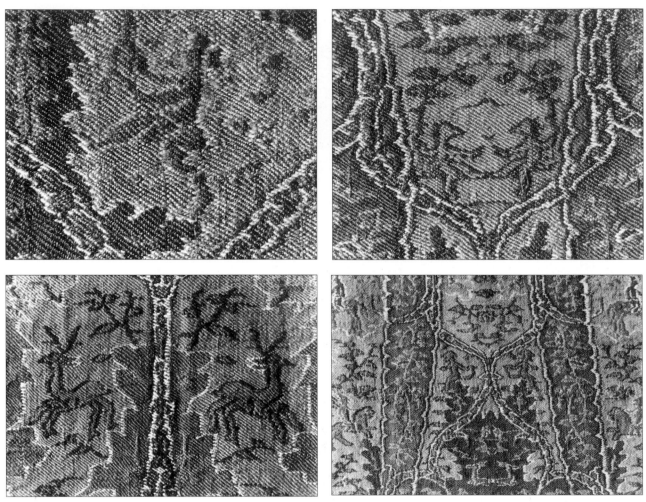

PLATE 8, a, b, c and d.
Details of Colour Plate 212, showing woven animals and people. Plate 8a shows a man dressed in turban and knickers, climbing a mountain with a pickaxe in his hand. Plate 8b shows two anthropomorphic creatures sitting on a bench facing each other under an arch of flowers. Plate 8c shows a pair of reindeer. Plate 8d shows a pair of devil-like creatures with long tails; below them sit a pair of reindeer.

remained in full force as late as December 1853: 'The Maharaja and his agents keep watch on every shawl made to get the 33% tax; and as soon as finished, the shawl is shown to them and the Maharaja's name marked in thread in one corner of all Cashmere shawls.'[31]

In the Dogra period, as during the Sikh period, shawl style was influenced by foreign events but even more directly. Through the constant demand and increasingly sophisticated imitation-shawl techniques developed in France, Kashmir's industry was quickly gearing its production to satisfy European taste.

Just how much exposure Kashmir had to European designs during the beginnings of the Jacquard loom (1818-1830) still remains a rather obscure question, although there are, without doubt, early Kashmiri patterns of this period which evoke definite overtones of English and French influence. The Jacquard loom did not advance technically before Deneirouse's innovation of

31. Ireland, p. 415.

PLATE 9.
Doruka (unfinished fragment). Dogra Period, c.1870. 28cm x 35cm (11 x 14in.). In all probability the last word in dorukas are those rare pieces which are entirely woven and without any embroidery at all. In this unique sample, the right half has no embroidery, but the left half is fully decorated by it, and we can clearly see how much the additional needlework becomes mandatory. Most dorukas were woven with embroidery in mind.

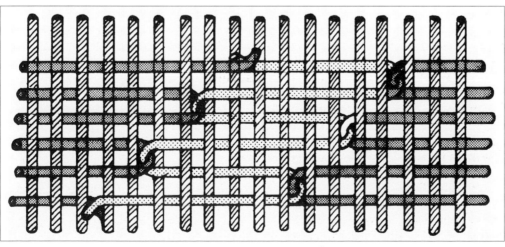

FIGURE 2.
Single-interlock weave of a doruka, a completely reversible shawl. Drawing by G. Vial.

1825 (see Deneirouse) which revolutionised the machine and the imitation shawl. And it was not until well into the 1830s that the resulting designs of increased dimensions became widespread and fashionable.

When French shawl agents arrived in Srinagar, the loom's 'art-nouveau' designs were automatically adopted by the Kashmiri. They revived the stagnant shawl industry with patterns that completely covered the shawl's ground, and left practically no open centre (matan). The Kashmiris were already geared up to this type of work as a result of their development of the large patterned 'tapestry' shawls of the Sikh period. The effect would have been the same if the agents had come with cartoon designs similar to those used by Gobelins or Aubusson.

Shawls of the Dogra period should thus be viewed in the context of French influence. The 'tapestry' shawl was a practical and rugged fabric employed for costume dress as well as for horses' saddles, tents, tent hangings and decorative curtains. It had become a necessity among the Sikhs.[32] The vast majority of these fabrics came from Amritsar and other surrounding areas of the Punjab such as Loudhiana, Lahore and Pathankot. But their wool was of a coarse quality and the designs were vulgar imitations of those of Kashmir.

This period was also marked by the discovery of more rapid ways of completing a kani shawl. Due to the large areas of design to be woven, the pattern was broken down into fragmented parts, each woven separately, at times on separate looms. These were sent to the rafugar, a shawl tailor or joiner who would work out which pieces went where. The Kashmiri people no longer know how such work was performed, or how the pieces were able to be fitted with such masterful perfection.

The designs brought to Kashmir by French agents represented various fashionable European styles. For example, the jacquard shawl's central field was frequently made of two distinct colours to give the impression that, when folded, there were two separate shawls (see Colour Plate 211). An Englishman, R.W. Chapman, working for the French firm of C. Oulman of Paris, actually received first prize for a design of this type at an exhibition of Punjab manufacturers. Thus, by the second half of the nineteenth century, the shawls of India were basically patterned after the French imitation – particularly the jacquard shawl. This did not belittle the design creativity of the Kashmir weaver for he was continually inventing new ways to assert his Indian heritage. French designs in Indian shawls were, in fact, an Indian interpretation of a French conception.

Although all foreigners had been expelled in 1844, they returned once political stability was achieved in Northern India, especially during the period following the Great Exhibition of London in 1851. Anand Koul offers a list of the French agents who came to Kashmir during successive years between 1856 and 1882, including the number of years each agent remained on duty and the company he represented. Included among them, for example, is the company Uhlan.[33] Koul also names Khwaja Amir Ju Gangu as one of the chief shawl traders of Kashmir.

A contemporary anecdote recounted by Ireland visiting Kashmir in December 1853 vividly exemplifies the bustling activities which the French shawl market created.

Most of the people were at work on a magnificent shawl for the Empress Eugenie of France, a white ground or center and it will be the most elegant one he [Hajji Mukhtar Shah] has ever made. He says thirty men have been steadily at work on it for 6 months and it will require three more months to finish it. The price when finished will be about 1,300 rupees or 650 dollars,

32. Soltykoff, p. 32.
33. Probably the French company MM Oulman fils.

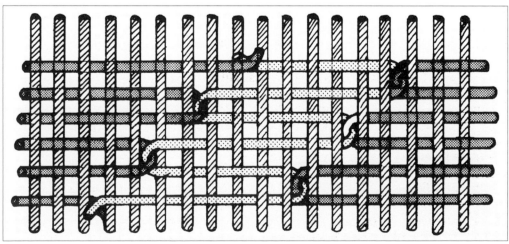

1825 (see Deneirouse) which revolutionised the machine and the imitation shawl. And it was not until well into the 1830s that the resulting designs of increased dimensions became widespread and fashionable.

When French shawl agents arrived in Srinagar, the loom's 'art-nouveau' designs were automatically adopted by the Kashmiri. They revived the stagnant shawl industry with patterns that completely covered the shawl's ground, and left practically no open centre (matan). The Kashmiris were already geared up to this type of work as a result of their development of the large patterned 'tapestry' shawls of the Sikh period. The effect would have been the same if the agents had come with cartoon designs similar to those used by Gobelins or Aubusson.

Shawls of the Dogra period should thus be viewed in the context of French influence. The 'tapestry' shawl was a practical and rugged fabric employed for costume dress as well as for horses' saddles, tents, tent hangings and decorative curtains. It had become a necessity among the Sikhs.[32] The vast majority of these fabrics came from Amritsar and other surrounding areas of the Punjab such as Loudhiana, Lahore and Pathankot. But their wool was of a coarse quality and the designs were vulgar imitations of those of Kashmir.

This period was also marked by the discovery of more rapid ways of completing a kani shawl. Due to the large areas of design to be woven, the pattern was broken down into fragmented parts, each woven separately, at times on separate looms. These were sent to the rafugar, a shawl tailor or joiner who would work out which pieces went where. The Kashmiri people no longer know how such work was performed, or how the pieces were able to be fitted with such masterful perfection.

The designs brought to Kashmir by French agents represented various fashionable European styles. For example, the jacquard shawl's central field was frequently made of two distinct colours to give the impression that, when folded, there were two separate shawls (see Colour Plate 211). An Englishman, R.W. Chapman, working for the French firm of C. Oulman of Paris, actually received first prize for a design of this type at an exhibition of Punjab manufacturers. Thus, by the second half of the nineteenth century, the shawls of India were basically patterned after the French imitation – particularly the jacquard shawl. This did not belittle the design creativity of the Kashmir weaver for he was continually inventing new ways to assert his Indian heritage. French designs in Indian shawls were, in fact, an Indian interpretation of a French conception.

Although all foreigners had been expelled in 1844, they returned once political stability was achieved in Northern India, especially during the period following the Great Exhibition of London in 1851. Anand Koul offers a list of the French agents who came to Kashmir during successive years between 1856 and 1882, including the number of years each agent remained on duty and the company he represented. Included among them, for example, is the company Uhlan.[33] Koul also names Khwaja Amir Ju Gangu as one of the chief shawl traders of Kashmir.

A contemporary anecdote recounted by Ireland visiting Kashmir in December 1853 vividly exemplifies the bustling activities which the French shawl market created.

Most of the people were at work on a magnificent shawl for the Empress Eugenie of France, a white ground or center and it will be the most elegant one he [Hajji Mukhtar Shah] has ever made. He says thirty men have been steadily at work on it for 6 months and it will require three more months to finish it. The price when finished will be about 1,300 rupees or 650 dollars,

32. Soltykoff, p. 32.
33. Probably the French company MM Oulman fils.

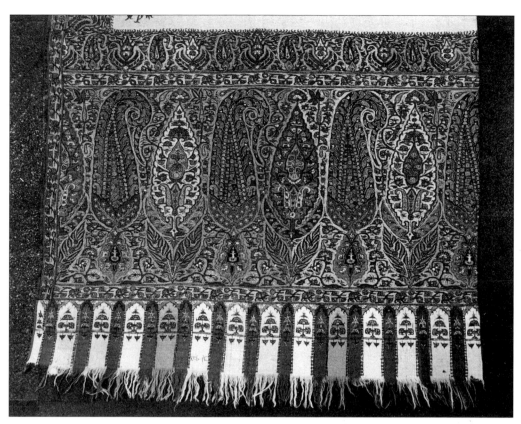

PLATE 10.
Doruka, reversible shoulder mantle. Dogra Period, c. 1870. 142cm x 330cm (56 x 130in.).

and such a shawl as would sell for about 4,000 dollars (!) in London or New York...my shawl took 15 men, 7 months to make. The workmen only receive one and one half annas (4.15 cents) a day.'[34]

DORUKA (THE REVERSIBLE SHAWL)

In the 1860s a new type of shawl was created which used a different weaving technique from the double interlocked kani shawls. The 'doruka' or reversible shawl enjoyed a tremendous success during the later part of the nineteenth century. According to Koul, 'it was in the time of Maharaja Ranbir Singh (1856-1887) that the "doruka" shawls or shawls with "face on both sides" were made. The inventors were Mustafa-Pandit and Aziz Pandit. These ingenious men also invented the "Zamin past qul bala" – shawls with raised floral work.'[35] This last term, 'Zamin past qul bala', recorded by Koul in 1915, may not, *per se,* imply embroidery at all but may refer to what has now become India's most prized collector's item, the 'dorunga', meaning literally two colours.

On elaborate 'jamawars' or gown pieces woven in the doruka technique, certain colour areas or often the whole ground of one side of the shawl were meticulously covered by a different coloured yarn of pashm using a couching stitch which followed exactly the direction and imitated perfectly the 'ribs' of the shawl's twill (see dorunga, Colour Plate 27). Such work is astonishing, for not

34. Ireland, p. 409.
35. Koul, p. 32.

51

only is it difficult to imagine but it is also almost impossible for the naked eye to discern such subtle contrast except by the use of a magnifying glass. In general the cheaper weaves required more embroidery to correct the defects in design expression. The weaving technique of both the doruka and dorunga are exactly the same. The dorunga is created from a doruka by adding the couching stitch to one of its sides, after it is removed from the loom.

Because of the doruka's high cost and its late arrival on the shawl market almost none of them was shipped to the West. The occasional piece today which does crop up at auction here and there was probably brought back by its owner personally from India. Therefore it is only recently that interest in this 'micro' weave has come about. The flat smooth appearance of the woven fabric is achieved by a single interlocking of the wefts' colours – a technique which eliminates the ridges on the reverse side (see Plate 9). This technique may be compared to those shawls woven in France or Russia in the early nineteenth century. It is very possible that agents from both of these countries encouraged its use in Srinagar.

The doruka shawl was known for its special design, which rarely resembled the large tapestry shawls. In the latter part of the nineteenth century, however, a technique was invented by which an 'imitation' reversible shawl was made, and this 'imitation doruka' became very popular. It was made by taking a kani shawl woven in such a manner that the pattern did not leave a mess of criss-crossing and hanging threads on the reverse. The embroiderer then outlined both sides of the shawl simultaneously by passing his needle from one side to the other, making sure that the ridges on the reverse were carefully concealed. By running the hand over both sides of the fabric, it is easy to feel the difference in texture. In the same manner, the perfection of an authentic doruka can be determined by the delicate way in which the skilled embroiderer has cleverly embellished his design.

DECLINE OF THE KASHMIR SHAWL

The shawl industry began to decline with the institution of the dagshawl tax system during the beginning of Afghan rule in Kashmir. The warring Sikhs sustained this system, perhaps not in name but in practice, if only to support their military exploits. The natural calamities of the 1830s caused the weavers to emigrate en masse to the Punjab, leaving their homeland. Finally, the master weavers refused to teach young apprentices their trade. As Jacquemont wrote in 1831, 'not one white beard was seen throughout the karkhandars'.

The arrival of the French agents gave the industry a tremendous lift which lasted for twenty years. The moving eulogy of Hajji Mukhtar Shah's narrative shows the Kashmiri's deep recognition of the French, who did so much to spur creativity and employment in a depressed industry. The Franco-Prussian War of 1870, along with a sudden change in European fashion, ended the European popularity of the shawl. Kashmir's shawl industry crashed brutally as a result, and received its final *coup de grâce* from the decimating famine of 1877. A prolific and rich era came to an end; the kani shawl had passed from a thriving actuality to the domain of legend.

CHAPTER TWO
Structure and Composition

It is important to understand the construction of the Kashmir shawl, not only for a basic appreciation of its aesthetic qualities, but also in order to date it within a particular historical period. Throughout Kashmir's history the shawl represents the numerous ups and downs experienced by the peaceful populace of Kashmir. Under Mughal rule the Kashmiris enjoyed a freedom of expression brilliantly mirrored by the arts and crafts in which they excelled, but with the arrival of the Afghans in 1753 and the Sikhs in 1819, political turmoil, oppressive policies and excessive taxation began to tear away at the basic fibre of this stoic race of people. Because it was a rich source of revenue, the weaving industry avoided being stifled completely, as is demonstrated by the many fine shawl specimens of the later period. By the beginning of the nineteenth century, however, radical changes in construction began to take place.

In spite of these changes, certain styles in design remained constant from the beginning of the seventeenth to the early nineteenth century. Such consistency was sustained by a ready market among people of conservative taste. Due to this, certain patterns often existed for many years before they came to be considered 'classic', and caution should be used when attempting to assign a specific date to a motif which developed possibly over a period of up to fifty years. The Kashmir shawl thus attests to the continuity of standard in fashion, and expresses the rich, elegant tradition of the Orient.

After the iconographic study of any given pattern, the next significant criterion for placing a shawl within a particular historical period is its basic construction. How the border (hashia) is attached, how the centre field is woven or twilled, how the design patterns are displayed, how the embroidery is applied, how many differently woven sections form the complete shawl and, lastly, what kind of dyes are used; all these give us clues regarding a shawl's origin.

There were basically three kinds of shawls: the dochalla or long shawl, the patka or waistband and the rumal or square shawl. It is possible that the patka may represent the earliest form of kani weaving; the decorated rumal (chandar) did not come into prominence perhaps until about the middle of the eighteenth century.

THE DOCHALLA AND PATKA – MUGHAL AND AFGHAN PERIODS

The dochalla, or long shawl, underwent a gradual evolution. The continuation of motifs over long periods makes it difficult to break down its development, but one can none the less divide it into the four main phases. Dochallas of the pre-Afghan period display prominent characteristics which clearly set them apart from later examples. In addition to the colours, which were usually of subtle and exotic tones, the ornamentation was strictly reserved for the extreme ends, or pallas, and for the narrow borders or hashias which ran the length of the shawl. The matan or centre field of the shoulder mantle was usually devoid of additional decorative weaving.

Because many shawls were made to special order for dignitaries of the Mughal court, their sizes may have varied. In 1668, Bernier commented that shawls measured about 114cm by 170cm (45 by 67in.) with a palla of about 30cm (12in.)

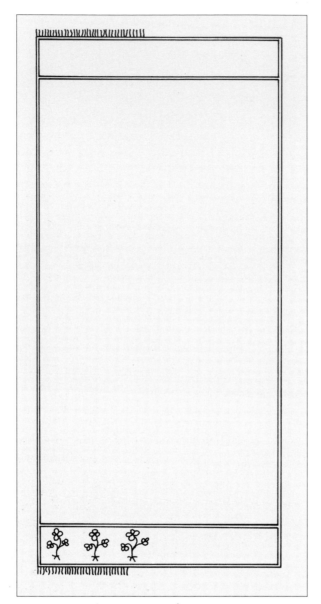

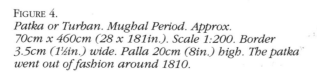

FIGURE 3.
*Dochalla, Mughal Period. Approx.
129cm x 280cm (51 x 110in.). Scale 1:200. Border
1cm (½in.) wide.*

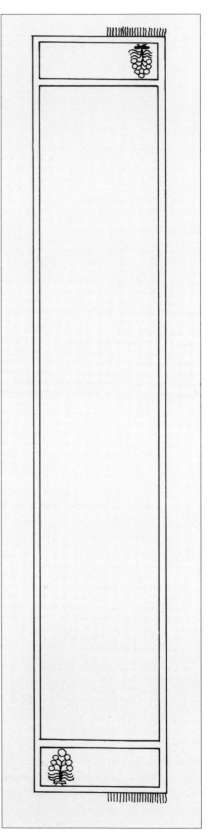

FIGURE 4.
*Patka or Turban. Mughal Period. Approx.
70cm x 460cm (28 x 181in.). Scale 1:200. Border
3.5cm (1½in.) wide. Palla 20cm (8in.) high. The patka
went out of fashion around 1810.*

FIGURE 5.
*Dochalla. Afghan Period. Approx. 131cm x 304cm
(51 x 120in.). Scale 1:200. Border 1.5-2cm wide.*

FIGURE 6.
*Tapestry shawl. Sikh Period. Approx. 150cm x 320cm
(59 x 126in.). Scale 1:200.*

high, and were decorated by weaving. His observations do not appear correct, and at the moment there are no existing shawls which support them. In general, it has been found that shoulder mantles of the period measure about 129cm by 280cm (50 by 110in.) (Figure 3), with a palla of about 18cm (7in.) high at each end. Shawls falling outside these dimensions were recut for one reason or another. These early shawls are rare indeed and it is always very interesting to discover them when two identical ones have remained sewn back to back (from the original idea of a dochalla or twin shawl). This reinforces the theory that during Mughal times it was the fashion for shawls to be worn in this way.

Although shoulder mantles were devoid of additional weaving (i.e. ornaments outside the pallas), this is not necessarily the case for the patka or waistband. Occasionally a patka may be found decorated with various overall patterns of small designs such as floral sprigs, stripes, or wavy lines, which further demonstrate the kani technique. Usually its size is approximately 70cm by 460cm (27 by 181in.) (Figure 4). The waistband, probably the oldest type of kani weave, died out around 1810 (see Chapter 4).

The Afghan invasion of Kashmir in 1753 had a drastic effect on the Kashmir shawl industry. As we have seen, the taxes levied caused the quality of the Kashmir shawl to deteriorate. Subtle nuances, such as whether the shawl's hashia was interlocked or woven with the entire shawl, became increasingly significant. Shawl-makers often attempted to escape the watchful eye of the tax collectors by manufacturing a shawl in several pieces in several ateliers and then fitting the pieces together. Such a technique, however, often had a negative effect on quality. Richard Strachey recorded in 1812, for example, that 'at most of the shops [at Srinagar] shawls containing much work are made in separate pieces at different shops and it may be observed that it very rarely happens that the pieces when completed correspond in size'.[1] It may be inferred then that fine shawls of this period which were permitted to remain on the looms until final completion came most likely from the royal ateliers which were immune from taxes. In other words, the way a shawl was pieced together or woven depended directly on the severity of the contemporary tax system. In contrast, shawls of the pre-Afghan period possess a rare diaphanous texture and were often woven in one piece with the finest of pashm. Most of them were royal pieces carefully preserved and stored away as heirlooms to be passed on to future generations.

At the end of the Afghan period the Englishman, Moorcroft, explained that a silk warp was employed to weave the hashia, which offered the advantage of a more prominent contrast of the dyed weft colours than could be achieved when just using plain 'pashm' yarn. This added strength and supported the rest of the shawl, which was disproportionately heavy. Although he claims that narrow hashias were woven with the shawl, there are actually few dochallas of Moorcroft's period which would make this claim a general rule.

DOCHALLA — SIKH PERIOD

There are two basic types of long shawls which characterise the Sikh period: the 'classic' and the 'modern'. The 'classic', demanded mostly by conservative taste, is defined by a continuation of earlier motifs which retained the appealing characteristics of eighteenth century shawl patterns.[2] But close scrutiny of the design composition reveals that significant changes came about. Besides the brighter colours, these shawls may often be distinguished by their 'modern' hashias. The graceful meandering vine composed of tandem repeats in the form of 'bent-tip' strawberries and 'pin-wheel' leaves, and the small flower buds of trefoils framed in hexagonal repeats, gave way to more abstract designs of meandering serrated leaves or branches alternating with sharply circular rosettes.

The 'modern' Sikh shawl on the other hand represents a clear break from traditional design. The important details of classic designs were suddenly

1. Strachey, p. 80.
2. Plate 190, although classified here as 'late Afghan', is nevertheless an excellent example as a transitional piece of this type.

56

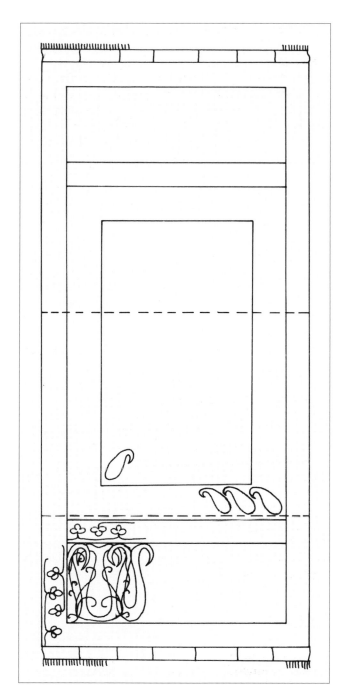

FIGURE 7.
*Dochalla. Sikh Period. Approx. 142cm x 310cm
(56 x 122in.). Scale 1:200.*

FIGURE 8.
*Dochalla. Dogra Period. Approx. 140cm x 330cm
(55 x 130in.). Scale 1:200.*

subordinated to stylistic conceptions of a fanciful and fantastic nature. No longer was the shawl designer limited to just the narrow pallas with their rows of botehs, which permitted so little freedom of expression. The increasing height of the boteh meant that a larger surface area of the shawl was included in the design pattern. This had the effect of ushering in further abstractions to fill the newly developed

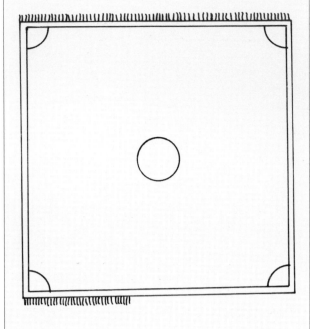

FIGURE 9.
Chandar. Afghan Period. Approx. 130cm x 130cm
(51 x 51in.). (Patka bashia standard.) Scale 1:200.
Border 3.5cm (1⅜in.) wide.

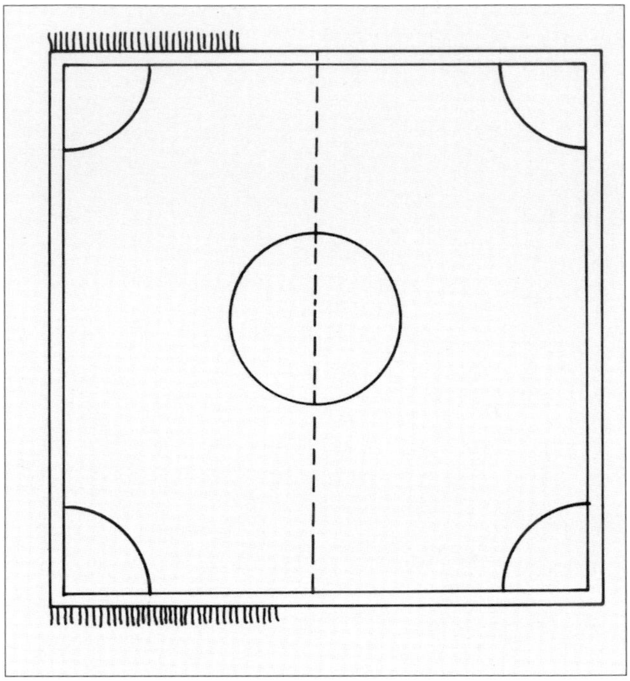

FIGURE 10.
Chandar. Late Afghan Period. Approx. 160cm x 160cm
(63 x 63in.). Scale 1:200. Border 3.5-4cm. wide.

ground space. A new type of shawl was created, the 'tapestry' shawl (see Figure 6).

The tapestry shawl was created by the 'modern' school of design. By 'tapestry' is meant those shawls which no longer illustrated simple boteh repeats on the palla, but often developed an underlying theme of abstract symbolism in which the sweeping boteh is reduced to a secondary role. The term also indicates a diminished matan or centrefield whose size is relatively small in relation to the remaining decorated portion of the shawl (Colour Plates 200-203). The hashias grew in size to about 10cm (4in.). On more elaborate shawls the palla design theme may invade the flanking hashias, but in general they were made separately and then sewn on. Such design intrusion was probably due to the jacquard shawl's influence towards the end of the Sikh period. The term dochalla is really a misnomer when applied to these types of shawls because they were obviously much too heavy to be worn in pairs. Nevertheless they continued to be made in this way and the term dochalla became a general term for all long shawls. Today the Kashmiri will say jamawar (gown pieces) to mean long shawl.

In the rumal it is rare that we come across the same full elaborate patterns found on the tapestry shawl, even on a diminished scale. The tapestry shawl continued up until the end of the kani shawl period, or 1877. Chavant's album (see Plates 62-68) permits us to date its early beginnings at least before 1837, and many of them are certainly contemporary with Jacquemont's visit to Srinagar in 1831. Last but not least we have Moorcroft whose 'Account of Shawl Goods' may date their real creative flowering at about 1820.

The 'jamawar tapestry' shawl was constructed of various borders, woven panels and embroidered fringes (see Figure 6). The central design of the pallas was usually made up of two or three rectangular panels which were then carefully meshed

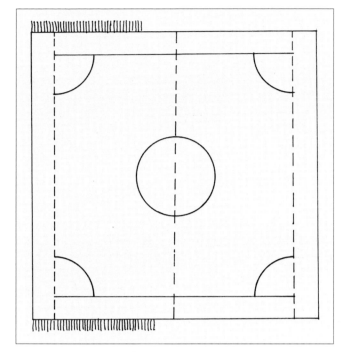

FIGURE 11.
Chandar. Sikh Period. Approx. 160cm x 180cm (63 x 71in.).
Scale 1:200. Border 14cm (5½in.) wide.

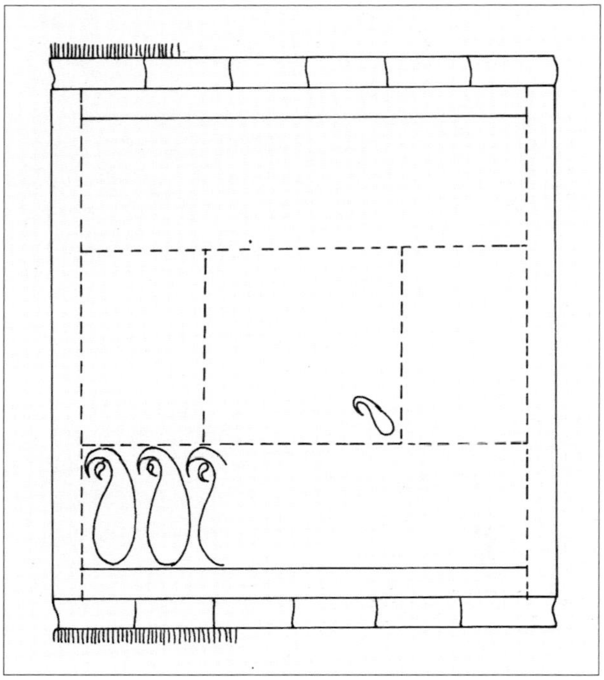

FIGURE 12.
Rumal. Sikh Period. Approx. 180cm x 180cm
(71 x 71in.). Scale 1:200.

together. Often this was performed so perfectly that the shawl must be flipped over to locate the invisible seam. Finer quality and specially commissioned tapestry shawls are usually found with their main end panels woven all in one piece. The matan was always sewn in and then flanked by rectangular panels which exhibited a motif similar but subordinate to that of the end panels.

Occasionally some jamawars of the Sikh period are found with what appears to be a peculiar type of construction. At first sight one would be tempted to say that the shawl was made upside down. But this can easily be explained from the knowledge of how the Sikhs utilised shawls. In this instance the pallas are reversed, i.e. instead of the botehs standing up where the hooks from the end of each palla are facing each other, the opposite is true. The answer for this is discovered in a painting by the Hungarian, Schoefft, of the Sikh Military court which illustrates the many uses of the Kashmir shawl. Here the shawl was employed as a curtain under the arches of the 'baradari' or open pavilion at the Red Fort in Lahore.

DOCHALLA – DOGRA PERIOD

During the Dogra period, which began in the 1840s, the method of construction remained basically the same but was modified slightly due to the sweeping designs generated by the Jacquard loom. The pieced panels, formerly of a geometric nature, were now often composed of all kinds of shapes, including circular forms. They ventured boldly and protruded frequently beyond the confines of the main panels. A fine tapestry shawl during the Sikh period was made up of as few as seven woven pieces; during the Dogra period it was often made up of dozens or more.

To this must be added the embroidered fringes, which were normally taken from standard stock and therefore required no extra time for their manufacture. During the second quarter of the nineteenth century, the town of Sealkot, about 200km (125 miles) south of Srinagar, became known for the weaving of hashias only. This accounts for the obvious differences in colour tones between the wools used in the main part of the shawl and its borders. Sealkot borders were often of a very coarse and cardboard-like texture, and the colour was usually of a pale green which rarely matched other parts of the shawl.

THE RUMAL

The popularity of the rumal appears to have increased during the late eighteenth century, while Kashmir was ruled by the Afghans. This popularity was probably due to the newly created markets in the Near East that had opened in 1753. Later, Europe also began its demands upon Kashmir's shawl industry, resulting in a rebound in popularity of not only the 'rumal' but all types of shawl goods. The rumal was cheaper in price and often took less time to weave and was, therefore, easier to sell than the 'dochalla'; at the same time it represented many of the fine decorative features and qualities of the expensive court shawls of legendary Mughal times.

Square shawls manufactured prior to about 1815 are almost exclusively of the chandar type, also known as moon shawls. There are few extant pieces which illustrate the boteh before this date. The centrefield contains a large circular motif filled with flowers and often centred on an open field of repeated buti (sprigs of small flowers), birds, or the chequerboard squares which were made for the Persian market.[3] Repeated motifs, in accordance with Islamic vernacular, were arranged in orderly transversal rows running across the matan or field. Each corner of the matan was ornamented with quarter circles of the same design theme as the central medallion (Figures 9 and 10). At present hardly any examples of the chandar exist which may be attributed to the Mughal period, but there are many of exceptional beauty from the Afghan period.[4]

During the Sikh period, as design dimensions grew, the rumal developed a new format. Four separate kani panels were carefully joined together to form a square, the middle of which was usually filled with plain black or white 'pashmina' measuring less than one square metre (one square yard). Of the four panels, the sides containing the two smaller panels were normally woven with the hashia, which was included within their design pattern, while the other two panels usually had their outer edges sewn to separately woven hashia strips. Finally, a fringe composed of multi-coloured strips of plain pashmina, without ornamentation, was added to two ends of the shawl, a traditional convention on shawls of the Sikh period (Figure 12).

The most frequently found rumal today is that of the Dogra period. It is composed of many pieces, each piece containing a part of the total design. If the pieces have been joined well, the shawl should lie perfectly flat without any buckling and its various motifs should match up perfectly. It is not difficult to find shawls of this type containing literally hundreds of pieces. These 'patchwork' shawls were made in great quantity after 1850. The traditional fringe of this period was made from many small pashmina strips of a variety of colours, each measuring about 8cm (3in.) in length. Each was embroidered with a mihrab-type motif.

Another type of rumal found in abundance during the latter half of the

3. Jacquemont, p. 289.
4. The finest collection of early moon shawls can be seen at the Benaras Hindu University Museum.

60

FIGURE 13.
*Rumal. Dogra Period. Approx. 180cm x 180cm
(71 x 71in.). Scale 1:200.*

FIGURE 14.
*Rumal. Dogra Period. Vase shawl. Approx. 180cm x 180cm
(71 x 71in.). Scale 1:200.*

nineteenth century was the 'vase' shawl (Figure 14). Void of the usual sweeping botehs, its busy design was composed of leafy vases or urns arranged in a complicated fashion and entangled with all sorts of strange botanical forms. This gave the shawl an overcharged aspect, as any fraction of the ground which might have remained plain was completely filled in with tiny, nondescript sprigs. The shawl's tiny centre normally was expressed by a sunburst medallion as the design's foliage merged from all corners towards the central axis. Another characteristic of the vase shawl is the special fringe which was manufactured expressly for it. It was made up of hundreds of small pieces of finely embroidered pashmina sewn together in an overlapping fashion and then embellished with additional embroidery which ingeniously hid the seams.

The last type of rumal commonly encountered is the 'foldover' or 'turnover'. A European innovation introduced in Kashmir, it was made with two narrow adjacent borders (sewn design side up) and two larger adjacent borders (sewn design side down). All four were of the same design. When the corner linking the two narrow borders is folded over diagonally, all four borders are aligned in the form of a chevron.

It is thus possible to discern the period when a shawl was made by examining the method of its construction. The general tendency, as the shawl developed through the late eighteenth and nineteenth centuries, was toward an increasingly fragmented construction as compared with the single-piece shawls made in Mughal times.

PLATE 11.
Shawl weavers of Kanihama, 1981.

CHAPTER THREE

Manufacturing Techniques up to the Present Day

WOOL

Traditionally, Kashmir shawl weaving employed a fleece derived from a Central Asian mountain goat. 'This type of goat is probably the most beautiful of all wool producing goats,' wrote S. Turner, England's ambassador to Tibet in 1783. 'I find it superior in beauty to the Angora goat. The colour of these animals varies. They have straight horns and are not as tall as the smallest sheep from England. The wool which serves to make the shawls is extremely fine and short. It is covered by other long and hard hairs which envelop the animal and conserve the delicateness of her first dress.'

The Angora goat mentioned by Turner derives its name from the city of its origin, Ankara, and it produced a greyish-yellow fleece. Similar species of goats were found in other locations such as Erzurum, Eastern Turkey, and Northern Persia. The Kirman province also produced great quantities of goat's wool which were exported along the caravan routes.[1] Vigne wrote in 1842 that 'goats producing the shawl wool are common in the countries west of the Caspian and excellent shawls are made there also.'[2]

Due to the varying political situation of the Northern regions surrounding Kashmir, the pashm (unwoven goat's wool; woven goat's wool is called pashmina) came from different places at different times: Yarkand, Khotan, Sinkiang, Lhasa or sometimes the Kirgiz steppe land region all supplied wool.

The ancient custom has not changed very much today, since wool is still brought down from the Eastern regions of Ladakh via the capital city, Leh. Even at the altitude of Leh's 3,500 metres (11,500ft.), among the scattered green, oasis-like hamlets of the Indus valley and where newly arrived tourists gasp for breath during their first week of acclimatisation, the local goats are incapable of producing the fine underfleece. The pashm cut-off point, below which the goats do not produce the special wool, appears to be at 4,500 metres (14,750ft.) in the Himalayan region known as Chang-Thang. This rugged and remote mountain region lies just east of Leh and runs north and south to cover a vast area of about 50,000 square kilometres (32,000 square miles). Approximately one half of Chang-Thang is controlled by Chinese Tibet. The legendary lake of Pangong, located at the centre of this region, is also divided in half by the Chinese Tibetan frontier.

The people who supply the goat fleece are known as Changpas, nomads whose livelihood depends on the herding of yak, sheep, horses and, of course, goats. Although some of the 'lena' (pashm in Ladakhi) slips across the border from Tibet, the greater portion of all the fleece supplied to Kashmir and the hill towns of Himachel Pradesh (Kulu, Manali, etc.) comes essentially from the Changpas of the Ladakhi side of Chang-Thang.

A tall robust race of herders, of whom 85% are Buddhist, the Changpas live in black yak hair tents called 'rebos'. Chang-thangi 'lena' merchants begin arriving in Leh by mid-July depending on the altitude at which their merchandise originates: the warmer the region the sooner their arrival; the colder the later. In any case, Leh receives a more or less continuous flow of lena up to about mid-September. According to Ladakhi dealers in the area of Lal Chowk, Leh's main

1. *Dictionnaire Universel de Commerce* etc. 2 vols., 1805.
2. Vigne, p. 126.

PLATE 12.
This shawl, of rather coarse quality, a product of Kanihama, will probably be sold at the Government Arts Emporium.

PLATE 13.
Preparing a 'hubble bubble' or hookah bowl with embers from the 'kangri' (small basket heater) for a moment of relaxation for this weaver from Kanihama.

boulevard, the annual quantity of raw, unclean fleece varies between 14,000 and 15,000 kilos (30,000 and 33,000lb.) per year. Of this seemingly large amount approximately one half finds its way to Himachel Pradesh through the Kulu and Manali dealers who journey to Leh in order to supply their own weaving centres. The bulk of the remaining fleece is bought up by a few Kashmiri dealers who in turn resell it to the shawl manufacturers of Srinagar.

Jammu and Kashmir residents can enter fairly easily the area of Chang-Thang but Indian residents, although not necessarily prevented, require special permission from the Deputy Commissioner. All other outsiders are restricted from entering and the recent Indo-Pakistan military clashes have, unfortunately, condemned this beautiful nomadic land to possibly many more years of isolation.

Not all prospective pashm dealers seek purchases through Leh. Some will go directly to Chang-Thang where a free and open market thrives. The best quality of fleece is derived from goats fed off the greenest pastures. In general, a Changpa dealer goes around collecting the pashm from the variously scattered areas where sometimes the herds amount only to a few goats. Once he has amassed a fair quantity he will offer the whole lot for sale. The buyer carefully inspects the wool by extracting several different samples, depending on colour.

COLOUR PLATE 28.
Domestic goats, Leh Valley, Ladakh.

The quality is quickly observed by his experienced touch and usually the finer the fleece the whiter it is. After the buyer has determined the various grades that he will end up with, an agreement is made on the final price. Thus the deal concludes very simply and honestly over a friendly cup of 'solja' or butter tea.

Lena comes in several shades: off-white, grey and sometimes black. In Leh, first quality sells for about 450 rupees a kilo; after cleaning, 400 grams remain. Second quality sells for 350 rupees a kilo, leaving only 300 grams cleaned.[3] The cleaning removes the longer wiry hairs which go into making 'namdas', embroidered floor mats manufactured in Kashmir.

Supply and demand and even the political situation can greatly affect the open market price. The Jammu and Kashmir government has established a price support system to provide Chang-Thang with economic stability. Since 1981, for a unity of standard exchange, or two kilos of pashm, 520 to 540 rupees is government guaranteed. Twenty years ago the price of fair quality lena was as little as 24 rupees.

Since 1975 when Ladakh opened its doors to tourism, the local shop owners of Leh and the local farmers have enjoyed a prosperity which make many of them take a rather blasé attitude toward trade in general.

Pashmina shawls are also one of the woven products of the handicrafts centre of Leh. The Jammu and Kashmir government is trying to promote artisan industries. In 1984 a pashmina shawl measuring one by two metres (39 by 78in.) could be bought for 550 rupees but although its warmth may equal those of Kashmir, visually it will never equal the work of woven art for which the Kashmiris are famous. The women in Kashmir are responsible for spinning the fleece and the quality of their hand spun yarn remains to this day unrivalled throughout the world. In 1984 Mr. Ali Raza[4] pointed out that two spinners from

3. Summer 1984.
4. The development manager of the Crafts Centre of Leh.

65

Srinagar were officially invited to Leh in order to show the Ladakhi women their fine technique. After only two months the project was abandoned and the women returned to Srinagar. It appears that the Ladakhis were incapable of adapting themselves to the tediousness of the work involved.

Many nations and regions have imitated the Kashmir shawl, but in general those woven outside Kashmir have rarely been made of the silky fleece from the Tibetan mountain goat and as a result have rarely been as fine in quality. From time to time, France and Russia have had access to a type of Oriental wool which greatly resembled that of pashm, and they copied Kashmir shawls, often achieving a startling similarity. Persia and Afghanistan made their own 'Kashmir' shawl. Some of the most important imitations came from India's Punjab region, where large quantities of shawls were quickly woven by the Kashmiri weavers who settled there during the early part of the nineteenth century.

In their haste to supply shawls to the European markets, the Punjabi weavers were forced to import Kermani wool from Persia and blend it locally, either with cheap goat or sheep wool. This is because Kashmir exercised severe control over its coveted pashm and did not relax this control until around 1860. By that time, however, it was too late, as the fashion market for such luxury articles had begun to draw to a close.

Nevertheless, the fashion market for shawls in India has endured as an elegant dress tradition, and among wealthy Indians a pashmina or shah tus (pronounced tooch) shawl is still considered a symbol of opulence. The seductive salesmanship of the Kashmir merchant is a sight to behold as he caressingly unfolds his billowing fabrics with an indescribably proud condescension. The old custom continues in which the client is permitted to take home a few shawls for a day or so before making his final choice, in much the same way as when buying a rug. Confidence between buyer and seller is an absolute must; the shawl represents more than just a fashionable purchase, it is an investment.

There are three main categories of natural wool used in Kashmir: rafle, pashmina and shah tus, and many variations exist in the quality of each. Today almost all common woollen shawls are woven from rafle, a machine spun wool derived from merino sheep.

The standard size for a modern woman's shawl is one by two metres. (39 by 79in.). One of top quality pashmina (plain woven goat's wool) sells at the Government Arts Emporium of India for about 200 dollars. But by far the world's rarest and most expensive wool is shah tus (king's wool). It comes from the ibex, a wild Himalayan mountain goat which grazes at extremely high altitudes. In the warm spring time the ibex rubs itself against rocks, thus shedding the fine short hairs which grow close to the animal's skin. The fallen fleece is then collected from the rocky slopes, packed and carried to the various weaving hamlets and towns. At present, the tus trade is controlled by Nepalese merchants who receive it from Tibet. Most of this trade is black market and with 1984 prices at 14,000 rupees a kilo (the equivalent of 1,000 dollars also on the black market), various clandestine methods must be devised to move the wool into India and on to Srinagar for resale. In Srinagar small measured mounds of the precious fleece are carefully weighed each morning on a jeweller's balance and then distributed to the few local women who are permitted to spin it by hand. Colours vary from charcoal grey to dark brown, and the price of the finest of the shawls made of this rich wool easily approaches ten times that of pashmina shawls of the same one by two metre (39 by 78in.) size.

In 1823 Moorcroft made a brief reference to 'asli' tus, which simply means genuine wool. A minute portion of the shah tus collected each year invariably contained a few white hairs, which were stored away and saved year after year. After perhaps ten or fifteen years of hoarding, it was possible to weave an all-white shah tus shawl. Because it was pure white, it was considered the world's rarest wool and accordingly its price almost inestimable. Such practice is long extinct.

Modern woven shah tus has an incredible warmth-giving quality which is felt immediately upon contact with the skin. In the traditional demonstration, the Kashmiri merchant squeezes it into a little ball, then tosses it up into the air; when he does so, it billows out suddenly to its full dimension. Shawl dealers refer to the shah tus as the ring shawl because in demonstrating the wool's amazing characteristics to the client the dealer takes great pleasure, in accordance with the ancient custom, in slipping the entire shawl through a finger ring. As shah tus ages it acquires a shiny lustre, and if it is white ibex dating back a few centuries the fleece develops a golden patina.

Most Indians will purchase this kind of shawl only from a Kashmiri, since the shawl's authenticity might otherwise be called into question. In addition, only the well-seasoned connoisseur would be advised to undertake this selection unless the purchase is conducted through a reputable shawl dealer. This is because there are numerous qualities which might fall under the heading shah tus or pashmina and therefore a certain amount of caution is necessary. The dealer will never have his shah tus cleaned to perfection, for to observe a few extraneous hairs within the weave is considered absolute proof that the shawl is genuine.

WEAVING TECHNIQUE

Since the unfortunate collapse of the kani-shawl industry in the late 1870s there has been no real attempt on the part of private industry to revive the ancient tradition. During the last one hundred years, the intricacies of the weaving technique have not only been lost but the numerous families who had once been deeply involved in making the shawls have also long since taken up other means of livelihood, often totally unrelated to their families' heritage. The last person reputed to have held the precious knowledge of many of the weaving techniques, Gulam Qadir Rangriz, died in 1979.

One cannot help feeling a certain compassion when listening to the conversations of Srinagar's inhabitants as they reminisce over the kani shawl's past and the once thriving industry which so enriched the culture of Kashmir. But in spite of the sincere efforts on the part of the villagers of Kanihama, under their present director, Ghulam Mohammud (who goes under the title 'technical cum marketing and production manager'), a lack of motivation is clearly apparent. The necessary stimulus might come about through demand and the financial backing of a free enterprise system, drawn from the weaving industry's private sector.

Furthermore, an almost insurmountable obstacle still remains: the guiding patriarchal heritage of the old weaving gurus, who were once able just by their living presence to convey the ancient tradition to 'children of the loom', and provide thereby an unbroken link with the past, is no longer there. The strong feeling remains that only they could ever offer the stimulation required to achieve success.

Today the specialists are gone, their work abandoned to the realm of legend.

Colour Plate 29.
Aerial view of the Kashmir valley, approaching Srinagar.

Colour Plate 30.
Street scene, Leh, 1984.

The 'naqqash' who wedded golden fleece to flower and colour, the 'rafugar' whose seams vanished, the dyer whose brilliant hues transformed texture into a chromatic scale of magic colours, and the master weavers whose dexterity baffled the onlooker, such craftsmen exist no longer. Only their woven masterpieces remain to echo sadly the legacy of a glorious artistic past. The weavers paid a heavy price for exercising their skills. Jacquemont had noted that almost all chalbates (weavers) were either crippled or blind before the age of fifty.

This loss of the traditional skills illustrates why it is necessary to pay careful attention to the eye-witness accounts of weaving by travellers to Kashmir in the nineteenth century. Moorcroft sojourned in Srinagar in 1823, and he provides us with one of the most valuable accounts of the overall kani technique:

Having ascertained the kind of pattern most likely to suit the market, the weaver applies to persons whose business it is to apportion the yarn according to the colours required. and when this is settled he takes it to another, whose function it is to divide the yarn into skeins accordingly and each skein is delivered to the dyer. Weft yarn is single but a little thicker than

the double yarn or twist of the warp. Its weight is estimated at one half more than that of the warp. The nakatu receives the yarn in hunks but returns it in balls and in one day he is capable of preparing the warp and weft for two shawls (dochalla). Next, the warps are stretched and clipped into a hot rice water solution which stiffens each length and sets it apart from the others.

It should be remembered that these yarns are being prepared for a manufactory process lasting as long as one year or more (cf. Allard's letter), depending on the elaborateness of the shawls. Here the yarn is given added strength and protection against fraying in order for it to withstand the constant friction due to the manipulation of the tojis.

We can also learn much about the technical construction of the shawl through an important discovery by the English linguist and cryptologist, G.W. Leitner, in 1870. His invaluable account provides important insights into the technical aspects integrating weave and design.

The warp of 'kani' is of three dimensions: 1) the smallest of 700 pairs of thread (a pair is technically called 'nal', 2) the middle size of 1300 nals, 3) the largest size of 1900 nals. These are the only three dimensions of which a warp can consist. Some fine extant shawls contain over 2200 nali. The warp is generally red although sometimes it is black or white.

A plan (naska) of the specimen of the shawl required is first drawn upon paper, and flowers of various colours are depicted. From this plan the number of nals required for the warp is estimated and spread on the loom. The specimen plan whose length and breadth are equal to those of the warp, is

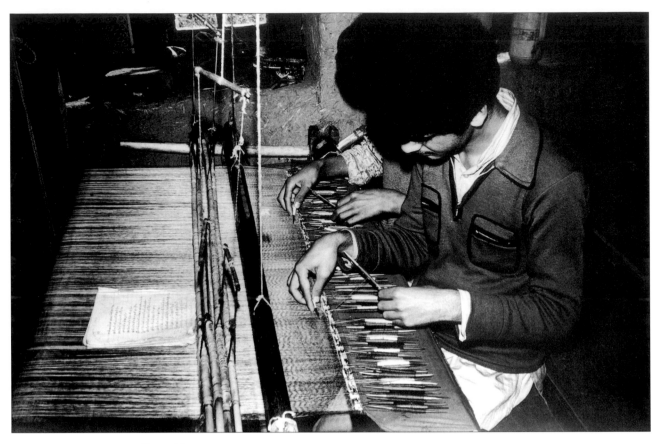

PLATE 14.
Young Kashmiris weaving a modern kani shawl in Kanihama, 1981.

then fixed underneath so as to allow the drawing to be seen through the warp. Keeping constantly in view the plan on the paper, the head of the manufactory (ustad) goes on repeating with marvellous rapidity in the language of shawl weaving the different colours and their quantity which he thinks would be required in the several nals in order to produce in the shawl the flowers and colours upon the paper. The other workmen, in accordance with these directions, take up the needles bearing the several colours and put them in where required. A clerk (talim nawis) is also present there and puts down upon paper, in the shawl alphabet, one after the other, the words as they are uttered by the head of the manufactory. The shawl numerals indicate the number of the nal and certain fixed signs which are placed on the right or the left of the numeral, the name of the colours. The plan of the shawl can be easily reproduced from this writing which clearly shows what colours are used in the different nals at any particular stage. Thence the great importance of obtaining as many of the older of these records as possible if any serious attention be made to revive the good old patterns.

Talam or talim is the name applied to the paper on which the process, as repeated, is put down. Each line of the talim is a clear representation of each stage (raftar) of weaving. The increase or decrease of colours, or the changes in their places necessary to produce the required flowers, are exactly

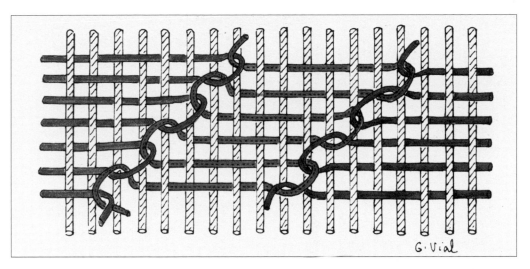

FIGURE 15.
The 'kani' weave. Twill tapestry woven shawl, reverse side. Drawing by G. Vial.

represented upon the paper. The aggregate of the number of nals, however, in each line remains invariably the same, being the total number of nals in the warp – this number is for remembrance sake put down on the top of the talam. Any mistake which might have occurred is corrected by a comparison of the parts woven with this paper.

Moorcroft had observed that:

The workman prepares the 'tojis', or needles, by arming each with coloured yarn of the weight of about four grains. These needles, without eyes, are made of light, smooth wood and have both their sharp ends slightly charred to prevent their becoming rough or jagged through working.

Under the superintendence of the 'tarah-guru', the weavers knot the yarn of the tojis to the warp. The face or right side of the cloth is placed next to the ground, the work being carried out at the back or reverse on which hang the needles in a row, and differing in number from four hundred to fifteen hundred,[5] according to the lightness or heaviness of the embroidery (woven-pattern). As soon as the 'ustad' is satisfied that the work of one line or woof is completed. the comb is brought down upon it with a vigour and repetition, apparently disproportionately to the delicacy of the material.

Silk is generally used for the warp on the border of the shawl and has the advantage of showing the darker colours of the dyed wool more prominently than a warp of yarn as well as hardening and strengthening and giving more body to the edge of the cloth. The warp differs in breadth, the narrowest consisting of twenty and the broadest consisting of fifty threads. The operation of passing the yarns through the needles is performed precisely in the same way as in Europe.

Three men are employed upon an embroidered (woven) shawl of an ordinary pattern for three months, but a very rich pair of shawls will occupy a shop for eighteen months. The weavers are all males and begin to learn the art at the age of ten.

5. Jacquemont has recorded as many as 3000 tojis.

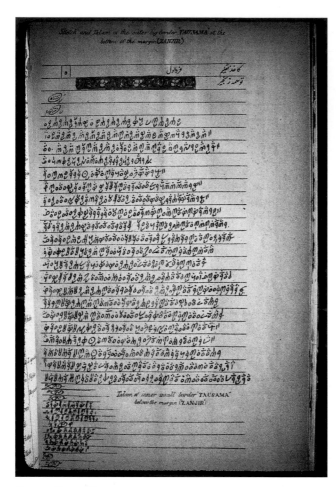

COLOUR PLATE 32a.
A sample of talim included in An Account of Shawl Weaving... *by G.W. Leitner.*

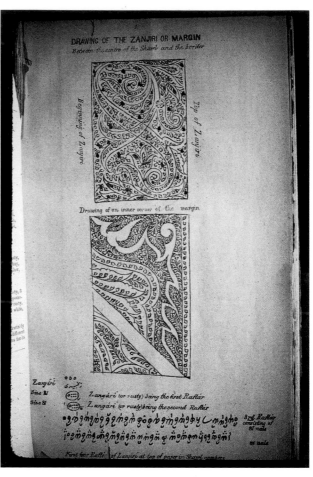

COLOUR PLATE 32b.
Shawl drawings with their corresponding Urdu notations, from An Account of Shawl Weaving... *by G.W. Leitner.*

TALIM AND TWILL TAPESTRY
by Peter Harris

Leitner and Moorcroft describe the set-up of a shawl weaving workshop, and Leitner includes with his commentary a sample of talim with tables of meanings for the number and colour symbols. But, rather like studying the same musical score and then attending a concert hall piano recital, one strains to see the pianist's fingers on the keyboard to understand how print is transformed into music. Without my own experience as a tapestry weaver observing shawl weaving for myself on a 1985 visit to Srinagar (see Colour Plate 34), I would not have believed possible the relationship between talim symbols and the structure and image of shawl fabrics.

The talim is a written listing of the sequence of coloured wefts for each weft pick of a shawl design (see Colour Plate 32a). It looks like rows of figures, aligned on the left, of unequal length; one small patch of weaving may easily run to many pages of talim, although designs are often used in repeat arrangements. The look of the design being described is not at all apparent from simply reading the lines of text (see Colour Plates 32a, 33a and 33b).

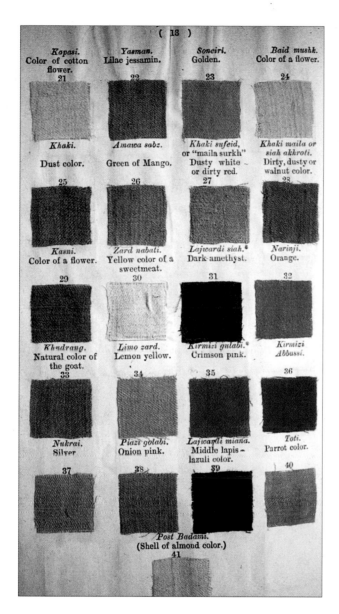

(13)

Kapasi. Color of cotton flower. 21	Yasman. Lilac jessamin. 22	Soneiri. Golden. 23	Baid mushk. Color of a flower. 24
Khaki. Dust color. 25	Amawa sabz. Green of Mango. 26	Khaki sufeid, or "maila surkh" Dusty white or dirty red. 27	Khaki maila or siah akhroti. Dirty, dusty or walnut color. 28
Kasni. Color of a flower. 29	Zard nabati. Yellow color of a sweetmeat. 30	Lajwardi siah. Dark amethyst. 31	Narinji. Orange. 32
Khudrang. Natural color of the goat. 33	Limo zard. Lemon yellow. 34	Kirmizi gulabi. Crimson pink. 35	Kirmizi Abbassi. 36
Nukrai. Silver 37	Piazi golabi. Onion pink. 38	Lajwardi miana. Middle lapis - lazuli color. 39	Toti. Parrot color. 40

Post Badami.
(Shell of almond color.)
41

COLOUR PLATE 32c.
Dyed woollen samples with their various Kashmiri names, from An Account of Shawl Weaving… *by G.W. Leitner.*

Each figure in a line of talim is a combination of two symbols, the main one specifying a number, with another placed above or below it indicating the colour of that number of stitches of weft (see Figure 16). Though some lines contain more figures than others, the total numerical value of each line is the same for the design of an area of weaving extending over a given number of warps. A sampling of shawl fabrics usually shows parallel pairs of weft stitches of the same colour, suggesting each line of the talim is used for two picks of weaving. Both of these rules are very helpful in confirming the accuracy of each completed pick for the weaver before he proceeds further. Symbols for colours may be either known by convention or specified by a colour card. The same talim system of recording designs continues to be used in the Kashmiri manufacture of knotted carpets. The hidden nature of the design information confers privileged access on the workshop which produced it, though at a price: subsequent handwritten copies may too easily add transcription errors.

Shawl weaving requires a loom with four harnesses, reed, and beater. Instead of a shuttle, many small bobbins provide a weft of the colour needed at each point across the width of the fabric, even if only a few different colours are used in the design. Most tapestry weaving employs a tabby or plain weave structure, a simple alternation of over one, under one, warp by warp and pick by pick. A feature of Kashmir shawls is their twill fabric structure, which may similarly be described as over two, under two, with the sequence for each succeeding pick advancing one warp to the right (as woven). Each time two harnesses are raised to make the shed for one pick of weaving, the warps appear two up, two down, etc., making pairs of warps at 100 warps per inch as visible to the weaver as single alternating warps at 50 warps per inch. Each pair of these warps is called a nal, the basic number unit of the talim, and a weft crossing one nal is what I have been referring to as a stitch.

Still, at 100 warps per inch, the scale of this weaving is extremely fine. Because in tapestry there is no continuous edge-to-edge weft, neighbouring wefts are linked to each other to prevent gaps in the fabric structure (see Figure 17). There are several styles of interlocking, but the one characteristically used in shawl weaving, called double interlock, has a couple of advantages: it provides a stable structure, as interlocked wefts are also linked from one pick to the next; in each pick all wefts move in the same direction and at each join the exchange of wefts is exactly the same. The boundaries between colours on the front surface are smooth and clearly demarcated, while on the back a visible, slightly raised ridge is formed. Because of this asymmetry the fabric is woven back side up, a stipulation that severely limits inspection of the emerging design visually, and makes the weaver dependent on accurate talim instructions.

Twill fabrics show a clear diagonal 'grain' or visual texture, as the parallel stitches of weft advance from one warp to the next in succeeding picks. In 2:2 twill a stitch of weft in the fifth pick will be placed over the same two warps as the first pick, but will appear to be connected diagonally to the stitch beside it. To keep the talim and weaving aligned vertically, remembering that each talim line is repeated in two picks, every second line of the talim begins and ends with a half unit, to clarify the position of those two picks in relation to the others.

Now I can put myself in the scene described by Leitner or Moorcroft, sitting elbow to elbow with one or two other weavers at a shawl loom. The first shed is raised and each weaver begins from a predetermined point, working from left to right, to pass a weft of the colour needed under a number of raised warp pairs, exchange it with the next weft and continue, as the head weaver calls out the combinations. When the pick is complete, the shed is changed, the beater is applied, and the same talim, read in reverse, is woven from right to left. This brings the working end of each weft back to the position it started from, ready for the next talim line. Instead of the clack-clack of a flying shuttle, the pace of work is slow, each pick taking some minutes to complete, and the only sound is the low chanting of numbers and colours. At 100 picks to the inch of weaving, more or less, even in their heyday shawls were luxury goods made possible by the low pay received for long hours of the weavers' work.

Leitner's description concludes reassuringly, 'Any mistake which might have occurred is corrected by a comparison of the parts woven with this paper'. Any inconsistency in the overall length of the woven pick signals that there is an error somewhere, and no doubt every weaver spends his share of time in impatient comparisons of the errant pick with the talim, with the locations of wefts established by previous picks, with his neighbour's portion of the weaving, or the two repeats of the talim line with each other. Weaving by following rote instructions requires a continuity of attention more strict than when the work can be conveniently inspected visually. But, a mistake in the current pick is relatively easy to correct. Because of the small scale of shawl weaving, the working surface obscured by interlocks and tag ends of wefts, and the high degree of consistency required in a repeat design, the detailed instructions provided by the talim amount to a highly technical system that works very well as long as it is followed carefully.

Twill fabric is more commonly used for garments because of its softer feel and drape than plain weave, so it was probably adopted as the weave structure for Kashmir shawls for the same reason pashmina was so highly prized as the material: its luxurious tactile qualities. Traditional tapestry, where the warp is completely covered by closely packed wefts, produces a thick, stiff fabric with limited uses in clothing. Therefore in the more open structure of a fabric woven under tension on the loom, warp and weft are both visible to a degree. Twill wefts crossing warps two at a time give a good impression of weft-colour predominance.

However, these stitches of weft crossing two warps, and in a diagonal arrangement, make it more difficult in tapestry to render clearly small details of the design. For example, weft stitches representing a narrow continuous vertical line will range over only two warps in plain weave, but five in twill. The drawback of this tendency to reduce design clarity may be what pushed shawl weaving to the practical extreme of small scale, limited by the fineness of yarns that could be spun and handled, and the weaver's eyesight to find and correct errors when necessary. Factors which made this work easier were: the visibility of pairs of warps (nals) compared with single warps, the routine manoeuvres of double interlock, and carefully following an accurate talim.

In the example just given, a strategy evident in the talim for representing a narrow vertical line is to indicate it only in alternate talim rows, which produces a dotted line more delicate and fluid than a continuous one. This goes beyond the basic mechanics of the system to a level of design expertise informed by weaving experience, and suggests the kind of lessons that might be gleaned from studying and comparing other talims.

The relevance and application of the musical score to a concert performance is fixed, objective, and repeatable, and so is the talim. But, like the musician's skill and interpretation, other undocumented contributions to the success of the weaving can only be inferred, such as the role played by memorisation for the weaver, or the use of techniques like spot brocading, to make the weaving easier and more effective. These are part of the lore too difficult to describe in words or diagrams, that the master weaver taught to his apprentices, through generations. While at first glance it appears arcane and mystifying, I think the talim provides an opportunity for better than usual understanding of this historic weaving technique, a rare artifact of the process that has left us so many dazzling products.

THE DYES

In addition to being known for the exquisite lustre of the goat's wool, the Kashmir shawl is famous for its beautiful colours. Pashm and natural dyes are two inseparable entities which, when properly prepared and combined, radiate remarkably brilliant colours. The whiter and finer the fibre of the wool, and the finer the yarn into which it is made, the more easily it receives a bright colour. This is one of the main reasons why the goat's fine white wool is preferable to that of sheep.

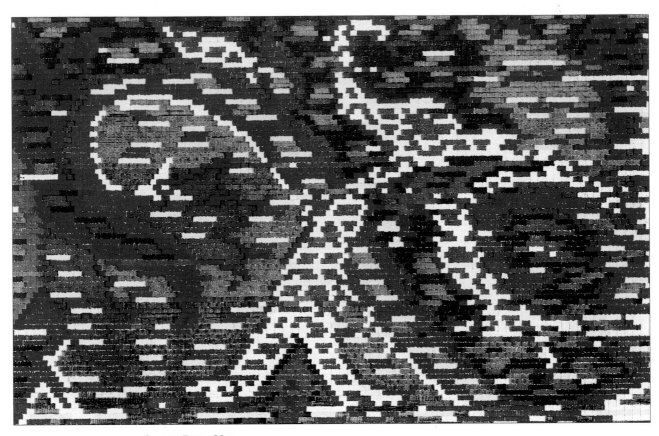

COLOUR PLATE 33a.
Graphed representation prepared by Peter Harris from talim of 'zanjir' given in G.W. Leitner's
An Account of Shawl Weaving…

COLOUR PLATE 33b.
Detail from a graphed representation prepared by Peter Harris from talim given in G.W. Leitner's
An Account of Shawl Weaving…

Hajji Mukhtar Shah claimed that the first shawls employed only red, saffron yellow and indigo blue. The colours, according to the earliest extant shawls, which date from the Mughal period, do indeed display few colours, but the tints used show a greater sophistication of dyeing techniques within the available chromatic range than existed in later periods. The subtle and exotic hues exude a colourful charm which harmonises closely with the Mughals' deep appreciation of nature. Moorcroft mentioned, for example, that over three hundred tints were

76

Colour Plate 34.
*A shawl weaver at his loom,
School of Design, Srinagar, 1985.
Both talim and graphed design
are shown in use as weaving
instructions. Photograph: Ellen
Adams.*

used during Mughal times. Although this seems to be an exaggeration, unsupported by the extant woven fabrics of the period, nobody can deny that India had long been the home of ancient dyeing techniques such as 'resist' and 'mordant', which held colours fast in spite of repeated washings well before other nations were aware that such techniques existed. But again, this is India; Kashmir remained a fairly isolated region for a long time.

The Mughal hues appear to have remained in vogue until the first half of the eighteenth century. At this time, strong indigo blues and bright bold reds from cochineal began to become increasingly evident in the 'transitional' shawl pieces of the period. Yellow was used sparingly.

With the arrival of the Afghans in Kashmir and the opening of new foreign markets, the shawl's popularity necessitated a larger scope of contrasting colours. But this did not mean that new dyes were invented. In 1823 Moorcroft mentioned that sixty-four tints were in use and that all were fast. At this time the dyer's art had already begun to decline. At the beginning of the nineteenth century a definite change is noticeable in the colours. Persia and Afghanistan not only demanded special shawl designs but also required particular colours. Among the kingdoms of Central Asia, for example, and especially in the markets of Kabul, a deep madder red was a traditional colour among the inhabitants. The ground colour on the Sikh tapestry shawls employed this madder red profusely and often it tended to drown the overall design of many of the

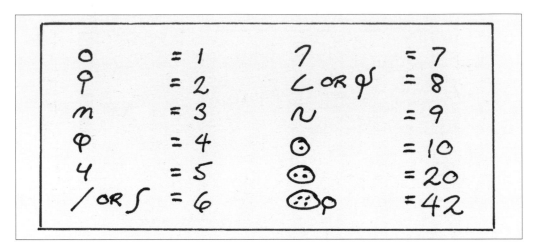

more elaborate pieces. This gives one the impression that many of the bright colours used before Moorcroft's time had disappeared.

Jacquemont arrived in Srinagar in 1831 and observed that 'very mediocre dyes' were being used; and he pointed out especially that yellow was not very fast. By the time Vigne arrived, about ten years later, the situation was not much changed, except for the fact that a new craft had been created to compensate for the earlier deficiencies. 'The colours of a shawl after it has been washed,' wrote Vigne, 'are often renewed so well as to deceive any but the initiated by pricking them in again with a wooden pin, dipped in the requisite tint.'[6] This supposes that yarns were uselessly dyed with full knowledge that their colour would fade drastically immediately after a first washing. One wonders why shawl makers even bothered to use them at all.

Moorcroft makes no mention of any defects in the quality of dyeing, but following his departure from Srinagar in 1823 many curious changes occurred within the shawl industry. In particular, one popular type of shawl represents a good example of this 'pricking' technique: the Sikh dochallas containing the bizarre hooked-vine motifs. Their wool was of a coarse nature and their normally dark muddy colours were a bit crude compared to the bright colours known in Kashmir. They might have been made in Lahore, the military capital of the Sikhs. If so, their singular design may have been related to the fashions of the court.

One possible cause for this decline in the dyeing techniques is the fact that many expert dyers emigrated to the Punjab, taking the secrets of their trade with them. Dyeing techniques are intricate processes which require carefully controlled conditions, and colours may be modified if the techniques are used elsewhere than in the original geographical region.

Reports of Kashmir and the Punjab of the early nineteenth century are filled with accounts of various towns which competed with each other for the manufacture of the 'Kashmir' shawl. The English and the French also vied with each other in this domain, luring away from Srinagar both dyers and artisans of the shawl trade.

By the close of the Sikh period dyeing techniques had improved and methods of making colours fast were rediscovered; as one enters the Dogra period with its large designs one rarely sees any of the 'pricking' which appeared all too frequently among the early Sikh period shawls. According to Hajji Mukhtar Shah, these improvements might have come about through the instigation of a Russian merchant from Kabul, one Yusuf Armani, who taught the local dyers new techniques in colour shading. Consequently, indigo was used with purified sulphuric acid while red was used with nitric acid. The Farahan rugs of the second half of the nineteenth century

6. Vigne. p. 131.

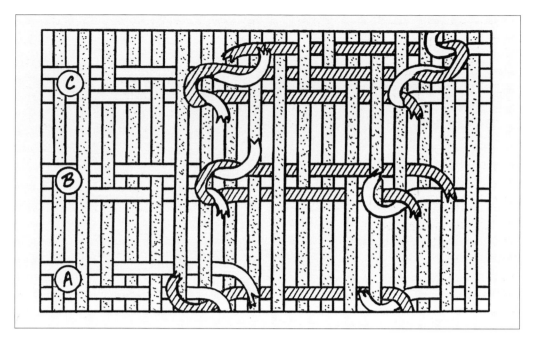

illustrate particularly well the effects of sulphuric acid dyeing, which gives the wool a greenish-blue colour.

The following list provides a general description of the colours in use and their sources, as recorded by the various visitors to Srinagar during the first half of the nineteenth century:

Crimson to violet: cochineal, kermes, logwood or any mixture thereof, pomegranate skins. Inferior tints were obtained from kermes
Green: English baize (broadcloth). Green was extracted from this cloth and reused in the shawl
Blue: indigo
Black: iron filings, iron sulphate, wild pomegranate skins
Light brown: wild pomegranate skins
Orange and yellow: carthamus and saffron
Drab (dull brown-yellowish grey): walnut skins
Alum (mordant): used for all dyeing.

Only Vigne ventured to record how a special tint was obtained:

The fine pale yellow colour of a new shawl is given by means of sulphur fumes. A hole is made in the floor about a foot [30cm] in diameter and six inches [15cm] in depth. Over this is placed a small square chimney of poplar-wood, open of course above. Some lighted charcoal is put in the hole and over it is sprinkled a small handful of bruised sulphur. Around the chimney and about two feet [60cm] distant from it is placed a horse or framework about five feet six inches [168cm] in height upon which four shawls are suspended and the external air is further excluded by another drawn over the top. When the sulphur is consumed the shawls are withdrawn and others are subjected to the fumes of fresh sulphur. They are kept until the next day, then washed again in water, dried and pressed several together between two boards.[7]

7. Idem.

79

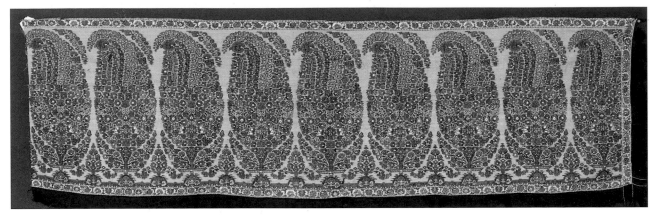

COLOUR PLATE 34a.
Palla fragment from dochalla. Afghan Period, c.1800. Balancing the boteh by its bulbous base is a vase posed delicately in the middle of the encircling arch of the two flower clusters. This multiple curvilinear style, set on a saffron ground, recalls the contemporary Napoléonic laurel crown. The symbol of the laurel became popular during the Consulate, extending well into the First Empire. The vertical and horizontal hashias consist of an uncommonly large floral repeat of eight or seven flower respectively.

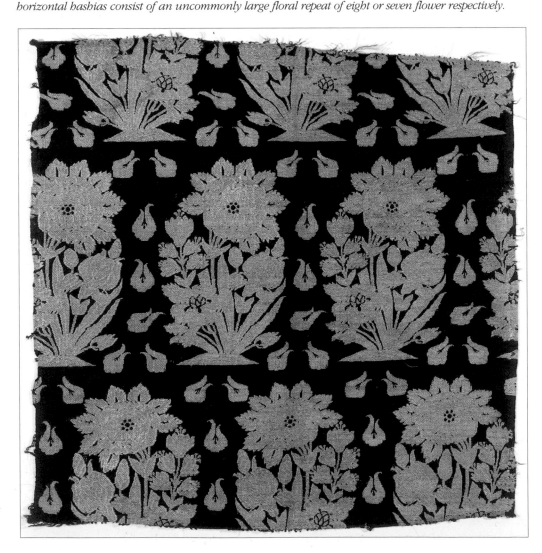

COLOUR PLATE 35.
Safavid silk fragment with gold threads, early 17th century.

CHAPTER FOUR
Symbolism and the Boteh

The key to understanding basic shawl design is to realise that its history is developmental. There is no fundamental break between, say, the high traditions of Mughal classicism and the work of the 'modern' artist of the Sikh period. To understand one artistic period of the shawl's history it is necessary to work through the others, much as a painter learns the important techniques of varying styles. The methods of weaving remained the same; the materials did not change; the colours varied slightly in their chromatic range. The slow and subtle evolution of the shawl's motifs can thus be understood by looking at the component parts of the shawl design itself, by carefully examining many shawl pieces.

Prior to the first half of the eighteenth century, shawls are extremely rare and this hinders the establishment of any firm theory for the various Mughal schools of design. And although there are many miniatures of the seventeenth and eighteenth centuries which depict people wearing the Kashmir shawl, extremely few may be positively identified as having a kani woven pattern. It is interesting to learn that almost all the known miniatures of the seventeenth century depicting a kani buta-patterned shawl are from the Deccan. The Muslims of the Deccan were of Turkish origin and the courts of Bijapur and Golconda glittered in ostentation equally with their Mughal rivals to the north (see Plate 17)

When we turn our attention to the court painters of Napoléonic France, although now we are looking ahead many more years, things change quite radically. The fact that the number of French paintings illustrating the Kashmir shawl during the Empire Period exceeds that of any other country is, in a way, indicative of the unique status that the French nobility had bestowed on it as an object of fashion. Style shows that the 'dernier cri' was undoubtedly the diaphanous long shawl, the extreme ends of which were patterned with stately botehs on a plain ground; buti patterns were also found though to a lesser extent. There are many shawl patterns which indicate that the artists of Kashmir were well aware of the ornaments that characterised the Napoléonic period. Some of the more popular floral motifs of the First Empire included the Greek palmette, laurel crown, garland, rectilinear leaf branch, cornucopia and split-leaf rosette. Animal figures included the winged sphinx and lion, and the swan; and in musical instruments, the lyre, flute and cymbal. Classical divinities, vases and urns were also used in decoration.

The Empire boteh usually contained compact flowers and followed a curvilinear and bulbous shape in which a vase and dish appeared. The apex, when it did not have a large flattened rose, was terminated by a sinuous play of racemes;[1] the botehs barely touched each other, the ground was free of ornament except near the top where a small detached branch of flowers, known as a 'coif', arched over the boteh's back, and at the bottom we find a buti or small cross of flowers.

One of the earliest paintings with a distinctive shawl pattern is a portrait of Madame de Sorcy-Thélussen, by Jacques-Louis David, painted in 1790. We observe a long saffron shawl with butis drafted in the Mughal manner, i.e. a small bouquet of three blossoms held by V-shaped racemes which in turn are secured by a possible Chinese character-like root; a hashia of similar flowers complements the palla. In the portrait of the coquette Madame de Recamier

1. Raceme (to borrow a term from the phyllotaxonomy of botany). Many of the aforementioned floral devices were simple variations on the Greek theme of the anthemion, a pattern of honeysuckle or palm leaves in radiating clusters forming a meander.

PLATE 15.
A portrait of Madame Rivière by Ingres, 1805.

(1805), Gérard reserves a dominating portion of the canvas for a long flowing saffron shawl. It too reflects a late Mughal style and the delicate hashia with a tri-lobed flower in the meander is very typical of this period. In Jean Mosnier's portrait of Madame Chakhovskaa, the shawl appears to clash with the date, 1806. The boteh is full blown, rather bulbous, and it sits on a large dish. The large rose at the apex is crowned by a tiny serrated leaf or stamen; the ground is free of ornaments. Because the shawl appears to have been cut down from another one

PLATE 16.
Portrait of the Empress Joséphine by Gros, 1809.

PLATE 17.
Portrait of the Empress Marie-Louise at St. Cloud by Jean Godefroy, 1810.

to form a square, indicated by the white palla and red matan, the palla itself may be older by several decades.

From the Empress Joséphine (1805) by Prud'hon we discover a number of revealing details: an all round 'dhor' pattern of large butis with serrated fronds and split-leaf flowers; an unusually large patka-type border flanked by large diamond-shaped dots in the guard borders; a sinuous vine device upon which the botehs are slightly raised. In David's 'Comtesse Daru' (1810) we again see this diamond guard border in the hashia but here is something new: a sinuous chain-like floral meander in the hashia (see Figure 17a).

A similar shawl to the latter is seen in Ingres' 'Comtesse de Tournon' (1812). The hashia shows a new meander composed of large split-leaf floral rosettes (similar to the ones on the Joséphine shawl) spaced within the interstices of a rectilinear vine (see Figure 17b). A running 'dhor' of tiny niches reminds us of Couder's later harlequin shawl painting, 1823, which is on display at the Conservatoire National des Arts et Métiers, Paris.

In two other paintings, notably 'Mme de Verinac' (1799), and also the 'Sermont des Horaces' (1785), both by David, we find a plain European shawl except for the extreme borders. The borders contain a narrow sinuous line pattern which

PLATE 17, a, b and c..
Courtly personages of the Deccan, illustrating the various ways the Kashmir shawl was donned in the 17th century.

alternates with greek palmettes. It is felt that this may have engendered the earliest 'dhor' patterns, first seen in Prud'hon's 'Joséphine'.

Finally, no review of European painting is complete without Baron Gros' 'the Empress Joséphine' (1809), a remarkable study in Kashmir opulence and revelation of character; Ingres' 'Madame Rivière' (1805), sinuously swathed in meticulous Kashmir; and Girodet's 'Revolt of Cairo' (1810), teeming with Oriental drama. The Empire style, as further research will undoubtedly confirm, demonstrates the links between courtly taste in India and France.

For a long time the Kashmir shawl has been characterised by the boteh (or buta, meaning flower in India), the principal motif with which the shawl is associated. This repetitive curvilinear shape has been known by many names since its first appearance on shawls in the eighteenth century including paisley, pine cone and mango.

The development of the Kashmir shawl is closely related to the development of the boteh motif; in fact, the motif's different forms express the different periods in the shawl's development. It began in the Mughal period as the flowering plant ('floral' boteh), evolved into a slightly abstract representation of flowers ('semi-floral' boteh) and then developed during the Afghan period into a more stylised curvilinear representation of foliage and flowers rising to a vertex at the top ('cone' boteh). By the middle of the nineteenth century, under the Sikhs, it had developed into an extremely stylised form of sweeping sinuous curves ('sweeping' boteh) far removed from any resemblance of nature's flora (see Figures 27-30).

The shawls shown in the Illustrated Guide (starting on page 253) have been chosen to illustrate the development of the boteh; by examining them and comparing them, the origins and evolution of this important symbol may be studied.

MUGHAL PERIOD

The Mughals adhered to a social structure ruled mainly by the laws of Islam, and their art, dependent to a large extent on Persian craftsmen, expressed a predominantly Islamic world view. It was a culture in which textiles held a significant place. Islam held a country's individual development within a unifying force, determining the themes and motifs which dominated its sacred and secular arts – arrangements of realistic flowers, abstract arabesques of geometric composition and calligraphic inscriptions – but eschewing the human figure.

The kani shawl of the Mughal period is marked by highly sophisticated woven patterns, a graceful, naturalistic rendering of the flowers of the boteh, and a carefully constructed hashia which served as a frame around the boteh itself. The remarkable artistic quality of the few extant pieces suggests the existence of a serious weaving industry centred around the court workshops of the Mughal emperors (see, for example, Plates 123-128).

There are difficulties, however, in interpreting the meaning of the realistic flowers identified with the Mughal period. The closer one approaches nature, the further removed one feels from anything abstract. Nevertheless, the Mughal shawl, despite the purity of its naturalistic motifs, has symbolic meaning. The boteh undulates gracefully as the leaves fold and twist gently about themselves in a play of light and shadow, while its peak culminates in a full bloom, which is often portrayed by a dominant flower blossom swaying at the top. The plant's reproductive organs are usually shown by the pistil which often protrudes beyond the top blossom. As the seed bearing organ, the pistil was a typical Mughal characteristic exemplifying the never-ending cycle of organic growth. On finer illustrations stamens can also be discerned (Plate 123). The open and semi-opened buds intertwining with the plant's sinuous stems provide a permanent reminder of the organic and regenerative forces of botanical life.

As much as this flowering plant – a key element in the study of seventeenth

FIGURE 17a.
Hashia tracing, showing an arrow-leaf meander, from the 'Comtesse Daru' by Jacques-Louis David, 1810.

century Mughal art – can be seen carved in stone and marble, pietra dura, knotted carpets, silk brocades and miniature painting, earlier Mughal art is almost totally devoid of this particular floral style. So how did it suddenly appear on the scene? Research has shown that the Mughal artist had copied botanical patterns directly from illustrated herbal books given as gifts to the Mughal Court by Jesuit priests in 1580. And at least three direct copies have been identified already as coming from the Carolus Clusius' 1576 *Rariorum Aliquot Stirpium,* published in Antwerp. This is very interesting indeed because Clusius, a Frenchman, was one of the most famous European botanists of the late sixteenth century and after many travels throughout Europe became the founder of the Dutch tulip industry.

In Chapter 1 we demonstrated how the French, under General Allard, exerted their influence on the nineteenth century shawl. Now, in a way, the 'herbal Gestalt' has been completed: what goes round comes round.

The earliest flowering plant in miniature paintings dates from the reign of Jehangir (1605-1627), at which time it appears that it was raised from the relative obscurity of the landscape of miniatures to become the main subject of attention

FIGURE 17b.
Split-leaf rosette hashia, from the 'Comtesse de Tournon' by Jean-Auguste-Dominique Ingres, 1812.

PLATE 18.
Royal souvenirs of the flowering plant exalted by delicate, carved, marble rococo mihrabs. Red Fort, Delhi. Built 1638-1648.

of the Mughal artist.[a] What were flowers like before his time? Does the Kashmir shawl really all begin simply with the introduction of a 'Frenchman's flower'. What about motifs before this period? After all, the earliest documentary references to the Kashmir shawl come from the reign of Akbar or the sixteenth century. But were these kani shawls woven? If we assume for the moment that kani shawls were woven during his reign then we should examine painting from that period and observe the fashion illustrated therein.

The miniature paintings from the reign of Akbar are essentially Persian in style and the textiles they depicted reflect contemporary usage. They were for all intents and purposes identical to those worn at the courts of Persia.

In reviewing, for example, the *Hamza Nama,* the story of Amir Hamza, an uncle of the Prophet, we find that gold brocaded costumes were the order of the day. The patterns consisted of palmette blossoms, birds, small cloud wisps, chintamani designs and often tiny floral sprigs – all rather simple and freely spaced.

The full rakish force of Oriental regalia was vented mainly through the rich patterns of rugs, tent hangings, turbans, patkas – not to speak of the overawing display of Islamic tile decoration. In such a dazzling repertoire, the cross-currents of Turkish and Persian art, we find the well-known swirling vines of the 'saz' leaf and rosette configuration, the spiralling split-leaf arabesque, again the chintamani design of three balls borne on the crest of wavy lines, etc. In addition, there is the cartouche, trellis, ogive, snake-like Chinese cloudband, and so on. Except for the Chinese cloud, none of these patterns seemed, at least according to extant evidence, to have gained admission to the shawl 'canvas'. True, one observes quite frequently the wearing of shawls which could easily be taken as pashmina,

2. Vivian Rich, *Mughal Floral Painting and its European Sources,* part of a Doctoral Thesis, 1981, School of Oriental and African Art Studies, UK.

FIGURE 18a.
Hashia detail of Colour Plate 116, Mughal.

but they are almost always without design and the absence of the flowering plant or boteh is obvious, both on the shawls and textiles in general.

Throughout this early Mughal style of ornamentation we find flowers drawn simplistically with little attempt at botanical accuracy. Before 1620, shrubs and small plants were a perfunctory addition to painting. As a quick solution to realism it was in general standard to hide roots with rocks or mounds. Fronds were plunked down at the flower's base, fanning out in an arching but conventional manner, while often a lonesome stalk or raceme rose tall to culminate in a pointed arch – a ploy frequently encountered perhaps to mimic the movement of a personage. Tree leaves were mostly spade-like in form with a slight bend at the tip and invariably both leaves and fronds were tinged all over with yellow.

The foregoing is really the persianate style and hitherto no shawls have been found which clearly reflect this style. Of course, things would have been so much easier if early patterns had incorporated the persianate style along with the fashion of the flowering plant. But this is not the case and the very lack of such stylistic commingling tends to confirm the theory that the Kashmir shawl as we know it began as early as the reign of Jehangir.

In contrast to shawls, seventeenth century Mughal carpets not only echo nostalgically of design elements in the persianate style but in many cases one can clearly witness the expression of two cultures arguing an established fashion.

In the conventional flowering plant under Jehangir the flowers were in general

FIGURE 18b.
Hashia detail of Colour Plate 117, Mughal.

PLATE 19a
The Bibi-ka-Maqbara, built by Auranzeb's son, 1679.

all of the same species, freely spaced on a plain background. Although they were at times woven in ways suggesting various states of growth and positions of suspension, the total effect was always that of a very specific plant. We also often find leaf stems at the base of the plants. As the boteh evolved towards a more abstract style, the stem became a kind of forsythia branch or raceme (stalked flowers arranged singly along a common main axis); the foliage was composed of either flower buds or tiny leaves, normally with two branches placed at the bottom of the boteh opposite each other (see Plates 88-89). From here the boteh evolved in one of two ways: either as its outline became more formal with the racemes arched upwards, becoming the proper curves of the general form; or else the racemes remained under the weight of the plant, still in the form of opposing leaves but taking the shape of a ram's horn curving outward and down. This effect is especially apparent on shawls which have multiple rows of small repeated botehs (or buti). The ram's horn or leafy fronds later appeared along with other flowers, pouring out of the base which had been added to the design. Finally, the motifs all blended together and eventually assumed the curvilinear shape of the vase which influenced greatly and set the pattern for the cone boteh of the Afghan period.

The hashia acts as a frame for the palla's row of repeated boteh. Often, and following strict rules, a key element of the flower was harmoniously incorporated into the hashia's meandering vine. In this way, the boteh's design was enhanced by the hashia which echoed and framed it. If the boteh's design was in itself aesthetically lacking, the hashia could compensate, and thereby preserve the overall aesthetic effect. The results were often surprising; the ingenious blending of rectilinear and floral movement in the high Mughal period demonstrates an acute awareness of the most subtle and delicate design techniques, the rules of which may have been established by the court workshops.

Later, hashia designs lacked artistic harmony but rather blended in either by force of matching colour or increased frequency of their vine repeats. Such is the style often displayed by hashias of the early eighteenth century. The palla's top and bottom hashias differ only from the long flanking ones in that the tandem repeats of the latter are shown compressed. This phenomenon appears to be reserved only for shoulder mantles.

There is reason to believe that certain floral forms of the boteh developed out of the Mughal social structure. For example, the Mughals' passion for flowers is undisputed and evident in their art. However, from time to time certain strange leaves and flowers appear on shawls in ways which do not allow logical conclusions concerning their provenance. They seem enigmatic in much the same way as the bizarre geometric motifs found on nomadic tribal rugs. Besides the shawl's colour, the mixture of flower blossoms and severely laterally pointed leaves might well have reflected a special system of rank, indicating the owner's status within the hierarchy of a rigid society (see Colour Plate 121 and Plate 90). More specifically, the patka shawl most often displays lateral leaf displacement. The patka is a band wrapped and tied around the waist. Soldiers, especially, were required to wear them, and kings and emperors bestowed them on their officers and nobles in recognition of services rendered. During Akbar's time the waistband invariably displayed geometric patterns, while a change to flower designs became noticeable under the rule of his son, Jehangir.

Except through brief and imprecise chronicles scattered here and there, extremely little is known about the kani industry of the early seventeenth century. A recent and major find by the Jagdish and Kamla Mittal Museum of Indian Art has brought to light new evidence of this obscure period of shawl weaving. The find consists of six palla fragments, illustrating altogether twenty-two floral botehs from a shoulder mantle. They were woven of a rare and exceedingly fine-spun shah tus, finer than any other kani piece known, probably during the early seventeenth century. The Mittal fragments were obviously part of an exceptional royal piece and possibly also part of a king's 'toshakhana' (imperial wardrobe) as observed by a faint stamp attached to one of the fragment's corners. Their beauty, execution and feathery texture exudes an aura of technical sophistication which could only have been achieved through an industry developed over an extended number of years. This find opens a new and early chapter in the history of Mughal art showing the existence of an elaborate arid unmistakably rich industry yet to be surpassed in intricacy of weaving and flawlessness of design (see Colour Plate 123).

Another of the earliest extant Mughal pieces known is composed of two palla fragments, one of which is conserved by the Calico Museum in India and the other by the Victoria and Albert Museum, London. Delicate flowers, captured in the process of blooming, form the motif. Here is the realism typical of Mughal shawls, achieved through the subtle play of undulating leaves and of frail curved stems. The buds and blossoms are slightly exaggerated in size, and the piece gives one the impression of the fragility of a perishable flower burdened by its

PLATE 19b.
Embossed brass floral decoration on door of the Bibi-ka-Maqbara.

PLATE 20, a, b and c.
Carved marble dadoes from the Red Forts of Delhi and Agra.

PLATE 21.
Cenotaph, Taj Mahal, Agra.

overgrown flora. The plant's stem seems to grow right out of the ground, although there is a slight attempt to show root growth, a peculiarity of early Mughal court shawls (see Plate 84).

Other extant shawls also demonstrate the subtle artistry of the Mughal period. Among the earliest surviving court pieces is a fabulous white shah tus shoulder mantle at the Boston Museum of Fine Art (Plate 83). The cut gem-like flower buds of the unidirectional hashia meander exhibit a characteristic free spacing in perfect harmony with that of the exquisitely drawn botehs to make this royal

PLATE 22.
Detail of shoulder mantle fragment (see Colour Plate 125), 17th century.

PLATE 23.
Flowers from the Dara Shikoh album, c.1635. During Jehangir's reign Western influence in the form of a flowering plant, naturalistic in appearance, became a favourite among Mughal patrons of the arts. Invading the upper flowers of this delicate plant is a menacing sky of grotesque Chinese clouds. This suggests how easy it was for the naqqash or shawl designer to re-interpret them into the scheme of Kashmir shawl patterns, where they eventually became part of the boteh.

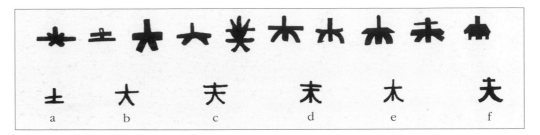

FIGURE 19.
Top line: tracings of root securing devices employed on Mughal shawls of the 17th century. Bottom line: Chinese ideograms and their definitions: a) t'u: earth; b) ta: great; c) t'ien: heaven; d) mo: branches; e) mu: timber; f) fu: a master of craft. These root drawings and their close similarity with Chinese characters suggest the possibility that Mughal artists were conscious of their meaning. (They may be seen in other works of Mughal art: See, for example, the lobed Nephrite bowl, 17th century, at the Metropolitan Museum of Art, acc. no. 02.18.762.).

piece one of the finest specimens of the Mughal period. Although Chinese clouds (see Plate 23) are absent from this piece, the Chinese influence is possibly seen in the device by which the boteh's stem has been rooted in the ground; this resembles the Greek letter 'pi' or more probably the Chinese ideogram 'Ta' meaning great. Although there have been many contemporary variations of this idea in shawls, this one possesses an undeniable curvilinear stroke making the influence of Chinese ideograms seem the more believable. The botehs of the Mittal fragment also have ideogrammatic roots. It appears this was a particular characteristic of the seventeenth century shawl and has not been observed elsewhere. The discovery of further pieces hopefully will shed more light on this subject. Figure 19a-f shows some of the more interesting root-securing devices from the earliest known shawls, and some Chinese ideograms with which to compare them. Notice the 'cloud roots' in Colour Plate 144.

By the mid-eighteenth century, the Chinese root device took on various abstractions until the development of the mound, after which time the vase and the dish came as additional non-botanical elements. One may speculate about the form which the mound takes. It is almost always stepped with heavy outlining, often in two tones, while spots decorate the mound's interior (Colour Plates 135 and 140). Keeping in mind contemporary Mughal painting, we find that court artists were unsurpassed masters at creating oblique perspectives by which depth perception was often translated into a full foreground view. If we follow this theory into weaving, what we may have here within these mounds are actually tiny fish in a pond or basin (see Colour Plate 140).

In the Chinese cloud patka, such as that in Plate 86, the top and bottom hashias contain an intentionally forced compression of rosebuds and cloud bands. Instead of the conventional oscillating design often reserved for the vertical hashias, here the clouds trail between the rosebuds and miniature clouds to connect them, all facing the same way. On the other hand, in the vertical hashia, bent tip 'roses' or 'strawberries' with appendages on the concave side have whiffs of clouds attached to the base of the flower in a similar manner to the botehs of the palla. In all probability, the bent-tip strawberry (Figure 20) was a rose which by force of Mughal fashion moulded itself into the compelling bends of the classic vine of the hashia.

In the earliest examples, the meandering-vine repeats almost always retained the same flower, while the later ones began slowly to incorporate as many as six

PLATE 24.
Wall decoration from Red Fort, Mahal-I-khas, Delhi.

PLATE 25.
Detail of sculptured marble interior of the Moti Masjid, built in 1659 by Aurangzeb.

different flowers. Where the blossom appears too large to be intelligently incorporated into the hashia in its entirety, only a part, or in some cases just one half of it, was used to achieve the proper equilibrium.

There is no doubt that the Chinese cloud shawls strongly influenced future designs, most notably the 'rank' shawl of the early eighteenth century whose lateral leaves were probably a further, more abstracted development of the Chinese cloud patterns (see Colour Plate 151) Plate 90, although a 'rank' shawl, continues to retain in its top and bottom hashias the Chinese inspiration. Colour Plate 121 is another good example of a continuation of the Chinese cloud-band idea. (For further discussion of rank shawls see page 24.)

In the Mughal period, the design of the patka differs in an important way from that of the shoulder mantle. Conventionally, the main floral vine of the patka's hashia is bordered on both sides by a fairly sophisticated geometric pattern, something which except for the chandar of the eighteenth century, is rarely found on the kani shoulder mantle. These guard border patterns usually further consisted of three rows of brocaded weaving on a common ground colour. The centre row often displays a kind of tiny rhomboidal pattern while on some specimens this angular shape actually takes the form of birds in flight (Figures 20 and 21). Flanking the guard borders is either a solid colour line of weft brocading or one filled with a series of contrasting flecks (see, for example, Colour Plate 122). This angular elaboration peculiar to the patka suggests that it may have played a much more dominant role in kani weaving – possibly before the use of the flowering plant and perhaps as far back as the Sultanate period (1215-1526). Therefore the Kashmir shawl as a shoulder mantle may still have been something of a novelty, as suggested by Abul Fazl, Akbar's court chronicler, and thus its use as a medium for the art of kani weaving may have also been a recent innovation. This leads us to the more ancient brocaded patka whose similarities in format approximated the shoulder mantle.

The patka designated the military or social rank of the bearer and it usually measured about .70m x 4 to 5m or longer. It was not until about 1640 that the

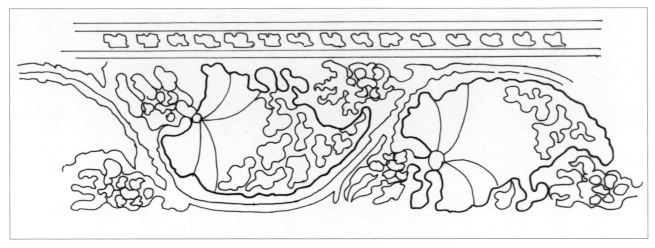

FIGURE 20.
Vertical hashia detail of patka shown in Plate 86, with Chinese cloud band and 'birds-in-flight' guard border. A 'bent-tip' strawberry meander, Mughal.

FIGURE 21.
Detail of the hashia of patka shown in Plate 90 with Chinese cloud band and a 'birds in flight' guard border, Mughal

flowering plant began to make its appearance on the patka.[3] Mughal painting of the first half of the seventeenth century shows that it was highly ornamented with geometric or Persian scroll-type patterns, often further embellished with gold covering large portions of the patka's ends and sometimes the whole piece. Apart from the brocaded ones and an exceptionally unique seventeenth century kani patka (Plate 81), however, no other kani patkas meeting this geometric or scroll description have at present come to light. Nor do we find large traces of arabesques or geometric patterns among the dozen or so extant patkas of the seventeenth century. None the less, on closer examination of the kani patka one detects a conventionally wide border or hashia of about 3.8cm (1½in.) of which the guard borders are always composed of running specks and tiny rhomboids. Paradoxically, although the shoulder mantle was much wider its hashia remained very narrow, less than two centimetres (an inch).

Following the decline of the Mughal empire, the classic Mughal style was

3. Kahlenberg, pp. 153-166.

FIGURE 22.
A reconstructed hashia repeat of the patka fragment shown in Plate 82. Note the angularity of the repeat.

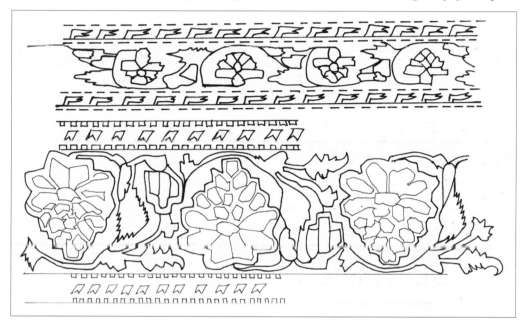

FIGURE 23.
Hashia details of Plate 87, Mughal.

perpetuated by many provincial kingdoms. Mukhtar Shah cites the example of Hyderabad, a predominantly Muslim state ruled by a dynasty of Nizams, as being a continuous outlet for the old, traditional court designs. The flora of such provincial shawls often represented state emblems of various kingdoms removed from direct Mughal domination. One might also cite the kingdom of Lucknow, whose ruler Nawab Asaf-ud-Daula was a generous patron to numerous artists, musicians and writers who were attached to the city in the late eighteenth century.

In conclusion, the Mughal boteh stressed the realistic representation of nature, along with an extremely delicate harmony of design. This emphasis was shared by the other impressive art mediums of the Mughal period, such as carpet weaving and even architecture. The Mughals, in fact, so venerated flowers that, even during the austere reign of Aurangzeb, they often used them for decoration. The Moti Masjid of Delhi's Red Fort (Plate 25), for example, remains a dazzling testament to an empire whose art was rooted in an inspired appreciation of nature.

Afghan Period

With the arrival of the Afghans in Kashmir in 1753, a long and fruitful period came to an abrupt end. The Afghans were great admirers of the shawl, but the severe hardships they inflicted on the Kashmiri weavers brought about a decline in the shawl's quality.

Under the Afghans, the boteh became more stylised. Its flowers began to be formed into bouquets of almost nondescript foliage. Flowers were not always completely unrecognisable, and in some cases the crocus, marigold, and rose retained a semi-naturalistic appearance. None the less, the boteh tended to move away from naturalism, towards more abstract forms. It was during the Afghan period that the cone buta first appeared, and its enclosing curvilinear walls (see, for example, Plate 105) perhaps reflect the restrictions on political and creative freedom placed by the Afghans on the people of Kashmir.

However, the historical origins of this motif are not entirely clear. Indian culture prior to the mid-eighteenth century offers very few clues to the origins of the cone. The Red Forts in Delhi and Agra are both ornamented in the flora idiom; even the sumptuous palaces of Rajastan, where no expense was spared, contain no motif resembling the cone. Nowhere in India had the cone been enshrined, ennobled or worshipped; and if it did ornament a few later monuments, miniatures or textiles, it was never a major motif, but always a minor part of the general design. The cone boteh appeared frequently, however, in Persian architecture as early as the eleventh century. It can also be found in Coptic weaving and Byzantine jewellery of the sixth and seventh centuries and so it is probable that the cone motif was borrowed from the cultures of Persia, Egypt or Byzantium. It is tempting to see it as an elemental shape representing the force of life itself and recurring in periods of cultural and artistic awakening.

Extensive analysis of hundreds of shawl designs strongly suggests that the cone boteh evolved as a result of the many stylistic changes in the floral boteh, especially in the important transitional period at the end of the eighteenth and beginning of the nineteenth century, though this does not necessarily preclude the notion of, say, Persian origins.

One of the most important features in the transition from Mughal to Afghan styles is the replacement of a single species of plant by a mixture of all different kinds of flowers. Another related change is the appearance of a vase and a dish, which was undoubtedly abstracted from the Chinese ideogram root. This was the first time that objects other than flowers were represented in the boteh's design.

The vase served to support the large number of flowers, which otherwise might have upset the aesthetic harmony of the design. Later the vase, often very small, became a purely ornamental feature, rarely in proportion to the huge array of flowers which was soon to develop. Such disproportion would never have been allowed in Mughal decoration, where harmony was considered as the primary aesthetic virtue.

The vase was an extremely important stage in the boteh's evolution (see Plate 97). It is believed that its appearance is contemporary with the emerging of floral variety. In addition, the vase's curvilinear form most likely encouraged the development of the cone boteh. The change toward a less specific representation of floral species had other effects as well. Towards the third quarter of the eighteenth century flowers were no longer drawn naturally but as abstracted decorations. The boteh was no longer a representation of nature, but an intense collage of colours within a curvilinear form. This was the cone boteh in its pure form.

FIGURE 24.
'Radial' flowers of the Afghan Period: a) detail from Plate 112; b) detail from Plate 105; c) detail from Plate 120 (millefleurs prayer shawl).

One of the earliest transitional patterns from the Afghan period is the 'Qajar' boteh (see Plates 104 and 105) so-called because of its similarities with a boteh pattern found in a pre-Qajar painting.[4] The significance of this painting lies in the fact that it is the only known eighteenth century source which portrays a typical Kashmir-shawl boteh. A glance at the illustrations in P.J. Falk's book, *Qajar Painting,* will demonstrate the importance of the Kashmir shawl in the Persian courts, especially the court of Fath Ali Shah (1798-1834). Although the Persians shunned its use as a shoulder mantle), they were widely worn as patkas, gilets, turbans, and also cut into every dress accessory imaginable, including socks and gloves.

A frequent Mughal element forming the base of the boteh had been the raceme (see page 89) usually shown growing up at opposing angles. The addition of the vase changed all this and the racemes began to move upwards slowly either within the boteh or pouring out of the vase. In either case, if they remained at its base they assumed the curvilinear form of the boteh. The important characteristic of the Qajar boteh is that the raceme has already worked its way to the top to 'sprout', forming an apex, the early beginnings of the pine cone. At the turn of the eighteenth century the popular theme was the sinuous protrusion of several racemes at a time forming the apex (see Colour Plate 169a). This style was meticulously captured in French painting by court artists such as Ingres (Plate 15), Gros and Girodet.

Along with the Qajar boteh came the 'radial flower' technique in which small flower buds appear attached like spokes on a wheel, orbiting a floral rosette (Figure 24). This had the effect of freeing the floral stagnation which arose from the curvilinear constraints of the boteh and creating a new graphic dimension. In the Boston Museum of Fine Art there is a particularly fine fragment exemplifying this technique (see Plate 105) and in a later version in the collection of the Victoria and Albert Museum the radial technique can be seen predominating in an early nineteenth century shawl (see Plate 132).

Another feature was added soon after. A curved branch detached from the boteh, but similar to the branches inside, was woven in an upward arch towards the top of the boteh. Occasionally it swept over the top. This 'coif' (Figure 28) was a clever ploy to balance the design of the repeated botehs which all leaned in the

4. Falk, p. 28, fig. 9.

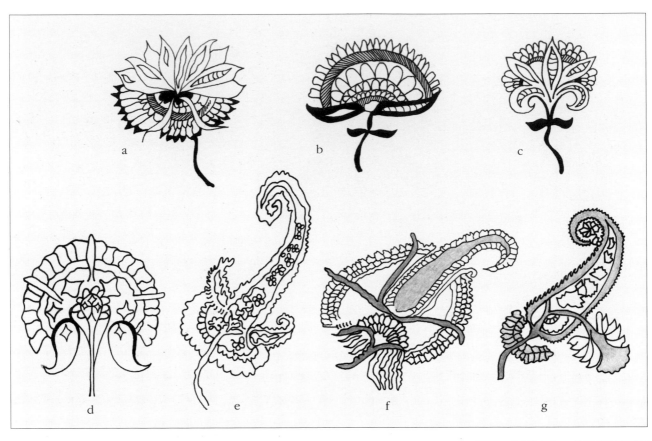

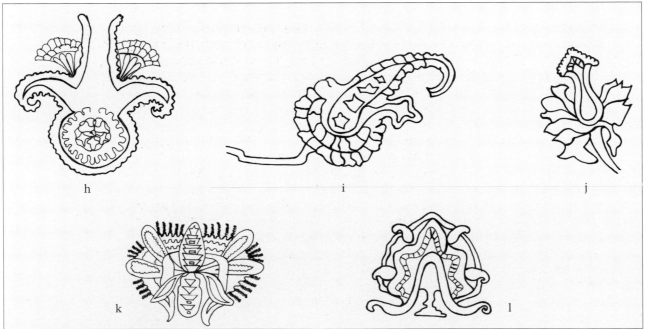

FIGURE 25.
Sikh Period floral details. A series of drawings showing the development of the fool's cap: a, b and c are taken from Moorcroft's drawings; i is a detail of Plate 159. The other tracings are from various shawls.

FIGURE 26.
Afghan-Sikh Period. A series of shawl tracings showing the development of the hooked vine.

same direction. It was developed by the Kashmiri artists into a strong conventional form, so much so that it often completely encircled the boteh (Plates 132 and 133), representing the beginning of the ground embellishment.

Other concentric forms followed. Encouraged by the coif boteh technique, weavers added a new dimension to the cone boteh, as ornamentation appropriated more of the ground. The hardened shape which crystallised in the transition from the Afghan to the Sikh period is a direct result of the encircling branch.

The heavily filled ground which developed had the effect of a halo encircling the cone boteh; this added a floating dimension which caused the boteh to appear completely detached from the ground and set against a floral setting. This marked the beginning of a new far-reaching style which was once referred to as 'transparent', but was wrongly attributed to European influence. The transparent boteh became an artistic theme for many future shawl patterns, both in India and Europe. Shawls of the tapestry type (discussed on pages 58 and 111) with lavish designs often display such scattered cones which are almost totally independent of the ground pattern (see Plates 166 and 169).

Finally, the detached branch was added back to the tilted rose at the top of the boteh, sometimes hanging over it, sometimes ending with a small flower. Branches inside the boteh also evolved toward increased abstraction. Early examples of the shawl portrayed slightly curved branches growing up almost vertically; later they began to cross over each other in a snake-like fashion. The branches eventually crystallised into two solid curved lines representing perhaps an abstracted form of heavy vines (Figure 26).

Under the Afghans, then, the boteh became more stylised and abstract. It no longer focused on a realistic representation of nature, but rather attempted to portray an intensity of colour within a curvilinear form. The central theme of the Afghan period was the evolution of the boteh into a cone-like shape. At the beginning of the Sikh period, this form crystallised even more when the effect of underlining was created by the fully ornamented ground. This had the effect of drawing a smooth, unbroken line completely around the boteh. The colour of the line depended on the ground dye.

During the Afghan period, the laws of Islam were graphically and repeatedly expressed within two-dimensional Euclidean space throughout the diversity of design patterns. Afghan shawls possessed a unity which enlarged one's perspective creating a sense of harmony by the geometric play of light and shade. The chandar or moon shawl was one of the main forms for such expression, especially through the tiny floral rosettes of the chandar's field. With its quincunx pattern, it was especially important since the central medallion played an important role in creating the illusion of a third dimension (Colour Plates 36 and 184 and Plate 108).

To conclude, the Afghans imposed severe exactions on the people and especially on the weaving industry from which they reaped huge financial gains. This in turn took its toll over the years upon the magnificent Mughal style which eventually degenerated into a confusion of packed flowers held within the confining walls of a new type of curvilinear boteh. The natural growth and development of the flowering plant slowly disappeared. The new stylistic convention was to more or less fill up the cone shape, cramming the flowers in wherever a free space permitted. Acting as catalysts to the development of this new shape were the vase and the dish.

SIKH PERIOD

As the Sikh Period began, design features reflected the influence of Western fashion, brought about in part by the influx of the French and the Industrial Revolution in Europe. There was a sudden decline in Islamic influence; the patterns which had represented the high point of Indo-Muslim exploration of the subtle symmetries of space began to decline. The Kashmir shawl reflected new and changing fashions. Napoléon's return from Egypt left an indelible impression in the Middle East that the Orient, including England's India, was not completely immune to military conquest. In addition, the lavish fashion of the Napoléonic empire left a clear mark on the fashion of the East.

Napoléon's fall coincided with the rise of another monarch, Runjit Singh. Although Singh's conquests lacked the elegant glory which the Western mind attributed to Napoléon, he was no less revered by a people who identified greatly with those who are courageous and cunning in war; Runjit Singh (Plate 2) became the great Maharaja of all the Punjab and the Kingdom of Kashmir in 1819.

The Sikhs broke all the sacred shawl design rules; they pronounced the might of an indigenous race, emphasising their genuine Indian heritage. The bold features of the Sikh Kashmir shawl do little to conceal the fervent militarism behind Sikhism. Such symbolism is not always defined in the form of a simple design component but rather it is often suggested by the image of the total composition. It is for this reason that the denomination of 'modern' art can be justly applied to those shawl designs created with the arrival of the Sikhs in Kashmir in 1819.

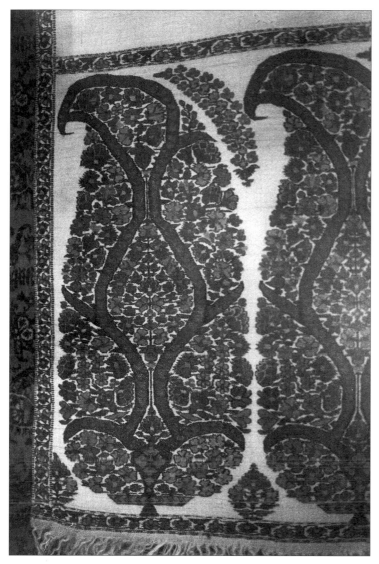

PLATE 25a.
Shoulder mantle (detail). Afghan Period, c.1800. The archetypal pattern for the hooked vine appears here to reach its final burgeoning form. (See Figure 26.)

PLATE 26.
Shawl pattern sent to England by Moorcroft in 1823. Lacquered tempera on paper, 36cm x 15cm (14 x 6in.). Inscribed verso 'Turquoise Colour by order of Mahummud Azeem Khan, Indian'.

The artist, whether his designs are woven in wool, carved on stone or painted on canvas, has at all times been the instrument and spokesman of the spirit of his age; consciously or unconsciously he gives form to the nature and values of his time. The shawls we find during this period of 'modern' art reflect the military bravado which moulded Sikhism. True to the teachings of the Sikhism's founder, Guru Nanak (1469-1529), the eclectic Sikh influence incorporated a rich variety of abstract images from all walks of Oriental culture.

This is one of the most fascinating transitional periods (1815-1820) in as much as one can see clearly the new infusion of Indian blood injected by the upsurge in symbolic content of the nascent shawl patterns. The pomp and splendour of the rich court of Maharaja Runjit Singh forms the background for this renaissance.

Although his patronage of the arts remains obscure, and little is known of his encouragement of the weaving industry (a few interesting references, however, do exist), the underlying theme of Hindu influence cannot be denied.

Besides the Golden Temple of Amritsar and a few building additions within the Red Fort of Lahore, the Sikhs left no resounding monuments which serve to stamp their esoteric culture with a personal style. Unlike the great Mughals, they never left any personal written accounts or autobiographies despite the omnipotent force their presence signified in Northern India.[5] But all this tends further to stimulate our curiosity in the search for the cultural outlets of an impressive race of people and to cause us to delve deeper into the expressive and prolific weavings of the Sikh period.

The earliest clearly-dated reference to some of the styles of the boteh during the Sikh period are Moorcroft's designs, which he sent to England in 1823. Apparently, Moorcroft sent back thirty-four drawings from Kashmir to England but, apart from eight which were acquired by the New York Metropolitan Museum of Art in 1962, little is known of their whereabouts, and so it is difficult to isolate the exact beginnings of important features which appear to have been introduced at the time of the Sikh conquest of Kashmir in 1819.

Moorcroft's eight boteh designs (shown as Plates 26-28) none the less offer us a rare opportunity to visualise cone styles popular in India, Persia and Russia in 1823. They contain important details which reveal some of the design ideas which became increasingly popular on later shawls. These show Indian – as opposed to Afghan – influence, and this influence accords logically with the ending of Islamic rule in Kashmir.

Plate 26 is probably the most important of Moorcroft's designs. It represents a vase, created by flowing cupped ferns whose neck and rim have been drawn in to define the top. Growing out of the vase is an exotic, flattened display of various stylised roses. Some appear to be in the process of blooming from buds surrounded by small leaves; others appear in full bloom but partly hidden by a strange array of what looks like unusually long 'lotus flower' leaves, of the type often seen in Indian miniature painting. The roses resemble a type of shield or perhaps an open fan.

The rose itself is composed of neat concentric circles of rows of equally sized and spaced minute petals. Sometimes the leaves are so large that they dominate the rose and are arranged in such a way that they could be taken for a flower themselves – perhaps a lotus flower.

The lotus-like rose was adopted as a convention of design, and variations were often employed in the meandering floral motif of the shawl's hashia until the very end of the kani shawl's history. It appeared especially on the Sikh tapestry shawls. Sometimes the rose splits apart to form a kind of stretched peacock's tail. Turkish velvets of the sixteenth and seventeenth century frequently portray a similar type of abstract design, often described as a carnation. At other times the 'lotus' leaves appear to grow directly out of the middle of the rose. In this case the leaves are either fanned out or grouped together in a kind of narrow cone boteh, similar to a type of anthurium flower.

This drawing suggests how the ubiquitous 'tilted-top' rose evolved into the lotus-rose which has by this time become integrated into the new language of the Sikh style. In all its forms, the rose, symbol of love and passion, appeared in every period.

The narrow cone boteh eventually detached itself from the mother lotus-like rose and broke away to become a separate and independent motif, retaining a small cluster of 'rose' petals at its base. The motif looks like a fool or clown's cap[6]

5. Archer, p. xviii.
6. Vigne, Vol. 2, pp. 133-4. Vigne confuses this subordinate motif with the major cone motif itself.

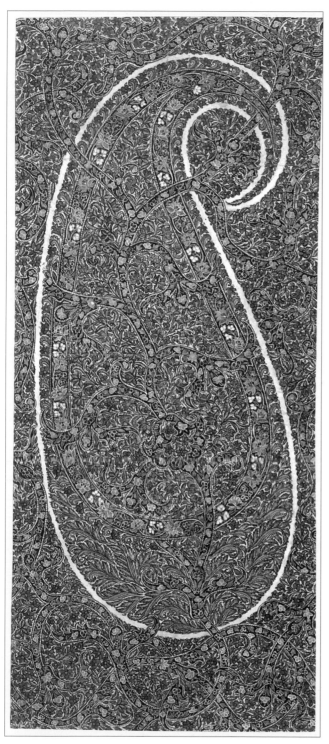

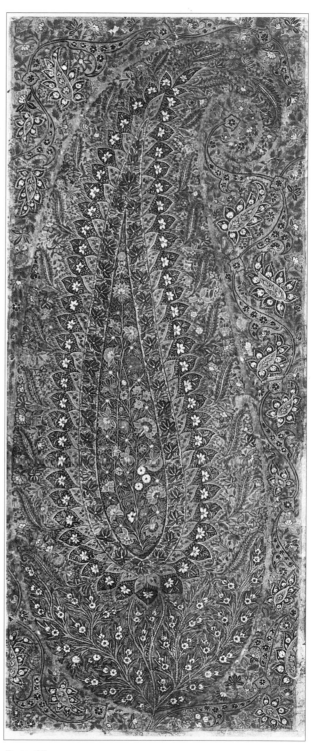

PLATE 27.
*Shawl pattern sent to England by Moorcroft in 1823. 35cm
x 14cm (14 x 5in.). Inscribed verso 'Yellow and betel colour
by order of Mahummud Azeem Khan, Russia'.*

PLATE 27a.
*Shawl pattern sent to England by Moorcroft in 1823.
35cm x 14cm (14 x 5in.). Inscribed verso 'Verdigris
colour, by order of Mahummud Azeem Khan, Russia'.*

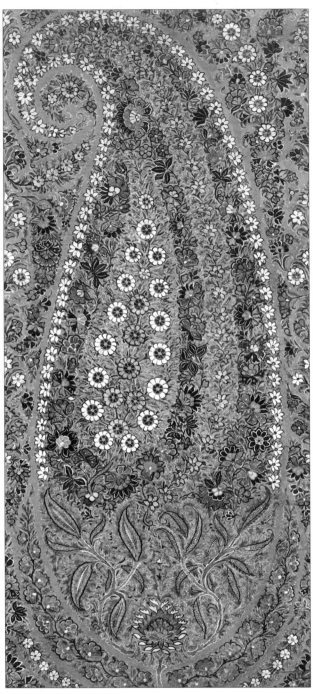

PLATE 28a.
Tempera on paper, lacquered. Inscribed verso 'Hindustan'.

Plate 28b.
35cm x 16cm (14 x 6in.). Inscribed verso 'Pomegranate colour, Hindustan'.

PLATE 28, a-e. (above and opposite)
Shawl patterns sent to England by Moorcroft in 1823.

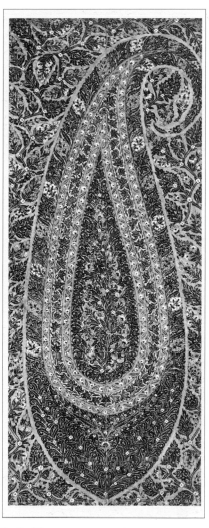

PLATE 28c.
Gouache on paper, 33cm x 13cm (13 x 5in.). Inscribed verso 'Elephant colour, by order of Shooja ool Moolkh, Persia'.

PLATE 28d.
35cm x 14cm (14 x 5in.). Inscribed verso 'Lapis-Lazuli colour, for Shah Zuman, Persia'.

PLATE 28e.
37cm x 15cm (14 x 6in.). Inscribed verso 'Dusty colour for Shah Zuman, Persia'.

but it has a striking resemblance to the jewelled ornament worn by the Indian and Persian nobles, called a 'jigeh' or 'aigrette', attached to the front of turbans as part of traditional court costume (see Figure 25i).

Another important design development was that of the hooked vine. This derives from an evolution in organic growth. Popular boteh themes of the late Afghan period displayed an increasing use of first vertical and then interlaced branches. The vine can be seen in its nascent form in Colour Plate 187 (see respective details in Figure 26) in which the boteh's inner structure has been built around the rising ogival pattern of leaves and tiny blossoms. Within a short time the vine hardened. In the National Museum, Delhi, there is a superb transitional shawl in which the vine is seen composed of pointed hooks menacing the restraining walls of the boteh's curvilinear form (Plate 25a). One can almost feel the pent-up energy and the need to break away that is generated by the bold visual impact of this revolutionary pattern. It radically underlines the unconscious social changes which took place. Furthermore it shows an absolute mastery of the synthesis of Mughal and Afghan styles. The lower flower clusters recall those of the 'Qajar' boteh while the radial flowers have been placed towards the middle. Cradled by the first hooks are two smaller vases while the small isolated floral ornaments (butis) lying between the coif botehs enhance the Mughal touch through the graceful arching of winged leaves. Although the raised dish appears slightly truncated, its chevron pattern combined with the cross-emblazoned vase effectively support the thick hooked vine which rises in an ogival fashion to dominate the boteh.

In another of Moorcroft's drawings, the boteh's inner cone is seen outlined with leaves arranged in the form of scales (Plate 27a). This is seen on many shawls woven during the 1840s and later the 'sweeping boteh' also assimilated this idea. We see here another detail not often found on Kashmir shawls: the arabesque which winds around the boteh as part of the ground décor. For centuries the Persians artfully employed this design on the elegant rugs of Isfahan and Shiraz. Classical rug designs such as the split arabesque, 'gul', leafy palmette, etc., found their way into Kashmir's rug weaving industry – an industry which enjoyed a success concurrent with that of the shawls. Yet, oddly enough, this motif is never seen on shawls. Perhaps the naqqash or designer felt that the use of such motifs would confuse his wealthy clients, who preferred not to mix the two design mediums. Or perhaps the idea of someone walking on rug designs and then weaving them into delicate shawls seemed almost blasphemous. Whatever the case may be, the unusually rigorous separation of these weavings further validates an art which developed within its own strong and independent sphere.

Plates 28a-e show further designs recorded by Moorcroft. Plate 28a is rather less elegant and interesting than the others; we see here a decline from the rare and exotic to the commonplace design abstractions which permit cheap imitations. In this drawing a snake-like form curls in the opposite direction from the boteh's tip – a variation of the earlier coif boteh technique. The boteh's centre is filled with three superimposed medallions above which is a kind of cypress tree or spear. The evolution of this ubiquitous, phallic element seems appropriate as a symbol of the Sikh force piercing through and melting away Pathan opposition. This motif demonstrates the declining influence of Islam on designs.

It is curious that pieces of such contrasting quality come from the same period, yet one realises when one tries to date textiles that such disparities are anything but rare. In addition to his drawings, Moorcroft left among his correspondence and notes a list of over eighty shawl fabrics, along with their corresponding descriptions and prices.[7] For example, he describes certain pieces as 'ornamented with flowers either in the corner or running all around the shawl between the border and the field', or 'green sprigs on a white ground', or 'large grounds of flowers somewhat in the form of the cone of a pine with the ends or points straight or curved downwards'. From this it may be implied that the bent-tip boteh was in vogue as early as 1822.

Finally, we come to a curious remark concerning the shawl fabric called 'hashiyadar Kunguradar'.[8] Moorcroft says: 'This has a border of unusual form with another within side, or nearer to the middle, resembling the crest of the wall of Asiatic forts furnished with narrow niches or embrasures for wall pieces or matchlock, whence its name.' This appears to be the first mention, from any source, of architectural ornamentation on shawls. The idea of forts, parapet openings and guns certainly coincides not only with the divergently 'modern' shawl styles but also with the Sikh's obsession with war. Vigne refers to a pair of

7. Irwin. 1955, pp. 37-45.
8. Irwin, 1955, p. 28.

PLATE 29.
Victor Jacquemont (1801-1832), a brilliant naturalist, died while exploring India.

woven shawls commissioned by Maharaja Runjit Singh representing his victories.[9] Perhaps in the future shawl pieces will be discovered that will shed more light on the early appearance of architectural motifs in Sikh weaving.

In the 1830s, Chavant, the well-known publisher and designer, published a drawing of a shawl made in 1825 (Plate 65). The drawing gives us valuable information concerning the boteh's development in the period immediately following Moorcroft's departure. We can see that around 1825 a new style of cone came into being. Instead of the curled-tip characteristic of Moorcroft's cones, the new boteh displays a stretched-out body. Instead of the tip curling about itself, it

9. Vigne, vol.2, p. 114.

assumes a kind of folded aspect with a sharp lance-like tip reaching perhaps half-way down, barely touching the side. This reflects the increased tapestry work which then began to cover a larger area of the shawl.

With this came a subordinate form of leaning botehs. They were reduced-size models of the lance boteh and were used for decoration of the 'dhor', the area surrounding the centre field of the shawl. Shawls at the beginning of the Sikh period show that the lance or folded boteh was clearly non-existent before this time. The lance boteh marked the last significant design innovation until twenty-five years later when French agents arrived to impose their style – the sweeping or zoomorphic boteh (see Figures 29 and 30).

Our knowledge of Sikh style is further expanded by the erudite Victor Jacquemont (1801-1832), a botanist sent by the French government to visit India (Plate 29). His clear description of the shawl trade in Loudiana, Islamabad and Kashmir offers us an intimate account, not only of the techniques of production, but also of the political situation and slave-like oppression suffered by the poor Kashmiri weavers.

Jacquemont arrived in Kashmir just eight years after Moorcroft, a timely arrival since just one year later Kashmir suffered a terrible famine which devastated the whole region. His stay in Srinagar provided some enlightening details about changes in style which took place during this important period (1823-1831). The measurements of the new boteh tend to corroborate the evidence found in Chavant's drawing relating to the increase in the boteh's size. His comments also suggest that a decline in quality had occurred by this time: '...the open field (matan) diminishes to almost nothing', wrote Jacquemont, 'by the enormous height of the palms (cones) which are now 0.70m to 1m long, and furthermore the designs today do not have anymore the agreeable bizarreness of those in the past; they are baroque. Those that the European taste would condemn the most severely are the most sought after in the Orient and the ones held in the highest esteem today represent indelicate figures of flower vases, houses and even animals.'

We see here Jacquemont's nostalgia for the earlier style of fine, delicately woven shawls so magnificently portrayed by artists such as Ingres and Baron Gros; the rare shawl of subtle woven fleece which fell in smooth, undulating folds, enveloping the feminine figure in voluptuous curves, now seemed to belong to the past, if not to the realm of legend.

The Sikhs' arrival, ending the Afghans' tyrannical rule, saw a veritable creative explosion. On the one hand, new designs flourished, and the decorations on Kashmir shawls became more ornate than ever before. On the other hand, the curvilinear boteh became less essential to the organic unity of these new, more abstract design patterns.

Under the Sikhs, the design of the boteh focused on the aigrette or fool's cap, the serrated leaf, the lotus-like rose, the 'leaning' and 'stubby' boteh (with lance tip), the hooked vine, the spear or cypress tree, stacked medallions, concentric cones, and certain unidentified architectural ornamentation (see Plate 60b).

Moorcroft's drawing shown as Plate 28a suggests that certain aspects of these changes had already started as early as 1823. However, the boteh had become but an echo of the past, a hollow skeletal form whose presence was necessary for economic reasons only, as a symbol without which the shawl could not be sold in many markets. There is thus little doubt that by the early 1830s the Industrial Revolution in Europe had created an ever-expanding consumer market and the influx of European fashion had combined with the years of foreign domination to alter the classic tradition of the kani shawl.

To conclude, the principal weaving associated with the Sikh period may be known as the tapestry shawl. The huge size of the sweeping botehs and the multitude of large architectural and curvilinear patterns began quickly to invade the whole surface area of the shawl. Hollow botehs detached themselves from the increasingly dominating ground designs to evaporate through scattered directions across a roaring sea of new images, exotic and enigmatic. The riotous agitation of the boteh's flora swept away practically all botanical reality in its path. It appears that in one fell swoop the Sikhs obliterated all graphic souvenirs which recalled the hard struggles against their Mughal and Afghan rivals to vindicate their rights to Northern India. The close look into this boteh microcosm provides a clear distinction of the evolving key elements which eventually emerged, fused and even re-separated to form the churning symbolism of the Sikh period.

Dogra Period

Few design innovations developed within the boteh style during the period which followed the death of Maharaja Runjit Singh in 1839. Raja Gulab Singh took over Kashmir in 1846 and within a few years French agents arrived there in large numbers with the latest Parisian shawl patterns. The abrupt change in political climate brought with it many foreign visitors, including a well-known English watercolourist, W. Simpson. He came to Srinagar to paint shawl weavers and embroiderers and the comments he made concerning the changing artistic scene are worth quoting:

> The great estimation in which Cashmir shawls are held in France, and the consequent demand for them, have induced some of the large houses in that country to keep agents in Srinugger [Srinagar]. One result of this is that the French design patterns in Paris and send them out to Cashmere for execution. Although their designs are all in the Oriental style, they are no improvement on the old work of the natives… [the French patterns] were perhaps purer than the old; they contained more free and sweeping lines, but they wanted the medieval richness of the native taste. It may be described as the difference between a piece of rococo ornament and what an artist of the· thirteenth century would have produced. There was a distinguishing character about the original style which is being rubbed out by this foreign influence.[10]

The Dogra period is indisputably intermingled with the sweeping all over patterns generated by the Jacquard loom. Practically all the kani shawls were of the patchwork kind, pieced together with sometimes as many as a hundred separate pieces, like a jigsaw puzzle (this was a feat in itself). Nevertheless, there are many surviving shawls which belie the idea that the kani industry deteriorated completely during the middle of the nineteenth century. On the contrary, the French presence in Srinagar greatly encouraged the kani weaving industry and was responsible for its revival. But the Franco-Prussian War of 1870 and changing European fashions virtually ended the shawl industry (see Figure 1). The style of this period is further discussed in Chapter 6, Shawl Weaving in France.

The shawls such as in Colour Plates 207, 209 and 210 represent the kani masterpieces of the post-Runjit Singh period, the period 1840 to 1877 when French influence dominated the weaving industry of Srinagar. Their design expression is often removed from the Islamic vernacular that patterns displayed before the arrival of the Sikhs in Kashmir in 1819. This is to say that as the import

10. Simpson, p. 5.

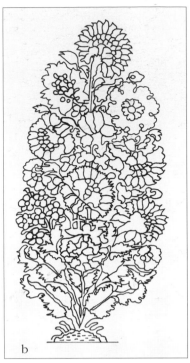

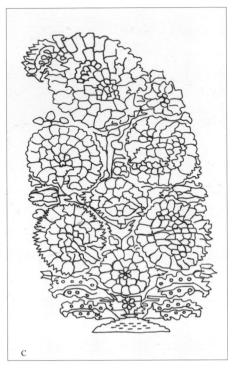

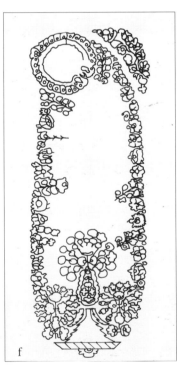

FIGURE 27.

a) Flowering-plant boteh with ideogram root, Mughal, mid-17th century; b) Multi-flora boteh with mound, Mughal, early 18th century; c) Large top-rose boteh with serrated-edge pistil and mound. Stylistic exaggeration. Mughal, mid-18th century; d) Qajar boteh with radial flower technique. Afghan Period, c.1765; e) large top-rose boteh, freely spaced flowers, millefleurs, with vase and dish, Afghan Period, c.1775 (Mughal transition); f) Mosaic coif boteh with large radial top rose. Afghan Period, c. 1800.

COLOUR PLATE 36.
Moon shawl (chandar), late Afghan style, c.1815. Medallions show typical characteristics of the flattened flower, 'radial' flower technique, the vase and dish, etc. The field is in 'Khatraaz' or striped style.

113

FIGURE 28.
Afghan Period. Arching raceme coif botehs. Tracings from: a) Ingres 1805; b) Baron Gros 1809; c) Girodet 1810.

demands of European markets increased, there was a corresponding decrease in the Islamic elements of design, either through abstraction or direct elimination.

French shawl designers of the nineteenth century such as Couder and Berrus left a profound imprint of their creative styles both on the industry of France and Kashmir. Indeed, Srinagar was, in a sense, the 'Gobelins' atelier for France's tapestry shawl market. At the time of the Great Exhibition of 1851 and onward, the Kashmir weaver rarely began his day's work before consulting the design and pattern books brought to Kashmir by Parisian agents.

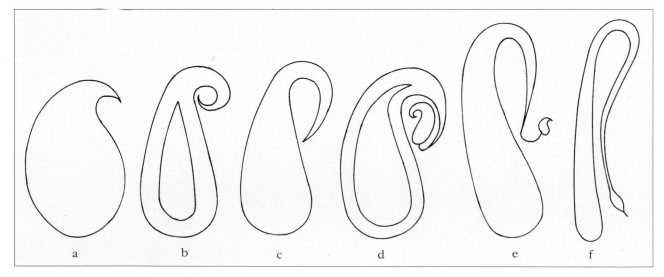

FIGURE 29.
Afghan-Sikh Period. a) Tea-pot boteh, 1800; b) hooked-tip boteh, 1820; c) bent-tip boteh, 1820; d, e) buti-tip cone, 1825; f) 'sweeping' boteh, 1825.

114

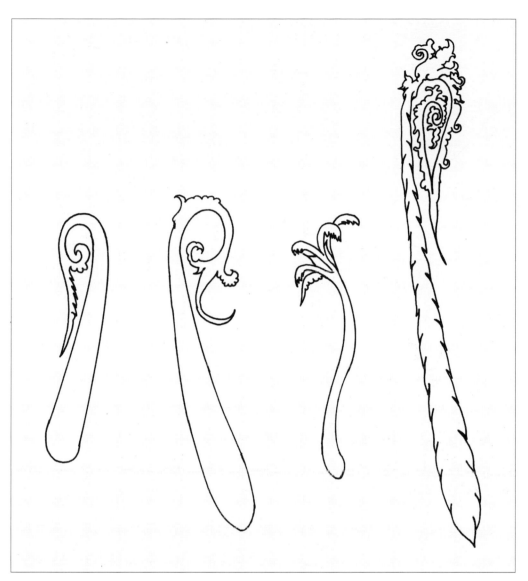

FIGURE 30.
Berrus' sweeping zoomorphic botehs, 'celery stalks', 1848.

PICTORIAL DEVELOPMENT OF THE BOTEH

The boteh sketches (Figures 27-30) do not necessarily demonstrate the evolution of the naturalistic flower boteh into the curvilinear cone, but rather clarify some of the working vocabulary employed in the text and captions. Research on the Kashmir shawl is still in its infancy, so it is difficult to be absolutely positive about a rigid chronological sequence of the boteh. Prior to the late eighteenth century, pictorial evidence is lacking. The drawings here are from pieces which in the author's opinion represent the artistic high points of Kashmir's weaving industry and thus express stylistic developments which one may associate with archetypal pieces.

Colour Plate 37.
Shoulder mantle, Sikh Period, c.1825. 140cm x 330cm (55 x 130in.). The tall botehs seem almost superfluous against the background of architectural paraphernalia which became fashionable at the court of Runjit Singh. The mihrab, with its spandrels round three scalloped circles, is Islamic in flavour. Other design features are an eight point star and a shield surrounded by spears. A close inspection of the fine detailed work which embellishes almost all the curving elements reveals a fascinating admixture of shawl school styles. Compare this with Chavant's drawing, Plate 63 (see Colour Plate 20a for detail).

116

COLOUR PLATE 38.
Long shawl, French, 1865-170. 340cm x 146cm (134 x 57in.). This unique shawl exhibits a very rare weaving technique (known as 'battant-brocheur') about which very little is known at present. It appears that the weft had been woven utilising special brocading shuttles which completely eliminated the floating threads on the back, thus avoiding the post-weave cutting procedure ('decoupage'). The shawl is woven all in one piece (see p. 155) for further discussion of this technique), cf. Le châle cachemire en France au XIX siècle, p. 90.

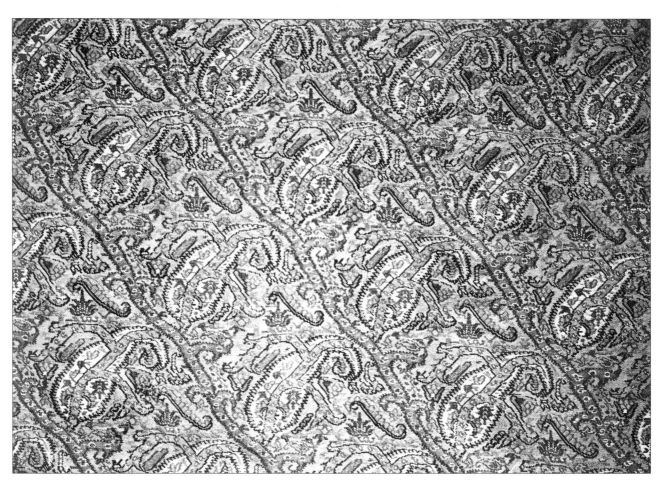

PLATE 30.
Persian kani shawl, Sikh Period.

CHAPTER FIVE

Shawl Trade and Shawl Fashions in the Orient

THE PERSIAN SHAWL INDUSTRY

Persia played an active role as intermediary for the lucrative commerce of Kashmir shawls but the date of the exact beginnings of her own shawl industry has yet to be established. Apart from what is known about shawl commerce, and various scattered references to Persian shawl weaving of the early nineteenth century, much of the industry's history remains in the dark. Travellers to the Orient, bent on finding out about the shawl-weaving industry, often focused on Kashmir, whose unsurpassed reputation was world wide, and ignored Persia almost entirely. The modern textile historian is, therefore, left with few sources of information regarding Persia's indigenous shawl weaving.

Some sources do exist, if not for the shawl at least for other textiles. One of the most valuable is the Frenchman Tavernier, who made many trips to the Orient in the middle of the seventeenth century, and who commented in some detail on the Persian textile industry. He was quick to discover the value of goat fleece and went to great efforts to export it to France. During his fourth voyage, in 1654, he was informed that such wool is not dyed and that it remains in its natural colours of clear brown, ash grey or, rarest of all, white. In addition to being very costly, the white wool was reserved for the muftis, mullahs and others of the law who wear only white, both for their sashes and for the veils with which they cover their heads during prayer. He also noticed a twill weave of a special type of wool so fine and delicate that the fabric was more beautiful and expensive than if made of silk.[1] Although Tavernier often mentioned rare wool being worked at Kerman, Yezd and Alep, nowhere does he use the word shawl.

The Persian nobility was, however, very fond of sashes (patkas), which they wore wrapped around their waists with the brocaded ends conspicuously displayed. The sash represented an important dress accessory to the court costume and, therefore, few were exported. Hanway observed in 1753 that 'even in the presence of Kings the Persians wore their sashes as turbans which were made of costly Kermani wool. Finer ones were valued at one hundred crowns compared to ones selling between eight and ten.'[2]

The Persians also wore a robe called 'cabaye', which fell just below the knees, and was made of very fine toile quilted with large stitches in order to hold a batting of cotton. Tavernier explained that such toiles would be a bargain if not for the fact that they did not hold their colour; as soon as a drop of water fell an embarrassing stain developed. The sleeves were long and hugged the arms down to the wrists. Similarly, the robe hugged the body just to the waist from where it fanned out. With the robe a beautiful silk sash was worn of which the ends were ornamented with flowers in gold. On top of this, they again wore another sash made from the fine wools of Kerman. The richest sometimes wore three sashes of which the first two were silk, and the third wool.[3]

From the Oriental travels of G.A. Olivier in 1794-98, we learn for the first time of an active shawl industry in Persia. Commissioned by the French government, Olivier, like many other learned emissaries, was sent to collect information on the Orient before Napoléon's incursion into Egypt. 'One million piastres worth of

1. Tavernier, vol. I, p. 172.
2. Hanway, vol. I, p. 331.
3. Tavernier, vol. II, p. 268.

COLOUR PLATE 38a.
Shirvan prayer rug, c.1800, 89cm x 114cm (35 x 45in.). Photograph Ralph and Linda Kaffel.

Kashmir shawls', noted Olivier, 'arrive each year in Bagdad by caravan and are distributed throughout Turkey. Sent by the Pacha, they often go to Constantinople by way of the Tartares [probably Turkestan]. Persia also exports Kermani shawls which have neither the beauty nor the fineness of the others.'[4]

Many shawls in the past have been perfunctorily, but probably correctly, attributed to Persian origin simply because of their coarser wool and inferior colours compared with those of Kashmir origin. The dyes, wool and even the designs appear conspicuously different. In spite of Olivier's criticism, however, some Kermani shawls did achieve a fair degree of quality. They were woven from the fleece of baby goats which grazed on the mountains surrounding Kerman. Olivier wisely remarked that the Kashmir shawl was woven from the fleece of the Tibetan mountain goat, a fact of which few people were aware at the time, especially in Europe where shawls were just beginning to become fashionable.

That valuable artifacts were made at all in eighteenth century Persia is especially amazing when one considers the hardships of daily life. It is difficult to imagine an atmosphere less conducive to the weaving of rich textiles than a country which witnessed incessant political turmoil, frequent wars, and absolute rulers who thought their survival depended on fratricide. Kerman was the scene of terrible slaughter in 1747 when Nadir Shah plundered the city, decapitated thousands and employed their heads in the construction of a tower. He left Persia in a state of devastation and left behind a legend of cruelty that spread throughout the world. Adrian Duprès of the French embassy wrote in 1807: 'The Persian Empire, one of the most beautiful in the world, has become more or less a vast cemetery since the death of Nadir Shah.' This ghastly image describes accurately the prevailing conditions at the end of the eighteenth century.

Duprès also carefully surveyed Persia's trade and left an illuminating account of the state of shawl commerce. It appears that Bagdad was the main entrepôt for foreign merchandise coming from Persia. Besides shawls made in Bagdad itself, others were imported from Kashmir, Kerman and Kashan.[5]

Duprès noted that Yezd also manufactured shawls, but they were a far cry from the rich brocades which had in the past dazzled the eyes of the courts of the Orient as far away as China. For example, Marco Polo had visited Yezd and was awed by the incredible silks and gifted weavers of the city's flourishing industry.

By the early nineteenth century, however, all that seems to have disappeared, for Duprès observed that shawls woven in Yezd were 'of an ordinary quality'. They were composed of different colours, solid or striped. Those made of long, yellow and red stripes, in a rough quality wool, were sent to the port of Bander Abbas. These were shipped in turn to Mascate and re-exported to India where they found a 'very active and competitive market'.[6]

While Kashmir shawls offer rich and varied shapes and designs, there is almost no such variety in Persian shawls. The earliest seem to date from just before 1800 and usually consist of variegated stripes of simple sprigs and other unrecognisable, small flowers.

During the Sikh period, however, design patterns became more pronounced. The Sikh style greatly influenced the numerous shawls of nineteenth century Persia. The lance-like bent-tip boteh, the boteh resembling a stubby hook with occasionally angular sides of a geometric nature, or the boteh in the form of a teapot without handle, are all found on the Persian shawls. These are the same styles which were initially popular in Kashmir in the second decade of the nineteenth century.

The design details popular with Kermani shawls of Persia are often blurred by

4. Olivier, *Voyage dans l'Empire Ottoman, Egypte et la Perse*, vol. 4, p. 446.
5. Duprès, vol. I, p. 196.
6. Ibid., vol. I, pp. 126, 252, 400; vol. II, pp. 160, 375.

the rather coarse weave of their wool. Nevertheless, they retain important features of Sikh abstract designs: the concentric cone, the stacked array of rose medallions; and the rustically hooked vine instead of the forked arabesque found in Persian court carpets. It is interesting that among kani Persian weaves probably made before the Sikh period practically no designs emerge which may be compared to the contemporary style of Kashmir. Between the simple sprig and the bold Sikh designs, we find no transitional development in Persian shawls of the boteh forms which were prevalent in Kashmir.

Persian shawls from regions other than Kerman also show strong Sikh influence. Kashan weavers used whole-component motif ideas such as leaning reciprocal botehs interspersed with tiny cone botehs resting on leafy fronds. These were widely used on carpets later on. Botehs were generally very small, rarely exceeding ten centimetres (4in.) in height and almost always scattered over the field.

These observations strongly suggest that the Persian shawl industry came to life during the Sikh period. The natural calamities which devastated Kashmir during the 1830s had caused mass emigration of the shawl weavers to the Punjab, and it is possible that Kashmiri weavers in need of work found employment in Kerman, in both the shawl and the rug industry. At the same time Kerman became a prominent supplier of goats' wool to the Punjab plains.

The study of the Kashmir shawl is aided by several sources of information. Not only do we have the rare sample pages of dye swatches found in the books of Watson (1877) or Leitner (1882) as a testimony to the chromatic past of the Kashmir shawl, but even today many an old shawl-weaving family in Srinagar still harbours, with great pride, the worm-eaten pages of a sample book containing early shawl fragments. Unfortunately, nothing of such nature has come to light concerning Persia's shawls. Chavant's *Album du Cachemirien* published in 1837 tells us, however, that in certain parts of Persia designs were not solely limited to the simple repeat patterns found among shawls assumed to be of Persian origin. This important document provides us with a few invaluable tracings of carpets from Teheran and Kabul, disclosing the early use of sophisticated Kashmir shawl designs. More important, however, is the disclosure of a large-patterned Kashmir shawl design woven in Teheran (Plates 63 and 64), disproving the notion that all Persian shawl designs must be of small patterns.[7]

Vigne, who travelled in the region in 1842, records that excellent shawls were also made in the Caucasus.

STYLE AND FASHION

The Persian shawl was used differently in Europe from in the Orient. From a noble shoulder mantle for men in the Orient it changed to a fashionable article of female attire in Europe. In Persia, its use was more as an ornamental fabric while in Europe it gradually shifted from high fashion to a more prosaic use: to keep warm in the cold winters and unheated houses.

Depending on the country and customs, the donning of the shawl had various symbolic meanings. In the Orient, however, it was a luxury article reserved only for the noble and the rich, and was considered an indispensable part of their wardrobe. By royal decree 'Princes by blood and great persons only shall be able to wear them as belts'; another edict required that narrow (Kashmir) shawls formerly worn around a bonnet (according to court etiquette) be replaced by the 'new fabrics now being manufactured in Kachân'.[8] This reveals a certain patriotism toward Persia's indigenous products, and at the same time hints of the

7. Chavant, *Album du Cachemirien*, pp. 2-3.
8. Duprès, vol. 2, p. 395

122

existence of a weaving industry that was still quite young.

Persian patriotism was also described by Baron Elphinstone. Dispatched to Kabul in 1809, he established an English embassy there and wrote: "The shawls exported to Persia are of a pattern entirely different from those seen in India or England. They were universally worn till lately when the king of Persia forbade the use of them with a view to encourage the manufactures of his own country.' The Baron was well acquainted with the industry of Kashmir shawls. His secretary who accompanied him to Afghanistan, Richard Strachey, had made 'many inquiries on the subject'.[9]

Elphinstone also describes a 'shawl carpet', found in one of the Kabul homes he visited:

> Carpets of highly wrought shawls are also used but this piece of magnificence must be very rare, from the enormous expense. Moolah Jaffer of Seestaun had a shawl carpet of great size, with separate pieces for sitting on, which was bespoke for Shauh Mahrmood, and which was bought for a quarter of its price after the prince was dethroned. Moolah Jaffer asked 10,000 pounds for it which he said was far below its value: he intends to try and sell it at the courts of Persia and Russia and if he fails, to cut it up and sell it in pieces to the Turks.[10]

Another type of shawl greatly admired by the Persians was the Kashmir 'khatraaz' which simply means 'straight lines' in Kashmiri. Khatraaz (Plate 31a) was a striped cloth of different colours containing either tiny repeats or a type of meandering floral design which ran the length of the stripes. It was normally woven in one piece, in the same dimensions of the standard long shawl, but rarely worn in the same way. The well-to-do cut it up and used it for vests, coat linings, stockings, and in general as a soft fabric worn close to the skin. 'The Persians seldom wear shawls thrown around the shoulders like the people of India' wrote Fraser.[11]

Fraser also recorded other styles popular in Persia at the beginning of the nineteenth century in his informative 'Account of the Commerce of Persia'. He wrote:

> Those which they chiefly admire are richly flowered all over, or spotted with pines [botehs] of great or less size on a rich ground, as black, blue, green, yellow, crimson or scarlet. A few of the striped patterns are liked but the former are the best.

In commenting about another type of shawl he alluded to the chandar or moon shawl: 'Square shawl-handkerchiefs are also required for the ladies; these should have a handsome centre ornament with a border to match.'[12]

Arabia and Turkey had also coveted these rich fashion articles long before Europe; and their taste for the finest specimens was without equal. The Count of Modave, while travelling in the Orient in 1775, noticed their extreme popularity. He related that '…there is not a son of a good mother, as the saying goes, who would not want a few [Kashmir] shawls at his disposition', though he considered that the Persians did not care in the least about wearing them. The Turks thought highly of the Kashmir shawl, which they required to be richly ornamented and of the best quality. Wearing it became an important event, especially during an outing through town which of course was never accomplished on foot; walking was considered a degradation. The nobles went about Constantinople, for example, on horseback, accompanied by a numerous group of lackeys and servants who attended them on foot.[13]

9. Elphinstone, p. 290.
10. Ibid., pp. 268, 269.
11. Fraser, 1826 p.369.
12. Ibid.
13. Bibliothèque National, The Costumes of Turkey.

PLATE 31a.
'Khatraaz' or striped kani cloth from Kashmir using hashia motifs.
Afghan Period, c.1800.

During the Afghan rule of Kashmir, Jacquemont offers us a clue to the design origins of those chequerboard shawl patterns often seen on late eighteenth or early nineteenth century shawls (see Plates 112 and 113). He describes a pashmina cloth of which the ground is always striped in length and breadth and divided into small squares. He noted, however, that its manufacture, although very popular under Afghan domination, was practically abandoned by the time he visited Srinagar in 1831. This pattern, called 'longui', was often woven in the same dimensions as a standard long shawl. It was the Afghans' favourite turban in the winter and it was frequently woven as a belt. The longui's colour was generally a dull dark blue, striped with red.[14]

14. Jacquemont, vol. 3, pp. 289-290.

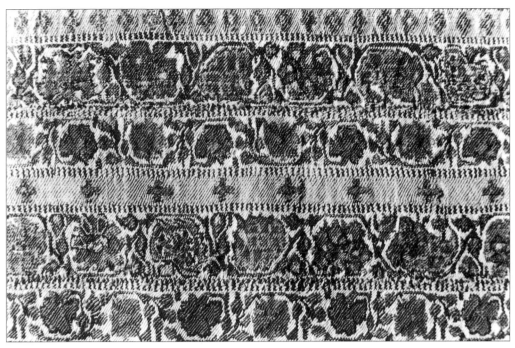

PLATE 31b.
'Khatraaz' or striped kani cloth from Kashmir using hashia motifs. Afghan Period, c.1800.

European Textiles in the Orient

Even before Kashmir impinged on Persia's weaving industry, the country was beginning to feel the first effects of Western design products such as fine printed goods. Western textiles were already enjoying an international reputation and France especially was on its way to establishing firm political and commercial ties with the Orient.

Fraser described the impact of French textiles such as chintzes and printed cloths on Persia in 1821-22:

> The French and the German manufacturers have been much more successful than the English in hitting the Persian taste; no doubt because they took care to have the best information upon the subject; and every bazaar had a full display of their rich and glaring chintzes, while many of our more sober English goods lay neglected on the inner shelves unasked for and unseen. It would not be easy to convey an idea of the kind that would suit the eastern markets, but novelty, united with rich and well-blended colours, seldom fails to please.[15]

The Persians were extremely fond of printed goods and manufactured large quantities. They were not equal in quality, however, to those imported from Mazulitpatam and other parts of India. French, German and English printed goods were in 'great measure' replacing those of Indian provenance. Fraser commented:

> The success of this branch of the trade depends very greatly upon the pattern sent, for fashion in this respect in Persia is to the full as capricious as in

15. Fraser, 1826, pp.367-369.

Europe, and the inhabitants will reject an excellent article merely because the pattern does not please them while they give extravagant prices for goods of a very inferior description merely because their gay colours happen to suit their fancy; for want of attention to this material point, there were hundreds of chests of printed cottons, that had been sent from Bombay, lying at Shiraz and Isphahan, totally unsaleable.

Fraser noted that French and German patterns were 'often preferred' to those of English origin. High luxury items such as silks, brocades and embroideries, chiefly supplied by the French, also captured the Persians' fancy.

From the Paris Exhibition of French National Products in 1819 we learn that French shawl manufacturers were enjoying new markets in Germany, Italy, and the Orient.[16] Constantinople, an entrepôt for European merchandise to the East, was renowned for shrewd and capable merchants accustomed to travelling exceptionally long distances. They represented trading companies across Turkey, Persia, Afghanistan and India. The French retained company agents in these countries and as many as twelve 'maisons' were being represented in Alep (Syria) in 1804.[17]

We have no account of just how France's exact imitation shawls were received in the Orient. Unusually fine shawls, featured at the national exhibitions of French products, were often exported and the exhibit reports often describe how exquisite specimens were *en route* towards Constantinople. These prized products represented France's highest artistic achievements, and were officially offered as cordial gifts in recognition of various political and economic agreements.

The English also sent shawls to India and although they were of inferior quality, their low price did attract a certain clientele. Fraser purchased two English imitation shawls in Bombay, at 40 rupees each, with the intention of selling them in Persia. They were of the turban type and measured 10 yards by 43 inches (915cm x 109cm). From previous trips he had an idea of Persian taste, but he appeared dismayed when he was able to sell them for only 100 rupees each. The Persians, it happened, objected strongly to the rough and ragged appearance of the shawl's reverse side. Fraser conceded '...if this could be made more to resemble the real shawls, it would tend greatly to increse their sale.'[18]

During the same period, Moorcroft also recounted how English shawls were received. In his letters from India he explained that 'they gave great credit to British artists for their close imitations, but considered them inferior to the Kashmeeree original.'[19]

TRADE ROUTES OF THE ORIENT

Kashmir shawls were exported, of course, first throughout the Orient, and then throughout Europe. Moorcroft has left an account of how the shawls were treated for export. The shawl was taken from the loom, inspected, washed and dried, and prepared for shipment.

The packages are of various dimensions but they are formed on one principle: the shawls are separated by sheets of smooth, glazed and coloured paper, and they are placed between two smooth planks of wood with exterior transverse bars which, projecting beyond the planks, offer a purchase for cords to tie them together. The whole is then placed in a press or under heavy

16. The French Consul Duprès along with the new ambassador, General Gardance, were dispatched to Teheran in 1805.
17. Olivier, vol.4. p. 181. See also Hanway, vol. I, p.48.
18. Fraser, 1826, p. 369.
19. Irwin, 1955, pp. 24-25.

weights for some days, when, the planks are withdrawn and the bale is sewn up in strong cloth. Over this a cover of 'tús' [?] or of birch bark is laid and an envelope of waxcloth is added and the whole is sewn up as smoothly and lightly as possible in a rawhide, which contracting in drying, gives to the contents of the package a remarkable degree of compactness and protection.[20]

The packages, or 'bedris' as they were sometimes called, exported to Afghanistan, Persia, and other destinations using overland routes, were subject to heavy taxes. In their journey towards Peshawar, north-west of Srinagar, and twenty days by caravan, the terrain was so rugged and mountainous that the route was nearly impossible, even by mule. At each resting station a toll was fixed, depending either on the bedris' weight or on just a cursory glance at the bundle. As a result, a shawl, when it arrived in Peshawar, had already been taxed up to twenty rupees. From Peshawar, shawls went on to Kabul where they were again subject to a new toll of 2½%. Following this, they proceeded to Meshed where the same fate awaited them.[21]

Information on road taxes was given by the English traveller, George Forster, who published an account of his travels *Journey from Bengal to England* in London in 1790. Forster had concealed his Western origins by disguising himself as a Turkish shawl merchant in order to slip unobtrusively into Kashmir, unvisited by any Western traveller since Bernier in 1668. Forster noticed a large number of duty stations, thirty in all, where goods were taxed between 3% and 4%, between Lucknow and Srinagar. 'This charge', noted Forster, 'with the expenses necessarily incurred in the course of a tedious and distant land conveyance, largely enhances the price of the shawls in the lower part of India'.[22]

In addition to these cumulative custom-duty taxes, the high cost of transportation was also a problem. It varied greatly according to the route. Furthermore, strict precautions had to be taken to avoid being attacked by marauding bandits. Jacquemont informs us, for example, that 'commerce had been practically annihilated by the state of anarchy devastating the countries to the north and west of Attock (between Peshawar and Srinagar) for the past twenty years, whereas formerly it was quite considerable between India, Afghanistan, Bukhara, etc.' The brigand Turkomans, a purely nomadic tribe similar to the Kirghiz, who found easy prey among the poorly armed caravans, were a constant threat.[23] Protection was necessary; ironically the Indians often had to pay four rupees per shawl to the chiefs of the robbers themselves. On the other hand, certain areas were well guarded; in the direction of Herat, Persian troops were stationed to assure the safety of the routes.[24]

A sophisticated level of finance supported this vast movement of merchandise, showing how important the shawl industry had become. Merchants conducted their affairs through a system of credit, loans, promissory notes and money lenders.

Passing through Isfahan in 1650, Tavernier recorded in detail the way in which the more than ten thousand 'banians', or money lenders, operated.

They are all bankers and very adept especially in the knowledge of money. The majority of money invested by the important merchants of Isphahan is in the hands of the 'banians', When in need of a large sum, a fair collateral will suffice for obtaining a loan the following day, provided a large interest is paid – sometimes up to 18%. But payment is made in secret due to the laws of

20. Wilson, p. 186.
21. Duprès, vol. 2, p. 395.
22. Forster, vol. I, p. 223.
22. Klaproth, 1829, vol. I, p. 48.
24. Duprès, vol. 2, p. 395.

127

Mohamet which forbids interest... Normally, loaned money is amortized in three months at an interest rate of from 6% to 12%. Merchants not actually residing at the place of their purchases are required to take out new loans to pay off the old. The new money is paid off at the city of their destination. For example money from Erzeroin [Erzurum] is refunded at Bursa, Constantinople or Smyrna. Money from Bagdad is paid at Alep.'[25]

Other travellers' accounts also describe the money lenders. Mir Izza Tullah, in his travels in 1812-13, found the 'wafarush' financing shawl manufacturers and the 'mugims' appraising shawls and observed 'All merchants made their purchases through the mugims.'[26]

Victor Jacquemont wrote:

Loudiana is the most frequented city between the Punjab and the countries to the North of Attock and India. A banker is never missing and they have their first correspondents in Amritsar, Lahore, Djeaodri, and Delhi; their relations stretch from Calcutta, Bombay, Kashmir, Attock, Peshawar, Cabul and Herat.[27]

The Kashmir shawls were exported by a number of different routes. Nearly all the imports and exports to and from the Punjab and other parts of India passed south through the Pir Panjal and Banishal passes, because the Jhelum Valley route was often closed to all trade during the early nineteenth century due to political disturbances. The Northern shawl trade with Tibet and Russia passed along the Ladakh and Gilgit routes.

The earliest account of shawl commerce and activity comes from a learned French military man, the Count of Modave, who travelled in India during the years 1773-76, about half a century before Moorcroft's detailed report of the same subject. According to Modave, most bedris taking the southern routes passed through the large depot at Lahore, then descended to Tatta near Karachi, by the Indus River. The 'banians', at times merchants but most often usurers, shipped them abroad via the Red Sea.

In their descent towards Tatta they also passed through the famous trading city of Multan, from where many of the Kashmir shawls were diverted to new overland routes to Persia. Multan enjoyed great prosperity during the seventeenth century as a strategic and key city of the Mughal Empire. In 1752 it was annexed to the Kabul kingdom and from 1771 was repeatedly attacked by the Sikhs before being taken by Runjit Singh in 1818.

Multan was renowned as a trading city; it was composed mainly of merchants and contained a larger number of factories than its rival city, Lahore. The Multanis controlled almost all commerce west between Hindustan (India) and Persia, their city being the point of reunion for caravans between the two.[28] Shawls shipped from Multan passed through Kandahar to Bagdad, joining Persian shawls woven in Kerman, Yezd and Kashan. From Bagdad they were sent on to Constantinople.

About sixty-five Multanis established a small colony in Astrakhan, under Afghan rule: it was witnessed by Count Jean Potocki who travelled through the Caucasus in 1797.[29] Kashmir, of course, at this time was also under Afghan domination and their leader, Zaman Shah, resided in Kandahar. After passing through Multan most merchandise from Hindustan was sent to Turkey, South Arabia and Persia via the cities of Surat and Tatta.

John Grose, in his voyage to the East Indies in 1757, noticed that Surat, in addition to shipping shawls also manufactured them, but remarked that there

25. Tavernier, vol.II, p. 155.
26. Sufi, p. 562.
27. Jacquemont, vol.3, p. 33.
28. Deloche, p. 336.
29. Klaproth, 1829, vol. I, p. 50.

PLATE 32.
The corner detail of a fragment of a moon shawl kerchief, c.1775. One of the earliest kani pieces illustrating an Anglo-Mughal pattern. The chunky flower rosettes, the heavy stem and the saw-tooth leaves point to a mid-18th century style. This is the only known chandar of this period that does not illustrate a purely Islamic style. Notice the atypically narrow hashias.

were 'but few and not many of the finest sort'.

Modave explains that the Kashmir shawls arriving in Tatta were practically the only article of merchandise transported to the Western countries. This was carried out by Indian merchants who, from the sixteenth to the seventeenth century, had established a series of colonies stretching from the Persian Gulf to the Caspian Sea, from Shiraz to Astrakhan and from Kandahar to Isfahan.[30] Basra, at the western end of the Persian Gulf, was the principal port-of-call for shawls arriving from Tatta and Surat. Quetta, situated between Multan and Kandahar, was also a principal shawl market. Apparently, the latter city contained a shawl-weaving community as early as 1794.[31]

On the north-west routes, the shawls that left Kabul for Bokhara were eventually traded by Khivan merchants in Russia by way of Orenburg and Astrakhan. These merchants resold some of the shawls in their home town of Khiva and the remaining ones were carried into Russia. In addition, Bokhara, Meshed, Kabul and Andijanin all had their own shawl-weaving production centres.

Bokhara, in spite of the political upheaval at the end of the eighteenth century, enjoyed a very active commerce under the influence of an impartial and calm government. It was situated on the great caravan route. Fraser remarked: 'There are two, not more, caravans per year which pass between Bukhara and Russia, but each consists of from 4,000 to 5,000 camels in a journey lasting three months.'

Shawls sent via the northern routes continued their journey to Tiflis, Georgia,

30. Deloche, p .329.
31. Singh, p. 95.

located mid-way between the Black Sea and the Caspian Sea. This important city was the major stepping-stone for Oriental goods departing for the great cities of the north: Amsterdam, London, Saint Petersburg, and Moscow. During the nineteenth century, the famous fair of Niji-Novgorod attracted quantities of rare merchandise which were purchased by merchants of all nationalities including many French who came from Paris.

France received her shawls through resident agents in Constantinople or Moscow; Marseilles received shipments coming from Alexandria, Smyrna and Constantinople. The Rhine frontier near Strasbourg gave entrance to shawls arriving from Marcarieff via Moscow and Vienna while Bordeaux's trade was limited to Bengal. The major French companies, however, imported directly from Kashmir.

Honigberger, in 1852, suggested that shawl transportation should not be by the long route round the Cape of Good Hope, but by the Red Sea and the Mediterranean, or if possible entirely overland because unless shawls are hermetically sealed they invariably suffer from the sea voyage.

In general, however, most shawls shipped to London went from Bombay via the 'John Company' or East India Trading Company. In London, auctions of the merchandise would take place for three days twice a year, in December and June, attracting dealers from many countries.

Through this variety of land and sea routes, then, the Kashmir shawl was brought to world-wide markets.

ORIENTAL RUGS

The development of Kashmir's curvilinear boteh during the eighteenth century appears to have been a phenomenon reserved only for the shawl and practically unrelated to carpet patterns. During the early Mughal period, however, both weaving mediums shared natural and freely spaced flowers. In the latter part of the eighteenth century, the boteh, as discussed in Chapter Four, underwent a radical transformation from a unique floral to an unmistakably curvilinear form; it was a fundamental part of the aesthetic evolution of the shawl. Yet a careful survey provides no evidence that the cone boteh was employed even as a minor design element in Oriental carpets and other weaving prior to 1800.

On the other hand, the nineteenth century saw a tremendous profusion of carpets, embroideries, etc. which utilised 'boteh' repeats and other Kashmiri patterns so often found in the kani shawl. Prior to this period Kashmir shawl designs may have influenced carpet weaving in the group of carpets popularly known as 'millefleurs'.[32] The origin of this distinctive group of carpets has been the subject of controversy, but it is now felt they were actually woven in India and that Kashmir itself is the most likely source of their manufacture. Their general design format is quite bold, consisting of a large central panel, the middle of which is shaped in the form of a prayer niche. The field is generally cluttered with flower blossoms and branches, hence the appellation 'millefleurs'. The field's symmetry is balanced and harmonised by the use of a large vase and dish elevated by a mound situated at the bottom of the niche. Important pieces of this group are found in the well-known McMullan and Biltmore collections in the U.S. (see Plate 32a), while the millefleurs shawl (the earliest of this type known, see Colour Plate 179) conserved by the Musée Historique des Tissus, Lyon, provides possibly the main link between this group and contemporary shawl patterns. The treatment and disposition of branches of flower blossoms (racemes), the graphic

32. Cf. Millefleurs carpet (17th century): Museum of Decorative Arts, Vienna, T1539.

PLATE 32a.
Millefleurs prayer rug, Kashmir, c.1800. Senneh knot, 120cm x 188cm (47x 74in.).

PLATE 32b.
Mughal rug, India.
Attributed to Shah Jehan
Period
(1628-1658).
137cm x 294cm
(54 x 116in.),
1258 knots per square
inch.

132

rendering of the top rose (radial flower) and of course the use of the vase, dish and mound, combine in late millefleurs carpets to suggest a close relationship between the 'millefleurs' carpets and Afghan-period shawls (1753-1819). Other examples of this carpet group can be seen in plates 30 and 32 of McMullan's *Islamic Carpets,* 1965. In the former we again find the apex flower drawn in the radial technique. In comparing Colour Plate 179, the apex rose shows the use of what the French called during the nineteenth century the 'caillouté' technique. Similarly, the dish's slanted or zigzag lines and the flower petals drawn on the vase itself, independently of the rest of the rug's flora, bears a strong resemblance to what might be found on a shawl woven towards the end of the eighteenth century.

Among the earliest carpets known at present which employ the Kashmiri cone boteh are those found in the region of Caucasus, in the village of Marasali.[33] These common prayer carpets display rows of boteh inside a mihrab (see Colour Plate 38a). Their unique main borders are flanked by two insignificant minor borders, characterised by a meandering vine pattern composed of 'bent-tip' strawberries (or abstracted roses) laid end to end and arranged within a sinuous geometric vine which runs over and under them in an alternating fashion. Horizontal lines placed in a staggered manner fill this special border, an obvious carry over from the Chinese cloud-band trails. Such meandering motifs were the main theme of the seventeenth and eighteenth century patka hashia borders.

The last carpet I would like to mention is a fabulous Mughal fragment, a masterpiece of Imperial court weaving, hanging in the Metropolitan Museum of Art (see Plate 32b). It is worth comparing the cog-wheel type flower in the rug's field to that of the shawl in Colour Plate 135. The mounds too, located in the rug's border, with their leafy protrusions, also appear to stem from the same school of design. The elegantly drawn floral meanders in the rug's guard borders relate stylistically to those hashias found in Colour Plate 123 and Plate 83. These comparisons are not necessarily to prove that Colour Plate 135 is of the same period as the rug but rather to demonstrate the transcending currents of art from one medium to another.

33. For examples of these carpets see *The Oriental Rug Collection of Mary Jane and Jerome Straka,* NY, 1978, pp. 105-106 pl. 102-103. Also, Schürmann, p.220, pl.78.

Plate 33.
A caricature mocking the Kashmir shawl's high fashion, 1795.

134

CHAPTER SIX

Shawl Weaving in France

In previous chapters the exposure of the Kashmir shawl to foreign influences has been discussed but the argument has been confined to shawls made in the Orient. In this chapter French attempts to manufacture a shawl which could compete directly with those arriving from the East are considered.

It has been suggested that the popularity of the shawl first began in England, and that it may have been the English who first began copying it. However, recent studies of the European shawl do not mention whether England ever employed the Indian weaving method. This chapter, therefore, discusses not only France's distinguished development of the kani shawl, but also France's great mechanical invention, the Jacquard loom, which eventually provided all of Europe with an efficient means of manufacturing the 'Kashmir' shawl.

When Napoléon returned from Egypt, the generals and officers who had served under him brought back mementoes of the Orient. Among these were Kashmir shawls which they wore wrapped around their waists as belts, and which had been plundered from the Mamelukes, the soldiers of the Egyptian Army. Contemporary artists vividly captured France's oriental exploits through portraiture, often depicting a subject dressed in full military uniform with a Kashmir shawl worn as a belt, as in the colossal painting by Baron Gros, where Napoléon is shown walking among victims of the plague ('Napoléon visitant les pestiférés de Jaffa', Louvre Museum).

Napoléon's return also brought important new trends in fashion. Feminine fashion simplified itself and women began wearing sheer white décolleté dresses. This caused a need for warmer outer garments, and the Kashmir shawl was an ideal solution in terms of beauty, warmth and texture.

The most important factor in the growth of the shawl's popularity, however, was the Empress Joséphine (Plate 16). She lived in a most creative period of female fashion and her clothes deserve to be studied as representative of the social history of her era. She was the first to adopt the 'robe de simplicité', and the triumph of the revolution made the fashion of a simplified dress universal. Endowed with infinite charm rather than beauty, Joséphine was the paragon of the well-dressed woman. Her extravagance in clothing and jewellery was legendary; she changed her dress ten times a day and never wore the same pair of stockings twice. Her wardrobe contained hundreds of the rarest of Kashmir shawls. When buying, she was reputed never to ask the price.

At that time England, with its virtual complete control of the seas and its mighty East India Trading Company, maintained an almost complete monopoly over goods coming out of India. Not only was France ruined financially by the Empire wars, but in 1786 she had signed a commercial treaty with Britain which turned out to offer many more advantages to the British than to the French. Despite the Continental Blockade of 1806 by which Napoléon had sought to isolate the British, much foreign merchandise continued to enter France as contraband. The silk manufacturers of Normandy and Picardy were completely crushed by British competition.[1] Much of the silk weaving was therefore phased out and their looms began the weaving of woollen 'Kashmir' shawls. Picardy was the major region for shawl production after the shawl prototypes had been designed in Parisian ateliers.

1. Martin, vol. 3, p. 319.

PLATE 34.
A First Empire shawl, 1804. The laurel wreath was then a popular theme in ornamentation.

PLATE 35.
A contemporary fashion illustration, c.1805, entitled 'The Modern Woman', a study in ostentation.

FIRST FRENCH SHAWLS

The French shawl during this transitional period was born out of the industry of ladies' scarves made of silk gauze with a plain weave. The borders were narrow, the botehs thin, slender and brocaded in silk in one or two colours. They were made on the drawloom and the wefts were left uncut on the reverse side.

In 1805 the first shawls with trimmed reverse sides (decoupés) were wefted in wool on silk warp with five or six colours. The use of more colours necessitated the operation of trimming as the shawl began to accumulate extraneous weight and lose its softness. The weave was not strong enough to prevent the wefts from falling out – a dire deficiency which had to be immediately rectified. Out of this urgency a system of heddle play *(jeu de lisse),* operated by the foot of the weaver, was invented to consolidate the weave. The method was called *'pas de liage'.*

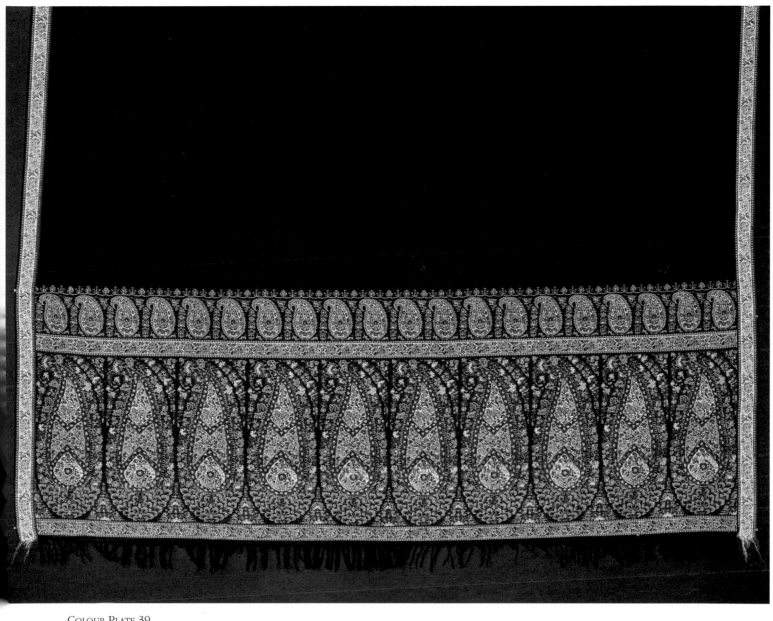

COLOUR PLATE 39.
French jacquard or drawloom shawl, c.1820. Pashmina wefts. The long borders are sewn on.
141cm x 298cm (55 x 117in.).

Although this strengthened the wefts, the pattern suffered because the warp covered half the point forming the flower.

In view of these technical difficulties and the very high demand for Kashmir shawls, dealers were thwarted in their attempts to satisfy the market. It is not surprising, therefore, that French manufacturers set about finding new ways to fabricate their own 'real' Kashmir shawls: first, exact imitations of the Indian original, and then new styles which followed French ideas of design and innovations in production technology.

In 1806 the production of shawls of silk warp and wool weft necessitated looms of a more complicated nature. The common drawloom contained four hundred pulleys arranged in eight rows of fifty each. Even with two warp threads assigned to each pulley it was impossible to make the design larger than twelve to fifteen centimetres (5 to 6 inches). In view of this limitation, a way was found to augment the number of pulleys to 1,200 in order to copy the Indian shawl. This became a complicated and expensive method since a second drawboy was required to handle the tremendous increase in drawstrings.[2]

THE EXACT IMITATION SHAWL

The 'exact imitation' shawl was made either on a real Indian loom, or a similarly constructed French loom, called 'espouliné' using a twill-interlock weave. These shawls were so well made that they were often sold not as imitations but as bona fide Kashmir.

The person credited with having first woven one of these shawls was Bellanger, a wool maker from Rouen, who was associated with Dumas-Desolme.[3] Since the first public exhibition of an imitation Kashmir shawl occurred in 1802,[4] we must assume Bellanger produced his shawl somewhat before this time. Subsequent national exhibitions of French industrial products often refer to him as having made and 'revealed the shawl to the commercial world'. It appears that he was sent a beautiful Oriental shawl by a far-sighted general of the Expeditionary Army and he immediately prepared a drawloom with a special harness invention and weave composition in order to copy it.[5]

Deneirouse, considered doyen of the French shawl industry, pointed out that Bellanger was 'a man who knew how to predict and prepare the future of an industry. He succeeded in producing a natural flower shawl conserved by his family with religious care, in perfect conformity to the most beautiful shawls of India.'[6]

Héricart de Thury, who followed closely the early developments of shawl weaving, remarked:

> The Maison de MM. Bellanger, Dumas and Descombes is one of the oldest in Paris. It is to this company that France owes her first 'shall' of silk and cotton with fringes, and they were the first having tried to imitate Kashmir shawls with silk and wool, with such success that France produced shawls worth 20 million francs during several years of which a large part were exported. This was achieved before Lyon's shawls in 'bourre de soie' or silk floss, came into favour.[7]

There had, however, been a possible precursor although whether Bellanger knew of it or not is open to conjecture. It appears that in 1785 there was an attempt to establish Indian weavers in Thieux, France. It is not known from what part of India they came or whether they were knowledgeable in kani shawl techniques, but it would appear that their work involved the weaving of toile or linen cloth.[8] A Monsieur de Montaran, Master of Petitions and Intendant of Commerce, was charged by the government to oversee and record the daily expenses of these weavers. The attempt was short lived as the work proved unprofitable.

2. London Universal Exhibition, 1851.
3. Bellanger died in 1829 whereupon his company was absorbed by the Ternaux family.
4. Rézicourt, Jobert and Lucas and Co., Reims, were the first to exhibit an imitation Kashmir shawl. They were associated with the Ternaux brothers.
5. Bellanger employed the same weaving technique as in India. Expo. 1839.
6. Deneirouse, *Traité,...* p. 10.
7. Expo., 1819, p. 10.
8. National Archives Paris F12-2414, letter from Héricart de Thury.

BAUSON AND GIRARD

The Indian technique, called 'châle espouliné', received its name because shawls made in this manner were woven with 'espoulins' or tiny wooden needles similar to the tojis used on the Kashmiri loom. Although Ternaux and a few other wool manufacturers had a small fraction of their shawls woven by this method, Bauson, a former associate of Bellanger, was the first to come up with the idea of establishing an atelier uniquely devoted to this type of weaving. Bauson's atelier received much public attention because he employed young orphan girls. He developed special weaving techniques using a loom of the Indian type. M. de Thury, in reporting his findings to the Interior Minister, described Bauson as being the 'inventor of certain processes which are particular to himself and not used in any other of the numerous ateliers which I visited and studied'.[9]

Bauson started his atelier in 1808 in Sèvres, and entreated the French government to give him financial aid on the grounds that his company 'contributed to the progress and perfection of industry'. His requests were not met and in 1815 he offered his company to the state in order to be made a national industry, similar to the tapestry manufacture at Gobelins. Bauson argued for this in a letter addressed to the Duc de Duras:

> If the atelier is given the title of 'Manufacture Royale', several weaving establishments of this type would be formed in various orphanages in Paris, an establishment which would have much in common with that of Gobelins, the only difference being that it takes a long time to train a weaver at Gobelins but very little for the Kashmir; the weaving is done mechanically without art and only two to six months are necessary for an apprenticeship.[10]

It became clear at this point that the government was turning a deaf ear, not only to Bauson but also to a great many anxious and industrially creative entrepreneurs eager to embark on new ventures. Financial aid was very scarce and the government was fiscally ruined by the costly Napoléonic wars. Furthermore, the Restoration of the Bourbons brought with it a large influx of foreign merchandise and the English took advantage of this opportunity with low-cost products resulting from their head start in the Industrial Revolution.

Bauson remained, however, obstinate in his demands to the Interior Minister, Le Comte de Vaublanc, since he felt that it was highly unjust that his company should not be nationalised. Finally in January 1816, the following year, he was asked to sketch an outline of the types of shawls he proposed to offer.[11] He supplied the following estimate of shawl prices:

Shawl, 2.5 x 1.5m, white ground and large cones and borders according to the fineness and richness of design: 900-1,500 francs
Shawl, 1.5 sq. m, flowered ground without borders: 390-550 francs
Shawl, 1.5 sq. m, striped with flowers, without border: 480-700 francs
Shawl, 1 sq. m, striped without borders: 400-500 francs
Shawl, 1 sq. m, flowers, without borders: 330-450 francs

Bauson then decided not to solicit any further subsidies either from the King or from the French government, but to attempt simply to obtain the privileged title of 'Fabricant de Cachemire de Son Altesse Royale Madame La Duchesse

9. Ibid.
10. National Archives Paris F12-2414, letter from Héricart de Thury.
11. Ibid., letter dated 18 Jan., 1816.

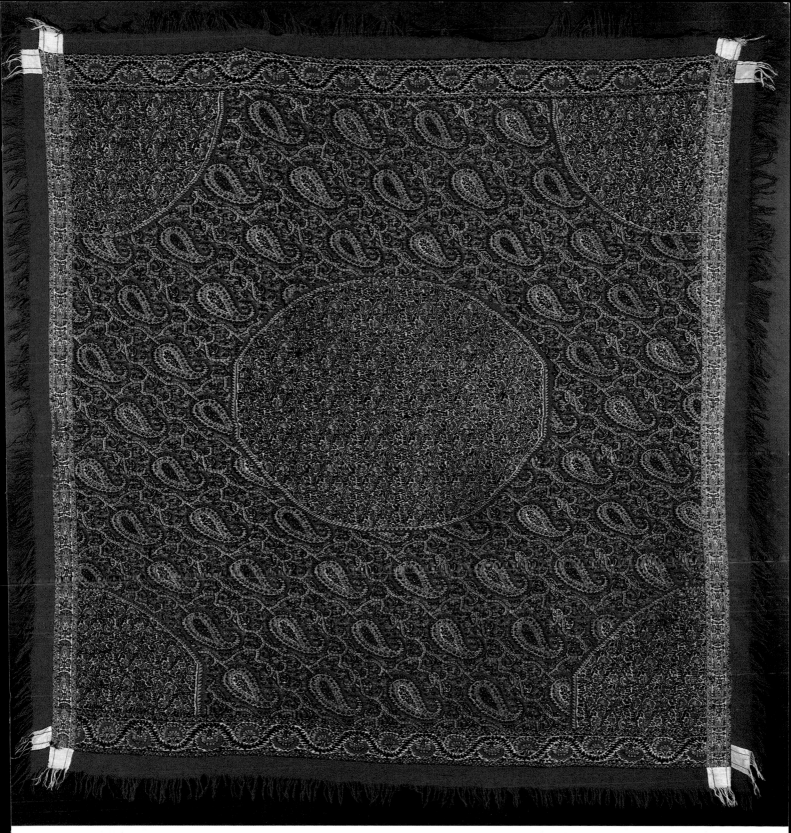

COLOUR PLATE 41.
French moon shawl, c.1835. 158cm x 158cm (62 x 62in.). This is a possible example of the espouliné technique with woollen weft and silk warps.

COLOUR PLATE 40 Opposite.
French jacquard shawl, c.1860. Pashmina wefts. 141cm x 365cm (55 x 144in.).

d'Angoulême'.[12] In this way his merchandise would receive preference over foreign goods, and he would be one of the exclusive suppliers to the Court of Louis XVIII. This concept caught the fancy of the Duchess and, after a few years, Bauson received her official sanction. Although consoled, he never seemed fully content. The Government insisted all along that Dumas and Descombes, as well as Bellanger and Ternaux, had all made imitation shawls before Bauson.

Bauson's work was finally exhibited in the National Exposition of French Industrial Products, 1819, where he received a silver medal for 'having imagined fabricating shawls, with an easy and prompt process, executed by children under the guidance of an experienced worker'. The Central Jury also said that 'the shawls made by Bauson are in every respect similar to the real shawls of Kashmir and can be delivered to the market at a lower price.'[13]

Bauson, however, was outraged at not having received a gold medal, and he wrote a letter a few months later expressing his disgust and disappointment with the government's attitude (or rather the attitude of the Central Jury) and boldly demanded a passport and permit to take his looms out of France into another country where he would be appreciated![14]

Bauson's anger was finally appeased by receiving a gold medal in the Exposition of 1823. The government, to reward his years of labour, also offered him a stipend of 300,000 francs.[15] His reputation had grown internationally and the King of the Netherlands, it seems, took a great interest in his shawls and offered to put a large establishment for the fabrication of Kashmir shawls under Bauson's direction.

A popular motif used by Bauson in his early shawls was the 'arlequiné' – a design very much enjoyed by Parisians (see Plate 53), first produced in great quantities in Srinagar. The arlequiné shawl consisted of a palla in which each boteh repeat was compartmentalised by a separate ground colour. He claimed to have achieved, through his own dye experiments, tonal nuances which imitated exactly and with 'absolute harmony those of India'.[16]

The loom techniques employed by this scrupulous shawl-maker were very similar to those of Kashmir, except of course for the fact that he engaged young orphan girls as weavers. An experienced worker sat in the centre and carefully directed two apprentices to his left and right. A shawl was woven at the rate of one and a half centimetres (half an inch) per twelve-hour day. Bauson's hand-woven shawl was the result of a long, tedious process; eighteen months were required for the completion of a long shawl. However, H. de Thury remarked, 'In spite of their cost, Bauson's shawls were selling daily as Indian ones without any suspicion they were made in France.'[17]

If Bauson was never completely satisfied in his relations with the government, he was probably even less happy in his relationship with a former associate, Girard, who also solicited government help. Girard established an atelier in 1819 using the knowledge of weaving techniques acquired from Bauson when they were close friends.

A case was submitted to the consultative committee of the Arts and Manufactures disputing whether Girard or Bauson had contributed most to the 'progress and perfection of industry'. Bauson had woven a long, white, superfine shawl to be presented to the committee as proof of his ability and technique. It had large, rich palms, borders and counter borders along with corner palmettes, and the complete shawl had been conceived without any lost stitches or seams. He was well aware that Girard's weaving methods were questionable: it was very easy to fabricate a shawl 'en bridant', by floating the wefts on the underside of

12. The daughter of Louis XVI.
13. Expo. 1819, Rapport du Jury Central.
14. National Archives, Paris, F12-2414, letter of 22 Oct., 1819.
15. Ibid., letter of 27 April, 1822.
16. Ibid., letter of 10 August, 1821.
17. Expo. 1823, p. 94.

PLATE 36.
The original jacquard weaving loom, 1804, surmounted by jacquard's mechanical invention. The mechanism is composed of hooked needles and spring-loaded pins which enmeshed with each of the successive pre-programmed punched cards to form the fabric's pattern.

PLATE 37.
Three views of Dencirouse's efficient espouliné loom without mechanism. The papier briqueté was not required and a separate reader at the opposite end of the loom counted and raised the warps.

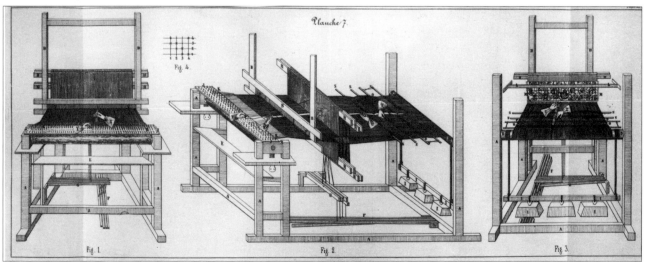

COLOUR PLATE 41a.
Reversible jacquard shawl in silk and wool. 165cm x 165cm (65 x 65in.).

COLOUR PLATE 41b.
Reversible jacquard shawl in silk and wool. 193cm x 178cm (76 x 70in.).

144

the shawl in such a way that the weaving would be accomplished with one hundred espoulins instead of the three hundred ordinarily required. The brocading of the wefts in certain areas of the motif was much simpler and quicker than the interlocking technique. Bauson, a meticulous craftsman, greatly resented this sort of trickery.

The outcome of this long dispute is unclear because neither man left complete accounts. Girard's company, however, did successfully establish itself in Sèvres, with twelve looms and fifty workers, all abandoned girls. Like Bauson, Girard had found a patron, Madame La Duchesse de Berry, and received a silver medal for his fine espouliné shawls in the 1827 Exposition.[18]

THE JACQUARD LOOM

France's strong inertia to modernisation was reflected by the long delay in her industrial revolution, and it was due to the influence of a few Englishmen that industrialisation finally occurred within the wool and cotton industry. Macloud had first introduced the carry-barry or flying shuttle to France in 1778, but its use remained very limited until 1815 when, due to Napoléon's encouragement, the cotton industry began slowly to adopt it. Undoubtedly the greatest impetus came from Douglas, an important muslin manufacturer from Manchester, who offered his knowledge and mechanical-engineering experience to the French nation.

As early as 1788 he had proposed the construction of new machines for spinning wool and preparing cloth, but here again resistance was encountered and his ideas were not adopted until 1802. Finally, a brilliant English engineer by the name of Cockerill, under the patronage of Ternaux, devised ways and techniques to improve the French wool industry.[19]

While French industry was busy taking advantage of English technology in Paris, Jacquard was perfecting his new invention in Lyon. In order to arrive at a final prototype, however, Joseph Marie Jacquard studied the eighteenth century inventions of Falcon and Vaucanson which had been stored away for years in Paris. The study was performed under the sponsorship of the government which finally recognised his ingenuity.

The invention of the Jacquard loom had an important effect on the history of the Kashmir shawl in France. Jacquard's popularity began with the public exhibition in 1801 of an eight-pedal loom for which he received the Bronze medal. In 1803 the Société d'Encouragement pour l'Industrie Nationale offered a prize for anyone who could come up with a rapid method of weaving fishing nets. Jacquard was invited to demonstrate his new loom. The members of the investigating jury were impressed, and he was awarded a patent on the 18 December 1805.[20]

During the same year the Society again offered a prize of 3,000 francs for a proper loom to fabricate all kinds of figured and brocaded cloth. Jacquard's creativity again prevailed and in 1807 the Comité des Arts Mécanique announced that he had found the solution to the problem and the 'usage is now generally adopted in Lyon'.[21] Until that time, we find absolutely no mention of its application to the manufacture of shawls. But the time was ripe and it appeared that at least a few far-sighted individuals began considering this new possibility. Jacquard was now a government employee fulfilling his contractual obligations. He received an annual stipend but asked a mere fifty francs per loom. For each group of machines that were completed and placed into service, he dispatched

18. Expo. 1827, p. 55. It is interesting to note that the Duchesse de Berry and the Duchesse d'Angoulême detested each other.
19. Lomüller, pp. 63, 95, 155.
20. Prat, p. xv.
21. Ibid., p. xvii.

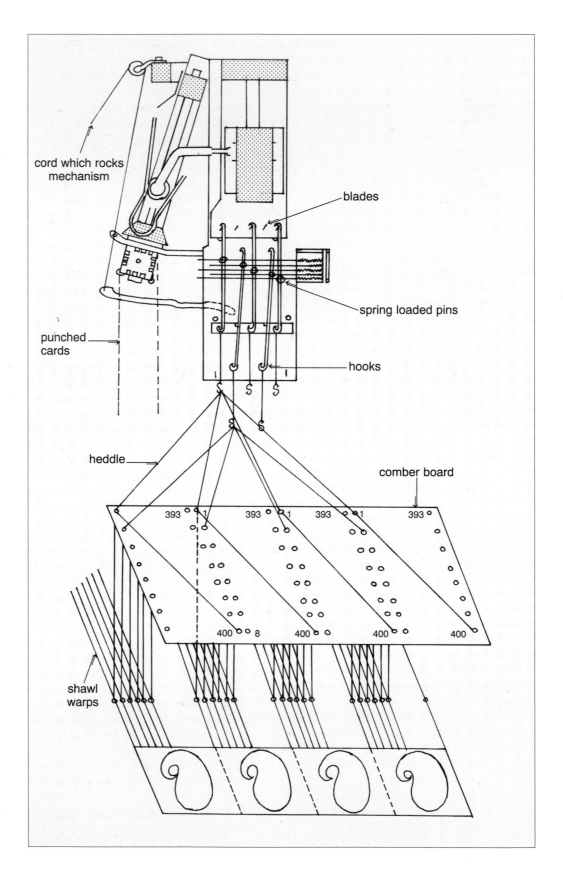

cord which rocks mechanism

blades

spring loaded pins

punched cards

hooks

heddle

comber board

393 1 393 1 393 1 393

400 8 400 400 400

shawl warps

FIGURE 31.
A cut-away view of an elementary jacquard loom.

146

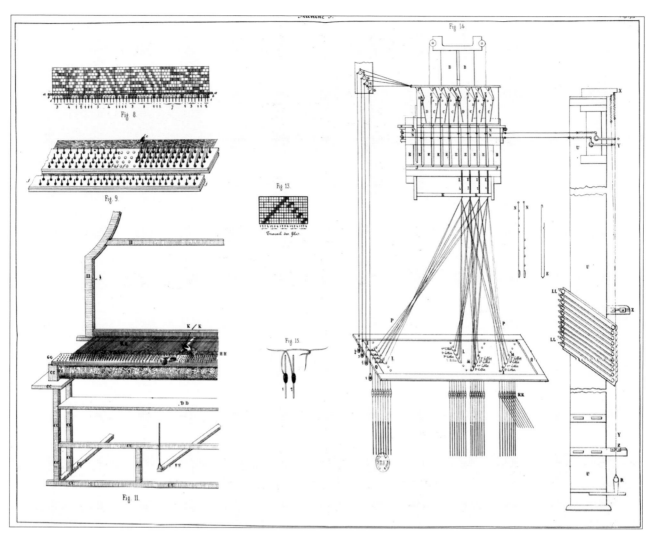

PLATE 38.
Deneirouse's special mechanical loom based on a stripped-down version of the jacquard machine. In fig 14 in this illustration, the reader, in pulling on the heddle cards (YY), raises the hooks which ride up on the blades of the 'griffes' (C). The weaver then steps on the pedal (EE, fig. 11) raising the warps (KK) and brocades with his espoulins (HH). fig. 8 shows the papier briqueté across which the heddle cords fall, shown by the numbers. Just below is shown the punched-hole board which organises the espoulins. fig. 15 shows how adjacent weft colours were interlocked with the espoulins (tojis).

an itemised account in a letter to the Chamber of Commerce requesting his due payment or 'prime' payable under an imperial decree of 1806. Fifteen looms were put into service during the period 21-29 April 1806, but only sixteen were completed during the first three months of the year 1811. All told, fifty-seven looms were made during the years 1806-11.[22]

Like many an innovator before him, Jacquard met with the traditional resistance to change, and to uncertainties of income. The authorities of Lyon, his home town, had stopped payments to which he was entitled. Rumours spread that Jacquard was in Paris seen talking with foreigners, and the Chief Commissioner of Lyon wrote to the authorities in Paris asking that Jacquard should be ordered back to Lyon 'before he sells his invention to the English'.[23]

22. National Archives, Paris, F12-2199, letter dated 2 May, 1811.
23. Ibid., letter dated 10 Nov., 1814.

It seems unlikely that Jacquard would have betrayed his country, however. When James Watt was commissioned by the English government to buy his invention, Jacquard replied, 'I regard it a sacred duty to leave to my native town a discovery which could furnish a foreign nation with a way to ruin our industry.'[24]

A critic at the 1834 exhibition observed that the Jacquard loom was introduced in Paris in 1816, 'not without difficulty', by Fournier Aîné and Co. (Fournier was most probably a shawl manufacturer.) This was the first time Jacquard's name was mentioned by an exhibition critic. The arrival of the Jacquard loom in Paris, in 1816, brought a relief from the difficulties inherent in the drawloom.

Jacquard's underlying intention was not so much to increase the speed of weaving and eliminate the drawboy, but rather the more humane desire to alleviate the excruciating forced child-labour prevalent throughout the industry where boys as young as ten were used to work the existing drawlooms. A boy would raise each of the warp threads through a system of cords. At each throw of the shuttle he was obliged to pull on these stretched ropes which were counter-balanced by heavy lead weights. Furthermore, he was required to call out the necessary weft colour as read from the design in order that the master-weaver could choose the right shuttle. This was an extremely arduous task for children to perform.

The operator of the drawloom had to depend on the drawboy to see that the warps were raised to the right height. If they weren't, the shuttle would often break some of the warps due to the lack of space between them. Another inconvenience of the drawloom was the time required for the boy to choose and pull the cord, not an automatic movement but one which demanded thoughtful hesitation.

The early use of the loom, however, brought new problems which could scarcely be overcome except by substantial modifications. Apart from the actual weaving itself, a whole new group of people had to be trained to use the loom and this of course accounted for a big delay in its initial operation. Before the drawloom could be abandoned it was necessary to reduce the immense quantities of expensive cards indispensable for each design on the Jacquard loom. This is why the loom was limited to small motifs in the beginning.

Just where the first Jacquard shawl was woven is not known, but it is very likely that the Parisians were the first to use the Jacquard loom for this purpose. One enterprising manufacturer proposed to the government, at the early date of 1817, the establishment of a 'new shawl industry using the Jacquard loom, in which three to four hundred workers would be occupied'.[25]

The early Jacquard loom ruined many of the businesses which used it; even after almost twelve years' use, employees still lacked motivation and showed resistance towards the machines. Nevertheless, larger companies were able to furnish themselves with more elaborate technology and with the perfection in the spinning of pure Kashmir wool, the obstacles which formerly impeded the use of the Jacquard loom were overcome.

By 1822 at least eighty Jacquard looms were being used in Paris to weave shawls of pure kashmir wool. This left a total of 3,190 drawlooms operating in Picardy and Paris together, of which 2,340 were being used to weave shawls.[26] The largest quantity of shawls sold in Paris were woven in Picardy, in such places as Fresnoy-le-Grand and Bohain.

How many Jacquard looms were operating in Lyon is not known but the exhibition of 1823 tells us that both Nîmes and Lyon were represented by twelve

24. Grandsard, pp. 108-109.
25. National Archives, Paris, F12-2414, letter dated 22 Oct., 1817.
26. Chambre de Commerce, Registre de Commerce T4, Rapport de Ternaux et de Bellanger sur l'Industrie Parisienne de Châles et de Gazes, Séance de Juillet, 1822.

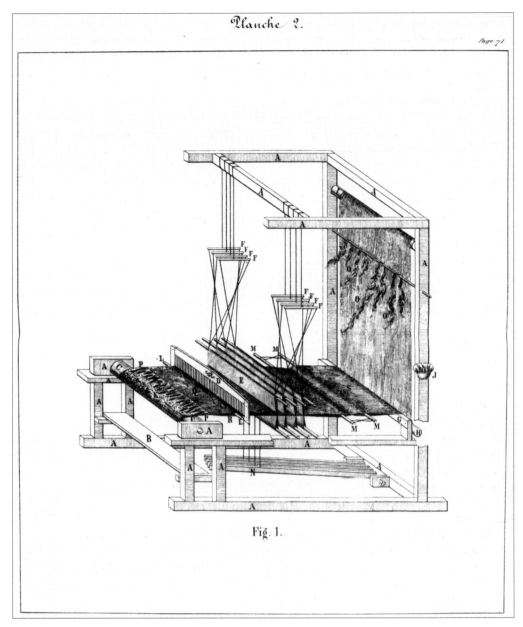

Fig. 1.

PLATE 39.
According to Deneirouse this illustrates the Indian loom 'in all its simplicity'.

manufacturers who certainly employed some Jacquard looms. Once again, the rejection of the loom within the weaving community is manifested by the fact that it was not mentioned at all in either of the two preceding exhibitions in spite of the fact that eighty were in full operation in Paris.

Later on in England the Jacquard loom was employed extensively in shawl making but remained rather unsophisticated up until the mid-nineteenth century. An important French manufacturer, commenting during the exhibition of 1851, ascertained that most of the British looms were lacking the most necessary technical improvements.[27]

27. Gaussen, 1851 exhibition, vol. 4, p. 7.

THE JACQUARD OPERATION

The Jacquard loom operates on the use of punched cards which, when pressed against spring-loaded metal pins, control the raising of the warps. Those pins which align with the holes are pushed through the card, forcing their corresponding crochet needles – or hooks as they are sometimes called – to be raised by vertically moving blades upon which the hooks become caught. Those pins which do not encounter a punched hole are pushed back, horizontally, moving the hooks out of the way so that the moving blades do not lift them.

The figure shown on page 146 is a cut-away profile view of an early Jacquard which exposes the pins and hooks in order to give us a clear view of the inner mechanism. This represents a very elementary version of a Jacquard, connected to a comber board which is threaded to weave a cone shawl. This is a very simplified drawing. Here each of the four cones would actually need 400 warps to make up the complete width of the shawl. It is, however, impossible to make a drawing rendering all 1,600 warps.

One can, however, imagine the same mechanism showing 400 hooks and warps instead of the five shown, to perform this weaving. As hook number one rises, it pulls with it four warps, one from each cone. The shuttle (not shown) is then thrown, using the appropriate colour, and the motif begins to form. As the blades descend releasing and picking up new hooks, according to the instructions read from each succeeding card, the next set of four warps is raised and the operation repeats itself. This action is done by the weaver who pulls a cord causing the card-carrying device to rock back and forth.

If the number of cones is increased to eight, four more cords would have to be tied to each hook. Therefore, it can be said that the number of times a motif is repeated is equal to the number of cords tied to each hook. Of course, as the repetition is increased, the array of cords from the Jacquard to the comber board becomes more complicated. As a matter of fact, a Jacquard loom set up to weave a shawl appears to be an absolute nightmare of threads spraying off in all directions.

As the cone (boteh) grew larger and more sophisticated in design, a larger number of Jacquard cards were required. On the other hand, the smaller the motif, the fewer the cards required. It is impossible to enlarge a cone motif without increasing the number of hooks. Figure 31 also does not show the 100 or more additional hooks needed for the weaving of the end borders so necessary for the embellishment of a shawl. The early looms did not have these hooks; because of this we find that the borders were made separately for the early shawls, and then sewn on (Colour Plate 39), once the shawl was removed from the loom.

Until Deneirouse (see below) and a few others paid serious attention to the improvement of the Jacquard loom, the designs were limited to small repeats not larger than 15cm (6in.) wide and a few years later to about 20cm (8in.) with looms utilising 600 needles. There was still a limitation to the number of needles which could be put into the mechanism without incurring enormous expense. Furthermore, the early Jacquard cards were large and bulky, and designs employing many colours increased their number. Storage was also a problem since they took up a large space.

The early Jacquard loom was thus unable to imitate the contemporary large Indian designs; the machine was originally made for the weaving of silk, and design effects were produced without the use of heddles. Its repeats were small compared with the large size of the Indian boteh which at this time measured about 50cm (19in.) in height. In order to weave larger patterns it was often necessary to return to the drawloom but here again it was impossible to enlarge the pattern beyond 12 to 15cm (5 to 6in.)

Jacquard, who had spent so many years developing his loom, abandoned making innovations entirely around 1812 and just supervised loom production. It was not until the end of the first quarter of the nineteenth century that something was done to alter the destiny of this revolutionary loom.

DENEIROUSE — SHAWL MAKER AND INVENTOR

Deneirouse, like Jacquard, is one of the great names of the French shawl industry, a shawl manufacturer and innovator who in 1851 published a treatise on shawl weaving in France, a work which had taken him ten years to write. The treatise had a twofold purpose. Firstly, at a time when France was going through an economic slump and when shawl makers were feeling the pinch, Deneirouse suggested a whole new industry which would alleviate unemployment, gain national approval and at the same time help the depressed shawl weaving centres of France, in Paris, Lyon and Nîmes.[28] Secondly, and of less importance, he wanted to defend his development of the 'papier briqueté', which had been wrongly attributed to another prominent shawl maker, F. Hébert, in the report of the 1839 Exhibition.[29]

At the Exhibition of 1823 two shawls had received attention for the remarkable colour effects and 'the beautiful execution of the palms and borders'. They were the work of Ysot and Eck, using new espouliné techniques. In the treatise, Deneirouse paid tribute to them and wrote: 'None of the "espouliné" shawls exhibited by any of us [Deneirouse also was an exhibitor in 1823] approached [them] either in design richness, beauty of the weave, colour vivacity or purity of design in perfect harmony with the fabric.'[30]

When the Ysot and Eck company was dissolved and their espouliné looms, designs and accessories were put up for sale, Deneirouse became aware of Eck's special 'encartage', where each 'duite' or combination of weft colours was painted separately on a card in a 'most complicated fashion'. Deneirouse commented:

> I was so taken aback by the admirable harmony in their shawls, absolutely similar to those of India, that I resolved to apply this system to the French shawl [drawloom or jacquard] of which the manufacture seemed to me much more important than using the Indian method.[31]

This system was the papier briqueté, which Deneirouse simplified, first applying it to the drawloom, and above all the Jacquard loom. Within a few years of his discovery, practically all shawl makers were using it.

The Indian designs, once woven, lost the curvilinearity they displayed formerly on paper to re-emerge with outline shapes in broken and jagged lines. Deneirouse's *mise-en-carte* took advantage of this fact. The *mise-en-carte* is the technique by which a pattern is transferred from sketch to special cross-hatch paper, which provides the loom with warp/weft instructions. Each coloured square of the paper represented the weft crossing over or under a warp. On the papier briqueté (a type of cross-hatch paper, see Plate 38) the artist was able to

28. Gaussen, 1851 exhibition, vol. 4, p. 61.
29. Ibid., pp. 18-22.
30. Deneirouse. *Traité...*, p. 19.
31. Ibid.

151

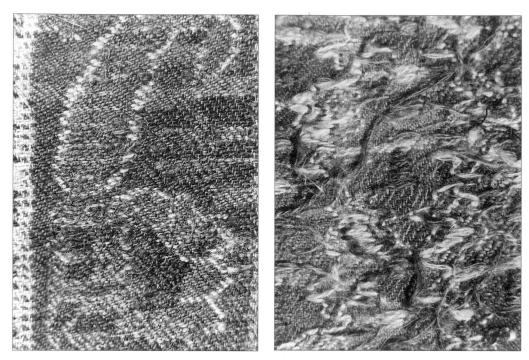

PLATE 40, a and b.
Magnified detail of the front and back of a coarsely woven kani shawl in merino wool.

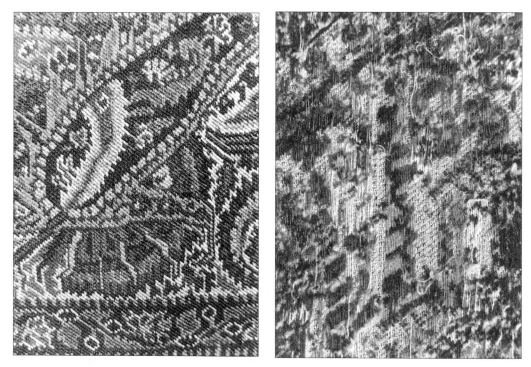

PLATE 41, a and b.
Magnified detail of the front and back of a finely woven French jacquard shawl.

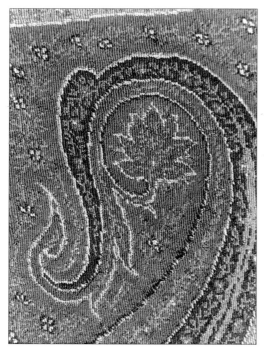

Plate 42, a and b.
Magnified detail of the front and back of a rare shawl known as 'battant brocheur', a weave which closely imitates the kani weave (see Colour Plate 38a).

draw freely and in total liberty without regard to the printed lines on the paper. Each square, or brick as it was called, represented four warp threads which could be raised by one hook of the jacquard.

Deneirouse realised also that within the Indian technique there were two weft passes, one exactly the same as the other. The same jacquard card had only to be repeated in order to imitate the 'caillouté' or rocky style. This had the effect of building up the flower in a step-like fashion, and imitating very closely the Indian shawls. This idea reduced the number of cards required by fifty per cent.

New techniques in shawl manufacturing were kept as closely guarded secrets and because of this Deneirouse worked in tight secrecy in his home town of Corbeil, without the knowledge of his colleagues, between 1824 and 1827. The repeating of the jacquard cards, along with the papier briqueté, reduced the cost of reading the designs by ninety per cent, and at the same time it was possible to make larger patterns.

Deneirouse's treatise explains the fundamental weaving technique of espoulinage, which involves a choice between two different looms, one of which was a stripped down version of the jacquard loom. The other loom was fairly similar to that used by Bauson.

The first method consists of a unit very similar to the jacquard mechanism but simpler (see Plate 38). Instead of the quantities of punched cards which formerly contained the design information, here we have drawstrings directly attached to the jacquard pins themselves. The other ends of the strings drop vertically alongside the loom, falling across rollers containing the coloured-in design drawn on the papier briqueté. Each 'brique', or grid, represents a minute fraction of the design which is translated to the cloth by a drawboy reader who pulls on the thin string (thin enough not to hide the grid). At the same time the weaver passes his espoulin (bobbin) through the warp threads with one hand and with the other he hooks or crochets the succeeding bobbin around the first one, thus interlocking the wefts. This is done until the complete width of the fabric is crossed once in both directions and the twill weave is completed.

Deneirouse pointed out that the advantages of using this method are twofold: firstly, whereas before it was necessary to employ a mechanism in complete harmony with the motif, it was now possible with the design *mise-en-carte,* a double-core loom, and a one hundred-needle machine, to execute the most complicated designs using the total width and length of the shawl. Secondly, a shawl made with only one repeat required only three workers: one to read the design and two to brocade.

The second method was much simpler than the first, in that no mechanism was employed. The only prerequisite was that the repeated motif did not exceed 40cm (15¾in.). This loom differed from that employed in Kashmir in that the Indian worker was obliged to count the warps himself and then brocade them, while Deneirouse's system allowed a separate reader to count them *while* the weaver manipulated his bobbins. Thus the weaver, who was formerly occupied with counting warps and then brocading, had only to pay careful attention to the brocade itself (see Plate 37).

It does not seem that the first method was very successful. Deneirouse wrote that he 'would have continued to make shawls by this process if [he] had been able to do the designs of all the widths which were asked of [him]'. One of the main advantages common to both methods, however, is Deneirouse's unique idea of a board, punched with holes, in which the bobbins are held in place while waiting to be used. If we imagine a weaver confronted with hundreds of espoulins in a confused pile and then having to choose the right one, this new method of bobbin allocation can be highly appreciated. Deneirouse argued that although the Indian weaver was extremely adept in counting the warps and choosing the tojis, whatever the dexterity of the worker, a certain lapse of time could not be avoided. The Deneirouse techniques saved time.

Rous, Comet and Co., a creative weaving concern from Lyon, went so far as to make shawls simultaneously using the jacquard and espouliné methods, thereby imitating the Indian shawls that did not require being shaved on the underside.[32]

Girard continued this technique, and received a gold medal in 1839, despite the pervasive influences of industrial mechanisation, for his '…perfectly successful, Indian-shawl imitation'.[33]

FURTHER DEVELOPMENTS OF THE JACQUARD LOOM

In the late 1820s Bosche, a shawl maker associated with Deneirouse, brought another innovation to the jacquard loom. This was called the 'double griffe' or 'mécanique brisée', meaning 'split mechanism' or 'split jacquard'. This technique placed an additional set of blades within the jacquard. Two hooks were now attached to each of the spring-loaded pins. When the blades rose they took the hooks with them. Those which normally remain at rest would work because of the new set of blades. Thus while one set of blades is rising the other is descending.[34]

The jacquard loom had now undergone a complete metamorphosis. The double griffe made two jacquard mechanisms out of one without increasing the

32. Expo. 1834, Le Baron Charles Dupin. p. 93.
33. Expo. 1839. vol. 1.
34. Prat, p. 96.

154

size of the unit. It was now an easy matter to place two of these jacquard machines on one loom which could be put into action with the weaver's foot. Designs of 175cm (69in.) in width could now result from the manipulation of 6,400 warps. The drawloom, even with the addition of more pulleys, was limited to designs of only 15cm (6in.) at the most.

By 1839 the main centres of shawl manufacturing, Paris, Lyon and Nîmes, each manufactured a different kind of shawl. Paris was the leading fashion centre and generally manufactured the finest shawls.

In Paris three types of shawl were woven: firstly, the 'cachemire pur', woven entirely with the goat fleece of Kashmir. This rarely had less than eight colours, usually ten to eleven, and sometimes as many as fourteen or fifteen. Secondly, the 'châle indou cachemire' which had a warp of silk 'fantasie' and a weft of pure cashmere but fewer colours were employed. Thirdly, the 'châle indou laine' which had a warp of silk 'fantasie' and a weft of fine wool with three to six colours.

In Lyon the 'châle tibet', with a mixture of wool and 'bourre de soie', woven in a square or a rectangle 3 x 1.5 metres (10 x 5ft.), and the 'châle en bourre de soie', with a warp and weft of silk, were woven, though by 1839 it was almost entirely the 'châle tibet'. The 'châle indou', with a warp and weft of inexpensive wool, was woven in Nîmes.

By 1857, Paris and its outskirts contained a total of 729 jacquards, of which 253 were inactive due to unemployment. Of those remaining in service, about ninety-five were working to supply furniture fabric. The following is the record of an independent worker using three jacquard looms, and shows his production during the years 1853-56:[35]

1853: 50 long shawls at 94frs each, 33 square shawls at 50frs each
1854: 24 long shawls at 94frs each
1855: 14 long shawls at 94frs each, 32 square shawls at 76frs each
1856: 24 long shawls at 94frs each

MASS PRODUCTION OF THE KASHMIR SHAWL IN FRANCE

During the Exposition of 1827, Rey exhibited an espouliné loom, but by the Exhibition of 1834 nobody was talking about espouliné shawls any more, most probably because of the tremendous advancements in the jacquard loom. This method, however, was not forgotten, for the French considered its lack of speed just another problem to be overcome by rapid mechanisation. Such mechanisation was not long in coming.

The 1844 Exhibition cites a certain M. Richard, who designed a machine called a 'battant brocher' to weave shawls by a type of brocading using the espoulinage technique. Although it had not as yet been perfected, the invention received praise for its ability to insert a weft crossing of twelve colours (douze lais). This was seven colours more than any previous machine and, therefore, represented a substantial advancement.

In 1862, Fabard, a shawl maker, invented a machine called the 'battant espoulineur', which seemed to solve many of the problems involved in espoulinage. Unfortunately, the national exhibition archives leave us with very little information regarding the shawls made with this technique, saying only that they displayed the 'same aspect, same rich colours and the same relief,...imitating fairly completely those of India'.[36]

35. *Ouvriers de Deux Mondes,* p. 301. Without doubt these were low quality shawls.
36. Expo. 1867, Rapport du Jury, vol. 4, p. 226.

The Exhibition review of 1867 contains two references to the mechanisation of 'les façonnés brochés'. 'The substitution of the motor for handwork in order to activate the shuttle of the battant brocheur' and 'the set-up of the simultaneous action of the battant lanceur and battant brocheur results in the complete elimination of the brides or weft floats'.[37] This is the first time that reference is made to automation in the shawl industry but in fact since the references concern the perfection of a technique one may assume that some looms had been operated automatically by the (steam) motor for possibly quite some time before 1867. The long shawl in Colour Plate 38 is one of the rare examples that illustrates the battant brocheur technique.

The importance attached to this developing industry should not be under-estimated. Since four million francs' worth of Kashmir shawls per year were being imported into France,[38] French manufacturers were anxious for new innovations, and Fabard's was an exciting one. In only twenty days and using twenty looms, a complete 'Kashmir' shawl could be woven. In 1862 orders were arriving from all over France with Paris as the centre of activity.[39] Fabard was adamant in asking the French government to prevent a wealthy English company from buying up this new industry. The British offer, of course, was not without several exacting conditions: the shawl maker and the looms were to be exported to England. Although information leading to the conclusion of this affair is not complete we can assume that the deal was not consummated because five years later, in the 1867 Exhibition, Lecoq and Gruyer were recognised for having made these shawls in France.

By this time, the shawl was on its way out of fashion. This 'counterfeit' sector of France's Kashmir shawl industry was mentioned by critics in the 1862 World Fair in London. A Monsieur Hébert, it was noted, had succeeded in applying an entirely new process of espoulinage and had been able to deliver to the trade, in a short period of time, about two thousand shawls for a total of 400,000 francs.[40]

COUNTERFEIT OR KASHMIR

Serious study into the fashion, design and weave technique of the French Kashmir shawl has only begun in the last few years. Setting the stage for the first major shawl exhibition was the Musée du Costume, Paris, in 1982, followed by the Musée de l'Impression sur Etoffes, Mulhouse, and most recently the Musée Historique des Tissus, Lyon. All three provided a starting point from which to uncover the many mysteries surrounding the prolific shawl industry of the nineteenth century.

This burgeoning interest has brought to light the problem of recognising the difference between a European Kashmir and a real Kashmir shawl. At present there is no extant exact imitation shawl which can be said with certainty to be of French origin. Unfortunately research in this field is lacking and only a chemical analysis of dyes and wool could provide us with positive proof. However, in spite of the lack of scientific information there are from time to time 'Kashmir' shawls appearing on the market which have an irrefutable wrong feel and look to them. The following brief discussion therefore attempts to show how a counterfeit may be recognised.

If we were working with hand and machine-made carpets, our task would be greatly simplified. This is because we would be dealing with large scale designs woven with heavy wool. The stiff patterns of the mechanical rugs would be

37. Ibid., vol. 9, p. 209.
38. Expo. 1851, p. 9.
39. National Archives, Paris, carton F12-2414, Personal letter to the Comte de Persigny, 20 Nov., 1872.
40. Universal Exhibition of 1862. London, official catalogue.

immediately detectable. With the Kashmir shawl, however, one is dealing with finely woven 'miniatures' whose designs must be closely inspected, often through a magnifying glass. This would be even more the case if shawls woven with Deneirouse's mechanical espouliné method are ever found.

To begin with it should be assumed that all shawls made in the Orient used the twill tapestry technique of interlocked wefts. These shawls will show on their reverse side many dangling loose threads, some ending in hand tied knots and others jumping from one colour area to another. But most important of all is the visible ridge formed by the interlocking threads between the large areas of colour.

One of the easiest shawls to copy was the moon shawl, possibly because of its small dimensions. During the second quarter of the nineteenth century many of them came from the Punjab. They were made of rough quality wool and their crude designs were so abstract that flowers simply became geometric areas of colour. Recently, a chandar or moon shawl with warps of red silk and interlocked wefts of thick merino wool was found in a private collection (Colour Plate 41). It was woven in one piece, which is rare for a shawl of average quality made for a commercial market. And because there are no central joins we find that the botehs run across the entire field all in the same direction. In view of these characteristics and the European-type colour dyes employed, it was most probably made in France.

The French had expressed their disenchantment early in the nineteenth century over the poor quality of shawls arriving from the Orient. Many shawls were made of different pieces which were often poorly sewn together or were badly woven and in need of instant repair. France's 'exact' imitation industry intended to counteract this problem by offering to the public a shawl entirely woven in one piece. A strong sense of pride was involved, as evidenced in the letter sent by General Allard from Kashmir in 1837 (see page 42). One criterion, therefore, for determining whether a shawl is an imitation is whether it is woven all in one piece. Very few Kashmir shawls were, even before the great period of patchwork shawls, and those which were are usually of exceptional quality and design suggesting that they came from court ateliers. A good example of a possible 'exact' imitation is found in the Textile Museum of Washington, D.C. It is a classic dochalla of few colours and although weft interlocking is completely absent, the shawl represents a very rare example of what the French called 'cachemire français'. Its weaving technique, called 'broché' or brocaded, was similar to the Indian technique in its use of the 'espoulins'. These were tiny thin sticks around which the thread was wrapped and which were used to insert the precious imported goat yarn with the same care used in the methods of brocading precious metals, like gold and silver.

Shawls woven on the jacquard loom are not called exact imitations because of the obvious differences apparent even to the unsophisticated eye. Examining the reverse side of a jacquard shawl one will find that the weft threads create thin coloured lines which dash across the shawl with a mechanical linearity. All loose and floating weft threads have been razor clipped with fine regularity. Running the hand over the reverse side, there is a touch sensation of rough flannel or of the low cut pile of a soft carpet. The jacquard shawl has embroidery only on very rare occasions: on the fringes of very fine French shawls. The finer ones frequently have fringe gates which are interlocked using the 'espouliné' technique, something the English fringes lack.

There is no difference in an early shawl woven on a drawloom from one woven on a jacquard loom. According to Gabriel Vial,[41] France's well-known authority on early weaving technology, 'it will be practically impossible to distinguish patterned cloth woven on a drawloom from that woven on a loom equipped with a jacquard mechanism'.

The first silk employed in imitation Kashmir shawls was called grenadine. It was composed of two silk yarns slightly twisted, but given a high torsion when combined together. Grenadine, supposedly, simulated very well the grain existing in the real Kashmir cloths. French shawls prior to 1813 were almost always made with a silk warp since the imported Indian goat fleece was too difficult for the contemporary French 'fileur' to spin. Consequently, imitations made entirely of pure Kashmir wool would most probably not have appeared until at least that time. The first yarn of pure Kashmir wool was spun mechanically in 1813 by Hindenlang, one of France's important shawl manufacturers.

Dye colours also play an important role when distinguishing real Kashmir shawls from their French imitations. The French were more able than the English to approximate closely the Kashmir colours, but variety was limited. The Kashmiri possessed an extraordinary sense of colour based on centuries of weaving experience. Shawls coming from the Punjab were heavier and bulkier with a predominating deep red colour. Jacquemont observed that the most popular colour in the Punjab and in India was scarlet, followed perhaps by white.[42] Amritsar was famous for making the best shawls of the Punjab and its dyes came close to those of Kashmir but the wool was limited to that from the local plains sheep and imported Kermani goat fleece.

The next criterion for determining the authenticity of a Kashmir shawl is the technique with which the centre field was joined. This was obviously a great point of interest for Moorcroft who was in Srinagar in 1821. The discrepancies he observed in the woven field are particularly interesting in light of this discussion:

> The cloth [matan] thus made is frequently irregular, the threads of some parts of the wool being driven up tightly, and in others left open, from which results a succession of bands, sufficiently distinguishable whilst without colour, but still more obvious when dyed. The open texture is, in a degree, remediable by the introduction of fresh threads; but there is no sufficient cure for that which had been much compacted. One might be led to suspect that there existed some radical defectiveness in the principle of this mode of weaving, not readily mastered, were not pieces of cloth found occasionally of an almost perfect regularity of texture. But the greatest irregularity is discoverable in those shawls which have the deepest and heaviest borders... Such indeed, in some instances, is the degradation of the cloth in the field, as to induce some foreign merchant to cause it to be removed, and another piece to be engrafted within the edge of the border.

It is odd that Moorcroft does not discuss the weaving competence of the Kashmiri rather than the 'principle of this mode of weaving'. He continues:

> But in this case there is no other remedy than a judicious selection of a sheet of the same breadth and fineness; for although two breadths of the narrow cloth might fit the vacant space, yet these must be joined by the rafugar in the middle; and although this can be so done that the bands differ *not in thickness* from the rest of the cloth, yet the join is discernible when held

41. Currently Secrétaire Général Technique du Centre de Documentation d'Etude et de Textile Ancien. Lyon. See Bibliography.
42. Jacquemont. vol. 3, p. 287.

between the eye and the light, from the threads in the joined breadth being *not continuous in the same line;* whereas any irregularity of this nature is drowned in the edge of the border. The best practice to insure a good field seems to consist in weaving the border, in every case separately, and inserting the field by the rafugar.[43]

Moorcroft does not mention that even when the matan was woven *with* the shawl, it rarely spanned the whole centre as one woven piece. Most fine Kashmir shawls contained at least one and often two seams in the matan where the border was *woven* with the field. These seams can be more easily detected, however, by locating the discontinuity in the hashia caused by the difficulty in aligning the design at the end of the pieces. Nevertheless, the hashia was so well joined that an observer might have trouble identifying the matan's seam, even if he held the piece up to the light. Occasionally, the enmeshed warp-ends protrude above the surface of the field; in this case, the seam is easily found.

Legoux de Flaix described how the Kashmiri employed a special darning needle, very long and supple, capable of meshing the warp threads together. Along with other highly specialised techniques, unique to the ancient craft, this has now been lost. If the matan has been entirely replaced, it would have either been sewn or spliced in but in both cases the Kashmiri was clever enough to conceal the front seam with delicate, floral embroidery.

THE REVERSIBLE SHAWL

FRENCH ESPOULINÉ

The reversible shawl was often made by the espouliné method. Legentil, a reporter of the 1844 exhibition, described how reversible shawls had been made in Russia for a long time, but in France only since 1827 and, until the time of his report, without success.[44] He does not mention reversible shawls originating from Kashmir, which he certainly would have done, had any been known at the time.

He describes in detail two reversible shawls displayed at the exhibition, exceptional for their quality and execution. They were shown by Heuzey and Marcel in collaboration with Deneirouse whose espouliné methods were used in making them.

The first was a long, richly designed shawl with a white centre, woven entirely of pure Kashmir wool; the second was an 'écharpe', or scarf, woven of very fine wool coming from a flock of sheep in Mauchamps, France. Both of these unusual products were part of a special commission and were to be exported to the Orient. Legentil wrote of the long white shawl:

There is a very curious shawl at the booth of MM. Heuzey junior and Marcel, following Deneirouse, and Lagorce. This shawl, in pure Kashmir and completely white, is brocaded [in this case he means espouliné] without a reverse side ['sans envers'] in natural flowers, with stems, leaves and scalloped edges. It is fine, soft and light, delicate and beautiful, of excellent colours and artistically designed. In 1817 something of this nature was tried: very pretty borders were made with reverse side unapparent; but the 'brocade' was finely cut off or clipped. While on the contrary, the former is full, solid with stitches which have some relation to the work of beautiful

43. Wilson, vol. l, pp. 181-183
44. Expo. 1844, vol. I, p. 205.

tapestry. Two things characterise this endeavour: first, the work does not give a reverse side, the warp finding itself enveloped in such a way that a relief is obtained which gives a vivacity simulating perfectly a velvetiness when woven with a twilled ground; second, the nature of the design breaks off entirely with all these 'crochets' [probably the hooked vine], floral designs ['ramages'], and eternal palms of Indian design, and reproduces here beautiful flower bouquets such as nature spreads before our eyes. The appearance of this shawl is an event. It encompasses, maybe, a whole revolution.[45]

The 'impartial' observations of exhibition reporters should however be treated with some caution. The shawl manufacturers of Paris represented a closely knit group and secrets of the trade were tightly guarded. Often a maker was part of the review committee or jury to the commission reporting on the exhibits. Fortunately, the National exhibitions were reviewed by various writers and one may hope to form an unprejudiced opinion by reading several different reports.

RUSSIAN ESPOULINÉ

During the early organisation of the shawl industry in Paris, competition from England and Germany was already recognised.[46] Ternaux drew his inspiration from the beautiful printed shawls from Vienna, while the Russians were beginning their shawl weaving industry, much like the French in 1800, by carefully dissecting the unique Kashmiri weave.

The Russian reversible shawl is described in an anonymous document found at the Musée des Tissus, Lyon.[47] It describes how the French ambassador to Russia, General Louis, Marquis de Caulaincourt and Duc du Vicence, recorded an account of Russian shawl weaving in 1808. During his second sojourn in Russia, he visited a famous weaving atelier in a small village called Skorodoumovka, near St. Petersburg. At the establishment of a Madame Merlaine he saw shawls and scarves which he considered more beautiful than those made either in France or in the Orient and he decided to purchase the most beautiful piece as a gift for the Empress Marie Louise. To the diplomat's great surprise, however, despite being offered the enormous sum of 10,000 roubles, Madame Merlaine refused to sell saying that as a devoted patriot, she was unwilling to let one of her most beautiful pieces of 'tapestry' out of her country.

Madame Merlaine had begun her atelier that year as a direct offshoot of the Kashmir shawl's popularity. Her success, due in part to the bondage of young serf women, was attributed to her patient and meticulous efforts. Her shawls were made with the Indian technique. Each weft was attached to the warp by a 'noeud special' and often separately woven bands were sewn together. This process demanded extreme, skilful attention so that the patterns and colours of the assembled pieces when joined would give the impression of having been made in one piece.

The distinction of the Russian shawls is that they have no 'wrong' side – each side is absolutely identical. Four times more work was required to make a reversible shawl than to make an ordinary one. The weft was not allowed to traverse the whole width of the shawl but only each specific area of colour, after which the thread had to be returned – a very tedious chore. The weaving progressed at the rate of 6 to 7mm (¼in.) a day.

Madame Merlaine was not alone in her efforts. Prince Nicolas Youssoupov from

45. Expo. 1844, Musée Challamel, p. 40.
46. National Archives, carton F12-2412, letter dated 20 Feb., 1808.
47. 'Châles tissés par les serfs Russes', Lyon. By 1841 Moscow recorded thirteen shawl makers, with a total of 284 looms (*Dictionnaire Universel du Commerce etc.*, vol. 2, p. 384).

Koupavinsk, Prince Enikeev of Penza, the State Counsellor Kolokolzov from Saratov and Madame Elisseev of Voronége, who began her atelier in 1813, all made shawls. Only Merlaine and Elisseev manufactured them in any quantity; the former employed fifty weavers, all serfs, with an output of forty-six shawls and five scarves per year, the latter, depending on the season, employed from thirty-five to fifty people.

The technique varied little from one atelier to another and it is impossible to attribute with certainty any one shawl to a particular maker, with the exception perhaps of those of Madame Merlaine, who wove the initials H.M. into her shawls. At the time of the Public Exhibition of Russian Products in St. Petersburg in 1829 her shawls were the object of great admiration. The Czar, Nicolas I, acquired a splendid piece for 12,000 roubles. With her achievements crowned by the reception of a gold medal, Madame Merlaine incorporated in her designs the Imperial Russian Eagle, woven in above her initials. This emblem measured 15mm (½in.) in diameter. The eagle was emblazoned with the Moscow coat of arms, an equestrian figure of St. George, the city's patron saint. The making of this woven emblem was considered a *tour-de-force* unequalled in the history of tapestry.

It was difficult, if not impossible, for Russian weavers to procure the wool of the Tibetan mountain goat. As a result, Elisseev was obliged to finance expeditions to the steppes of Western Siberia in order to assure her own personal supply of the wool. After appropriate sorting, the wool was soft, silky and very light. In 1802 a special scraper was devised to remove impurities from the goat's fleece but, although this gave a fine lustre and softness to the yarn, not all impurities were completely eliminated. It was then necessary to remove the remaining impurities with a tweezer once the shawl had been woven.

In France, Ternaux also had problems obtaining this rare fleece, and as a result undertook an expedition to Western Kazakhstan in 1818.[48] Earlier his purchasing agents in Russia had smuggled the coveted fleece into France where its scarcity was due in part to foreign shawl manufacturers who went to expensive extremes to satisfy a lucrative market.

Towards 1820 Russia gained direct access to the Kashmir shawl trade and at the same time allowed France to establish a consulate in Tiflis. This city, located mid-way between the Black and Caspian Seas, represented an important trading centre for Kashmir and Oriental shawl goods converging from the East and then heading towards the major cities of Russia and the rest of Europe.

Evidently the Russians experienced the same initial difficulties as the French in processing the goat fleece. Not until 1813 did Hindenlang in France develop a spinning method whereby, for the first time, pure Kashmir wool could replace silk or 'organsin' as warp threads.[49] In Russia, by 1823, banks of warp measuring 4,500 metres (4921 yards) and weighing not more than 13 grams (½oz.), were spun with remarkable skill.

For someone who has never come in contact with any of these reversible shawls, it is difficult to imagine the intricacy of their design. They are so fine that even when compared with similar weavings such as those of Huari, Peru or the Chinese 'K'ossu' their complexity still confounds the imagination. The sensation of touch, due to their softness and lightness, is similar to handling a fine piece of silk satin. Only a country with slavery was capable of producing such articles: the work required was inhuman. However, in the case of Elisseev, who enjoyed universal respect for her kindness, the female workers were completely freed after ten years of work in her ateliers; nevertheless most of them were by then

48. See Irwin for a detailed discussion of attempts to naturalise the Oriental goat used for shawls in Europe.
49. Although 1813 is the date given for the discovery of a method proper for spinning Kashmir wool in France for shawl weaving, it appears that several large companies and especially Ternaux had conquered this difficulty at least three years previously (see *Bulletin de la Societé d'Encouragement pour l'Industrie Nationale*, Nov. 1810, Vol. 9, p.278).

almost blind. It is clear that the working conditions in Russia were no different from those in Kashmir or even France. Elisseev founded a hospice for blind weavers, unique of its type, regarded as an act of outstanding charity at the time.

In France neither Bauson nor Girard, who operated weaving ateliers, discussed these hardships, but nevertheless they were very real. Even a jacquard weaver, working from 5am to 9pm in the summer or from 7am to sundown during the winter, was lucky if he still retained his eyesight at the age of forty-five, so difficult was the chore of following the disposition of the yarns, and as a result many were forced to abandon their profession.[50]

JACQUARD LOOM

The reversible loomed shawl, characterised by its traditional square format, small repeat pattern and few colours, is familiar to collectors of European shawls. It was often made of pure silk, or at least the warp was silk. Reversible shawls other than those made by the espouliné method were known to exist before the 1844 exhibition.

In 1827 Deneirouse and Gaussen senior exhibited a reversible shawl and a model of the drawloom on which it had been woven.[51] Another reversible shawl known as 'châle sans envers' was made popular by Ternaux.[52] The English also acknowledged the novelty of this type of shawl during the 1820s, calling it a 'double shawl', but as yet it is impossible to be certain when the first one was woven on the jacquard loom.

The technique was based on the use of two sets of warp threads that served to weave two shawls simultaneously back-to-back. Simplicity of design and sparsity of colour were a prerequisite in order for harmony to be achieved. The normally large number of floating wefts was reduced in such a way as to make the shawl as thin, and thus as light, as possible, and to allow the wefts to form the design. Since each weft shot served to pattern both sides of the fabric at the same time, it followed that the ground on one side would correspond to the figured work on the other.

It is not clear whether the reversible shawl originated in an attempt to weave two shawls simultaneously which would then be cut apart, but certainly a 'new' technique was presented at the 1844 exhibition in which two competing exhibitors each presented a method for manufacturing two shawls at the same time. The concept was similar to, yet different from, the above technique; the aim here was to slice the 'double' shawl in half and thus provide the commercial market with two saleable products. The same procedure is being used today in Pakistan to create two carpets at once, achieved by slicing the pile side of two parallel semi-mechanically produced carpets.

50. One is recorded as having become a vegetable merchant. *Ouvriers de Deux Mondes,* vol. 1, p.38.
51. Expo. 1844, vol. 2, pp.213-4.
52. Expo. 1827, 'Rapport du Jury etc.,' vol. 2, p.67.

CHAPTER SEVEN
The French School of Shawl Design

When the Kashmir shawl's boteh was introduced in the West at the end of the eighteenth century, people were immediately intrigued by its meaning and form. The boteh excited interest more by its colour and shape than by its composition, which was rather confused, and the French were inspired to adapt uniquely French designs. In Europe, except for clothing made of colourful printed cottons, most ornamentation had been added by the laborious process of rich embroidery. People must have been quite astonished when they first came into contact with these polychromed woollen fabrics, for clothing made by tapestry weaving was unprecedented.

CHRISTOPHER-PHILIPPE OBERKAMPF (1738-1815)

Christopher-Philippe Oberkampf was a leader in textile fashion who set up a cotton printing factory in Jouy-en-Josas. The brilliantly coloured motifs for which his establishment became famous acquired the popular name of 'toiles de Jouy'. Inspired by Indian and Oriental designs, these glowing fabrics were envied by all Europe.

Oberkampf began to copy the various boteh patterns found on the shawls brought back by the officers of Napoléon's Egyptian Army. A notice on the frontispiece of an important design album (Plate 44) found among the vast collection he left following the 1840 demise of his factory, reads: 'Most were copied from the first shawls and scarves which were introduced in France at the beginning of this century [1800] by the officers of the Egyptian Army.'

Oberkampf was not a shawl manufacturer, but the boteh patterns he collected represented a significant addition to his design repertoire. He miniaturised them into tiny, repeat motifs for his printed cotton production. Small repeats were very

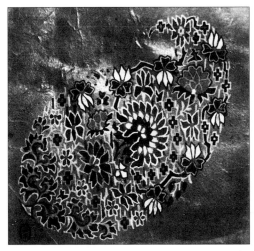

PLATE 43.
Boteh tracing from Oberkampf's early album, c.1800.

FIGURE 32.
Patterns for printed cloth, Oberkampf, 1808.

PLATE 44, a and b.
Shawl tracings from Oberkampf's early album, c.1800.

popular at this time and were regularly employed on early printed imitation shawls of cotton and silk.

This miniaturisation is illustrated in one of Oberkampf's albums entitled 'Etoffes Imprimées' or printed cloths. The album is important because it shows the various design changes which occurred between the years 1804 and 1811. We find that he did not actually incorporate the boteh into his printed goods until 1808. Oberkampf employed mainly the outline, or form, of the boteh and avoided the confused floral 'filling' which would have encumbered the overall design. His style shows a cubist-like reduction of the Indian idea into geometric pieces, much as the French created a mélange of African and cubist art one hundred years later (Figure 32).

PLATE 45, a and b.
Fantasy patterns for printed cloth, Favre Petitpierre, c.1800.

PETITPIERRE, FAY AND BRULÉ

Another textile manufacturer, Favre Petitpierre, further illustrates the early development in France of the boteh, or cone, as it was frequently called. A contemporary of Oberkampf, he too elaborated upon the Indian cone in the designs of his cloth-printing productions in Nantes. One of his albums shows exquisite hand-painted motifs in handkerchiefs and neckerchiefs. Here we begin to see the boteh in its full Western form: a kind of zoomorphic convolution with definitely elongated and bent-over tip. There were also other changes; instead of a compact shape filled with irregular and uncommon flowers we see a simplified design, which resulted in a composite abstraction more suited to European taste (see Plate 45).

These fantastic conceptions foreshadowed future generations of boteh patterns. As a matter of fact they might have been one of the moving forces which engendered the boteh revolution. Already the bent tip of the cone had a rococo element, with one drooping tip as a ribbon which suggested a series of repeated end-to-end parallelograms (see Plate 45b).

The French, with their innate artistic sense and curiosity, were naturally intrigued; not only did they desire to understand these strange Oriental images but they also wanted to transform them into something more suited to their own textile industry. A remark by a reviewer of the 1844 exhibition of French industrial products provides insight into how they viewed the boteh: foreign patterns were '...confused and condensed motifs which end in points...bizarre fruits and crawling branches which wrap around adjacent objects, a confused mass where the eye hardly recognises either the form or the object....'[1] This remark was typical of those heard earlier in the century as well.

That the Orient represented an exotic mélange of mysticism, religion and customs is demonstrated, perhaps, by the alien paintings exhibited by the 'Orientalists'. The French attached a religious meaning to the boteh symbol, while in reality, as we have seen, it was the result of various floral and vase designs evolving over many years.

In addition to the boteh, floral patterns were also a fashionable design motif on shawls, scarves, and dresses at the beginning of the nineteenth century. The Empress Joséphine again serves as an example. She ran into debt just to be able

1. Expo. 1844, Musée Challamel, vol. 1, p. 39.

PLATE 46.
Empire shawl, design possibly from Fay's atelier, most likely woven in Spitalfields, England, c.1815.

to appear for a single evening in an astounding sheath gown to which fresh rose petals had been carefully sewn. The gown was also profusely embellished with the rarest of exotic feathers and brilliant, dangling pearls.

Two Parisian designers, Fay and Brulé, also demonstrate the importance of floral fashion (see Figure 33). They maintained artist ateliers during the periods 1809 to 1824 and 1810 to 1815, respectively. Fay's creations of botehs (palms) and embroideries of 'cashemire' were displayed at the 1823 national exhibition.[2] A contemporary album at the Musée des Arts Décoratifs contains dated drawings of both artists.[3] We see that shawl patterns of a floral nature were not only employed but were also very popular, years before Isabey's famous sketches (see below).

TERNAUX AND ISABEY

The exhibition of 1806 had already shown evidence of industrial progress; most enterprising gauze manufacturers turned towards the woollen shawl as the fashion for gauze waned. However, the imitation shawl was having certain problems in the French market. A few years later the well-known industrialist, Ternaux, wrote to the Minister of Interior, Montalivet, of a plan to remedy this situation:

> You know, Monseigneur, with what fury luxury seeks the Kashmir shawl; what quantity of revenue this import takes away, and how much one scorns everything which calls itself imitation. The prejudice concerning this is carried so far that women, agreeing that a 'cashemire français' of 600 francs is as good and as beautiful as that which comes from India at a cost of 1,800 and often 3,000 francs, reject the first just because it is 'imitation'.[4]

The imitation shawl was, after all, only an imitation. Ternaux, a penetrating observer of fashion's caprices, saw that the moment had come to modify its

2. Expo. 1823, Rapport du Jury, L.H. de Thury, p. 78.
3. See album No. BB31 Musée des Arts Décoratifs.
4. Lomüller, p. 179.

F<small>IGURE</small> 33, a-g.
Seven 'Cachemire' designs for embroidery. a) Fay, 1811. b) Fay, 1811, for the King of Rome, born March 20, 1811. c) Fay. d) Fay, January 25, 1817. e) Brulé, July 17, 1812. f) Brulé. g) Brulé, December 18, 1810.

design, not only for his benefit, but also for that of the industry. He continued: 'One is beginning to get tired of these palms [cones] from India without getting weary of the fabric.'

Ternaux asked Napoléon to order twelve shawl designs from the well-known mIniaturist and colourist J.B. Isabey. On 31 December 1812, twelve shawls were handed over to the Emperor. Napoléon offered them in turn to his new wife Marie Louise. Although her influence upon fashion was not nearly as dramatic as that of her predecessor, the inspiration of the first lady was always of great importance, and Marie Louise thus played her part in setting the fashion for the 'châle français'. She gave several shawls to her ladies-in-waiting, and also wore them to promote this latest trend. The new style was a triumph. On 1 February 1813, just a month later, the *Moniteur Universel* announced:

> The shawls of MM. Ternaux are a perfect product and the weave has the necessary solidity. The designs are the work of our best artists, and far from the bizarre and confused designs that one sees on foreign shawls. The palms [cones] are replaced by bouquets and garlands imitating the most beautiful European flowers whose clear colours and fine nuances have something of the appearance of painting.[4]

Parisian society followed Ternaux and Isabey's example; people sought out the 'châles ternaux' which became the latest word in fashion. The flower shawl became popular as Ternaux began to divert women's attention away from the Kashmir shawl of India towards the new French one.

Unfortunately no trace of Isabey's shawl sketches has been found, nor has any shawl yet been found which may be attributed with absolute certainty to Isabey's winter collection. However, the Musée de la Mode et du Costume of Paris, in their recent exhibition devoted to the French Kashmir shawl, uncovered three interesting shawl specimens which may very well represent part of the missing collection.

Two of them were lent to the exhibition by actual descendants of the Ternaux family, who had preserved them as heirlooms and considered that they were originally woven by Guillaume Ternaux. The first one is a white shawl measuring 274cm by 146cm (108 by 57in.) with a 11.5cm (4½in.) border composed of a natural flower meander, having nothing in common with Oriental botany. The second, exhibiting similar attributes of draftsmanship and dyes, is a long cream coloured shawl measuring 264cm by 134cm (104 by 53in.) with palla ends patterned with botehs in the form of naturalistically drawn bouquets of European flowers. The stems of the bouquets are secured to the right of the boteh's base by a graceful snake-like vine which forms the remainder of the bulbous shape. The bouquets culminate at the top in the form of an arching raceme, imparting a final delicate touch to a design of extreme elegance. The third shawl, conserved by the Musée des Arts Décoratifs of Paris, is identical to the second one (see Colour Plate 43).

All three shawls were woven in the espouliné technique and display incredible craftsmanship comparable to the fine shah tus shawls of the Mughal period. This is all the more bewildering when we consider that the twill interlock weave was virtually unknown in France a little more than a decade earlier![5] A report given to the Société d'Encouragement pour l'Industrie Nationale described the shawls as 'beautifully executed and of fine and tight weave differing from those of India only by the *economy of manufacture which accelerates the work*' [author's italics].[6] This implies that there must have been an efficient loom weaving system which predated Deneirouse's by at least twenty years. From the provenance of

5. It is well known that Ternaux was acquainted with the espouliné technique because of his close association with Bellanger.
6. Alcan, 1847, p. 269.

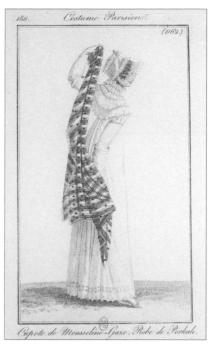

COLOUR PLATE 42 a, b, c, d, e and f.
Shawl fashion in France, from Costume Parisienne, *1809 to 1821.*

these pieces, their superior weave, and the similarity of their design to that described in 1813, we can say that at least part of the Isabey collection has been found.

French designs earlier in the century were stagnant at times but not because

PLATE 47.
Square shawl. Couder inspired, c.1839. This 'renaissance' shawl is obviously a simplified rendition of a cross between the 'Isfahan' (Colour Plate 98) and the 'Nou-Rouz' (Colour Plate 58).

talent was lacking. In turn-of-the-century Paris classical Greek and Roman designs were all the rage and a Parisian woman just was not up to date unless she was dressed in sheer white muslin, with a high waist and low neckline, and draped in a genuine Kashmir shawl. Not until the 1823 exhibition did the floral motif attain large scale commercial popularity. Its success appears to have lasted throughout the 1820s but it waned by the time of the 1834 exhibition. Perhaps the French public grew tired of the floral motif. Nobody can deny, however, that it provided the groundwork for the first major school of French design.

We have seen how early imitations borrowed traditional ideas from the Orient, as well as depending heavily upon floral designs, the fashion craze which swept Paris early in the century. The discovery of the jacquard loom not only revolutionised the production of textiles but also opened doors to new areas of design creativity.

With the advent of the imitation shawl there was a sudden need for talented designers. In 1826 shawls valued at 32,000,000 francs were manufactured of

PLATE 48.
*Corner detail of a square shawl by Couder, c.1839. Manufactured by Gaussen. Eleven colours.
190cm x 194cm (75 x 76in.). No mention of this spectacular jacquard-woven piece has yet been
found in French literature. The cartouche repeat of the border recalls the contemporary patterns
of the Savonnerie carpet factory.*

which over a quarter were exported.[7] In 1820 and 1822 laws had been passed
which prohibited the importing of 'cachemires et les soies de l'Inde',[8] and France
relied heavily on purchases made in London from the East India Company. Shawl
manufacturers engaged in a desperate search for new motifs.[9] By the Paris
exhibition of 1834, however, the ban on wool imports was abolished and
Kashmir shawls were freely entering the country on payment of customs duties.[10]

JEAN BAPTISTE AMÉDÉE COUDER (1797-1865)

Jean Baptiste Amédée Couder, well-known industrial designer, writer, and
brother of the painter Louis-Charles Auguste Couder, was the first artist to
distinguish himself in the field of shawl design. He opened an 'atelier de dessin'
in Paris in 1820,[11] in which work was not limited to shawls, but included many
original designs for tapestry, embroidery, rugs and furniture. He is most famous
for his series of shawls known in France as the 'renaissance' shawls.[12]

Couder travelled to India several times; his long and perilous voyages served to
sharpen his innate talents and offered him the opportunity of combining two rich
cultures. He was a man of intense human understanding and, far from being
preoccupied with his own self-interest, he devoted a great deal of his time to
teaching industrial artists. Still, as much as he influenced the French shawl, many
of his ideas often ran counter to the general mood and taste of shawl fashion,

7. Expo. 1827, vol. 2, p. 66.
8. Sée, Henri *Esquisse de
l'evolution industrielle de la
France de 1815 à 1848*,
Paris, 1925. These
regulations were demanded
at the insistence of the
French manufacturers who
felt undercut by the
increasing amount of
contraband.
9. Fichel, p. 6.
10. In 1796 a law prohibited
the importation of 'etoffes
tissées' or woven cloth
mixed with silk and animal
fleece, Lomüller p. 180. Rey
claims that Parisian shops
openly sold Kashmir shawls
which had been smuggled
into France.
11. Expo. 1855, vol. 3, p.
1,223.
12. The best known of
these shawls are the 'Nou-
Rouz', the 'Odalisque' and
the 'Isfahan'.

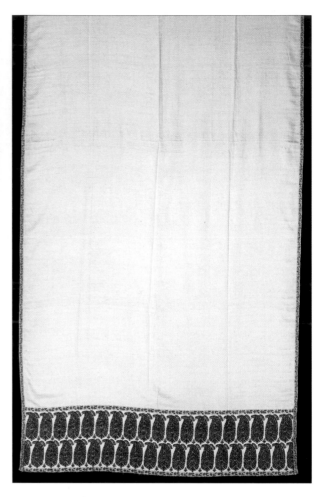

COLOUR PLATE 43.
Detail of long shawl, Paris, First Empire. The design is attributed to Isabey, and woven by Ternaux. It is a very rare example of French espouliné weaving with silk warps and cotton wefts, 48 threads per cm. 12 colours. 134cm x 264cm (53 x 104in.).

COLOUR PLATE 44.
Early French 'dochalla' type shoulder mantle, c.1800. 121cm x 280cm (47 x 110in.).

COLOUR PLATE 45.
Detail of long shawl, France. c.1820. 142cm x 318cm (56 x 125in.).

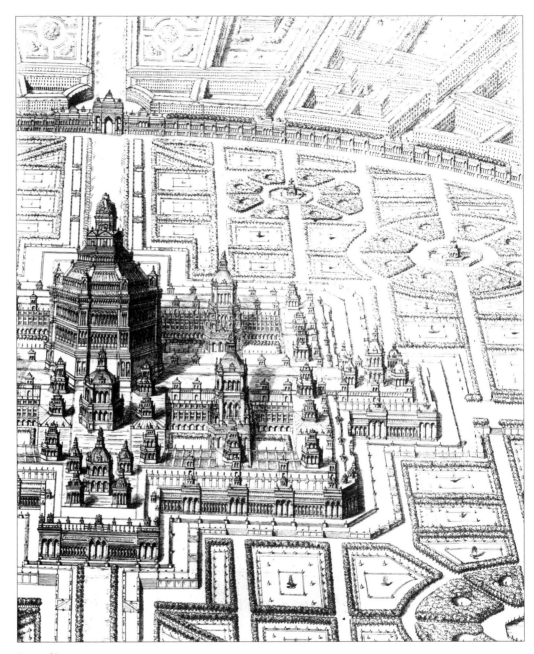

PLATE 49a.
Three-dimensional aerial view of Couder's great architectural project, Palais des Arts et de l'Industrie. 1840.

perhaps because his designs, based upon strong architectural concepts and luxurious if not baroque ornamentation, often carried over too much of the now dated Empire style.

Couder was well liked and admired by his colleagues. In 1835 the Central Jury of the Exhibition of French National Products awarded him the title of France's most outstanding industrial designer. In 1850 a petition was signed by the most distinguished shawl designers of Paris requesting his nomination to the Legion of Honour.[13]

13. National Archives, F12-5115, letter dated January 3, 1850.

PLATE 49B.
Detail of the central edifice showing Couder's obsession with columns and arches and meretricious ornamentation.

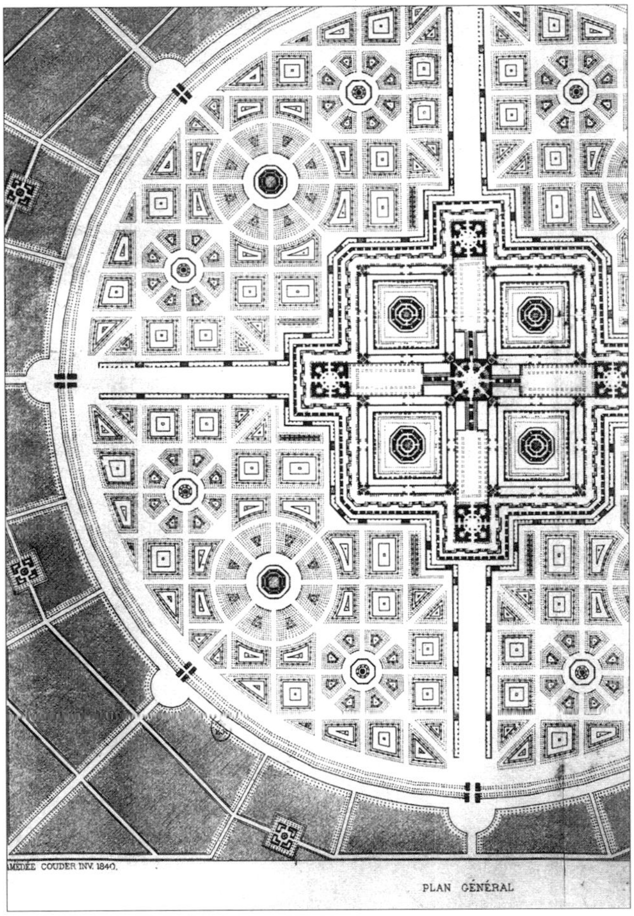

PLATE 49C.
Detail of aerial view of the general plan for the Palais.

Couder's interests in industrial design were extremely varied, and he later devoted much time to architectural endeavours. In 1840 he proposed a full plan and description of a 'Palais des Arts et de l'Industrie', the only known copy of which exists at the library of the Victoria and Albert Museum.[14]

The curious thing about this work is that the frontispiece is dedicated to a Monsieur Willson, possibly a reference to Stephan Wilson, the person who first introduced the jacquard loom into the British Isles.[15]

Apart from a half dozen or so extant woven shawls, a few decaying vellum sketches and his published articles concerning his spirited if not extravagant ideas on the moral aesthetics of art and architecture, we know little about the man himself, his youth, his early development as a fledgling artist and even his schooling in architecture.

Born in the wake of the French Revolution and in an artistic family socially immersed in it, Amédée was a true product of his time. While Napoléon was carving up Italy as the spoils of war, the leadership of France's Directoire Period was being argued among the revolutionaries, royalists and the military. One could only imagine in such a charged atmosphere the powerful impressions of

14. A. Couder,
L'Architecture et l'Industrie comme moyen de perfection sociale, Paris, 1842.
15. Rothstein.

175

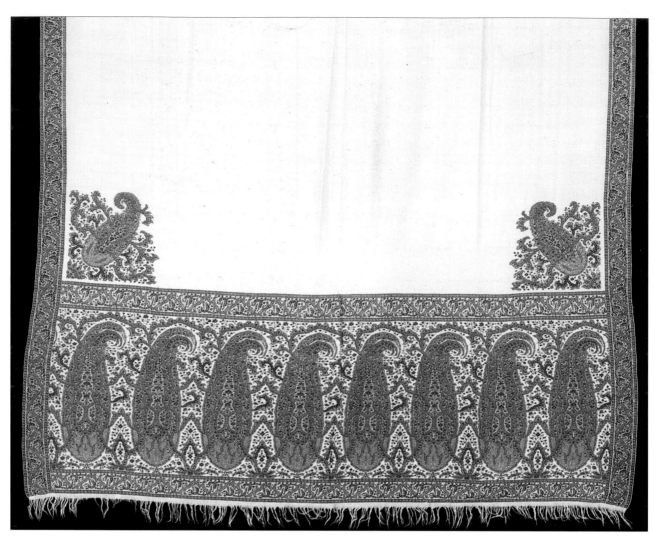

COLOUR PLATE 49.
Long shawl, France, c.1835, hooked vine pattern borrowed from Sikh Period, India.

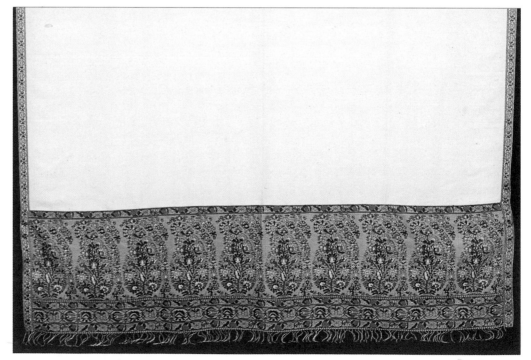

COLOUR PLATE 50.
Napoléonic Period, all silk, rich gold field and pattern of compartmentalised botehs based on the theme of the 'coif'. c.1810. 127cm x 259cm (50 x 102in.).

176

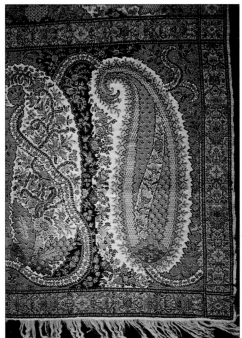

COLOUR PLATE 52.
French 'moon' shawl. Silk and wool, 165cm x 165cm (65 x 65in.). c.1835. In synthesising design ideas from Kashmir and Europe the French developed a brilliant version of a jacquard moon shawl in this superlative example recalling the Gothic stained glass windows of medieval churches. The hooked vine and flattened flower blossoms, both characteristics of the Sikh Period, were magnificently arranged around a central motif depicting an effulgent if not exploding sun. The straight-line hashia or border in which all this is enclosed is wrapped with boas of floral garlands celebrating the typical Indian meander that decorates it.

COLOUR PLATE 51.
Detail of long shawl showing design ideas borrowed from India and earlier French floral patterns. c.1820.

L'INTELLIGENCE OFFRE A DIEU LA RECONNAISSANCE DES HOMMES.
COURONNEMENT DE L'EDIFICE CENTRAL

PLATE 49D.
The capping ornamentation to the central edifice of the Palais.

pomp and glory and the lasting effect they had on the young Amédée Couder as he held his father's hand in the streets of Paris to the drum beats of Napoléon's victory parades.

Although Amédée is well talked about as being an architect, and indeed he has left us with several published projects, we know of no buildings of his which have actually been constructed. As a young architect and growing up during the first quarter of the nineteenth century, it would be difficult to find another city more inspirational than Paris. Between the fall of the First Empire and the rise of the Second, Paris was nothing short of an urban laboratory. All buildings were based on a standard model and reflected desire for monumentality in the city's appearance. The sound of stone cutters from such great projects as the Madeleine, the Stock Exchange, the Arch of Triumphe, must have been echoing throughout Paris, not to mention the construction taking place on properties formerly owned by the Church and now in the public domain. These were exciting times. The Revolution saw the end of feudalism and ecclesiastical tithes and the rise of free trade within the country. Freedom of enterprise and of profit without any restriction was opening the way to a new economy. Much of this enthusiasm, of the opening up of new horizons, was quite apparent in Amédée's exuberant writings, as we shall see further on.

His brother, Louis-Charles, seven years older, did a stint at the Ecole des Beaux Arts in Marseille, his mother's natal town, finishing up in Paris, where he won his first prize at the Salon of Apollo in 1817. By 1830, his reputation firmly established, Louis-Charles went on to paint hundreds of portraits of well-known French characters such as army generals, field marshals, officers of the national guard, the mayor of Paris, as well as scenes from mythology. His prolific works can be found in many museums. One of his works 'The Triumph of Yorktown', Washington and Lafayette at the surrender of Cornwallis in 1781, is part of the French embassy collection, Washington DC. Louis-Charles received the Cross of the Legion of Honour in 1841. He often lectured at the Royal Academy of Painting and Sculpture, and collaborated on its *Dictionary of Fine Arts*. In his book, *Considerations on the Moral Goal of Fine Art,* in which he attempts to explain

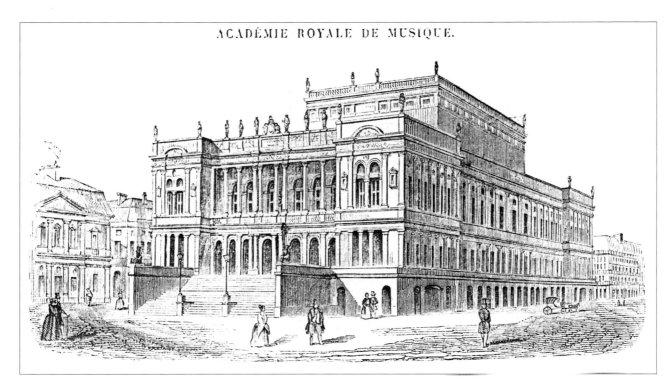

ACADÉMIE ROYALE DE MUSIQUE.

PLATE 50.
Couder's Royal Academy of Music project. 1845.

the nature and sentiments of the artist, Louis-Charles felt that he was living in an era of 'virile force' of which the fine arts were a reflection. Invoking the names of the world's great artists and philosophers and their moral views, and sermonising on the definitions of beauty, line and colour, the book attempts to define a musical thread tying together the creative energies of all the arts.

According to one source Amédée worked at his father's place and his first designs were of Persian carpets; in another he studied painting and obtained a prize at the Salon of 1836. Whatever the case, one thing is certain, at the young age of twenty-three he opened his design atelier in 1820. Three years later he exhibited his first shawl painting of a harlequin pattern at the National Exhibition of French Products. Looking at the harlequin shawl we already see the development of domes, rectangular compartments and a central rosette, foreshadowing his development of the more architectural 'Isfahan' shawl. Amédée's exuberance, as expressed in his writing, appeared to mirror very similar thoughts his brother set forth in his articles on the theory of art.

At about the time of the 1834 French exhibition, he began working on architectural plans for a gigantic building complex titled *Projet d'un palais des arts et de l'industrie*. Couder, obviously not a man of excessive modesty, describes his monumental project as 'one of the greatest works of our age' where national exhibitions would take place every year and universal exhibitions every five years. Indeed, one look at his three dimensional aerial view recalls monuments easily the size of Vatican City with the equivalent of Saint Peter's basilica at the centre.

The project was planned for Montmartre and was to be a permanent building for universal exhibitions, containing libraries and museums. It called for an

COLOUR PLATE 53.
*Long black centre
with Sikh pattern
and brilliant vegetal
colours and fine
pashmina wool
combine to create a
stunning masterpiece
of weaving. c.1825.*

enormous open circle divided into quarters by walkways measuring 30 metres (98ft.) wide leading to monumental gateways opening at cardinal points to the city. At the centre stands a tall, massive hexagonally sided, gothic structure whose four story spire is crowned by a statue titled 'Intelligence offre à Dieu la Reconnaissance de l'Homme', a statement which could only have meaning through the understanding of the deep religious convictions of the times. The statue is a winged woman standing with open arms, head raised to the sky and surrounded by a dense crowd of bearded personages.

Impressed by the Great Universal Exhibition in Hyde Park, and having seen the number of exhibitors explode from just a few hundred in the year V1 (1798) to

COLOUR PLATE 54.
Square shawl with rare, truncated pattern. Sikh design features. 190cm x 190cm (75 x 75in.).

COLOUR PLATE 55.
Rare and unusual square shawl with concavely indented sides and pattern relating to the Couder school of design, c.1835-1840. 188cm x 188cm (74. x 74in.).

COLOUR PLATE 56.
Long shawl of fine pashmina wool and fabulous rich dyes. Transitional Sikh-Dogra Period patterning borrowed from the India shawls. c.1845. 160cm x 350cm (63 x 138in.).

COLOUR PLATE 57.
Moon shawl with contemporary Sikh Period design showing the 'fool's cap' and mother and daughter botehs aligned in a wonderful graphic pattern. c.1840. 168cm x 170cm (66 x 67in.).

181

Scarf designed by Couder, Paris, 1834. 3m x 77cm (118 x 30in.). It has the same inscription as the 'Isfahan' shawl.

18,000 in 1851, Couder sought to bring the Universal Exhibition to France. With his reputation already established in the industrial arts, Couder longed to make his mark in architecture. His *Architecture and Industry as a Way of Perfection*, written in sanctimonious if not demagogic language and laced with soaring prose, became a manifesto, designed to strike at the moral and religious prejudices of man.

It is interesting to note that Berrus left us with a large corpus of his personal design albums but nothing in writing from which to gain an insight into himself as an artist, whereas Couder has left us a profusion of articles but almost nothing in actual designs, except for the Isfahan and Nou-Rouz shawls and a few architectural drawings. Indeed, in the section on 'Moral Causes', in which he reveals his ideological differences with the Orient, Couder felt that if the Orient did not attain the degree of civilisation as in the western world then the latter would not be worthy of its godly achievements, 'as revealed by nature'. It is obvious that Couder got caught up in the grandiosity of the post Napoléonic fever.

Couder's manifesto becomes a mission attempting to define the concept of industry as a kind of saintly mystery achieved through secrets of cult initiation, a kind of sanctuary of intelligence.

In his 'Character of Monumental Art', architectural ornamentation will always find its source in nature and vegetation. Couder provides the reader with a brief history of the development of high architecture through the geometric dignity of the straight line and flat surface as expressed by the ancient civilisations of Greece, India, the Etruscans and Egypt. He states that 'In understanding the symbolism of architecture the precise expression of each line and figure should be viewed as a secret language'.

Couder goes to great lengths to develop the concept of symbolism in great architecture, which he feels expresses the immutable truths, the soul of generations and the poetry of the human race and concludes his windy chapter with '...Monuments that speak high to the thought are necessary, that reflect civilisation, that communicate on eternal religion to the heart; that when they will have disappeared, still leave a profound teaching; the last traces on earth must

COLOUR PLATE 58.

The Nou-Rouz shawl, designed by Couder for the 1839 exhibition, Paris. 165cm x 389cm (65 x 153in.). Warp: Spun cashmere and silk; 40 threads/cm. Weft: cashmere; decor: 40 shots/cm; ground: 160 shots/cm. Twelve colours.

    The Spring's equinox is celebrated as the first day of the year among Persians and called Nou Rouz. It is one of their principal holidays. During the 19th century, cannons and musical instruments were heard the whole day while the Shah received the homage of dignitaries of his empire, each offering him presents according to his rank. Here, Couder expresses his great affinity with Persian culture combining it with European Gothic art. As in the Dream Window, Couder uses the stage setting where the 'actors' are groups of oriental personages dancing and merry-making under a vast and intricately designed Byzanto-Gothic piece of architecture. An enormous structure of seven vaulted arches, pediments, niched turrets and further supporting columns is all beautifully held in place by eight pairs of multicoloured Corinthian columns. All this has been meticulously patterned with pseudo-Islamic calligraphy, floral meanders, arabesque scrollwork, and geometric mosaics imitating tile work. Under the central arch presides a Queen flanked by frolicking women. Hanging from the stage is a series of oriental carpets the ends of which terminate in mihrabs, reflecting the architecture above. At the top we can glimpse part of the procession of camels, horses and people that make their way toward the Shah.

    The shawl, manufactured by Gaussen, was woven with red warps and displayed a green ground. More than 101,000 jacquard cards were employed to weave this complex design which in fact only occupies one quarter of the surface of the whole shawl. Running the cards backwards and forwards four times was required in order to achieve this symmetrical section of the full image. This shawl was exhibited in Paris in 1982 and Lyon in 1983. Locations of the six other known examples are: Victoria & Albert Museum, London; Museum für Angewandte Kunst, Vienna; Le Musée Historique des Tissus, Lyon; The Etro (2) collection, Milan; and the author's collection.

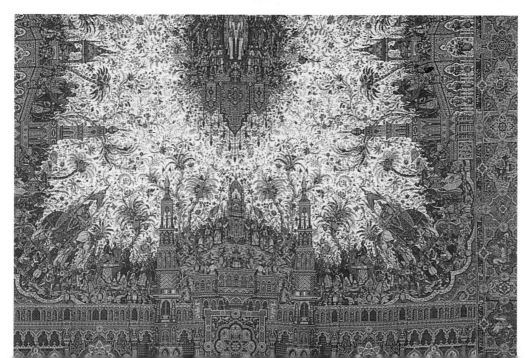

COLOUR PLATE 58,
a, b, and c. Details of the Nou-Rouz.

185

teach us that our monuments were like an immense throne, from where the voice of truth, sublime, persuasive, incessant, drove humanity to the culminating point that God has designated.'

Finally, in his *Necessity of Making a Palace*, Couder reveals in his prose some words which may lead to our further understanding of his design concepts as woven into the shawls. For example, in arguing for the acceptance of his opus magnum he exclaims that 'A great coup belongs to France, to strike and break the shackles that hold its spirit to the doors of its yet greatest empire – the greatest empire being one, of course, that would see the completion of his project which he immodestly calls 'the most gigantic chefs-d'oeuvre of antiquity'. (This calls to mind the window left ajar in the 1851 shawl 'Dream Window'.) Couder felt that his project should not only be considered a work of art but be considered in the light of philosophy and religion – not only an obvious statement but a redundant one also.

Couder's other known project was called the *Royal Academe of Music* which was published in 1845. In this article he also set forth an idea to expand the Louvre (then under construction) to the Tuileries by extending the galleries or promenades which lead to the museum's entrance, adding large public squares and huge fountains. Couder acknowledges the fact that other architects have addressed the same important question but felt that 'in the clash of opinions some light might emerge'. Of course it was Charles Garnier's famous opera house project that won out in 1860. Described as an eclectic neo-Baroque style, his opera became one of the most famous buildings of the nineteenth century and a symbol of Second Empire taste.

It is interesting to muse on why Couder devoted so much time to such monumental architectural projects. Perhaps they were originally conceived during his days as a student at the School of Fine Arts (SFA) for one of their competitions. The competition, called the Prix de Rome or Grand Prize, was the last obstacle in the education of the nineteenth century architect and the highest possible achievement for the student at the SFA. However, in order to compete you had to be under thirty years old. Couder published his projects during the early 1840s, which of course would have put him well over the age limit.

In looking at his grandiose Palais project one could see a multilevelled façade profusely decorated with columns, niches and statues in such an overwhelmingly crowded style that one could easily understand his difficulty in getting support for its construction. The style ran counter to the neo-classical style which dictated geometric simplicity. After the French Revolution the old orthodox school of architecture was revived by the then prominent designers, chief among them Pierre Vignon (the Madeleine), A.T. Brogniant (the Stock Exchange) and of course the two most famous architects responsible for the transformation of Paris, Charles Percier and Pierre François Fontaine. Although Couder was well known in the industrial arts, obviously he was by no means in the same league as the aforementioned giants of architecture.

A painting of Couder's first known shawl is on view at the Conservatoire National des Arts et Métiers, Paris. The shawl was first exhibited at the 1823 Exhibition of French Industrial Products, at the Louvre. Although little is known about immediate public reaction it is clear that several of its unique features were to have a lasting influence on future shawl designs.

In the painting shown in Plate 53 we can see repeated mihrabs or arches lining the middle field, or 'dhoor', of the shawl, an important pattern which was soon afterwards transferred to the end fringe. This fringe pattern was very popular on succeeding generations of shawls.

PLATE 53.
Long shawl painting by Couder shown at the 1823 Exposition, Paris. Five different botehs decorate the 'harlequin' palla.

PLATE 54.
Long shawl painting, signed Couder, c.1851.

Couder used the fringe pattern again on his 1834 Isfahan shawl (Colour Plate 98). It was used by the firm of Chambellan and Duché for their 'Hindus shawl', exhibited in 1839. Berrus made liberal use of this pattern in his shawl designs prepared for the Great Exhibition of 1851 in London. At the same time, the fringe pattern reached Kashmir where it was adopted as a convention for practically all shawls destined for European export.

We can also see in Plate 53 Couder's unique placement of the boteh within the framework of the mihrab. He believed the boteh to be a religious symbol, and it is not unlikely that his interpretation was drawn from early Persian prayer rugs of the sixteenth and seventeenth centuries. This idea was to have a lasting effect on shawl design.

Couder was the first to employ the total surface area of the shawl fabric as his design medium, drawing his inspiration probably from the well-known medallion carpets of Persia or from the square moon shawl whose matan was always decorated. Prior to this, the jacquard long-shawl's matan was never used

COLOUR PLATE 59.
Square shawl attributed to Couder. c.1835. 186cm x 189cm (73 x 74in.).

for decoration. In Plate 53 we can see that Couder dismissed the convention of repeating the same boteh design and offered instead five variants repeated to make a total of ten. He also used variegated coloured ends, an idea adopted from Kashmir shawls typical of the 1820s in which often the end warps had been dyed to produce this effect. This was called the 'harlequin' shawl.

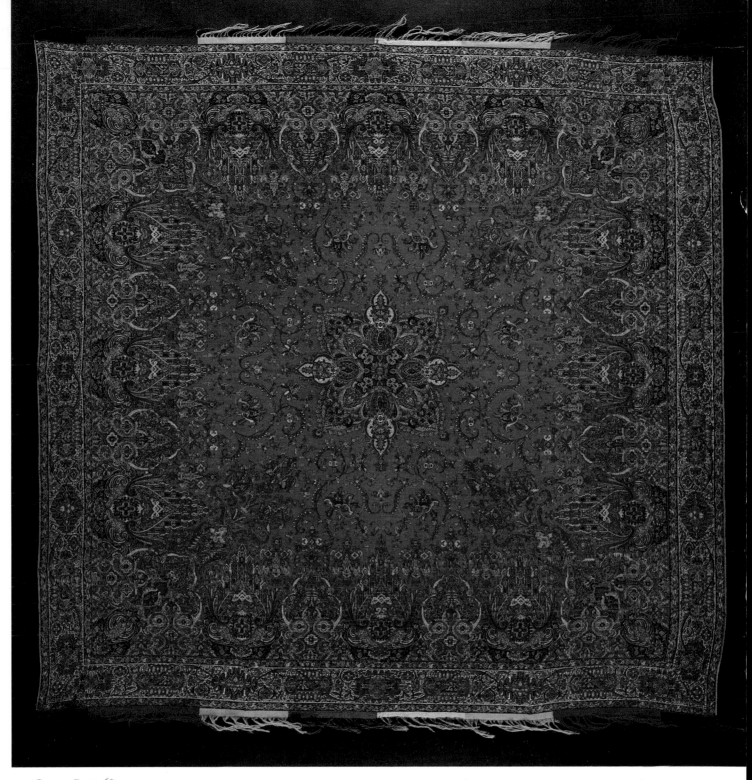

COLOUR PLATE 60.
Square shawl, attributed to Couder, c.1835. 187cm x 190cm (73 x 75in.). Notice the endless Chinese knot within the pointed cupolas. This is a typical Couder characteristic, also found in the Isfahan.

The quality of the real Kashmir shawl was rapidly deteriorating, and new design techniques had to be developed. Up until this time France's shawl industry had received its design inspiration from India. This was no longer true. Srinagar had been reduced to a ghost town by the famine of 1834 and the few shawls that reached Europe were rough, cheap imitations from the surrounding cities and countries such as Persia, Afghanistan and the Punjab.

Rey, in his 'Study', severely criticised the Kashmir shawl:

> One can say there is such a shawl composed literally of pieces and fragments; the cones from one end of a long shawl do not resemble each other nor those of the other end. If they do look alike in form, they differ in colour tint. The corner motifs of a châle à rosace [moon shawl] are not the same as the centre, or they might be embroidered when the centre is brocaded. The rosace itself might be composed of two unmatched halves. But above all, the imperfections abound in the châles à fond plein [i.e. shawls of which the 'matan' or centre field has been worked with a pattern]. It is not rare to find them streaked by a variety of four or five designs....[16]

The economist Jerome-Adolphe Blanqui, acting as head of the Conservatoire des Arts et Métiers, also criticised the shawl. He wrote in 1836:

> ...the narrow borders [the shawl's hashia] had given way to large ones, the cones had become very large and the lively colours had disappeared. Almost always, the Indian shawl, that our women were proud to put on their shoulders, were already worn and the colours faded; in this case they were revived and repainted by colourists without the women's knowledge. Still better, not only were the shawls old, dirty and threadbare but they were even patched-up.[17]

Couder was convinced that the smooth contours of Oriental designs could be achieved through a careful *mise-en-carte* which would avoid the 'cassures' or jagged edges that appear in Kashmiri weaving.[18] He also took advantage of the recent improvements of the jacquard loom, especially the papier briqueté invented by Deneirouse, and the 'double griffe' which allowed a pattern repeat of 1.75 by 3.5 metres (69 by 138in.) (see Chapter Six).

The French seemed to have tried everything to divert attention from Kashmir shawls, and after the 'natural flower' period and the commercial failure[19] of Couder's 'renaissance' shawls new tactics had to be found. No wonder, therefore, that Couder and other artists paid serious attention to the new cones from Kashmir, and began to incorporate them into their own creations. That the scope of the design was virtually unlimited appeared a perfect way for testing the versatility of the jacquard innovations. Thus, with the advent of the 1844 Exhibition of French National Products, a new turning point in the history of shawl design seemed to be approaching.[20]

Of Couder's designs, at the exhibition, one observer wrote:

> ...a large shawl inspired from India where one finds charming details; instead of these heavy palms [cones] rounded-off at the lower ends leaves are seen ending in the form of a lance ['feuilles lancéolées'] which attach themselves to their light stem with rare elegance....[21]

The shawls in the 1844 exhibition represented a transition from the bizarre Indian designs to those typifying the smooth contours later to be called Art Nouveau. Who can say whether Hector Guimard (1867-1942) was not influenced by these swirling, sinuous lines of woven fabric? Or, for that matter, Alphonse Mucha (1860-1939), the artist best remembered for his posters and who immortalised Sarah Bernhardt?

ANTONY BERRUS (1815-1883)

Another important shawl maker was Antony Berrus, who founded his atelier in 1840. Berrus was one of the most creative and prolific artists of the nineteenth century. He requires special attention not only for his school of design but also

16. Rey, p. 143.
17. Blanqui, 'Conservatoire des Arts etc.', pp. 420, 425.
18. Couder, 'Analyse du dessin etc.'. 1834, pp. 3, 4.
19. Expo 1844, Musée Challamel, vol. I, p. 39.
20. Expo 1855, Rapport du jury mixte, vol. 3. p. 122. A royal decree admitted industrial designers to compete in the national exhibitions only from 1834 onwards.
21. Expo 1844, Musée Challamel, vol .1, p. 40.

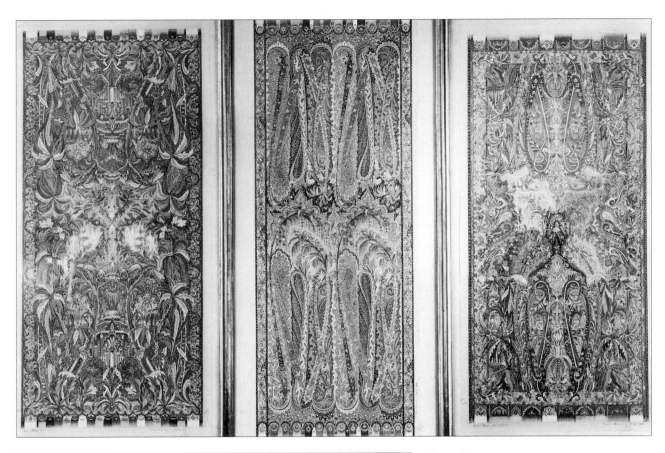

PLATE 55.
Shawl paintings shown at the Universal Exhibition of 1851 by Berrus.

PLATE 56.
Detail of a spectacular square shawl of fantasy design showing strong Couderesque influence. c.1840

191

COLOUR PLATE 61.
Square shawl attributed to Couder, French, c.1835. 186cm x 188cm (73 x 74in.). Again, the endless Chinese knot is seen within the painted cupolas.

COLOUR PLATE
62a.
Dream
Window, 1851.
*See page 194
for caption*

193

Dream Window, 165cm x 388cm (65 x 153in.). French shawl woven for the Universal Exhibition in London in 1851, where it was displayed at the Crystal Palace. This shawl (according to the original invoice) was bought by the buyer for Alex T. Stewart & Co. (which later became Wanamakers) of 96 Grand Street, Broadway, New York, brought to the United States of America and sold to a Mr. E.P. Christy Esq. on 16 September 1851, in whose family it had remained for ninety-six years. The initials D B C can be found on one of the flags flown atop the minaret-type columns. They have been attributed to the well-known shawl manufacturers Deneirouse and Bloisglave, while the C most likely stands for Couder.

This shawl is of paramount importance to the study of early jacquard shawl technology in so far as the complex pattern it illustrates articulates just about all the then known technical capabilities of the loom. Although the design repeats itself at both ends, it does so in a very rare manner called pivot, and thus it is also known in French as a châle à pivot. Pivot shawls are indeed the rarest of jacquard weavings because of the high sophistication demanded of the loom. The colour palette, high warp-weft resolution, wools, and the masterly design, all point toward a shawl which was woven probably during the 1840s or perhaps within a few years after the appearance of the Nou-Rouz (1839).

Because designers at the time usually remained anonymous, it was the custom to sign or initial unique patterns on very finely woven shawls with the initials of the manufacturer rather than with those of the designer, who was considered simply a paid employee. However, in this case, the design is one which obviously begs attribution to the hand of Amédée Couder because of its strong architectural and theatrical affinities with the Nou-Rouz. And, indeed, his initial has been flown on the flag along with the others. Couder was a master industrial designer but a frustrated architect, having published several important works for the construction of large building monuments which never were realised. This architectural impulse comes across clearly as much in his first masterpiece, the Isfahan, as in the Nou-Rouz and Dream Window.

The pattern begins much the same as the Nou-Rouz in that an elaborate table is placed right at the end of the shawl, upon which is draped a sumptuous cloth covered with fine lacy doilies with pompoms. The table is decorated with a fine collection of Chinese bowls and vases filled with a variety of flowers. As we proceed into the picture we face strange climbing trees and tree trunks whose spraying and drooping leaf clusters make every attempt to camouflage the awesome architecture which awaits us.

Entering the third pattern register, we find three gothic arches of which the middle is flanked by tall minarets bedecked with an array of swirling flags. At the centre of each arch are curious gazebo-type buildings with sinuous staircases and pagoda roofs which, almost hidden behind the dense branches of the burly trees, appear to rise up organically within the vaulted arches.

The viewer is further drawn into this co-mingling of East-West by the deepening perspective of staggered arches that draw closer together as they recede into the distance. All the supporting columns are intricately patterned with geometric tiles. The building within the central arch shows a large window left ajar, whence the shawl's sobriquet, Dream Window. Perhaps the idea was to create the impression of one sitting in his living room while contemplating the mysteries of the Orient.

The centre of the shawl is neatly divided by swooping pyramidal shapes whose fanciful decoration is composed of kaleidoscopic snowflakes on a brick all ground pattern. At the base of these shapes we find a strange building resting under a minutely patterned rainbow of tiny paisley-filled cartouches and Chinese-looking tents or domes. The building resembles a church, though instead of a steeple we find a thatched-roof, silo-looking structure. The church's slanted roof falls well beyond the walls, forming a portico on thick, round columns. The entrance to the church, flanked by two large potted trees, is a large gothic arch whose doors stand ajar, while looming up behind the church beams a bright multicoloured halo.

The pyramid's exterior walls when viewed from the side are decorated with sharply pointed, sawtooth-edge, cloud shapes that seems to waft into the sky. Within the interstices of the clouds can be seen hanging different types of Chinese lanterns. The shawl's borders are decorated with small cameo scenes of pagodas or Chinese lantern-like structures, flower-filled vases and parasols.

COLOUR PLATE 64.

The Procession Shawl, 1867. 162cm x 336cm (64 x 132in.). Mention of this important shawl is first found in the committee report on the Paris Universal Exhibition of 1867, where it was first exhibited. It was designed by a Monsieur Pin whose workshop was established in Lyon. The Procession has been exhibited at the Yale University Art Gallery in 1975 and later at the Textile Museum, Washington D.C. in 1986. At present there appear to be about eight of these shawls known in various public and private collections, including the Metropolitan Museum of Art, New York and the Museum of Fine Arts, Boston.

The Procession shawl is one of the last great jacquard masterpieces of the 19th century. As a weaving depicting scenes from the Orient with people, animals and architecture, it represents an important historical document in the iconography of shawl design, reflecting not only the contemporary and state of the art concepts of shawl art but, just as importantly, the artist's view of the mysterious east. The high resolution of the warp-weft density combined with the extreme fineness of the pashmina wool has brought a striking plasticity to the fullness of the woven figures and a true feeling of dynamic movement to the procession as it winds its course towards the Great Temple. The artist has obviously revelled in modelling his personages and animals in all sorts of postures in order to articulate to the fullest the then highly advanced sophistication of the jacquard loom, an achievement not easily attained except by a highly accomplished industrial artist. The shading of each article of clothing, the expression of each face and the muscular contraction of each of the animals has not been spared the intense scrutiny of the artist's eye. Compared to the figures of the Nou-Rouz, which appear flat and static, the Procession shawl (1867) is a stunning example of the amazing advances that had taken place in loom engineering since 1839. It is known that a little more than a hundred thousand punch cards were cut for the making of the Nou-Rouz (1839). It is not inconceivable that at least that many were required for the Procession shawl.

As the name implies, the theme is one of an imposing parade of oriental dignitaries and animals that appear to meander sinuously along the half-length of the shawl, starting from the middle of the shawl and extending toward each of the four corners. The packed crowd of bright white prancing horses, caparisoned white elephants and camels, slave-carried palanquins, parasol bearers, horn blowers, and retinue, all set against a stark black ground, suggests a special evening temple ceremony. Arriving at the corner of the shawl, the parade appears to enter and pass through a large dome-covered structure bedecked with minarets and three large mihrab-type windows of which the two flanking ones provide a glimpse of the parade. Within the central mihrab is found ensconced a four-arm Hindu deity in lotus position atop a white caparisoned elephant. The parade exits and then, at the very centre of the shawl, re-enters a smaller mosque-type edifice that apparently leads to the inner sanctum of the jama majid or grand mosque of the shawl's central end field

The mysteries of the parade are revealed to us through the clever device of a keyhole-type of cameo design; and within this tear-drop delineation the viewer espies the sudden awesomeness of oriental ritual in full progress.

Inside the grand mosque and among the elaborate Mughal decorated columns can be seen the crowd of standard bearers, horn blowers and drummers as they press closer to the main subject of the ceremony, another large four-armed Hindu-type deity ensconced on a lotus-type pedestal. Prostrating themselves before this awesome deity are six devotees on an elaborate oriental carpet. Looking up, as the towering mosque with its enormous dome and tall minarets reach toward the heavens of stars and draping pearl necklaces one could almost hear the ring of music and chant in the air. It is clear at this point that the artist has, in order to create these fantasy images, intentionally mixed the ideas of Hinduism and Islam.

Further highlighting the celestial nature of the cameo design are the large flanking paisleys that sweep up majestically through a virtual ornithic garden of paradise. At least fifteen different bird species can be counted, the feathers and posture of each tending to mimic the organic flow of floral pattern. Moving our attention toward the centre of the shawl is a cartouche with pointed mihrab spandrels within which another procession is taking place, one of dancing women. Among lotus-positioned statuesque deities, the women, dressed in bellydancer, midriff costumes, appear to be dancing in gay and sensuous movements to the rhythm of tambourines. Perhaps this central panel is meant to illustrate the women of the harem.

The Procession shawl can be found in the following other collections: The Metropolitan Museum of Art, New York, The Museum of Fine Arts, Boston, The Textile Museum, Washington D.C., The Yale University Art Gallery, New Haven, and the author's collection, New York.

Literature: Exhibition catalog The Kashmir Shawl, Yale University Art Gallery, 1975, Plate 28. Textile Museum Journal, 1986, Vol. 24, p. 54,

COLOUR PLATE 62b.
Detail of the lower part of 'Dream Window'.

COLOUR PLATES 63a and b.
Two details from a sumptuous and magnificent chinoiserie shawl at the Brooklyn Museum. Notice the similarities in design to the 'Dream Window'. Pashmina wool, c.1845.

196

COLOUR PLATE 64, a and b.
Details from the Procession Shawl showing the incredible definition of weave.

COLOUR PLATE 64.
*The Procession Shawl,
1867. See page 195 for
caption*

PLATE 57.
A rare masterpiece of French shawl design, probably by Berrus. Woven in Kashmir in kani weave, c.1850. 157cm x 370cm (62 x 145in.).

22. The Musée des Arts Décoratifs, Paris, contains the largest collection of Kashmir design albums in the world. Fifty alone can be attributed to Berrus.

for the enormous influence he exerted both in Europe and in the Orient.[22]

Berrus was born in Nîmes where he attended the recently established School of Design and, like Couder before him, started out by designing carpets. In 1838, he landed a job with Nîmes shawl maker, M. Gélot, who was shifting his business to Lyon, from where Berrus quickly moved up the ladder to become his associate. But Paris was where things were happening and for an extremely talented designer such as Berrus Lyon must have seemed very provincial. Understandably,

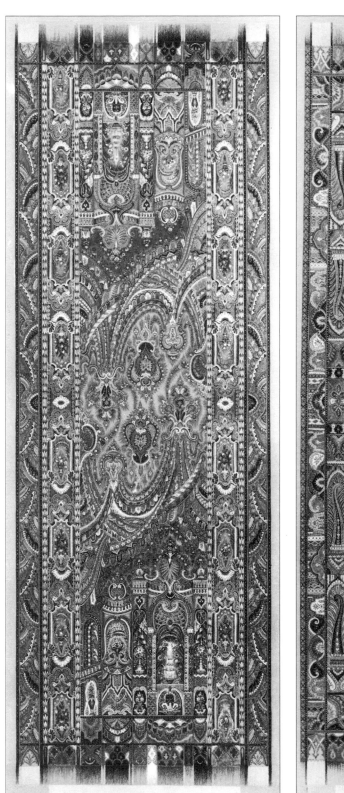

PLATE 58, *a and b.*
Shawl paintings by Berrus shown at the Universal Exhibition of 1855.

COLOUR PLATE 65a.
Spectacular all-silk shawl. Little is known about this masterpiece of extremely high-definition, jacquard weaving. Signed Chanceau, the shawl exhibits here and there little amorous vignettes, chinoiserie motifs and Hispano-Moresque architectural features. Apart from the fact that it was made on a jacquard loom, fits the format of the standard European long shawls and displays an otherwise brilliance in creativity, its style really runs counter to the trend in woollen Kashmir shawl designs. c.1850.

COLOUR PLATE 65b.
Detail of the Chanceau shawl, showing the incredible painterly definition of the artist's hand.

200

he found himself in Paris two years later with his own atelier.

More than a few of Berrus' shawl creations were influenced by Couder's 'renaissance' style. The repeated mihrab arches found in Couder's early shawls were subsequently employed by Berrus in a *chef-d'oeuvre* of shawl design. The painting portraying this shawl is now on display at the Conservatoire National des Arts et Métiers, Paris. It was featured at the 1855 Exhibition and shows the boteh as a divine symbol, illuminated by a burning red ground and framed in a tall Gothic arch capped in mihrab style (Plate 58b). Berrus' general and most commercially popular style, however, might best be described as fantasy. He employed ideas from the Far East with bizarre forms of fantastic flowers and tropical forests (Plate 55). His famous animal-like botehs and Persian calligraphic-type trellis work produced shawls of such great beauty and originality that his fame spread quickly throughout Europe. The zoomorphic boteh became one of the trade marks of his atelier and was profusely copied, not only by major shawl centres such as Paisley, Vienna and Lyon, but also by the Kashmiri weavers themselves (Plate 57).

Berrus personally sketched all designs coming from his atelier. He received an honourable mention at the 1844 National Exhibition, just four years after having founded his workshop. The designs he displayed were judged as being in the Indian style where the contours were pure and unbroken. By 1855 Berrus' shop employed over a hundred workers, compared to the thirty working there in 1844. They were engaged in translating designs for the *mise-en-carte* of the jacquard loom. Monsieur Delacour, Berrus' right-hand man, was responsible for enlarging his sketches and making samples of all the shawl details, while a Monsieur Gourdet was responsible for colouring and *mise-en-carte*. At this time his company attained a turnover reaching 250,000 francs.[23]

Berrus was the first to break away and develop his own individual style. In contrast with Couder, who was more of a scientific innovator, Berrus was a pure artist who confined his talents wholly to the shawl's canvas. In essence, he took Couder's theory and put it into practice. The idea was actually simple: to break away from the jagged edges of the declining Kashmir shawl and transfer the smooth contours of the new sweeping botehs on to the jacquard cards so that a faithful reproduction of the design would appear in the woven fabric. Berrus created an efficient task force to accomplish this feat; the effort involved in manufacturing the cards was still enormous and required unlimited patience. All this was a prerequisite for the weaving of his designs, which, by the time of his arrival in the shawl business, was already far removed from the Oriental image.

Berrus, Parquez,[24] Vichy, Braun, Chebeaux, and of course Couder, were all graduates of what was by then a firmly implanted system of design ateliers throughout Paris, Lyon, and Nîmes. They represented the élite of this field, and their talents were greatly admired abroad. Braun sold 50,000 francs' worth of shawl designs to the firm Montis, Glasgow, during the 1851 Universal Exhibition.[25] Chebeaux's creations were sold to the firm of John Monteith, James Black and Hamiel, also of Glasgow, and to the firm of Simpson, Young, Buttersworth and Brook of Manchester. The shawl artist was not only compensated by a good salary, his talents brought additional rewards of fame during the 'campaigns' of the national and the international exhibitions. Since 1834, when the industrial artists were first recognised and allowed to present their works, shawl designs along with manufactured articles were often the featured attraction. One critic felt that shawl designers, just as sculptors and engravers who sign their names to their work, should enjoy similar recognition. Indeed, many

23. Expo 1855, Rapport du Jury etc., vol. 3, p. 1,223.
24. Parquez, ostensibly, was in possession of the collection of design albums originating from the then defunct Oberkampf factory. He probably purchased these valuable books either just after Oberkampf's death in 1837 or more likely during the auction sale of the company's assets in 1844.
25. Expo 1855, vol. 3, p. 1,222.

COLOUR PLATE 66.
French long shawl, extremely finely woven with pashmina wool in ten colours. The reverse side contains a gold seal stating that it was woven by the firm of 'AC', Amédée Couder. Couder's son carried on the business after his father's retirement. c. 1865. 160cm x 345cm (63 x 136in.).

COLOUR PLATE 67.
French long shawl. Signed Couder Jeune & Cie. Extremely finely woven with pashmina wool. 163cm x 343cm (64in x 135in.).

COLOUR PLATE 68.
French long shawl. Signed 'AC', initials woven into the centre. Extremely finely woven with pashmina wool. c.1870. 157cm x 325cm (62 x 128in.).

COLOUR PLATE 69.
Finely woven French shawl with pashmina wool. Signed in the black centre in semi-legible script, A. ? Cachemire pure. Possibly from the Couder workshop, c.1870.

COLOUR PLATE 70. *Extremely finely woven pashmina French shawl with a brilliant chromatic harmony of colour tones. The date 1855 is woven into the corners and indicates that the shawl was made for the Universal Exhibition of that date. 160cm x 353cm (63 x 139in.). For a shawl of the same design see* The Cachmere Shawl, *p. 138.*

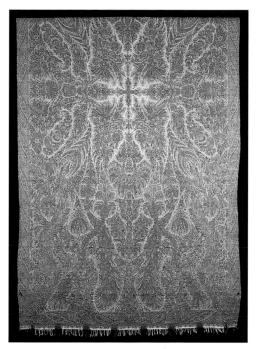

COLOUR PLATE 71.
Berrus shawl woven from cartoon (Cabinets des Dessins, no. CD 5275 F.) found at the Museum of Decorative Arts, Paris. Berrus' famous jungle period, c.1848-1850. For colour illustration of the cartoon see The Cachmere Shawl, *p. 99.*

COLOUR PLATE 71a.
Very fine French shawl woven with pashmina wool, attributed to Berrus. c. 1867. 157.5 x 358cm (62 x 141in.).

COLOUR PLATE 72.
French long shawl initialled in each of the four corners 'LF' (Léon Frères). c. 1850. 168cm x 335cm (66 x 132in.).

long jacquard shawls were initialled, usually on the extreme ends within one of the arches or 'gates' of the fringe (Plate 59).

MID-NINETEENTH CENTURY SHAWL DESIGN

By the mid-nineteenth century the school of shawl design was divided into three categories: 1) traditional Indian shawls characterised by classic Oriental style, accurately copied right down to the smallest detail; 2) designs subject to the caprices of fashion, where the motifs were modified substantially and were fantastical in character; 3) a combination of the first two where the Indian outline was conserved but detail expressed imaginative changes.

Each school served a very definite function, satisfying the special needs of either domestic or foreign markets. The Indian school agreed principally with the demand of French taste while, on the other hand, the whimsical, exotic designs satisfied a particular foreign market. The former catered to the conservative palate of ladies desiring a loyal copy of the Indian product, while the latter suited the avant-garde.

The proprietors of the large establishments which successfully grew up in Paris, Saint-Denis, Puteaux and Essone followed Oberkampf's example. Before long, designers were attached to all branches of the textile industry. Among the most remarkable 'dessinateurs' at the end of the eighteenth century were two Lyonnaise artists, Philippe de la Salle and Bouy.

In 1847, Paris had sixty-six artist-workshops employing 721 people. These workshops catered to industries of many foreign nations and built a reputation for successfully forecasting coming fashion. At the same time representatives of these nations came to Paris looking for artists willing to direct their ateliers.

The superiority of French design had been respected for a long time in Europe. The Austrians, as far back as 1751, had commissioned French artists to instruct their apprentices in the art of velvet weaving. Seven years later an industrial

PLATE 60.
Shawl advertisement, Paris, 1847.

design school was founded with the adoption of French techniques and staffed, also, by French instructors.[26]

British firms frequently sent for Parisian shawl designers, both to renew old styles and to create new ones. In Paisley, for example, the company Keer, Scott and Kilner often used France's best talent to enrich their knowledge of colouring and *mise-en-carte* techniques.[27] Soon after, this situation was reversed, and the English found it easier to dispatch their chief artists to Paris, for three or four months of apprenticeship.

26. Geijer, p. 163.
27. Expo 1862, Rapport du Jury. p. 122.

COLOUR PLATE 73.
French long shawl of Berrus' 'jungle' period. Notice the chinoiserie vignettes woven into the fringe gates. c.1850. 163cm x 317cm (64 x 125in.).

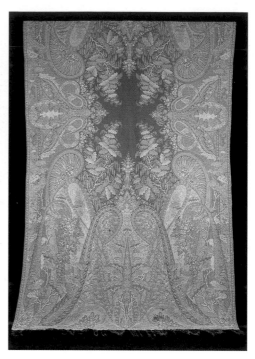

COLOUR PLATE 74.
Long shawl with chinoiserie pattern attributed to the Berrus school of design. c.1850. 160cm x 338cm (63 x 133in.).

COLOUR PLATE 75.
Long French shawl initialled in each of the four corners 'EC' (Eugène Cailleux). c.1850. 160cm x 312cm (63 x 123in.).

COLOUR PLATE 76.
Berrus shawl, 1865-1866, woven from its original sketch as seen in Plate 61.

COLOUR PLATE 77b.
Fine long shawl by Berrus. Identical to Colour Plate 77a except for the unusual way the pattern sweeps around to one side towards the middle of the shawl. Called in French a Bernous pattern, it is extremely rare to discover two woven shawls both exhibiting such uncommon features and both of exceptional beauty and weave. c.1865. 163cm x 330cm (64in. x 130in.).

COLOUR PLATE 77a.
French jacquard shawl, known as châle à pivot, c.1867. 163cm x 351cm (64 x 138in.). Pivot shawls are extremely rare and this one, which can be attributed with a high degree of confidence to Antony Berrus, was most likely woven for the Universal Exhibition of 1867. It can be noted how the rising cluster of paisleys dash toward the centre and, crossing it, spill into the opposite side to interlock with its 180 degrees mirror image. Thus the artist revels as much in the new-found marvels of the pivot technique as in the sinuous, narrow black centre that accentuates it. This pristine shawl, with its original glossy patina, is woven with the finest quality pashmina and a very high warp-weft density.

PLATE 60a.
French long shawl (detail), c.1815. Compare this to Plates 132 and 133.

PLATE 60b.
Jacquard shawl fragment, probably French, c.1835. 59cm x 135cm (23 x 53in.). All the essential Sikh design characteristics appear in this fragment.

One of the most prestigious British companies of the early shawl era was Gibbs and Macdonald. Their high quality products, woven during the period 1804-36 were, for the most part, modelled after the French imitation shawl, especially after the defeat of Napoléon in 1815. At this time Mr. Macdonald made it a habit to visit Paris every year to obtain new designs.[28]

In 1834 there are records of an English shawl artist, Thomas Barker Holdway, who was sent to Paris to study the latest techniques in this field. His visit was due to the fortuitous results of a first prize and forty pounds which he won for his shawl designs.[29]

Throughout this cultural and cooperative exchange of artistic ideas Paris remained the centre of creativity and production. Practically all important foreign production centres had their *mise-en-carte* performed in Paris. This method made for tremendous reductions in industrial expenses which were simply translated into the purchase and transportation of the pre-programmed jacquard cards. Therefore, nobody was ever absolutely sure whether the shawl was woven in Paris, Glasgow or Vienna!

FLEURY CHAVANT

In spite of the creation of a school of industrial design, few books of Kashmir patterns were available to aid and provide manufacturers with working guidelines to achieve successful imitation shawls. In 1837, however, Fleury Chavant, an industrial designer turned publisher, produced a periodical entitled *Album du Cachemirien*. Its utility lay in the full scale drawings traced from recent shawls of new designs which were woven in Lahore, Isfahan, Kabul, Kashmir and Chandahar. English shawl makers also procured editions of Chavant's work and both the Paisley and Norwich museums today contain examples of his album.

Shawl makers everywhere were now well informed of the latest Oriental trends in shawl weaving and designs arriving monthly from the East.

28. Whyte, p. 23.
29. Whyte and Swain, 1962. p. 61.

PLATE 61.
*Rough sketch by
Berrus in crayon,
chalk and charcoal
in preparation for the
cartoon of the shawl
in Colour Plate 76,
found at the Museum
of Decorative Arts,
Paris, Album 4, cl
20303, inv. xx47.*

It is highly plausible that the *Cachemirien* was based on the very shawls sent from India by General Allard after his return to Lahore in 1836. Poitevin, the reviewer of the 1867 Exhibition, explained that this large group of Kashmir shawls was exhibited in the boutique of the dealer Gagelin, the same dealer who 'instructed' Allard before his return to India. Poitevin wrote: 'This occasion created such publicity that it set the style for other dealers to follow'.[30]

Before this time Europe was largely unaware that the Kashmir shawl was so widely imitated in the Orient. The *Cachemirien* proved an invaluable guide for those whose sights were aimed at the export market – especially at the Middle East where heavy overland taxes on shawls from Kashmir made them extremely costly. The Kashmir shawl was, for example, often more expensive in Arabia or Turkey because of the overland taxes imposed on the caravans. Industrialised Europe's cheaper shawl competed favourably against those woven by hand in the Orient and satisfied a ready middle-class market.

Chavant's influence on design was thus undoubtedly strong and, although he himself did not create any new designs, he wisely engaged the most reputed Parisian artists. They either copied from existing woven designs or produced original ones and their names greatly enhanced the prestige of his publications.

The *Cachemirien* clarifies, in a small way, some of the developments of the 'boteh' in Europe, as Chavant carefully points out earlier motifs which prevailed during the Rey, Ternaux, Bellanger and Lagorce period. The first botehs are described as caillouté (literally tiny stones, but the word 'mosaic' would be more appropriate) which was the style of the 'naissance du cachemire'. Other styles were called the 'Bengale', 'à rubans', 'à palme superposée' and 'à pagode'.

In another of Chavant's albums, entitled *Le Dessinateur de Cachemires*, coloured drawings similar to the drawings in the *Cachemirien* are shown, but with the additional features of some delicate drawings in chinoiserie style. An occasional pagoda is found. This Far Eastern style reappears in a shawl manufactured by Chambellan and Duché at the Paris Exposition of 1839 and is also reproduced in Chavant's *Souvenir de l'Exposition de 1839* along with a few 'renaissance' shawls as mentioned above. Chavant published about twenty-five albums altogether.

30. Expo 1867, p. 173.

COLOUR PLATE 78.
Chinoiserie shawl, c.1840. 183cm x 183cm (72 x 72in.). Wool: Pashmina and silver wrapped threads. This unique shawl represents probably the earliest known chinoiserie pattern from Europe. Only two other major exhibition chinoiserie shawls are known and they are both long shawls. One is in the Brooklyn Museum (see Colour Plates 63a and b), while the other is known as the 'Chinese Fairy Tale Plaid' and is located in the Paisley Museum, Scotland.

In this shawl the vegetal colours and weave format indicate a date contemporary with shawls of the period 1835-1845. And, more importantly, because the cartouche pictorials all face the same direction, it can be deduced that it had been woven originally as an exhibition shawl. Although a rare reference has been found among the scant reviews of the international European exhibitions indicating that indeed metal wrapped yarns had been used, this is the only shawl known at present to exhibit this feature. The shawl's field is composed of ten parallel 'poles' supporting an array of chinoiserie cartouches highlighted by an ornate field of meandering flower vines and exotic birds. Two designs decorate the cartouches. The first cartouche shows a Chinese dignitary enthroned in his tent and accompanied by three attendants and a flag bearer, witnessing a battle between two of his soldiers. In the second, we find perhaps a princess and her attendants listening to a mandolin player. Four of each of the cartouches are strung along the poles unidirectionally alternating with smaller oval medallions featured with peacocks. Surrounding the field lies a narrow border of another chinoiserie design in a repeat pattern. Here, we see a sheep herder wielding a stick in each hand with a knobby hillock behind him and two smaller occupied tents, one with a person standing, the other with a person sitting down. And finally, three other standing personages and several palm trees.

COLOUR PLATE 79.
Shawl designed by Frédéric Hébert and signed in the centre 'H, Cachemire pur', the typical mark of the Hébert weaving atelier. In fine pashmina wools and with a fringe gate mimicking the contemporary shawl pattern from Kashmir. c.1865.

COLOUR PLATE 80.
Shawl designed for the 1855 Universal Exhibition in Paris. The date can be found woven four times into the fringe gates. A shawl of exceptional quality and weaving, and its design is possibly from the Hébert atelier.

211

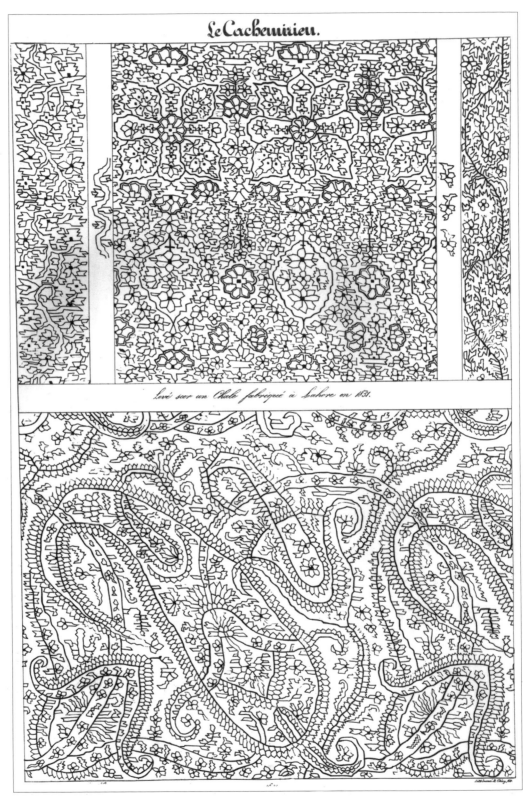

PLATE 62.
Tracing from Chavant's Le Cachemirien. *Top, c.1800; bottom, shawl woven in Lahore in 1831.*

212

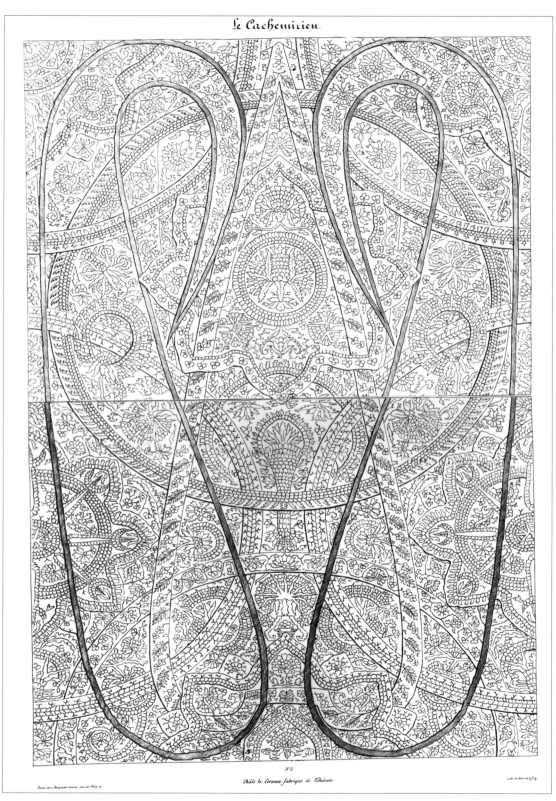

Le Cachemirien.

Châle le Cerceau fabriqué de Téhéran.

PLATE 63.
Tracing from Chavant's Le Cachemirien. *A shawl woven in Teheran.*

COLOUR PLATE 81.
Fine French shawl attributed to Berrus.
c.1860. 155cm x 307cm (61 x 121in.).

COLOUR PLATE 82.
Sumptuously ornate and unusually large
French shawl attributed to Berrus. c.1860.
152cm x 355cm (60 x 140in).

COLOUR PLATE 83.
A fine Berrus long shawl with an all over
plaid pattern without any plain central field.
c.1867. 155cm x 333cm (61 x 131in.).

COLOUR PLATE 84.
A fine Berrus shawl with red centre, 1867,
163cm x 335cm (64 x 132in.).

COLOUR PLATE 85.
Pivot shawl attributed to Berrus. Pseudo-calligraphic and illegible signature in black field. c.1855. 157cm x 366cm (62in. x 144in.).

COLOUR PLATE 86.
Fine and unusual, exhibition-type shawl designed by Berrus. Its cartoon can be found in the album 47XX, 1861-1864, at the Museum of Decorative Arts, Paris. An inscription in the weaving reads: 'IL n'y a de Dieu que Dieu', there is no God but God. 155cm x 330cm (61 x 130in.

COLOUR PLATE 87.
Fine Berrus shawl woven of pashmina wool. c.1862. 152cm x 356cm (60in x 140in.).

COLOUR PLATE 88.
Fine Hébert shawl woven in the pivot technique and signed in the centre 'H Cachemire pur'. c.1867. 153cm x 361cm (60in. x 142in).

PLATE 64.
Tracing from Chavant's Le Cachemirien. *A shawl woven in Teheran.*

216

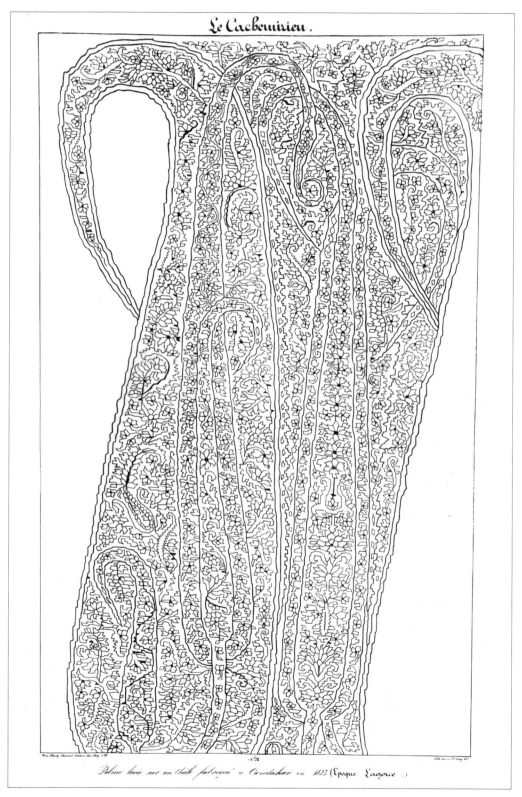

Le Cachemirien.

Palme tirée sur un chale fabriqué à Candahar en 1825 (Epoque Lagorce.)

PLATE 65.
Tracing from Chavant's Le Cachemirien. *A shawl woven in Kandahar in 1825.*

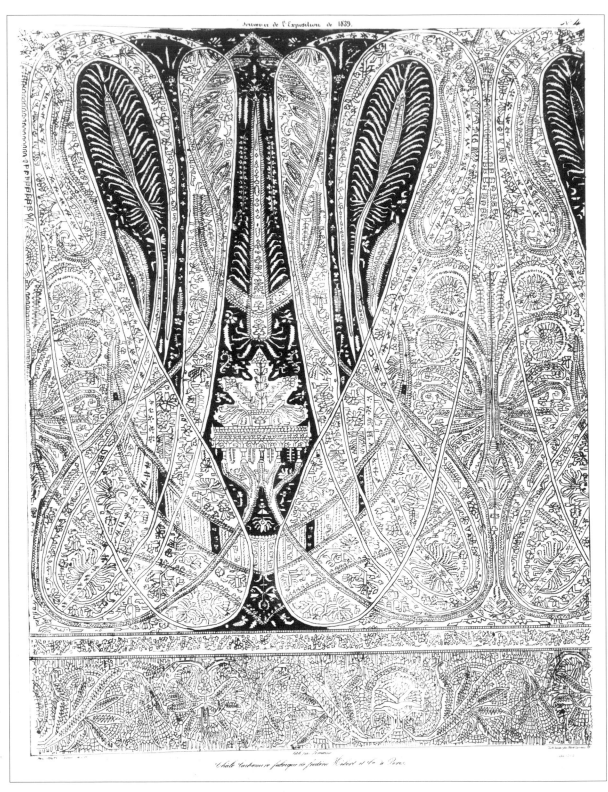

PLATE 66.
Tracing from Chavant's Souvenir de l'Exposition de 1839. *A Kashmir shawl manufactured by Frédéric Hébert and Co., Paris.*

PLATE 67.
Tracing from Chavant's Souvenir de l'Exposition de 1839. *A 'Hindu' shawl manufactured by*
M.M. Chambellan and Duché, Paris.

Plate 68.

Tracing from Chavant's Souvenir de l'Exposition de 1839. *Shawl woven with pashmina wool by Bournhonet, Ternaux's successor.*

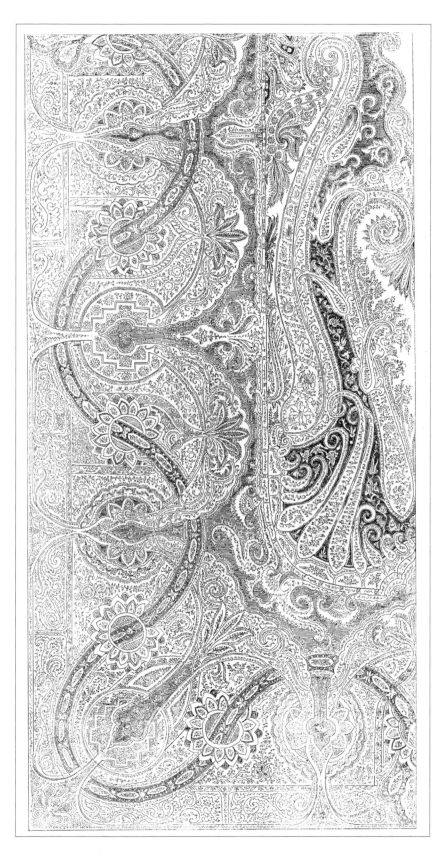

PLATE 69.
Tracing from Victor Delaye's album
Indo-parisien, *1850-1867, showing*
quarter section of a long shawl.

221

PLATE 70.
Tracing from Victor Delaye's album Indo-parisien, *1850-1867, showing quarter section of a wonderful square shawl pattern.*

PLATE 71.
Tracing from Victor Delaye's album Indo-parisien, *1850-1867, showing quarter design for a long shawl with motifs borrowed from Gothic architecture and early printed cloths.*

PLATE 72.
Tracing from Victor Delaye's album Indo-parisien, *1850-1867, showing quarter design for a square shawl.*

PLATE 73.
Tracing from Victor Delaye's album
Indo-parisien, *1850-1867, showing*
fantasy design for woven cloth and
not necessarily shawls.

COLOUR PLATE 89.
Fine Hébert shawl having a gold embossed stamp on the reverse side reading 'Seule Medaille d'honneur 1840-1863'. With a signature in the central field it was most likely woven in 1867. 157cm x 338cm (62 x 133in.).

COLOUR PLATE 90.
Fine Hébert shawl with signature in the centre, 'H Cachemire pur'. c.1860. 147cm x 335cm (58 x 132in.).

COLOUR PLATE 91.
Fine Hébert shawl with signature in the centre, 'H Cachemire pur',.c.1860. 163cm x 323cm (64 x 127in.).

COLOUR PLATE 92.
Fine square shawl with initials in each corner, 'FM' (Fortier & Maillard). The French devoted many more of their finer productions to long shawls than to square ones. This one displays nine colours with brightly 'lit' fringe gates. c.1860. 185cm x 188cm (73 x 74in.).

COLOUR PLATE 93.
Fine French shawl with signature in the centre, BM, indicating perhaps Bonfils et Michel? c.1867. 160cm x 358cm (63 x 141in.).

COLOUR PLATE 94.
Fine Berrus shawl, c. 1865. 165cm x 343cm (65in. x 135in.).

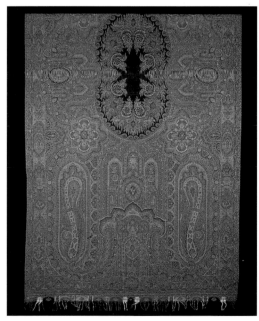

COLOUR PLATE 95.
Fine French shawl patterned with intricate architectural details of pagodas and mihrabs. Also, love birds and lanterns and even Chinese boats can be found woven into the design. Signed 'SL' (?) in the fringe gate, the shawl was probably woven around 1865. 160cm x 338cm (63 x 133in.).

COLOUR PLATE 96.
Fine French shawl signed in each of the four corners 'MBC' (?). c.1860. 173cm x 325cm (68in. x 128in.).

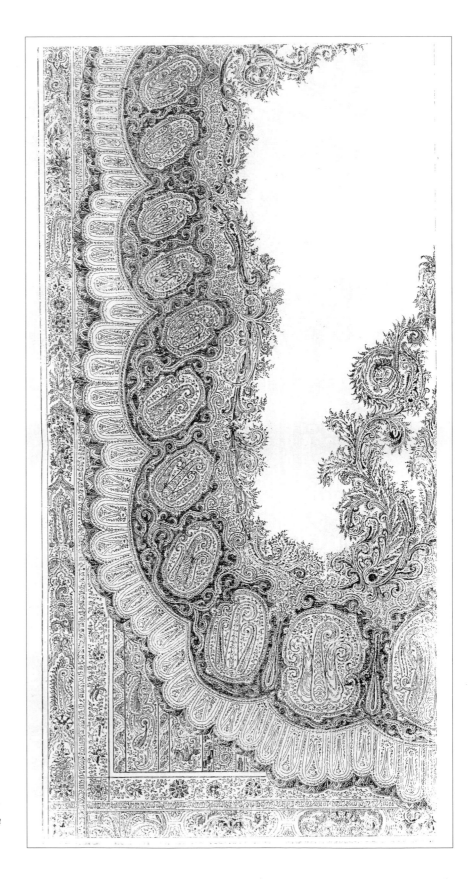

PLATE 74.
Tracing from Victor Delaye's album Indo-parisien, *1850-1867, showing quarter design for a long shawl.*

228

PLATE 75
Tracing from Victor Delaye's album
Indo-parisien, *1850-1867, showing*
quarter design for a long shawl with
unusual zoomorphic rococo motifs.

Four Seasons' shawl, France. Shawls with a four colour central pattern began appearing around 1860. 160cm x 317cm (63 x 125in.).

The Isfahan shawl, French. Eleven colours. 184cm x 184cm (72 x 72in.). This mandala-like shawl, of which only one known example survives, is of paramount importance in the history of European Kashmir shawls. Queen Marie-Amélie, impressed by a painting of the shawl exhibited at the National Exposition of 1834, ordered a woven copy of it. Amédée Couder, its designer, combined the then newly advanced and highly complex jacquard-loom technology with the severe requirements of the shawl's sophisticated design in colour contrasts and high warp-weft resolution. Persian inscriptions are found in the centre and under the trio of minarets in the shawl's corner. They read respectively: 'Couder and Gaussen 1834', 'Isfahan' and 'Exhibited at the Exposition of French manufactured products 1834'. See exhibition catalogues, Lévis-Strauss, 1983, pp. 56, 64, 65, and 1982, p. 82. See also Ames, 1982, p. 59.

COLOUR PLATE 99A. *(Far left) 'M. B. Cie' woven into fringe tab. Initials unidentified. (See Colour Plate 96.)*

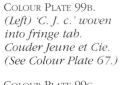

COLOUR PLATE 99B. *(Left) 'C. J. c.' woven into fringe tab. Couder Jeune et Cie. (See Colour Plate 67.)*

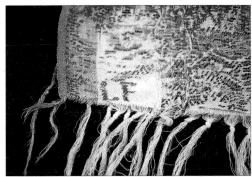

COLOUR PLATE 99C. *(Far left) 'L. F.' woven into fringe tab. Léon Frères. (See Colour Plate 72.)*

COLOUR PLATE 99D. *(Left) 'E. C.' woven into fringe tab. Eugène Cailleux. (See Colour Plate 75.)*

COLOUR PLATE 99E. *(Far left) 'F. M.' woven into fringe tab. Fortier et Maillard. (See Colour Plate 92.)*

COLOUR PLATE 99F. *(Left) 'J. C.' woven into fringe tab. Possibly John Cunningham. (See Colour Plate 112.)*

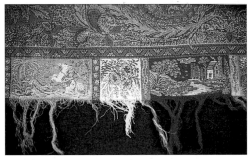

COLOUR PLATE 99G. '*55' woven into fringe tab. Woven for the Universal Exhibition of 1855. (See Colour Plate 80.)*

COLOUR PLATE 99H. *Interesting pictorial vignettes woven into all fringe tabs of Colour Plate 73. This not uncommon idea usually appears on shawls woven with few colours but often with wonderful designs from the mid-19th century.*

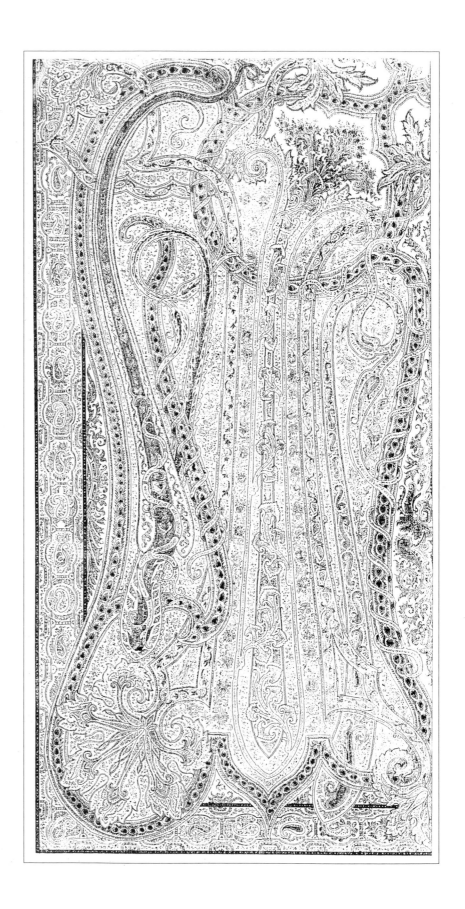

Plate 76.
Tracing from Victor Delaye's album
Indo-parisien, *1850-1867, showing*
quarter design for a long shawl.

232

VICTOR DELAYE

Victor Delaye is another name that comes up on the roster of known shawl artists. His album, called *Indo-Parisien,* contains about fifty pages of beautifully drawn shawl patterns apparently sketched during the years 1850-1867, which he claimed were applicable to carpets, vests, lace, ribbons and all kinds of weavings. In looking at these drawing it becomes obvious that Delaye was a gifted artist and creator of fabulous fantasy designs. Capturing moods from the architectural mysteries of the Far East and Egypt, as well as the French rococo and majestic gothic styles of Europe, the album offers a rich and exotic world of unusual patterns replete with celestial cherubs, monkeys, children, strange personages, sphinxes, pagodas, Islamic and geometric interlacings, etc. Many patterns depict the 'paisley' in its zoomorphic state while other patterns are reminiscent of Berrus' seaplant style and at least one pattern had been featured at the Regional Exhibition of Rouen.

NÎMES SCHOOL OF DESIGN

Nîmes enjoyed a prosperous textile production during the eighteenth century competing with Lyon in silks and woollen goods and by the beginning of the nineteenth century had established its first free School of Design for the textile industry due to the direct influence of council merchants and manufacturers.[31]

The school's directors were all gifted artists in their own right, some former students of the great David and Girodet. Begun in the 1820, classes were given on the theory of weaving, loom application, textile sketching, printing and the making of jacquard cards *(mise en carte),* until it doors finally closed in 1907. The Musée du Vieux Nîmes conserves a series of interesting drawings which trace the important steps taken by the artist to transfer his initial design pattern to the final coloured *mise en carte* paper utilised for the actual weave of the shawl. First the student outlined his floral pattern in white or coloured ink by utilising tiny lines that mimicked the *mise en carte* of the jacquard loom. Curved lines had to be avoided as each line represented either a weft shot or warp thread. The artist drew on transparent, glazed paper *(papier verni)* and then gouached the open floral spaces from the reverse side. The result was a design that came very close to the final woven shawl. Several artists might work on one *verni.*

From Nîmes came many well-known shawl artists and manufacturers who either stayed on in their natal city or trekked to Paris where the shawl fashion was in. Jean Gaussen, the silk manufacturer, had two sons both named François who each made their mark in the shawl business. While in Paris, François Gaussen, Sr. teamed up with Deneirouse, another Nîmes shawl maker, where they took over the established shawl firm of Largorce and won a gold medal for their products at the 1827 National Exhibition. The two separated but Gaussen Sr. soon distinguished himself in gold again at the 1834 and 1839 National Exhibitions by weaving two of the most important shawl designs of the nineteenth century: the Isfahan and the Nou-Rouz, Couder's celebrated masterpieces.

Also from Nîmes, François Grillet won a patent on a new type of *mise en carte* paper for silk, and went on to Lyon where he became partners with François Trotton and they wove shawls. They applied for a patent on a new type of loom procedure that reduced by half the number of weft shots on brocaded shawls. By 1840 Grillet was again working alone and applied for yet another patent (1843) which called for the use of two warps. One was used for the ground colour and

31. *Nîmes et le châle,* Musée du Vieux Nîmes, 1988, pp 21,22.

COLOUR PLATE 100A.
(Right) Illegible signature on shawl attributed to Berrus. (See Colour Plate 85.)

COLOUR PLATE 100B.
(Far right) 'Cachemire' woven into centre field.

COLOUR PLATE 100C.
(Right) 'A. C.' woven into centre field of Colour Plate 66. Amédée Couder.

COLOUR PLATE 100D.
(Far right) 'A. C.' woven into centre field of Colour Plate 68. Amédée Couder.

COLOUR PLATE 100E.
(Right) 'A. S. Cachemire'?. From Colour Plate 69.

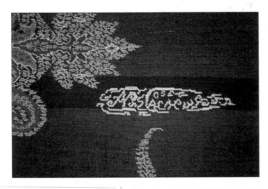

COLOUR PLATE 100F.
(Far right) 'H. Cachemire pur', usual mark of Frédéric Hébert. (See Colour Plate 88.)

COLOUR PLATE 100G.
Sewn on label from the company (unidentified) D. A. D. Jne B&Cie, Paris, with the dates of 1844, 1849, 1851, 1855 (twice) 1862 and 1863 commemorating the gold medals they had received at these national and universal exhibitions for their shawl products.

COLOUR PLATE 100H.
Sewn on label from the company 'C. P. B., Fabrique de Châles, Paris' (company unidentified)

234

the other for the pattern and by the National Exhibition of 1844 apparently his shawls made quite a stir.

In a brief review of the National and Universal Exhibitions, we see that from 1823 to 1867 many Nîmes shawl makers won recognition with their innovative products and special weave techniques. In 1834 we find for example the firm of Barnouin and Bureau using designs by their own hand, the first to weave shawls using the actual pashmina wool. The 1839 archives note that Nîmes is exporting to North and South America as well as Spain, Belgium and Holland, and by 1844 striped shawls are being shipped to the Orient. Several firms are even competing successfully with Paris and Lyon in so far as quality of weave is concerned. What we find among the many archival reviews is that nothing prevented the various shawl weaving centres from weaving whatever quality of shawl they deemed necessary.

Nîmes produced shawls mostly of the Indo-wool and Tibetan category and excelled in weaving inexpensive shawls too. In order to reduce costs several modes of production were necessary. First the size of the shawl was reduced; second the weaving was not as tight (less warps and wefts to achieve the same design); third, by a careful choice of inexpensive wools and silks; fourth, simply by reducing the number of weft passes alone.

In the latter procedure, all the colours of the shawl are woven in by each pass of the shuttle. That is, if a shawl's pattern uses seven colours then seven weft shots are required for each 'line' of wefting. If the shawl has 40 lines per centimetre then we have 40 times 7 or 280. Thus the weaver has to throw his shuttle 280 times per centimetre. An expensive shawl with many colours could take a long time to make. From 1849, intermediate colours were obtained by a new procedure called 'colour marriage' whereby the weaver, in the same weft line, placed say a red thread and one yellow thread thereby creating the colour orange.

CONCLUSION

In this chapter we have revealed the principal artists and manufacturers whose legacy of accomplishments predominate the annals of nineteenth century France. Through Ternaux we sensed the intense drive of a great industrialist to harness the compelling force of fashion. Couder jolted the shawl industry awake with his Indo-Gothic architecture, glittering Oriental figures, and caparisoned elephants and camels. Berrus mesmerised the public by the sheer force of his 'inner-sanctum' designs, in which the boteh was enshrined, and temples camouflaged by fantastical jungle foliage, evoking 'A Thousand and One Nights'. In the field of invention and loom technology it was not so much genius that counted but hard work and determination to satisfy an urgent need. Jacquard, Bauson, Deneirouse, Fabard and doubtless many others played a crucial role in elaborating on the loom's sophistication. The French Kashmir shawl exemplifies a fusion of art and industry. Together with its Indian progenitor, the kani shawl of Kashmir, they represent two inseparable textile art forms of the nineteenth century.

PLATE 77.
Part of border of shawl counterpane, 1793. Woven by P.J. Knights at Alderman Harvey's manufactory. 3.65m (144in.) wide with no seam. Silk warp and wool weft. Design in silk. This design alternates round the border with the arms of the ancestral families in the tree of John Hobart, 2nd Earl of Buckinghamshire and his wife Caroline Conolly. The design, taken from the Indian boteh, was worked in darning stitch by children as the drawloom at the time was not capable of weaving in such a complex pattern. National Trust, Blickling.

CHAPTER 8

British Shawls in the Indian Style
by Pamela Clabburn

While shawls were being made in France in the Indian style Britain also grasped the opportunity to keep her weavers at work. Although there were several towns where weaving was the principal trade, there were three which had the right background for making fashionable shawls. These were Norwich, Edinburgh and, a little later, Paisley. Through the eighteenth century all three were skilled in the weaving of light-weight fabrics, with Norwich making mainly half-silks and fashionable dress materials, Edinburgh weaving damasks, and Paisley specialising in muslins and silk. The looms of all three towns could be and were, after considerable trial and error, adapted to weaving shawls in imitation of the Indian.

This imitation only went as far as the designs, which were at first slavishly copied. The techniques employed were very different. Making a shawl (or a pair of shawls) in India using the twill tapestry method was intensely time-consuming with a pair of shawls (worn back to back) taking in general eighteen months to two years to weave. Though they were eventually sold in Britain at a very high price, reaching 200 guineas in some cases, the Indian weaver was paid a mere pittance, and though the British weaver was by no means well paid the sum he earned was princely in comparison with that of the Indian. The slowness of the Indian method also meant that few shawls could be produced, which did not suit the ideas of the British merchant.

By the beginning of the nineteenth century each British centre was using the same technique, a plain twill weave, generally using a silk warp for fineness and strength, with a wool weft, and nearly always weaving in the design with wool. This was a much quicker method than the laborious tapestry weave, and when two shawls are put close together, one being Indian and the other British, if the colour and the design are similar, as they so often were, it is difficult to tell which comes from which country without a close inspection.

One question which always has and still does bedevil everyone from museum curator to anyone looking at the first shawl they have seen is how to tell Indian from British at first sight and then, much more difficult, how to tell from which British centre it comes. It is in only a few cases that anyone can be completely certain of the answer. For though the three centres started in different ways they came together almost too well for easy differentiation. The question of design has always been a stumbling block. For most of the first seventy years of the nineteenth century Indian designs, especially the boteh or pine shape, dominated shawls and many of the designs used in Britain came from India via France. There are several references to manufacturers either going to France themselves to collect patterns, or buying patterns from France. For example, it is known that Mr MacDonald of the Edinburgh firm of Gibbs and MacDonald went to France every year to collect designs, and in the accounts of Grout of Norwich for 1834 is the entry '6 French handkerchiefs bought for patterns.'

Equally, many firms were not big enough to have their own designer or design team and bought their patterns from free-lance designers, probably based in London. Though these men would not have sold the same pattern in different towns there is always a family likeness and technique in designs from the same

COLOUR PLATE 101.
*Square shawl,
Paisley, Scotland,
c.1810-15. 152cm x
152cm (60 x 60in.).
A very early shawl,
all silk. The small
motifs over the
ground have been
put in by the 'finger
spotting' method,
where the weaver is
helped by two girls,
one each side of the
loom, who 'put in'
short lengths of yarn
with their fingers.
See p. 244.* Private
Collection.

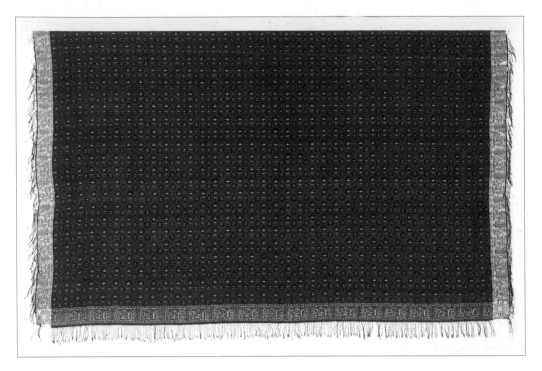

hand, which makes identification difficult. Lastly, there was the very thorny question of plagiarism. In broad terms the quality of Norwich weaving was better than that of Paisley, and when Norwich had put a new shawl design on the market it was quickly copied using inferior yarn and selling at a considerably lower price.

By 1839 the industry was in such straits that a Commission to Report on the Plight of the Hand-loom Weavers was set up by the Government. Mr Etheridge, a Norwich manufacturer, complained to the Commission that 'he had brought out a shawl of a most beautiful pattern and it was taking well and yielding a good profit; but he had just received a letter from his London agent, telling him that his pattern had been imitated by the Scotch, and advising him to discontinue it immediately'. He added:

> When the Scotch take up a pattern they inundate the market with such an abundance that the article becomes quite common and ladies of property will not buy a shawl of which there are so many imitations.

This point of view was certainly that of Norwich because Norwich was making the better article for the 'ladies of quality' while in most cases Paisley was trying to attract the less well-off, and succeeding very well. This, then was the main bone of contention between the three centres and had the result that the popular design (the Indian) had too few differing elements to allow room for the three centres to promote their own ideas.

The result of the Commissioner's report was that by 1842 it was possible to register shawl designs at the Public Record Office (PRO) in London. For one shilling a design could be used only by the firm registering for either three or six months, which gave time to get a design on to the market before it could be copied, added to which the design could be used in various forms, possibly by putting elements from two of them together, or moving them to make a different pattern. From shawls in the collection at Norwich it appears that differences in colour were also allowed.

COLOUR PLATE 102.
Long scarf, Spitalfields, England, c.1820. 248cm x 48cm (98 x 19in.).
Twill woven in fine silk with design in thick silk. The village of Spitalfields in East London was famous for its silk weaving, many of the weavers being Huguenots who fled from France in 1685. They mostly wove fine silk dress fabrics but also this type of shawl or long scarf. Private Collection.

Colour Plate 104.
Long scarf, Norwich, 1935-40, printed, 253cm x 60cm (100x 24in.).
Woven by Towler Campin & Co. The leno (gauze) ground has the 'trade mark' of the fine printed shawls made by this firm, consisting of 2cm (¾in.) of double weaving 1cm (⅜in.) inside the edges all round. This made the fragile fabric less likely to tear. This characteristic has not yet been noted by any other firm anywhere. Private Collection.

COLOUR PLATE 103.
Long scarf, probably Paisley, c.1825-30. 254cm x 65cm (100 x 26in.).
All wool. The design on this shawl is unusually sparse with little definition. Private Collection.

PRINTED SHAWLS

As well as woven shawls there were many which were printed. The wooden blocks used were in themselves works of art and it is sad that so few have been saved. They had been used in shawl manufacture since the end of the eighteenth century when they traced the outline of the pattern for the children to fill in with darning stitch.

As far as is known there are no extant shawls from the first thirty years of the nineteenth century which were printed, though there seem to have been many made. It was not until the 1830s that shawls made of fine woven silk or gauze (leno) were made as suitable for summer wear. They had the same style of design as the woven and most are beautifully printed. The blocks used, judging by the few in existence, were built up in layers of different woods to minimise warping, with a thumb and finger hole on top for the operator.. The wooden surface then had the design inked on, and fine brass or copper wires were hammered in. Each colour had a separate block and great skill was needed by the printer to make sure that the colours did not overlap. Some shawls were printed in the town where they were made, but in other cases the plain woven fabric would be sent to specialist printers, the best being Charles Swaisland of Crayford in Kent. From 1842 designs for printed shawls in the PRO and those in existence show how charming and decorative they were.

STYLES OF SHAWLS

As with all dress accessories the shape of a shawl followed the fashion of the day and, considering that a shawl is basically an unstructured square or oblong of fabric, it is amazing that so much variety of pattern and expertise by designer, weaver and printer is shown.

At the turn of the eighteenth century women were wearing simple light-coloured dresses of cotton, fine silk or fine wool, falling straight from a high waistline. The shawls which they wore both complemented the dress and provided the necessary extra warmth. They were known as 'long shawls' and were on average 250cm long by 100cm wide (98 by 40in.) woven generally with a silk warp and wool weft. They can be seen in many portraits of the time, both French and British. In the 1815-20 period, though the long shawl never lost its appeal, more square shawls appeared. They were all silk with sprigs of flowers over them, with or without a border, about 150cm (60in.) square. They, unlike the long shawl, seldom had a pine shape in the design. They evolved, in the 1820s-30s into what were known as 'turnover shawls'. These were square, with a plain centre and either a border the same width (about 3cm – 1in.) all round or two borders, one about 3cm (1in.) and the other about 8cm (3in.). In either case two adjoining sides of the borders would be sewn on one way with the other two reversed. When the shawl was folded diagonally the borders, placed one pair above the other, all showed the right side and formed a V down the back of the wearer.

With the spreading of the skirt during the 1840s into the wide crinoline of the 1850s shawls became larger, usually rectangular, sometimes square. The designs filled the ground to the exclusion of the field and pines became longer and thinner, waving and crossing each other. Looking closely at the designs and noticing the intricate fillings of empty spaces with dots, flowers and small shapes is to wonder at the invention of the designer, while sometimes deploring the general 'busyness'. In part, all this welter was due to the Great Exhibition of 1851 when each manufacturer tried to outdo the rest.

The late 1850s and 1860s saw some superb all-silk Jacquard shawls, glowing with colour. These were in two sizes, one a comparatively modest and very wearable 175cm (70in.) square which was often in the 'zebra' style: i.e. horizontal stripes of pattern often divided by plain narrow stripes. The other style was an enormous weaving 350cm long by 150cm wide (138 by 160in.), beautiful, with deep pine borders and often a large plain rectangle in the centre in a rep weave.

At this time it was very noticeable that these shawls, however well woven, with brilliant, jewel-like colours, were relying more and more on the same motifs in the design being placed in different ways to give a new look to what was an old pattern. The manufacturers had begun to realise that the shawl, which tottered on into the 1870s and even to a much lesser degree into the 1880s, was on the way out.

EDINBURGH

The story of shawl-making in Edinburgh is a short one and necessarily incomplete because it was 1942 before museums in the city were even sure that there had been a shawl industry there at all The certainty came in 1960 when Margaret Swain, a well-known textile historian, found references to the industry in the records of the Board of Trade for Agriculture and Fisheries, but even then there were no known shawls and it was not until 1973 that authenticated specimens appeared.

It seems that shawls 'in imitation of the Indian' were being made in Edinburgh before 1792 by William Mortimer and George Richmond, and that by 1792 there was an established manufacture. In 1793 the Board of Trustees started to give premiums or prizes for this type of shawl, and by 1800 a thousand people were said to be employed in the industry. From then on until 1820 the manufacture flourished; then there was a recession. By 1830 the trade had revived but by 1847 the last loom making Edinburgh shawls had stopped.

One of the principal shawl-making firms was that of Gibbs and MacDonald, and it was in 1973 that a descendant brought a varied collection of shawls, border samples, medallion centres and corners to the National Museum of Scotland. The collection is very interesting. The shawls are woven of wool with the pattern put in with silk, in contrast to a Norwich shawl where the pattern is nearly always of wool. Another distinguishing mark is that there are black warp threads in the borders, though this may be a distinguishing mark of this firm only. In the collection are individual motifs of centre medallions and corners and where these appeared on the shawls they had been sewn on rather than woven in. Did they weave a row of medallions and a row of corners, cut them out and sew them on?

From the billhead of Thomas Summers of Princes Street, Edinburgh, dated 1855, it becomes clear that shawls from all the centres were sold in each others' towns as well as abroad. Thomas Summers styles himself Shawl Merchant and Manufacturer in spite of the fact that Edinburgh is said to have stopped making shawls in 1847. He also states 'India and British Shawls, Dyed Cleaned and Repaired' and 'Shawl Borders, Middles and Fringes Sold Separately or made up to Order'. This explains why so many shawls seem not to fit into any category. If they could be put together at the whim of a buyer, and if the components had not been assembled by one designer, it is no wonder that some shawls have a very uncertain or odd look. The last note on this extremely helpful billhead states 'Plaids Altered into Shawls'.

COLOUR PLATE 105.
*Long shawl,
Edinburgh, Scotland,
1930s, 210cm x
142cm (83 x 56in.).
Woven, Cashmere
and wool. This shawl
is a replica of one
woven by the firm of
Gibbs & MacDonald
of Edinburgh. It has
the characteristic of
four corner botehs
sewn on to rather
than woven into the
ground.*
Private Collection.

COLOUR PLATE 106.
*Long scarf, Paisley or
Norwich, 1830s,
254cm x 126cm (100
x 50in.).
Silk warp and wool
weft. The background
colour of this shawl,
a beautiful coral
pink, is most
unusual. Possibly the
shawl was a special
order, perhaps for a
bride.*
Private Collection.

COLOUR PLATE 107.
Arab shawl, c.1845-50, Norwich. 322cm (127in.) along the top.
Wool and cotton, printed. This type of shawl is shaped as an oblong with the two corners of one long side curved, forming
a flat semi-circle. They were known as 'Arabs' by the manufacturers E. & F. Hinde, but as 'Burnous' by the fashion world.
In this example there are two distinct designs, one in each half meeting centre back. The shawl could be worn with either
design showing. There is no fringe along the top. Private Collection.

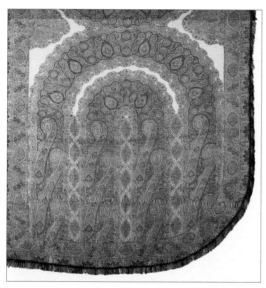

COLOUR PLATE 108.
Arab shawl c.1845-50, Norwich, 322cm (127in.)
along the top.
Silk leno (gauze), printed. A light summer shawl in
contrast to Colour Plate 107 which is much heavier
for winter wear. The design is strongly horizontal
and each half is the same. The three-toned fringe
does not extend to the top. Private Collection.

COLOUR PLATE 110.
Long shawl, Paisley, 1860s. 334cm x 150cm (131 x 59in.)
All wool. This is a typical Paisley shawl of the late 1850s and 1860s
with a long, heavy border full of pattern reaching to a small, nearly
plain centre. The mixture of red and green in the pattern giving an
indefinite look is often seen at this date. Private Collection.

COLOUR PLATE 109.
Square shawl, 1844, Norwich, 172cm x 172cm (68 x 68in.).
Made by Towler, Campin, Shickle & Matthews. The striking colour of
the ground is known as Norwich Red, a colour perfected by the dyeing
firm of William Stark. The design is derived from one registered in the
Public Record Office in 1844. Private Collection.

It seems that the shawl trade in Edinburgh was never very large, but it was important, partly because it was the earliest of the British/Indian shawls (1790) but also because the surviving shawls show that the standard was very high indeed.

PAISLEY

The story of shawl weaving in Paisley starts rather later than in Edinburgh or Norwich. The first references to it appear at the start of the nineteenth century, some fifteen years after the other two centres. Paisley had in the late eighteenth century a flourishing trade in muslins with excellent weavers, and when Edinburgh had a large amount of work and too few weavers they took some operatives from their near neighbour, Paisley, These men after a while took the extra skills they had learnt back to Paisley and started their own 'imitation of the India' trade there.

As with the other centres the first shawls woven at Paisley were very simple. The loom they used was adapted from the one they used for their muslins, and the designs were of very stylised, simple sprigs placed all over the ground. Sometimes these sprigs were put in by hand, and for this the yarn was cut into lengths of about an inch (2.5cm). When the weaver raised the spotting shed a girl stationed at either side of the loom deftly inserted the figuring yarn. Sprigs of this kind were woven face up and as there were no long floats on the underside these did not need to be cut off and there was no waste. From their method of insertion these were called 'finger spots'.

William Cross, writing in 1872 on 'changes in the style of Paisley shawls', discusses what must have been these 'finger' spots and he describes them as 'perverse, wry-necked sprigs in one colour, generally green, or made up of little bars of various colours, like so many chips of painted wood built into the required shapeless form'. There are still some of these early shawls to be seen, and once it is known what to look for they become obvious.

Another type of shawl made in both Paisley and Norwich in those early days was the 'Angola' which was a copy of a fur shawl. They had a great, if short, vogue in the 1830s. William Cross says that James Robertson, the chief manufacturer,

> had great trouble in getting cotton spun suitable for it and then woven into the texture best calculated to produce the required effect. The fabric had afterwards to be raised by cards or teazels to make the loose spun cotton of which it was composed, show a fleecy surface like the original Angolas... But, cheap though they were, and showy, they were found to be very unprofitable and inconvenient to wear. A shower spoiled their appearance and the necessary looseness of texture caused them to give off flakes of fibre at every touch, so that any gentleman giving his arm to a lady wearing an Angola shawl was made to look as though he had been in a cotton mill.

In 1822 George IV went to Scotland amid great excitement. Tartan shawls were immediately fashionable with some having floral patterns arranged to fit the squares of the design. At the same time the 'blue style' was in vogue. In this the ground was cream and the design was put in with a predominance of a deep gentian blue. What was known as a 'kirking shawl' was also fashionable. This was a long shawl with a cream ground and a design usually in two shades of gentian blue and one red. These shawls were worn by a bride to church the first Sunday after her wedding and afterwards as a christening wrap for the babies. Although they were less showy than many they were undeniably beautiful and there are still many of them about as they have been carefully kept. They were also made in Norwich, but were not used necessarily as kirking shawls. They are said to have been designed by 'two London pattern-drawers of the time, Messrs Knight and Grace whose designs were much sought after'.

Production of shawls in Paisley grew very quickly with a considerable overseas market especially in the Middle and Far East. By 1818 they were selling in Persia and Turkey and in 1820 they were also selling in India as the 'Paisley Kashmir'. The trade had come full circle.

During the 1820s another fashion became popular. This was the 'harlequin' style where the borders of whatever design were divided into blocks of different strong colours. Sometimes these different colours extended upwards and included large border pines, though often they only included the narrow outer edge border. By the 1840s the blocks could each cover a quarter of the shawl so that when it was folded it was possible to wear one of four different colours as the main colour, down the back.

As with other towns, Paisley had both good and bad times, her worst being between 1841 and 1843 when the whole town became bankrupt, and in 1842 it was stated that 14,791 weavers were receiving relief, an enormous number. However, trade improved and the shawl manufactory flourished, probably partly because they could and did weave some shawls of excellent quality and great beauty, but on the whole she went for the middle and lower market and so was able to weave more shawls of less quality to be sold more cheaply.

NORWICH

The early history of shawls in Norwich is different from that of Edinburgh or Paisley though it, like them, was very soon based on the Indian designs. It was in 1785 that Alderman John Harvey, a manufacturer and member of a very influential Norwich family, was asked to try and weave a shawl from exceedingly fine wool spun by a Miss Ann Ives of Spalding in Lincolnshire. John Harvey's weavers must have been extremely competent as they managed to weave a woollen shawl 1½ yards (137cm) square which weighed only 3oz (85g). Unfortunately the sheep's wool they used was not nearly as fine and silky as the Indian cashmere and already Harvey was wanting to emulate the Indian shawls as it was their texture which was so enviable. Many yarns were tried but in the end Harvey decided that a silk warp and wool weft was the best solution to the problem.

Having decided on a twill weave which was comparable to the Indian, the manufactory started making shawls and other articles such as men's waistcoats, ladies' turbans, and counterpanes in the same style. At this time the looms were not capable of weaving in a design and so the pattern was printed in outline on the fabric and then darned in in coloured wool. This technique was very successful and one man who worked for Alderman Harvey, P.J. Knights, in 1792 prepared a counterpane on these lines which was presented to Queen Charlotte in 1793. It was so innovative that it won a Silver Medal from the Society of Arts. The design consisted of the Royal Achievement in the centre with a border of trailing plants, including the rose, shamrock and daffodil, and in the four corners representations of the Garter Star. The citation from the Society of Arts states that the Medal was for 'a shawl counterpane 4 yards [365cm] square, manufactured by him [P.J. Knights], which on examination appeared to be of greater breadth than any goods of equal fineness and texture, hitherto produced to the Society [of Arts] or to their knowledge woven in the Kingdom'.

As far as is known there are only two of these counterpanes in existence, one

COLOUR PLATE 111.
Square shawl, Norwich, 1860s, 164cm x 164cm (65 x 65in.). All silk. Made by Clabburn Sons & Crisp. The design is an amalgam of motifs seen in many of this firm's shawls in the 1860s. It is brought up to date by the brilliant colouring, but the lack of innovation heralds the end of the shawl era. Private Collection.

COLOUR PLATE 112.
Turnover shawl, Norwich, 1860s, 157cm x 157cm (62 x 62in.). Probably made by Clabburn Sons & Crisp. A very unusual shawl in that turnovers are not known so large, nor as late as the 1860s. They were fashionable in 1825-35. This one appears to have been made from two pieces of border fabric mounted on to a black twilled fabric and was possibly made from factory leftovers. The workmanship of design, weaving and mounting is meticulous. Private Collection.

246

COLOUR PLATE 113.
*Square shawl, Norwich, 1865-75,
160cm x 160cm (63 x 63in.).
Made by Clabburn Sons & Crisp.
Reversible shawl with silk warp
and wool weft and silk stripes.
The basic fabric without the
stripes was also sold for
upholstery, so obviously the end
of the shawls was in sight.*
Private Collection.

COLOUR PLATE 114.
*Paisley, Scotland, 1832. 25cm x
170cm (10in. x 67in.). Although
the major exhibition shawls often
display people and animals, this is
the only known shawl featuring a
portrait. In fact, this is perhaps the
earliest of all pictorial shawls.
George Washington, first president
of the United States, is featured at
each end of the long narrow scarf.
Under him, in three cartouches, is
written 'Georg Washington', 'Born
Februa. 22, 1732, died Dec. 14
1799' and 'E Pluri=bus Unum'. At
the fringe gates we find three
American flags displaying twenty
stars. The number of stars would
tend to indicate an earlier date,
but by 1822 there were twenty-
four states in the Union and the
number was growing fast, too fast
for anybody really to keep up with
it, let alone manufacture a new
flag every year. The actual floral
pattern and especially the muted
dyes tend to confirm the date of
1832.*

frail but whole in Strangers Hall Museum in Norwich which is the prototype of that given to Queen Charlotte. The other is cut up and has been made into a bedhead and valance in the Chinese bedroom at the National Trust house, Blickling Hall, near Aylsham in Norfolk. This has the Achievement of John Hobart, second Earl of Buckingham, and his second wife, Caroline Conolly. The border, which has been cut off and made into a short valance for the bed, is very interesting in that alternating with the arms of the Hobart family and that of Conolly are bunches of flowers. The shape and style of these bunches are very reminiscent of the Indian boteh of the mid-eighteenth century and it is the earliest near-copy of the Indian allied to completely Western motifs that we have in this country.

In a letter to the Society of Arts Knights explains that the counterpane 'cannot be retailed at a price less than 20gns, to be 16 quarters square, as it is; and 15 if 12 quarters, embroidered in the same manner: if plain, with a fringe only, it will come up at 8 guineas, 16 quarters; and 6 guineas, if 12 quarters fringed. Please to observe, the middle being left plain, it is intended for the coat of arms of the purchaser; to be embroidered, if they please, and at their own expense, by sending down the drawing and size'. As Knights does not mention the design of the border it would be interesting to know if other counterpanes, if there are any, had the border in an Indian design, or, possibly, with arms only.

The approval of both royalty and the Society of Arts helped the infant trade enormously. The Queen and Princesses wore shawl dresses, Knights was appointed Shawlman to Her Majesty with designs being sent down from Windsor, and influential members of society patronised the manufactory. By 1800 there were some twenty shawl manufacturers in Norwich, the shawls were being exported abroad, even as far as Australia, and the outlook was cheerful.

The only clue we get as to the style of the shawls made by these early manufacturers is from a letter written by one Richard Bidwell in 1796, listing the articles he wove in the same style, as 'Scarfs, Scarf Cloaks, Undress Shawls, Common Shawls, (all embroidered), White Scarfs, Embroidered Rich Scarfs, Bordered and Cornered Scarfs, Waistcoat Shapes, Embroidered Shapes, and Rough Embroidered Shapes'. A shape is the garment cut and embroidered but unmade, which can then be sewn to the measurements of the customer. This list shows that the industry was moving towards different types of shawls only, but had not got there yet. They needed other articles to sell in the same style.

In the first twenty years of the nineteenth century the shawl trade was successful and was helped by the current fashion in women's dress. These were of lightweight fabrics, straight from a high waistline with little, if any decoration, and a bright shawl was not only warm but also gave much needed colour and emphasis to what could be an insipid dress. The paintings of the time generally show the shawl as an accessory rather than as a garment, but there can be no doubt that in cold weather they were essential wear.

In the 1830s a Norwich dyer discovered how to dye silk and wool exactly to the same colour. Formerly the usual combination of silk warp and wool weft meant that the field colour had to be cream, and the coloured design was put in with wool. If a coloured field was wanted, plain silk was used, with, as usual, wool used for what was known as the 'fillover', that is, the design. By now all designs were put in on the drawloom and as far as is known darned designs stopped about 1820, though the drawloom was in use well before that. The Jacquard loom began to be used in the 1830s but it appears that though it was used extensively for the fabric trade it took much longer to be accepted for the shawl trade.

Both in Paisley and in Norwich the designs of shawls posed a big problem.

There was no question but the French designs were far more attractive. Design in France had always been taken more seriously than it was in Britain. France had excellent Schools of Design early in the century and all the training of the students was towards Manufacture rather than Art. In Britain it was very different. Training in the Schools, which started in the 1830s, consisted mainly of copying from the antique. Designs for manufactures were not considered important. The result was that firms had few good local designers on whom they could call. They often sent to France for ideas but they also used freelance designers based in London, and they copied from each other. This makes it difficult, except in a few cases, to differentiate between shawls from Paisley or Norwich. Both places often used the same designer, and as both were basing their work on the ever popular pattern of the Indian boteh there was a good deal of similarity.

After 1842 it becomes easier to differentiate, at least for our generation. In Norwich between 1842 and 1876 three hundred and fifteen designs were registered at the PRO and several shawls in the collection have, for example, part of one design and part of another, or only part of a design, the rest being of an unregistered pattern. The three hundred and fifteen are an enormous help to curators or owners wanting to know the provenance of a shawl. It also means that quirks of particular designers, even if their names are unknown, have been discovered and so shawls, some earlier than 1842, and therefore unregistered, can be assigned to a certain firm.

The strange thing is that all these registered designs were produced by only seven firms, and at that time there were at least twenty-six manufacturers of shawls. It would seem that at only one shilling a design with the possibility of using the same design many times in different colour ways, and with different parts of the pattern prominent, it was an economical way to get a new shawl on to the market before the design was used by a competitor. But for some reason the majority of firms did not take the chance. We have no idea how many shawls were woven in the mid-nineteenth century, but there is in the Bridewell Museum at Norwich one order book for 1847/8 belonging to the firm of E. & F. Hinde which lists twenty-nine types of shawl, and it appears that in that year alone Hindes sold 27,000. It seems a large number from one firm but in the late '40s virtually every lady would own at least one shawl and sometimes up to a dozen or more to match her various costumes. Partly this was because the style of dress in the 1840s to 1870s made the wearing of any type of coat or even a cloak impracticable. From the 1840s the width of skirts increased, and with the advent of the crinoline in 1853 they became enormous. No fitting garment would sit over them and a shawl was the only possible covering. Thus the size of the shawls increased to match the size of the skirt.

1840-1870 was a period of very large exhibitions dominated by the Great Exhibition of 1851 in London. The exhibits were of all types of manufactures, but they had classes for textiles, and both in France and England the shawls from Paisley and Norwich won prizes. These exhibitions were a wonderful showcase for the manufacturers and many shawls were sold, the buyers ranging from Queen Victoria downwards, and where royalty bought many others followed suit.

In keeping with mid-Victorian taste and the natural wish of manufacturers to show off the skill of their workers, the designs of the shawls became more and more complicated. The boteh in general became thinner and longer. The pines proliferated, overlapped and writhed, backed by numerous smaller motifs, until there was no plain ground left, except perhaps a small central patch of the main colour. In Norwich many of this type of shawl were woven of silk only, on the Jacquard loom.

By the end of the 1860s the day of the shawl was coming to an end, the main reason being that the style of dress was changing. Large skirts had been in fashion for twenty years or so, and gradually they became smaller, first with less fabric in front and then with all material pulled to the back. With the advent of the next stage, the bustle, it became difficult and unnecessary to wear a shawl. A coat once more became a practical garment. The end of the shawl era was also hastened by the Franco-Prussian War, and the collapse of the French trade.

AMERICAN SHAWLS
by Frank Ames

At present, there are no historical records which could shed light on the industry in America, although it is known that American manufacturers had been engaged in this competitive field since 1851. At that time, the Universal Exhibition review archives cite at least three companies from Boston, namely the Upham & Appleton Co. making 'guingams, cachemires', etc., F. Skinner & Co. making 'cachemires', and Stone Lawrence & Co. making 'chales et cachmires'. New York was represented by the company Macy & Stanton which exhibited woollen 'cassimeres and cachemires de laine'.

PLATE 78.
The lady should have been prepared before attempting to wear a voluminous hoop in public transportation. The coachman on this old American stereo card announced, 'Very sorry, mam, but leave yer krinerline outside'. The shawl she is donning has the obvious look of an American paisley.

250

COLOUR PLATE 115.
American shawl, wool, jacquard loomed, c.1875. 178cm x 180cm (70in. x 71in.).

How does one go about distinguishing an American shawl from a European one? I can only answer this question based on my travel experiences and having lived for many years in Europe. The American shawl appears almost always to be decorated with hand embroidered fringe gates that frame the square shawl on all four sides. They were invariably woven with heavy wools and in dark colours of green and red and contain a very small black centre. Some long shawls also have been found in this style though with simply the ends bordered with fringe gates. I have never come across this aforementioned style in Europe.

AN ILLUSTRATED GUIDE
Showing the development of Kashmir shawl patterns from the 17th to the 19th century

PLATE 79.
Detail of complete shawl. An exquisite specimen of 17th century weaving illustrating the idea of the Chinese root securing device and the wavy fronds which appear to add a spirited buoyancy to an already beautiful bouquet of identifiable flowers.

PLATE 80.
Shoulder mantle (fragment). Mughal Period, c.1700. 18cm x 21cm. (7 x 8in.). This is part of a collection of kani fragments found in a jacket belonging to the Sultan of Mysore, Tipu Sahib. In contrast to the previous piece the difference here between leaves and flowers is more distinct. The needles on the branches imply a rose bush. The Chinese cloud hashia may appear slightly incongruous with the botehs' style. A charming aspect is provided by the turned-over flowers. Notice also the ideogram root-securing device which coincidentally means earth in Chinese.

COLOUR PLATE 116.
Shoulder mantle. Mughal Period, 17th century.
In this exquisite shawl in the collection of the Textile Museum, Washington, a very narrow palla is decorated by freely spaced leaning tree shrubs on a rich salmon ground. The bases of the trees rise from 'barred-cross' roots and support a slightly sinuous branch axis of angular leaf clusters and flowers in faded rose-violet and pale green. In the unique hashia, also freely-spaced, teardrop flower buds alternate with small angular blossoms along a trapezoidal meander.

COLOUR PLATE 117.
Waistband (hashia fragment). Mughal Period, early 17th century. 17cm x 5cm (7 x 2in.).

COLOUR PLATE 118.
Waistband (hashia fragment). Mughal Period, early 17th century. 6cm x 9cm (2 x 3in.).

Two incredible specimens of the finest known kani weaving in the world. Their texture is like silk to the touch and one would believe that they were actually woven from pure shah tus.
Obviously, by the width of their borders, they are pieces from a patka or waistband. Indeed Colour Plate 118 is surely from the fabulous palla fragment now conserved in the new Kuwait Museum (see Islamic Art in the Kuwait National Museum, *p. 155) and, although it is not shown here, it is still worth commenting on. It is without doubt a very rare specimen of floral design in shawls. There is a queer aesthetic quality about it which tends to repudiate the classic Mughal school of floral representation where so often we find gracefully outstretched leaves and branches. The Kuwaiti piece seems to be devoid of this cliché-type elegance: the leaves are stiff, sharp and pointed, the flowers appealing and the bizarre leaf-securing stem catches us completely by surprise with its unnaturalness.*
A tracing of Colour Plate 117's angular meander can be seen in Figure 18b.

254

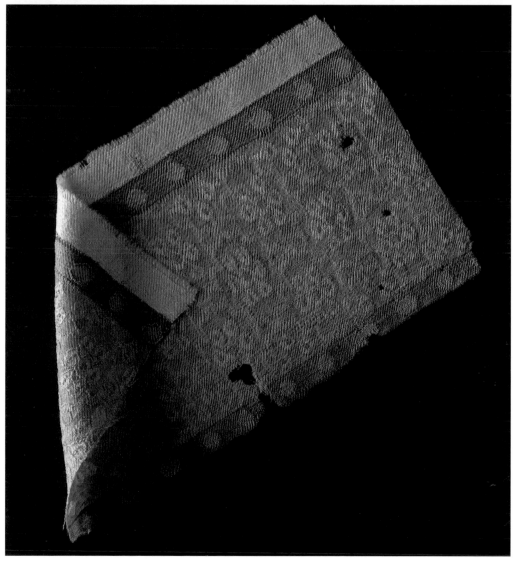

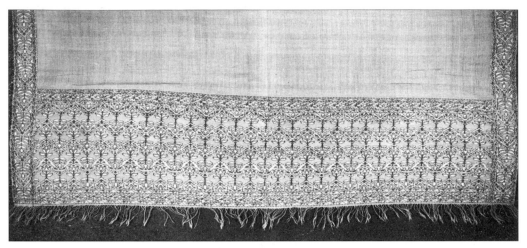

Plate 81.
Waistband. Mughal Period, c.1700. 68cm x 410cm (27 x 161in.)
Probably one of the oldest forms of the kani shawl is the patka. Archetypal patterns are often found in the kani patka which may have been popular during the Sultanate Period of pre-Mughal India. The chevron pattern on this 'garden shawl' (see Plate 94) is often depicted in Mughal decoration and it frequently suggests the idea of running water. The thin trapezoidal meander decorating the zig-zag lines relates closely to the hashias in Plate 82 and Colour Plate 120. Because of the similar colour tones of burnt orange, white and pale green, Plates 81 and 82 may be contemporary pieces.

Plate 82.
Waistband hashia fragment. Mughal Period, 17th century. From the motifs on the hashia of this tiny fragment we may speculate on the design of the lost palla. The sharply angular meander is composed of a claw-like cluster on a running and unusually thick vine, which alternates around a group of three 'star' flowers. It is possible to reconstruct a full cycle of the meander's repeat with the design information found in the fragment (see Figure 22). In the guard borders we again find a trapezoidal pattern which has a certain Coptic look to it.

256

PLATE 83.

Shoulder mantle. Mughal Period, early 17th century. 126cm x 337cm (49 x 132in.).
Another masterpiece of Mughal court weaving relating in extreme rarity to Colour Plate 123.
The hashia's unidirectional flower meander follows a rather rigid geometrical draftsmanship.
However, its meticulous detail is beautifully completed by the running rhomboidal specks of the
guard borders. Oddly enough, the boteh's flowers with their hanging petals appear waning
despite the appearance of new buds. The veining of the large opposing leaves at the bottom is
unique. A striking thing about this elegant kani piece is the way the stems are secured. It is the
only known piece in which the root securing device actually approaches the curving strokes
found in Chinese ideograms. Similar design characteristics may be found in a piece conserved
at the Association for the Study and Documentation of Asian Textiles, Paris (accession number
1276). The latter's whimsical design suggests hovering butterflies (see Colour Plate 124).

PLATE 84.

Shoulder mantle (fragment). Mughal Period, early 17th century. 18cm x 56cm (7 x 22in.).
This charming pattern in its pure simplicity again confirms the direct link of the kani shawl
industry to the Mughal court workshops. The opening rose bud counterbalances the large tilted
rose of madder red, pale yellow and indigo blue. The bud is incorporated into the hashia's
meander which highlights the palla's overall effect. However, the heavy use of red on the leaves
just above the ideogram root appears to lose the intended effect of leaf folding. The boteh's
windblown leaves are of faded greyish green outlined in pale blue.

257

COLOUR PLATE 119.
Complete palla fragment. Mughal, c.1700. 16cm x 135cm (6 x 53in.).

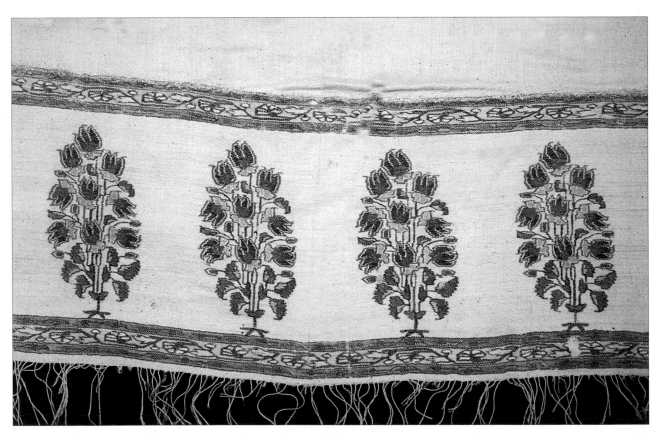

COLOUR PLATE 120. *Shoulder mantle (fragment). Mughal Period, 17th century. 51cm x 136cm (20 x .53in.)*
Decorating the light saffron ground are botehs composed of dark blue flower blossoms outlined in white and tomato red. The stems, emanating from a vase-like object, are arranged in a parallel fashion. The green leaves at the boteh's base are tinged with dark yellow to expose their undersides. The whole of the boteh is balanced carefully by a single stem resting on the ideogram root.

COLOUR PLATE 121.
Waistband. Mughal Period, 17th century. 70cm x 460cm (27 x 181in). See Plate 90 and Colour Plate 130 for further details and comparison.

See Plate 90 and Colour Plate 130 for further details and comparison.

Below
COLOUR PLATE 122.
Waistband. Mughal Period, early 17th century.
This is one of the most beautiful and perfect patka specimens in the world, part of the Bharat Kala Bhavan's magnificent collection. Although the boteh's base, in the form of a Chinese ideogram, appears heavy compared with the rest of the plant's principal stems, its style embodies the very quintessence of early 17th century Mughal shawl artistry. An archetypal shawl pattern is implied when the palla's hashias and boteh share common botanical elements and a fine balanced symmetry is elegantly attained.

The boteh's overall beauty is cleverly enhanced through the effects of pale yellow outlining. The resulting chromatic aspect is surprising and suggests a bush of flowers glistening with rain drops in the sun. Illuminating the centre of each of the pale blue flowers are the bright yellow and vermilion specks which also provide a warm, uncanny illusion of flickering lights. The shawl's rare wool and the incredibly soft touch sensation offered by its diaphanous folds is derived from the finest shah tus which after more than three hundred years of excellent conservation still emits a shimmering golden lustre.

259

Forming the main theme of these rare and exquisite patkas (waistbands) are of course the Chinese clouds. The botehs' blossoms are rather bizarre. They look like 'bent-tip' strawberries or they may be a kind of rose abstraction. The accumulation of cloud wisps at the botehs' base in the form of leaves suggests a drifting or floating sensation. In Plate 86 the colour combination is unusual: white outlined, dark blue blossoms and yellow outlined pale green leaves contrast against a rich cochineal ground.

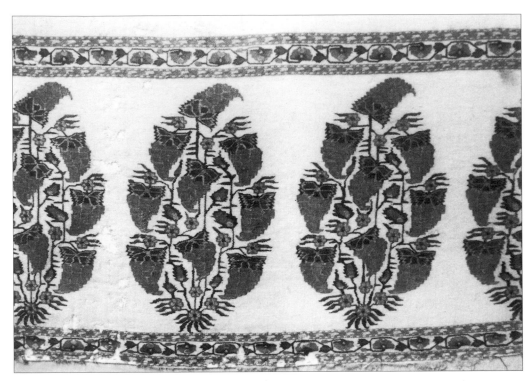

PLATE 85.
Waistband. Mughal Period, 17th century. 68cm x 484cm (27 x 190in.).

PLATE 86.
Waistband. Mughal Period, 17th century.

PLATE 87.

Waistband. Mughal Period, early 17th century.

In this illustration the shawl has been folded over to reveal the meticulously fine weaving of the underside. From a distance it would be very difficult to guess the back from the front side. It is surprising to discover patka hashias on a shoulder mantle. The boteh which patterns this light brown shawl consists of pale-red roses and faded blue leaves outlined in lilac. Supporting the stems is an anvil-like Chinese ideogram. See Figure 23 for a line drawing of the hashias.

PLATE 88.

Waistband. Mughal Period, 17th century.

In this magnificent patka conserved by the Calico Museum, Ahmedabad, we find beauty and grace in a rose boteh pattern. Rising sinuously within the boteh's centre is a branch which instils an inner movement to the flower clusters. Below, one of the four racemes terminates with a curious device resembling an insect. The racemes are winged on to a bespeckled and irregular mound containing four queer protrusions that may at one time have indicated cloud whiffs.

COLOUR PLATE 123.
Shoulder mantle (fragment). Mughal Period, early 17th century. 18cm x 69cm (7 x 27in.). This superb piece is an unparalleled example of Mughal court weaving. Set like cut diamonds in a bracelet, freely spaced multifaceted flowerbuds reflect the finely detailed hashias of the shawl fragment's palla. Expressed through the vertical stem's triple flexion, a smoothly rising undulation draws the observer's eye to the large flower cluster at the boteh's top. Again we find the roots secured by a strange device in the form of an ideogram. Colours: pink, crimson red, light and deep bluish green.

COLOUR PLATE 124.
Shoulder mantle (fragment) Mughal Period, mid-17th century.
This exquisite 17th century fragment ranks among one of the finest in Mughal shawl artistry. The graceful and free-flowing movement of the boteh's exotic flowers and curvaceous stems epitomises the romantic mood inherent in the courtly life of Renaissance India. Only the palla of this once long shawl survives. It is in three separate fragments, each containing four full identical botehs. The boteh displays six flowers: two in full bloom, two in half bloom and two as yet unopened. A curious phenomenon of jagged wing like leaves, heavily outlined in yellow and red, and sporting a deep-blue ground, speckled with white dots, appear attached to four of the rose blossoms. This deft artistic touch evokes a visual sensation of butterflies hovering at play and it wonderfully enhances the boteh with a mellifluous charm. Indeed, on even closer inspection, the bulbous shape of the cross-hatched flower buds resembles with astonishing realism the abdomen of an insect. These speckled leaves re-occur from time to time in other contemporary shawls designs. Superimposed on this comic fantasy of 'winged' flowers is a note of serious naturalism struck by the breezy fern-like fronds which engulf the boteh. Some of them show slight yellow tingeing – a technique which indicates that the leaf by exposing its back is partly folded. One is surprised by the height attained by them as they reach up to overtake the upper-most blossoms. The root securing device is another off-beat curiosity much as the Chinese ideogram root discussed earlier. Here we encounter two small out-stretched leaves attached to a strange rectangular body which rests on two legs in the shape of pointed leaves. Crowning the top of the body are two pairs of arching fronds.

262

COLOUR PLATE 125.
Shoulder mantle (fragment). Mughal Period, 17th century. 23cm x 135cm (8 x 53in.).
*Early bouquets of freely spaced flowers are rare and this one is a beautiful example of irises,
carnations and rose buds all enjoying their own space to blossom and move about. The
characteristic of the fish-pond mound and the centrally located upside-down flower and the
wonderful harmony of floral arrangement, all combine to create a stunning work of high
Mughal art.*

COLOUR PLATE 126.
Patka or waistband, Mughal Period, 17th century. 24cm x 56cm (9 x 22in.).
*Extant textiles from 17th century Mughal India are rare and rarer still are the Kashmir shawls
from this period. In this example we find a distinct persianate flavour. Despite the orderliness of
the boteh's impressive array of rosebuds, the artist has imparted to them a subtle grace of
movement. Branches rise from the boteh's stem vortex to spray forth five or six tandem flowers,
each carefully underlined by a tiny green leaf. One also notices that the leaf edges are tapered
and recede quietly toward the background creating an illusion of volume. Perhaps a light wind
is stirring as observed by the swaying of the top to the left, yet the actual overall movement is
from left to right, if one focuses on (starting from the left) vertical rows two to four. The scattered
symmetry of the six large leaves, sharply drawn with realistic vein markings and feathered edges,
add to the boteh just the right equilibrium. This pattern, simplistic at first glance, is really a fine
work of art and it is not inconceivable that it could have been a product of the Mughal court
ateliers. This patka illustrates the fact that the flowering plant was raised from the relative
obscurity of the landscape of miniature paintings to become the often sole subject of Indian
decorative arts under the reign of Jehangir.*

PLATE 89.

Waistband. Mughal Period, 17th century.

According to 17th and 18th century literature, pure white shah tus was reserved strictly for kings and dignitaries of high rank. In view of the elegant artistry of the exquisite white patka it may be attributed to a Mughal court workshop. A curious addition to this rose boteh is the line just above the Chinese ideogram root which supports the two leaf branches. The branches, apart from the main stem, do not follow a similar style to earlier specimens. Often in 17th century kani botehs and especially in Mughal carpets, branches are arranged in a stiff vertical fashion, almost parallel to each other. The large vertical hashias mimic the botehs' floral elements by a bold meander of identically repeated rose blossoms, rose buds and leaves. In the horizontal hashia the guard border's rhomboidal flecks and slanting lines of the angular meander give vibrancy to an otherwise compressed design.

PLATE 90.
Waistband. Mughal Period, 17th century. The designation 'rank' shawl is applied to this type of shawl. Rank or military grade may be implied by the stacked array of stiff leaves. However, their development into this abstract form was by no means immediate. It is felt that they evolved slowly through an ever increasing abstraction of the 'Chinese cloud' shawls.

264

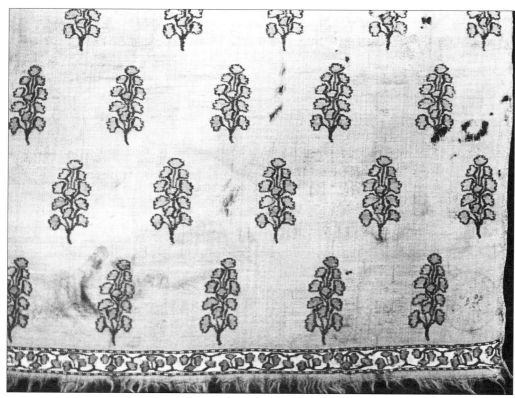

PLATE 91.
Shoulder mantle (fragment). Mughal Period, early 18th century. 74cm x 127cm (29 x 50in.).
This charming little Mughal fragment of black outlined tree shrubs provides a nice addition to
our knowledge of early 18th century shawl patterns. The hashia, with its freely spaced trifoliate
meander and arching stroke is from the same fine artistic hand as the main pattern.

PLATE 92.
Shoulder mantle (fragment). Mughal Period, early 18th century. 129cm x 168cm (51 x 66in.).
A shawl pattern of distinction is offered by the fine harmony of red roses on saffron ground and
their perfectly symmetrical butis.

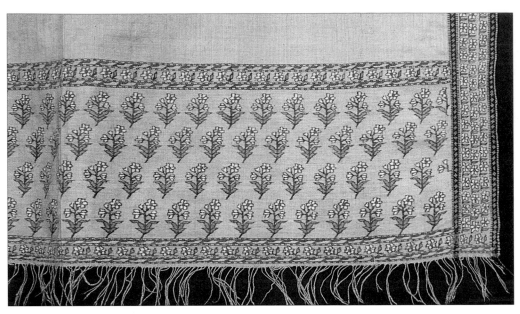

COLOUR PLATE 127.
Waistband. Mughal Period, c.1700. 63cm x 341cm (25 x 134in.).
This piece from the Bharat Kala Bhavan, Banaras, embodies the fine characteristics by which
Mughal shawls are known. On a soft salmon-pink ground, white sprigs form four regular rows
across the shawl's palla. The butis' laterally pointed leaves, inspired from the rank shawl idea,
may indicate a possible early 18th century date of manufacture. The hashia design is unusual,
with rows of disconnected sprigs rather than a meandering vine.

COLOUR PLATE 128.
Shoulder mantle (fragment). Mughal Period, 17th century. 133cm x 280cm (52 x 110in.).
These bold and human-like poppy flowers with their buds curled up toward the central stem
appear to exude a powerful charm aimed directly at the observer. The red dye which shows signs
of running and the unusually coarse wool employed in the weave would tend to indicate a
product not woven within the auspices of the Mughal court. Or, perhaps it may have been woven
in Lahore where the Mughals made an earnest attempt to weave fine Kashmir shawls but
experienced difficulties in good dyeing.

COLOUR PLATE 129.
Waistband. Mughal Period, 17th century. 70cm x 420cm (27 x 165in.).

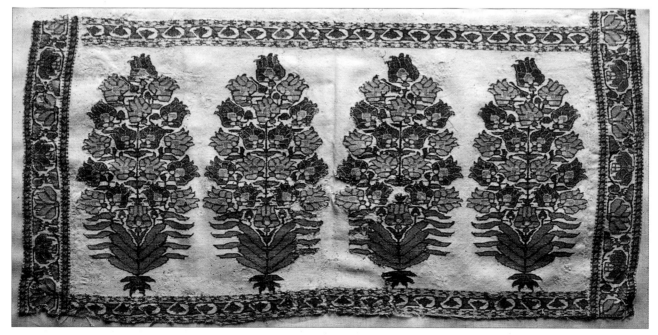

COLOUR PLATE 130.
Waistband fragment. Mughal Period, 17th century.

267

PLATE 93.
*Shoulder mantle (fragment). Mughal Period, early 18th century. 68cm x 21cm (27 x x 8in.).
Rose blossom butis are finely illustrated by this kani piece which has a similar but more
constrained hashia pattern compared with Colour Plate 138. The tips of the serrated leaves rising
from the 'Chinese' root are well drawn to support the two opposing tilted rose blossoms.*

PLATE 94.
*Shoulder mantle.
Mughal Period, 18th
century. 135cm x
306cm (53 x 120in.).
The chevron was a
popular Mughal
ornament, often used
to suggest running
water. Variations of
this theme can be
seen in the well-
known 'garden'
carpets of Persia in
which the troughs
that distribute the
fountain's water are
indicated
traditionally by a
chevron pattern, Thus
'garden shawl' would
have been an
appropriate sobriquet.
Colours: blue and off-
white.*

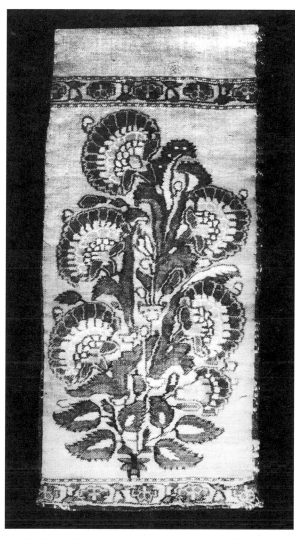

PLATE 95.
Shoulder mantle (fragment). Mughal Period, early 18th century. 19cm x 13cm (7 x 5in.).
The assemblage of four rose pots is unusual for this period. They provide a device for elevating the tinged red and blue perfoliate leaves which, opening in a kind of cornucopia fashion, pour forth large oval-shaped flowers. Flower blossoms which predominated in various boteh styles of the mid-18th century became exposed to the popular fashion of circular floral shapes such as those seen in Colour Plate 140.

The use of flower pots and the leaves place this piece around the middle of the 18th century. However, the group of small serrated base leaves, secured by an anvil-like device, and the delicate hashia possibly suggest an earlier date.

This piece offers a glimpse into the little known transitional styles immediately preceding the Afghan Period.

PLATE 96.
Shoulder mantle (fragment). Mughal Period, mid-18th century.

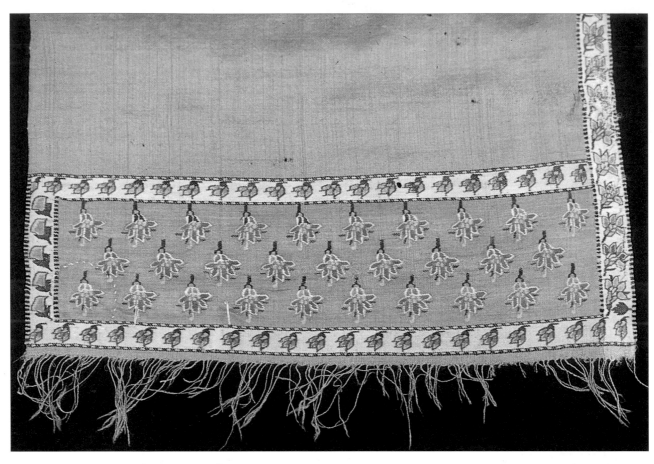

COLOUR PLATE 131.
Turban. Mughal Period, c.1700. 25cm x 327cm (10 x 129in.).
This uncommon orange-saffron kani piece appears to be a kind of sampler of various hashia patterns.

COLOUR PLATE 132.
Shoulder mantle fragment, Mughal, early 18th century.
It is possible to observe the effects of the ikat dyed warps at the top of the palla. Although the indigo blue has remained strong the lacklustre quality of the dyes in general indicates that it was perhaps woven outside Kashmir. See Colour Plate 10 for boteh detail.

COLOUR PLATE 133.
Waistband or shoulder mantle, Mughal Period, early 18th century. Approx. 1m x 5m
(39 x 197in.).

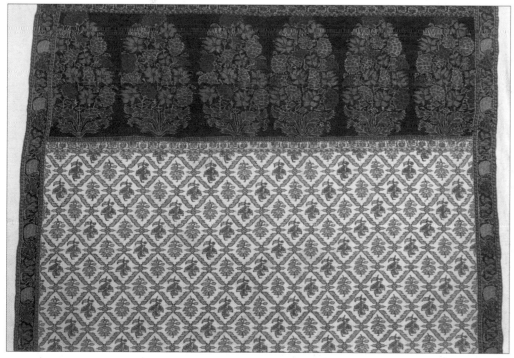

COLOUR PLATE 134.
Shoulder mantle, Mughal Period, early 18th century.

PLATE 97.
Shoulder mantle. Mughal Period, mid-18th century.
This pairs well with the cog-wheel boteh of Colour Plate 140, especially with its drooping serrated leaf, although its weaving execution does not come even close to the latter.

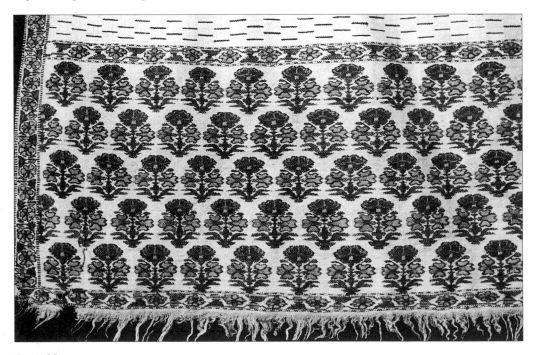

PLATE 98.
Shoulder mantle. Afghan Period, late 18th century. 125cm x 300cm (49 x 118in.).
Rose-tulip buti on an 'anvil-like' dish line the palla. The staggered rows of short lines in the matan blend harmoniously with the sharply pointed leaves of the buti. Only two other known pieces have such a decorated matan. One is at the Association for the Study and Documentation of Asian Textiles, Paris, accession number 1691. The other is conserved by the National Museum, Delhi, accession number 56-153/1.

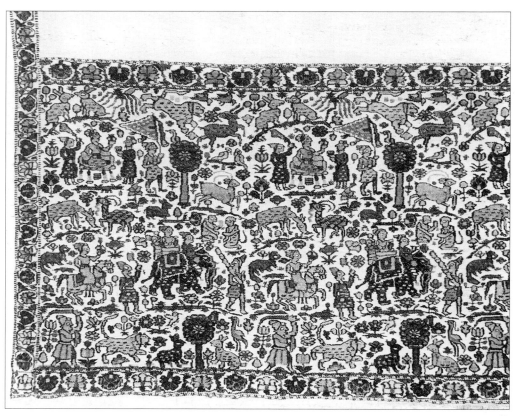

PLATE 99.
Shoulder mantle. Mughal Period, mid-18th century.
132cm x 320cm (52 x 126in.).
Another Mughal hunting shawl contemporary with
Colour Plate 145 and in a similar style. Although more
finely drawn, the scene is nevertheless much less
dramatic as no actual combat is depicted except for a
leopard in the lower left corner, chased by a retainer
brandishing a sword and shield. In the upper left corner
an important Mughal personage appears enthroned,
waited upon by two attendants while a third is waving
a large banner. A Mughal on horseback admires a
bouquet of flowers while in front a caparisoned
elephant carries another Mughal and his two
attendants. Colours: chrome and mustard yellow,
orange, pink, fawn, crimson red, grey, bluish green,
blue and indigo, blue and black on a white ground.

PLATE 100.
Shoulder mantle. Afghan Period, c.1770. 190cm x
133cm (75 x 52in.).
This buti-palla was supposedly brought from India in
about 1770 by Thomas Coulson. The hashia, similar to
that in Colour Plate 144, offers a small but interesting
transitional link in shawl iconography due to the
shawl's known purchase date. These particular hashia
patterns were then quite popular but disappeared
almost completely by the end of the 18th century.

COLOUR PLATE 135.

Waistband. Mughal Period, 17th century.
Botehs containing a mélange of flowers are rare indeed. In this impressive patka conserved by the National Museum, Delhi, a perfect floral balance within the bouquet is achieved. The pivotal point for this balance is provided by the lower rose which is hung upside down like a pendulum. The cog-wheel flower and the mound with its curious protrusions should be compared with similar features found in the Mughal carpet.

COLOUR PLATE 136.

Shoulder mantle. Mughal Period, early 18th century, 135cm x 325cm (53 x 128in.).
In this unique and complete shawl of brilliant cochineal pashmina and naturally flowering plants, the high tradition of Mughal art is carried forth at its finest. In general, red ground shawls are problematic to the achievement of chromatic harmony and a well-organised design. In this piece it is obvious through the careful choice of colours and execution of weave that we are dealing with a master craftsman. Not only was the weaver required to remain within the confines of a limited number of colours, such as the deep indigo blue, forest green, pale blue, bright saffron yellow and the rich teal, but his design had to be bold and strong in order to withstand the intense and almost overpowering ground colour. And bold and strong it is, for the blossoming array of poppy flowers are brought to luminescent life by the bright saffron petal clusters radiating through the blue nexus of each flower.

Shoulder mantle. Mughal Period, c.1700. 141cm x 312cm (55 x 123in.).
Besides the 'bent-tip' strawberries at the boteh's base, the colour scheme of rose red on a green ground is unusual. The small 'leaf-flags' attached to the frail stems and the claw-type root are important design elements associated with shawl pieces of this period. An identical shawl to this piece is conserved by the Calico Museum, Ahmedabad.

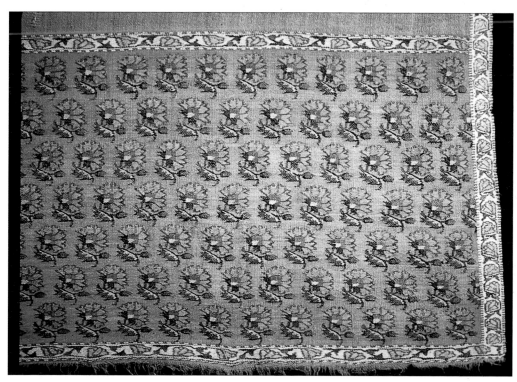

COLOUR PLATE 138. Shoulder mantle. Mughal Period, early 18th century. 133cm x 320cm (52 x 126in.).

In Persian and European literature the rose is the flower of love and poetry. In miniature paintings of the 17th and 18th centuries Mughals are often seen posing while holding up a rose blossom in one hand or while extending it to their favourite concubine. Shawls of this type may have been offered as sentimental gifts.

Contrasted by a pale green ground the 'winged-leaf' buti's tilted rose blossom is outlined in dark red. The winged leaf indicates the 'fold-shading' by a yellow tinge on its up-turned surface. The long sweeping branches and crocus flowers of the hashia are of a style popular during this period.

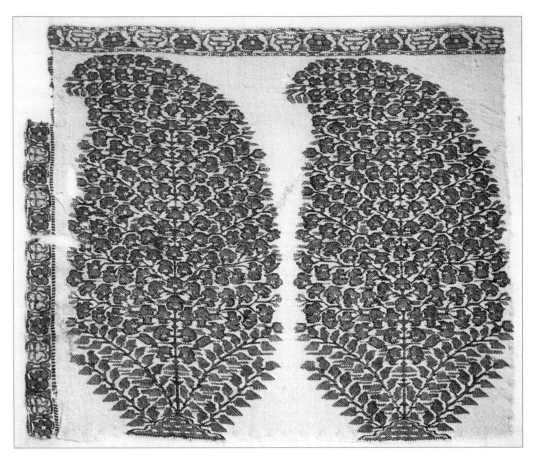

PLATE 101.
Shoulder mantle (fragment). Mughal Period, mid-18th century. 20cm x 23cm (7¾ x 8½in.).

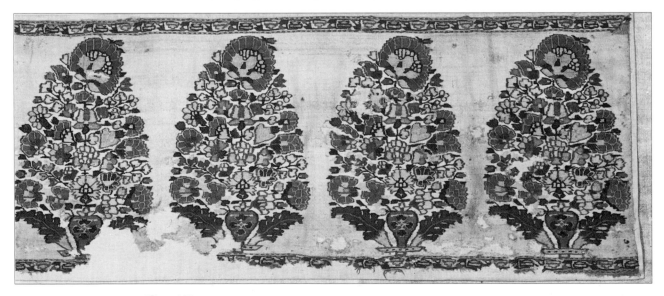

PLATE 102.
Shoulder mantle. Mughal Period. Early 18th century.
In this vase and dish mounted floral bouquet we find enough significant spacing between the botehs and identifiable flowers to give it a fairly early date.

276

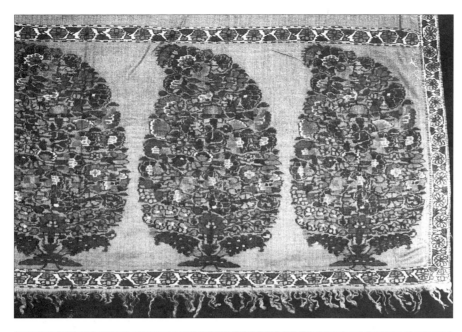

PLATE 103.
Shoulder mantle. Afghan Period, 18th century. 137cm x 321cm (54 x 126in.).
The floral content is somewhat cluttered and the boteh has a stubby and mosaic appearance with an unusual amount of white thread highlighting that became popular around 1800.

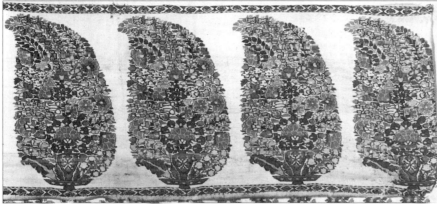

PLATE 104.
Shoulder mantle (fragment). Afghan Period, mid-18th century. 19cm x 106cm (7 x 42in.).

PLATE 105.
Shoulder mantle. Afghan Period, mid-18th century. 117cm x 279cm. (46 x 110in.)

COLOUR PLATE 139.
Shoulder mantle.
Mughal Period,
c.1700. 324cm x
142cm (127 x
56in.).
We find here a novel
respite in design style
which breaks away
from conventionality.
The idea of these
unusually large
round flower
blossoms borders on
the absurd; yet the
bold spherical effect
subdued by the
angularity of the
frail stems creates a
surprising charm.

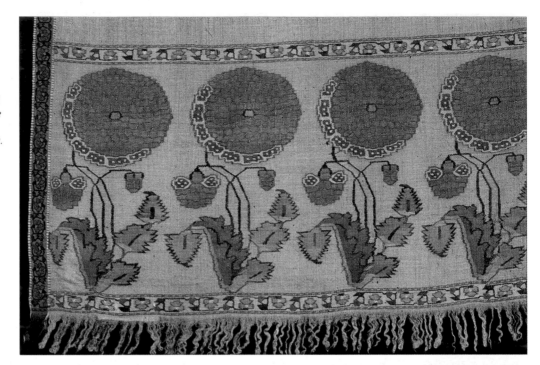

COLOUR PLATE 140.
Shoulder mantle. Mughal Period, mid-18th century. 315cm x 135cm (124 x 53in.).
The continuing popularity of a large, if not exaggerated tilted blossom at the boteh's top is a
major theme of 17th century Mughal art. This piece at the Bharat Kala Bhavan is a stunningly
beautiful Mughal court example of this technique. At its base is a jagged blue mound with red
dots possibly representing fish. Distorted perspectives are often found in Mughal miniature
painting allowing the artist to show both interior and exterior views simultaneously. This boteh
style suggested by the large circular flattened flowers represents undoubtedly the precursor of the
radial flower technique – a technique which became popular during the third quarter of the
18th century.

COLOUR PLATE 141.
Waistband. Mughal Period, mid-18th century. 127cm x 220cm (50 x 86in.).
The luminescent peach ground, the rather bulbous botehs with their full-blown tilted roses and
the expansive strokes of the draftsman's hand have indeed created a special charm in this patka.
Despite the curvilinearity of the boteh's exterior and the orderly arrangement of flowers, the artist
has made an earnest attempt to space the floral elements freely.

COLOUR PLATE 142.
Waistband (full view of fragment). Mughal Period, mid-18th century. 22cm x 30cm. (8 x 12in.).

279

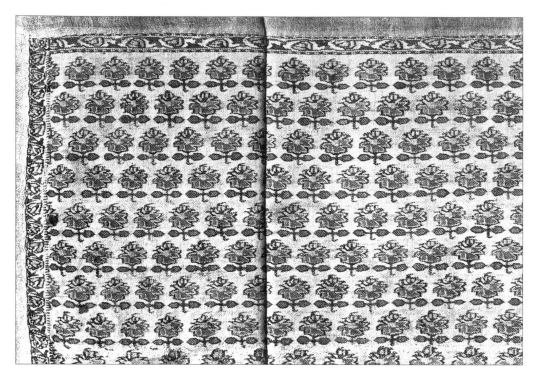

PLATE 106.
Shoulder mantle (fragment). Mughal Period, early 18th century, 30cm x 26cm. (12 x (10in.).

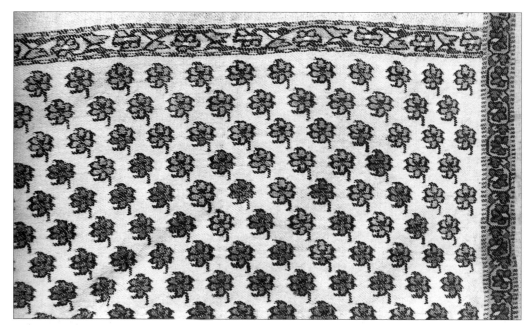

PLATE 107.
Shoulder mantle (fragment). Mughal Period, early 18th century.
These two fragments provide us with a clear picture of the crocus meander, found in their hashias. It is interesting to observe how this sweeping pattern with its long flower stem meander suddenly finds itself compressed in the vertical hashia of Plate 106. This compression is frequent and is invariably due to the fact that the long narrow hashias that run the length of the shawl are made with silk warps. Again observe this phenomenon in Colour Plate 138 and Plate 93.

PLATE 108.
Kerchief or 'moon' shawl. Mughal Period, mid-18th century.
Chandars of the 18th century drawn in a naturalistic or even semi-naturalistic style are rare indeed. The floral inspiration of this extra fine tus kerchief is, for the main part, Mughal. This is evident from the crocus and pin-wheel type flower of the three-flower repeat which describes the outer circumference of the central medallion. The crocus disappeared in Kashmir patterns after the last quarter of the 18th century. See the hashias of Plates 106 and 107. The pin-wheel type flower can be seen to predominate in the boteh of Colour Plate 121, probably at a time when it was very popular. However in later patterns we find it was relegated to a minor floral detail, such as here, or in hashia designs up to the first quarter of the 19th century.

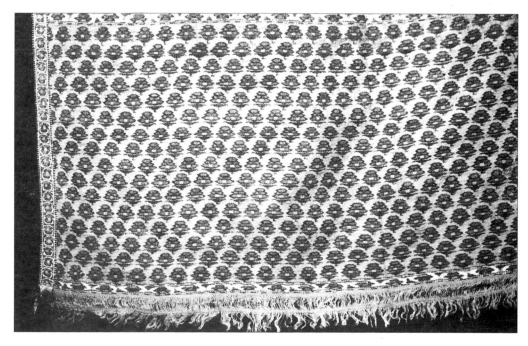

PLATE 109.
Shoulder mantle. Afghan Period, mid-18th century. 127cm x 300cm (50 x 118in.). The pagoda-like sprigs on a rich salmon ground are distinguished by the angularity of their green flower petals, stacked in three levels. The well-designed hashias, which retain the pagoda theme, blend harmoniously with the palla's elegant pattern.

281

COLOUR PLATE 143.
Kashmir shawl (fragment), Mughal Period, early 18th century, 22cm x 152cm (8 x 60in.).
This Mughal border fragment with its undecorated ground and freely spaced botehs represents
an important link between the inchoate, curvilinear boteh and the 17th century patterns. The
link is reinforced by the nature of the floral details which appear to be directly inspired from
17th century archetypes. At the top right we find the cog or pin wheel flower, a distinct Mughal
floral device found only in 17th century patterns, and although it was not perfectly drawn as
such, enough of it is there to make it nicely identifiable. Also, in the hashia, we come across the
crocus meander which further points to a shawl woven early in the 18th century.

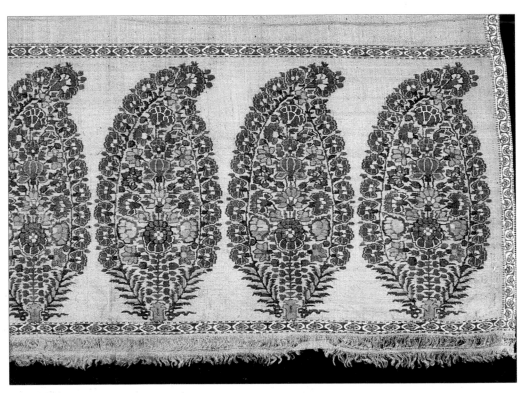

COLOUR PLATE 144.
Shoulder mantle. Mughal Period, mid-18th century. 139cm x 330cm (55 x 130in.).
One of the most beautiful shawls of the 18th century. The exterior wrap of red roses is supported
by a curved stem which forms the boteh's interior cone. The stem rises from tall fern branches
which flank a central raceme. The latter extends upward from a vase-like object. The vase is
secured in place laterally by two Chinese clouds which enhance the narrow base of this
otherwise very elegant boteh. The distinct flower in the boteh's centre is a blue iris, outlined in
yellow and red. The hashia is composed of a contemporary pattern of tiny oval flower buds set in
a kind of hexagonal opening formed by the angularity of the foliate meander.

COLOUR PLATE 145.
Shoulder mantle. Mughal Period, mid-18th century. 138cm x 318cm (54 x 125in.).
A Mughal hunting shawl, with people and animals portrayed in a splendid array of bright crisp
colours on a rich salmon ground. In the shawl's top left corner two attendants are warming
themselves around an open fire. In contrast to the rest of the palla's salmon ground, the top row of
animals appear on a green ground. Many objects are unrecognisable, for example underneath
the white horse appears a thick blue line resting on three yellow 'wheels'. Four vertical grey stacks
rise curiously from this line. On the other hand, blue is used to colour the caparisoned elephant
upon which sit a stout Mughal and an elephant boy. A hunter, with raised spear in hand,
mounted on a white horse, is seen attacking a leopard. Another leopard is shown in the process of
devouring a fallen white deer. Behind the horse stands the hunter's retainer. In the lower left
corner stands a chimerical figure outlined in bright red, and wearing a large yellow turban or
hat. The remaining colours are pale yellow, saffron, reddish salmon, black and beige.

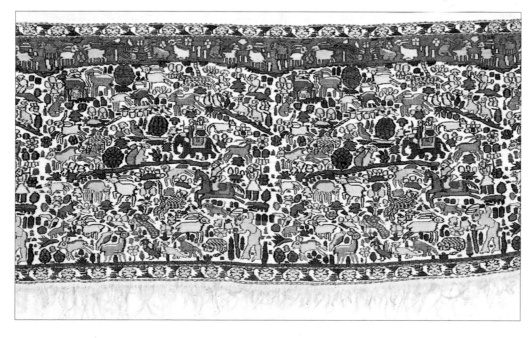

COLOUR PLATE 146.
Shoulder mantle with
hunting scene,
Mughal Period, mid-
18th century.

283

PLATE 109a.
*'Moon' shawl. Afghan Period. Late
18th century.*
*A luminescent saffron-yellow field and
white-ground medallions patterned
with polychrome flora of mustard,
pink, madder red, bright sky blue and
forest green all combine to make for a
very attractive piece. Through its
dazzling display of colours (although
only seen in black and white here) this
fine shawl, possibly shah tus, despite its
rather abstract pattern, evokes the
exotic spirit of the Orient. Due to the
gross variations in weave the corner
shown does not distinctly illustrate the
small vase and dish which are more
readily visible in the other corners.*

*These corner details focus on the
difficulties of solving the
field/medallion weave integration, one
of the most difficult feats in moon
shawl weaving. Twisted fringes were a
common finishing touch on patkas
and chandars made during the
second half of the 18th century.*

PLATE 109b.
*Moon shawl. Afghan Period, late 18th
century.*

284

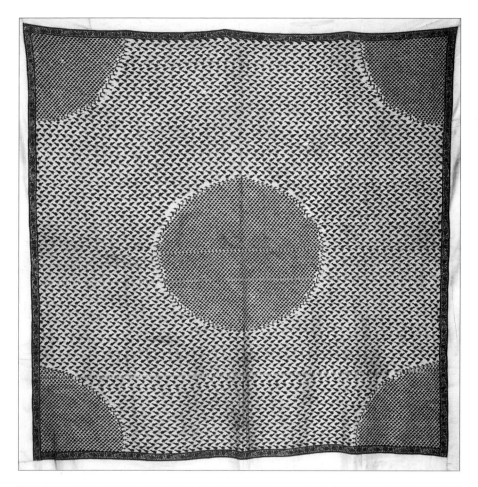

PLATE 110.

Moon shawl. Afghan Period, early 19th century. 180cm x 180cm (71 x 71in.).

Close inspection of the chandar or moon shawl reveals a unique field pattern of small ducks facing the same direction in alternating rows. The zigzag arches of the quarter medallions have been 'pricked in' with a pale-green dye. Enclosed inside the medallions is another pattern of pagoda-like sprigs similar to that of Plate 109. The cloud-band hashia (sewn on) of 'bent tip strawberries', roses and 'pin-wheel' flowers is beautifully executed with a rare fineness. The horizontal line across the centre reveals where the two separate halves of the shawl were joined. The irregular spacing where the ducks approach the medallions' circumference indicates that a proper pattern weave solution was not achieved – something extremely difficult with a pattern of this nature. The large size of the medallions tends to preclude the dating of this piece before 1815.

PLATE 111.

Waistband. Afghan Period, late 18th century.

The magnificent stately botehs which pattern this waistband represent the finest woven specimens of their genre. At the base is a large raised dish which supports a curious bell-shaped object surmounted by a tall vase. The vase is enclosed on either side by two hanging arched and serrated fronds, the undersides of which are illuminated by tinges of yellow to illustrate leaf-folding. Serrated leafy fronds of this type were closely associated with Ottoman court embroideries. Flanking these fronds and enclosing the boteh's base are two large racemes, one in blue and the other in red.

The novel ikat-dyed warps of the khatraaz field represent an interesting artistic intrusion into the palla. Identical boteh patterns, but less fine, are conserved by the Calico Museum, Ahmedabad, and the Victoria and Albert Museum, London. (See Colour Plate 13 for boteh detail.)

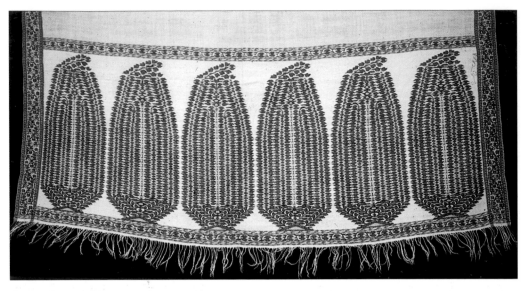

COLOUR PLATE 147.
Waistband. Mughal Period, mid-18th century. 466cm x 72cm (183 x 28in.).
A truly stately effect has been ingeniously created by the use of racemes arranged in stiff rising columns of regimented rectilinear flower buds. The blue and yellow flowers are outlined in black, as are the mound's diverging racemes.

COLOUR PLATE 148.
Shoulder mantle. Mughal Period, mid-18th century. 113cm x 137cm (44 x 54in.).
This joyful little pattern makes a big Mughal statement and represents a brilliant distillate of many of the design ideas of the 17th century.

COLOUR PLATE 149.
Shoulder mantle. Mughal Period, mid-18th century. 219cm x 135cm (86 x 53in.).
Pale salmon-coloured marigolds appear joined in horizontal rows by their pointed blue leaves on a white ground. The normally monotone bashia of hexagonally enclosed flower buds is here enlivened with red, blue and yellow.

COLOUR PLATE 150.
Shoulder mantle. Mughal Period, mid-18th century. 142cm x 316cm (56 x 124in.).
Despite the heavily charged multi-floral bouquet, an overriding Mughal impression persists in this beautifully coloured, khaki ground shawl. Again we come across the use of the spotted mound.

PLATE 112.
Moon shawl. Afghan Period. Late 18th century. 148cm x 149cm (58 x .58in.).
Although in terribly poor condition the chequerboard moon shawl from the Boston Museum of Fine Arts is nevertheless the only surviving example of its type. It is interesting to point out the large difference in weaving precision between the central (only a quarter of which is visible in this illustration) and quarter medallions and the winged buti flowers of the shawl's field. The latter are more finely drawn. Also it can be seen that a proper weaving solution was not arrived at where the chequered field meets the quarter medallions. This indicates that the shawl was probably not woven in a court workshop. However, despite this, we find an unusual design element here, something which is generally reserved only for the botehs of long shawls. This is the combination of vase, dish, leafy fronds and radial flower. Although hardly visible, one of the flowers in the hashia's meander contains Islamic calligraphy.. (See Colour Plate 17 for corner detail.)

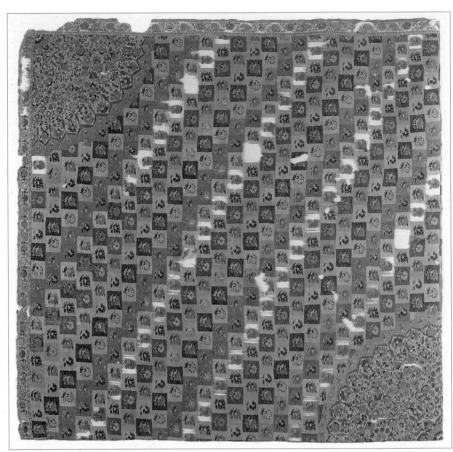

PLATE 113.
Patterned kani fabric. Afghan Period. Late 18th century. 75cm x 295cm. (29 x 116in.).

288

PLATE 114.

Shoulder mantle (fragment). Afghan Period, late 18th century. 75cm x 54cm . (29 x 21in.).
Whether this small fragment originally represented part of a palla's decoration or an overall
field pattern is not certain. A good guess would be that it is a fragment of the latter as this
particular design has not yet appeared on any known pullu. The compactness of the hashia's
floral meander indicates that it was of the vertical type, which had probably extended the full
length of the shawl. Note that the lower foliate part of the winged butis relates to that of the
chequered moon shawl in Plate 112. The butis are contained in a rhombic trellis pattern of
sawtooth leaves. This sawtooth style prevailed at the turn of the century and can be clearly seen
in other pieces.

PLATE 115.
'Khatraaz' shoulder
mantle. Afghan
Period, late 18th cen-
tury.106cm x 375cm.
(42 x 147in.).
Normally woven in
the same dimension
as the long shawls,
i.e. approximately
1.35m x 3.20m (53 x
126in.), this intricate
'millefleurs' pattern
must have taken at
least two years to
complete. This type of
tapestry fabric was
also used for such
clothing as trousers,
vests, socks and hats.
The end hashia is
unusual in that it
contains the same
pattern as the vertical
hashia except for the
bent-tip strawberry.

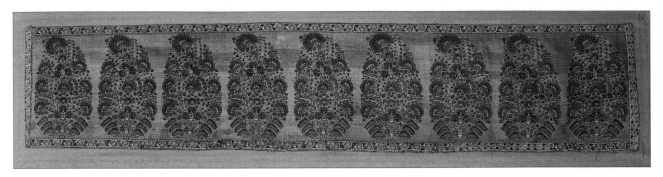

COLOUR PLATE 151.
Shoulder mantle (fragment) Mughal Period, 18th century. 26cm x 123cm (10 x 48in.).
The idea of the rank shawl is suggested by the vase's flanking rows of serrated leaves. The vase itself is decorated by a floral cross which became the convention until the end of the 19th century. Note the other small vase just above the central rose. The boteh is constructed around the symmetrical play of large roses. What sets this particular pattern apart stylistically are the thick rose stems.

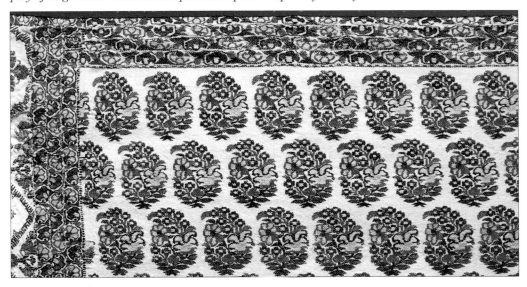

COLOUR PLATE 152.
Shoulder mantle (fragment). Mughal Period, mid-18th century. 48cm x 88cm (19 x 34in.).

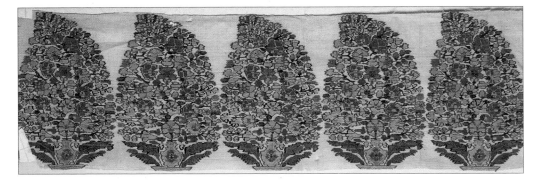

COLOUR PLATE 153.
Shoulder mantle. Afghan Period, c.1770. 20cm x 93cm (8 x 36in.).
Very little elbow room is provided for the regiment of botehs in this example, something which may tend to confuse the shawl's chronological sequence. Perhaps if the hashias were not missing we would be able to decipher more clues.

COLOUR PLATE 154.
Shoulder mantle (fragment). Afghan Period, c.1770. 136cm x 21cm (53 x 8in.).
Looking at this pattern, we can say that life would have been humdrum and simply academic if it were not that the artist had drawn a bold curvilinear outline around what should have been a beautiful, and 'unmolested' Mughal floral pattern. True, the conventional vase, leafy fronds and speckled dish are there in full force, but a close look at the floral elements compares little to that found in what we might consider late 18th century botehs. The hashia, a key element in this study, relates only to other shawls which consensus of opinion would undoubtedly place to mid-18th century.

Finding an answer to the reason why the artist chose to 'imprison' this fine bouquet and surround it with an aggressive red ground colour is intriguing. Perhaps the artist, reared in the Mughal school, perfunctorily succumbed to the new wave in fashion that demanded the cone form.

COLOUR PLATE 155.
Shoulder mantle (fragment). Afghan Period, c.1770. 21cm x 136cm (8 x 53in.).

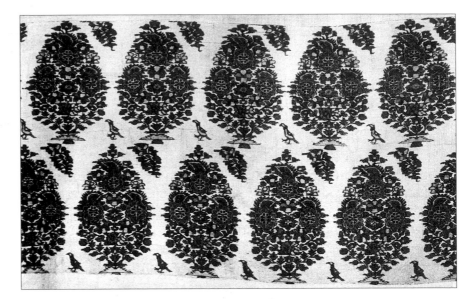

PLATE 116.
Shoulder mantle (fragment).
Afghan Period, late 18th century.
21cm x 97cm (8 x 38in.).

PLATE 117.
Shoulder mantle. Afghan Period,
late 18th century. 129cm x 308cm
(51 x 121in.).

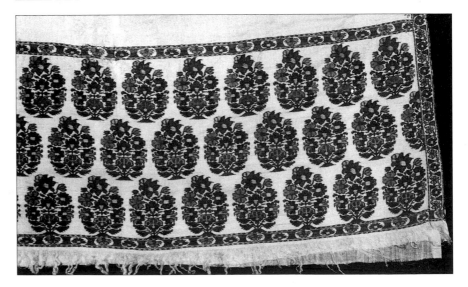

PLATE 118.
Shoulder mantle. Afghan Period.
c.1800. 134cm x 317cm (53 x
125in.).
The butis in this example are
gracefully woven and coloured in
rich earth tones of cochineal,
madder red, saffron and an
unusual amount of forest green.
The winged fronds provide a light
touch to a buti pattern in which
the flowers are woven with a
charming delicacy. It is apparent
here as in many other elegant
patterns that the shawl artist
carefully considered the entire field
design as a complete ensemble
rather than as a series of isolated
elements.

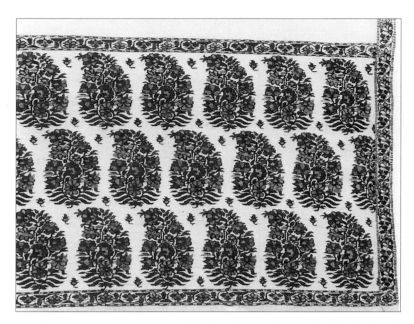

PLATE 119.
Shoulder mantle. Afghan Period, late 18th century. 124cm x 315cm (49 x 124in.).
This elegant palla from the Jagdish and Kamla Mittall Museum of Indian Art, Hyderabad, contains several transitional features worthy of attention. The tiny solitary flowers foretell the arrival of ever-increasing ground embellishment. At the same time the vertical hashia exhibits an unprecedented trilobed flower which may have formed the prototype for later hashia patterns as in Plate 117. The fine movement created by the arching interplay of the two central flowers set on wavy leaves attests to a sophisticated level of Mughal artistry. In one corner of the palla an inscription in Devanagari reads: 38 Narayan 52. Colours (on white ground): mustard yellow, fawn, pink, crimson, red, bluish green, indigo and black.

PLATE 120.
'Millefleurs' prayer hanging or mat. Afghan Period, c.1815.
This magnificent 'millefleurs' kani piece derives its name from the Oriental carpets in which this rare type of design is found. Under the 'rolled' arch which suggests cloud formation is seen a profusion of flowers, racemes, vase, dish, etc. The 'radial' flower arrangements echo clearly the important shawl style which became popular during the late 18th century. Nevertheless the guard hashias flanking the large outer border demonstrate a compressed variation of the 'bent-tip' strawberry and 'pin-wheel' leaf pattern – a variation which developed about 1800. The top border's pattern is alternated by large palmettes and squares each emitting concave white stripes arranged diagonally. The bottom border eliminates the palmettes and organises the strips in a spiral fashion. In style and chromatic range this piece relates closely with Colour Plate 174, especially by the profusion of white outlined flowers. (See Colour Plates 179, 180 and 181 for more 'millefleurs' prayer rug types.)

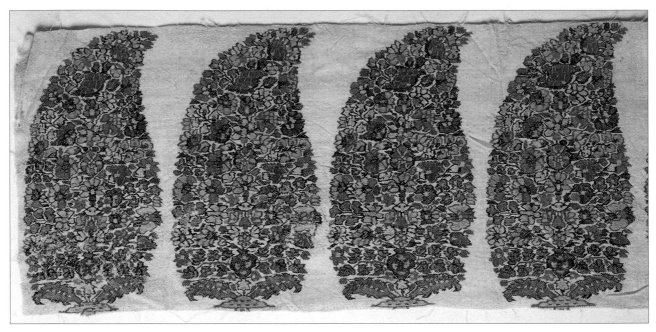

COLOUR PLATE 156.
Shoulder mantle (fragment). Afghan Period, c.1770. 19cm x 115cm (7 x 45in.).

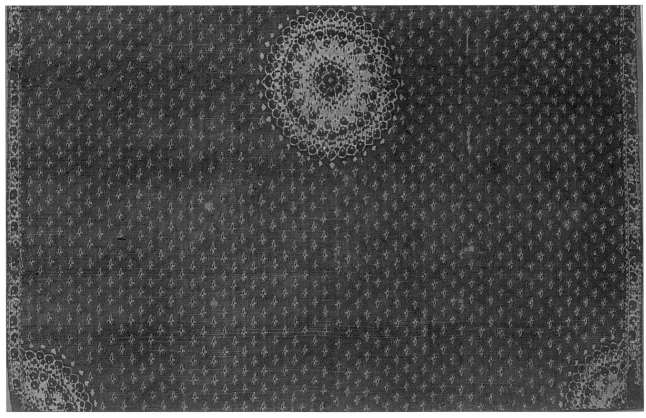

COLOUR PLATE 157.
Moon shawl (detail). Afghan Period, c.1770.

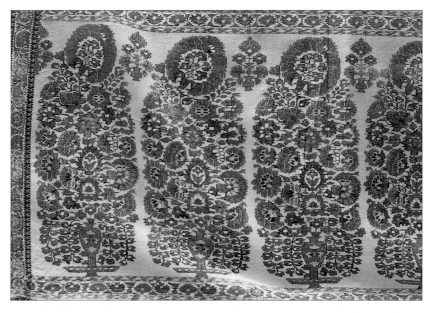

COLOUR PLATE 158.
Waistband. Afghan Period, late 18th century. 385cm x 135cm (151 x 53in.).
Although the delicately woven flowers are reminiscent of an earlier Mughal style, the large vase, dish and racemes would tend to date this patka boteh well into the Afghan Period. Other design devices which advance this argument are the two palmettes in the boteh's centre and of course the separate vase of roses between the botehs.

COLOUR PLATE 159.
Waistband. Afghan Period, late 18th century. 69cm x 640cm (27 x 252in.).

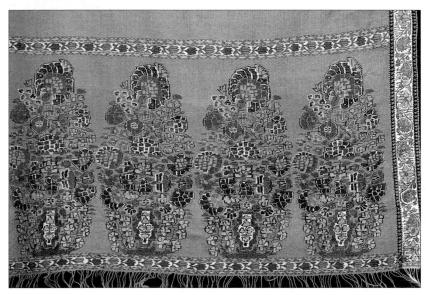

COLOUR PLATE 160.
Waistband. Afghan Period, late 18th century. 636cm x 67. 5cm (250 x 26in.).

These two pieces are variants of Colour Plate 158 and are grouped here because of their unusual vase similarities and chromatic range. In Colour Plate 159 the white-outlined flowers of pale blue, grey, green and various shades of red are all artistically highlighted by the patka's exotic ground colour of rosy peach. In Colour Plate 160 we find a wonderful 'burnt' orange tone highlighting a beautiful array of freely spaced 'chiselled' flowers.

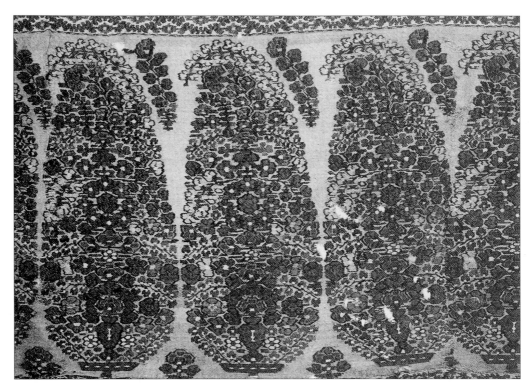

PLATE 121.
Shoulder mantle. Afghan Period, c.1810.

PLATE 122.
Shoulder mantle. Afghan Period, c.1800.
The style of this Kashmir shawl is similar to Plate 121 though much less finely woven. The soft pastel colours on a 'burnt' saffron ground make the shawl very attractive. The thin delicate hashias are representative of the period (see also Colour Plate 168). The vertical hashia is a repeat of three flowers; a yellow 'pinwheel' type, a small nondescript flower of blue, red and yellow, and a red and yellow rose bud. Note again the serrated-edge boteh in the cone.

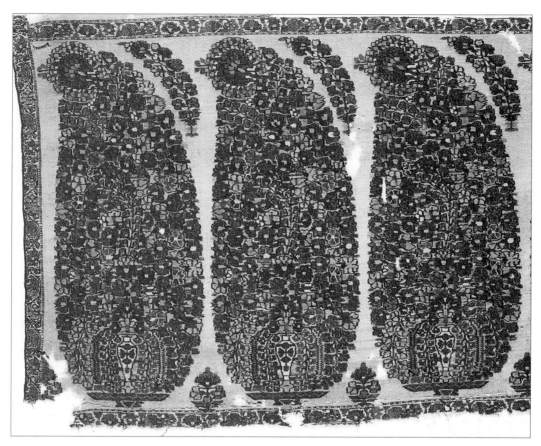

PLATE 123.
Shoulder mantle (fragment). Afghan Period, c.1800.

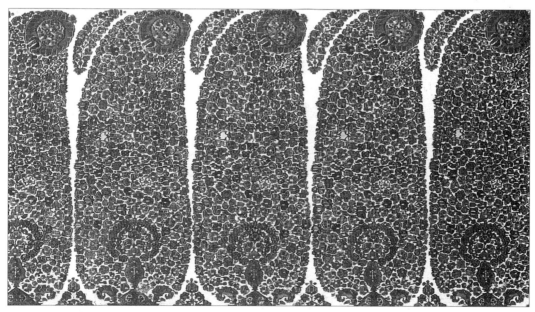

PLATE 124.
Shoulder mantle (fragment). Afghan Period, c.1800.

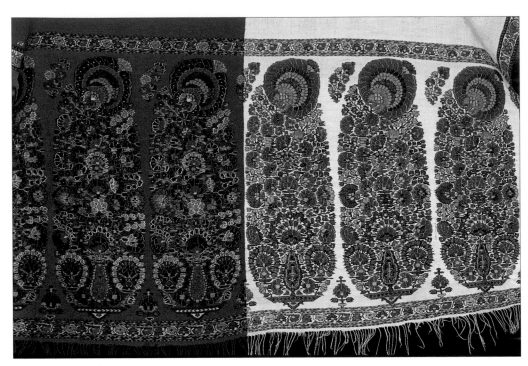

COLOUR PLATE 162.
*Kerchief or 'moon'
shawl. Mughal Period,
mid-18th century.
113cm x 114cm (44 x
45in.).
This is probably the
earliest known moon
shawl. The white
stripes of the hashias'
guard borders flanking
the unusual white
rhomboidal specks
indicate an archetypal
pattern and a distinct
departure from the
standard patka
patterns normally
employed. A unique
beige rose coloured
ground illuminates the
diapered field of jewel-
like flower buds whose
stems terminate in an
umbrella-handle
shape. Red roses and
dark green leaves
outlined in black form
the matching vine
meander of both
hashias. The small size
of the central and
quarter medallions
provides further clues
to a very early fashion
of decorating the fields
of head cloths.*

COLOUR PLATE 161.
*Waistband. Afghan Period, late 18th century. 896cm x 74cm (353 x 29in.).
Although entirely woven in one piece, the full length of this unusually long patka is divided in
half by the red and white matan whose colours extend into the palla. Representing the initial
developments of the 'coif' boteh technique are the detached flower branches alongside the boteh's
top. At the bottom, touching the hashia, are separate botehs which represent variants of the 'bow-
tie' style. A true product of the Afghan Period, the lower half of the boteh is distinguished by three
'radial' floral arrangements the centres of which are dominated by roses and vases.*

*These corner details
focus on the
difficulties of solving
the field/medallion
weave integration,
one of the most
difficult feats in
moon shawl weaving.
Twisted fringes were
a common finishing
touch on patkas and
chandars made up to
the end of the 18th
century.*

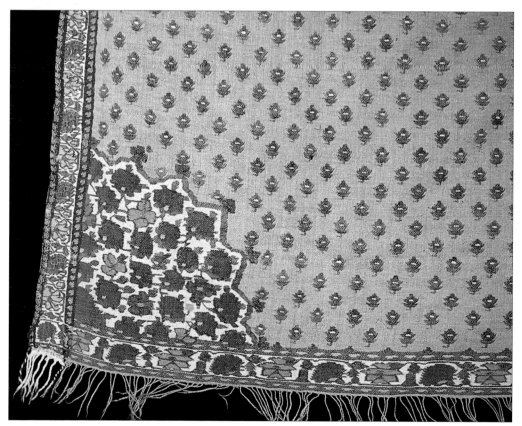

COLOUR PLATE 164
*'Moon' shawl.
Afghan Period, late
18th century. 127cm
x 134cm (50 x 53in.)*

PLATE 125.
*Shoulder mantle (fragment). Afghan Period,
c.1800.*

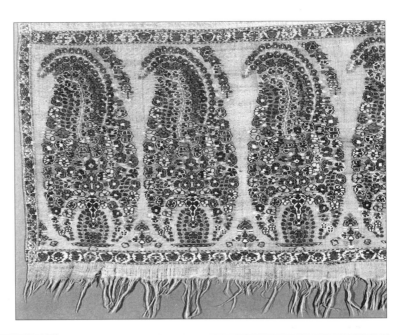

PLATE 126.
*'Moon' shawl. Afghan Period, c.1810. 140cm x
154cm (55 x 60in.).*
*A finely executed moon shawl, this piece
embodies the beautiful qualities of the late
Afghan style. Smooth curving arches described
by the medallion's spandrels, and detailed
polychrome flowers all evenly spaced, are just
some of the few characteristics immediately
noticeable in this tight detail. A pair of large
'radial' flowers are highlighted under the
pointed domes within the quarter medallions.
Exceptional care was taken to ensure that both
hashias were identically woven – not an easy
feat considering that silk warps were used for
one of them.*

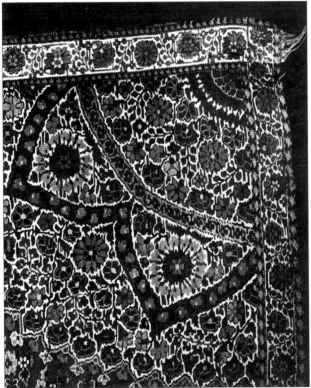

PLATE 127.
Shoulder mantle. Afghan Period, c.1815. 270cm x 127cm (106 x 50in.).
*The hashia's 'chain' meander and guard border's hexagonal flecks developed into a popular
pattern in early Sikh Period shawls yet the boteh's floral arrangement remains steeped in late
Afghan style. This may be observed in the two large round roses and especially the crooked
branch which creeps up from the dish to surround the circular rose invading the rest of the
boteh's interior. Many of the coif boteh's colours show signs of having been 'pricked in', notably
the mint green and saffron yellow which have left smudge traces.*

PLATE 128.
'Moon' shawl (centre detail). Afghan Period, c.1815.
In the moon shawls of this period we come across another distinct design pattern which enjoyed a large popularity. A central medallion is composed of rosettes in the form of flattened flowers uniformly arranged in pairs and in an orbiting fashion round a large central flower (see also Colour Plate 183). The medallion's field contains a dense foliage of scattered racemes.

PLATE 129.
Patterned kani fabric (pieced fragment). Afghan Period, c.1800. 100cm x 73cm (39 x 29in.).
This all-over plaid kani fragment and that in Colour Plate 176, both very worn and patched, represent rare patterns. Although the flowers are better defined in Colour Plate 176, both fragments share a similar dense floral nature and mosaic construction of geometric shapes. These shapes also bear resemblance to the whirling border pattern of the prayer hanging in Plate 120. What strikes us most here is the unusual amount of leaf outlining in white thread. Also seen are small serrated-edge 'botehs' similar to those in Colour Plate 173. Adopted from patterns such as those found in Colour Plate 140, these 'botehs' crystallised into an independent motif at the turn of the century, a fact which readily dates such patterns to around 1800.

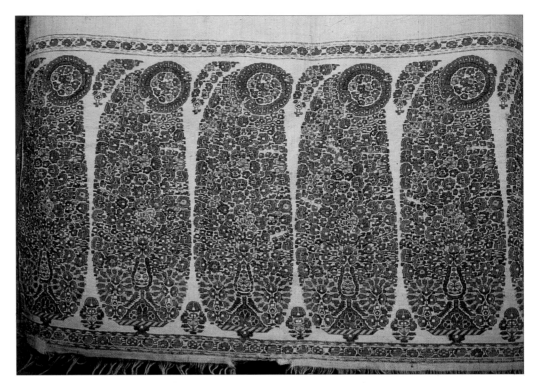

COLOUR PLATE 165.
Waistband. Afghan Period, c.1805. 73cm x 389cm (29 x 153in.).

It seems that the number of boteh styles is endless but, when several of the same species can be conveniently grouped together, finding a common denominator in the form of a descriptive appellation, it can often prove very useful. 'Mosaic coif boteh with radial top rose' seems to apply quite conveniently to these two.

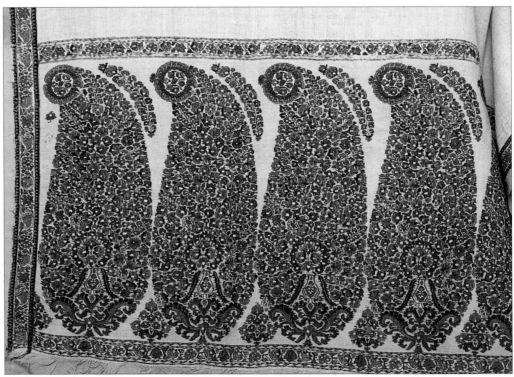

COLOUR PLATE 166.
Waistband. Afghan Period, c.1805. 75cm x 488cm (29 x 192in.).

COLOUR PLATE 167.
Kani shawl material, late 18th century. 90cm x 80cm (35 x 31in.).
Kashmiri weavings which display Islamic motifs are rare and in this fragment we discover the bold use of a style reminiscent of Koranic border decoration. The freely-spaced floral infill of split-leaf serrated flowers and irises on a fairly light ground colour provides just the right touch to make this pattern distinctive and Middle-eastern looking. For an identical fragment see accession number CIRC 4-1948 at the Victoria and Albert Museum.

COLOUR PLATE 168.
Shoulder mantle. Afghan Period. c.1800.

PLATE 130.
Corner detail from moon shawl in Colour Plate 184a.

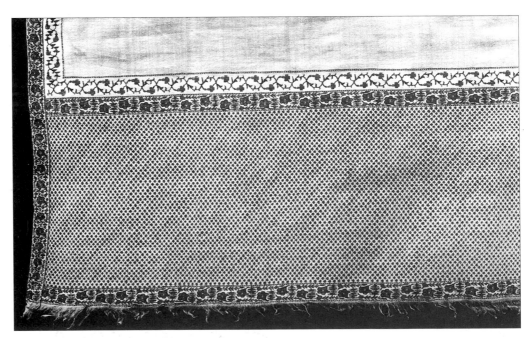

PLATE 131.
Shoulder mantle. Afghan Period, c.1810. 130cm x 312cm (51 x 123in.).
Recently a number of shawls have been found exhibiting the delicate style of fine draftsmanship seen here; woven products of a distinct atelier. The dense diapered field is framed by a marvellous hashia pattern featuring rectilinear branches, a motif popular during the First Empire. Often the predominant colour is a pale green. (The AEDTA collection, Paris conserves three fine examples from this school of draftsmanship.)

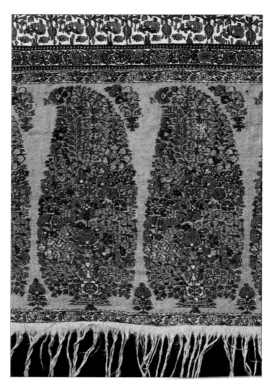

COLOUR PLATE 169.
Shoulder mantle. Afghan Period. c.1800

COLOUR PLATE 169a.
Shoulder mantle. Afghan Period. c.1810
The double hashia and rare khaki colour suggest a military aspect to this well-drawn, flamboyant piece. The delicately woven, four flower bud repeat in both vertical and horizontal hashias is further enhanced by an excellent choice of rich colours. The vertical hashia pattern relates to Plate 122 by the double separation of buds and the squareness of the angular vine meander. The squareness results from the continued fusing of foliate meander elements which lost their naturalness over time. The artist has taken full advantage of this transmutation, enlivening them with bright alternating red and green thread. Each flower of the hashia stands out sharply and distinctly due to the illuminating effect of carefully detailed outlining. Some of them assume the aspect of cut gems.

COLOUR PLATE 170.
Shoulder mantle. Afghan Period, c.1815.
136cm x 330cm (53 x 130in.).
The new innovation of compartmentalised botehs by
alternating ground colour appears to have received its
initial start from patka pieces such as in Colour Plate 161.
Again, as in Colour Plate 174, the small 'serrated-edge'
boteh which appears intermingled within the coif botehs'
floral collage is the main style characteristic of this piece.
Also the matan's chequerboard pattern of 'winged-leaf' buti
represents the continued popularity of a century old pattern.
At the botehs' base is the floral-cross decoration normally
woven on the missing vase.

COLOUR PLATE 171.
Shoulder mantle. Afghan Period, c.1810. 135cm x
274cm (53 x 108in.).
If the Renaissance painters Lotto and Holbein have
preserved a particular style of Turkish carpet in their
work, then certainly France's court painters Girodet, and
Ingres may stand equally as a point of stylistic reference
for this particular boteh style. The style may be described
as the arching-raceme coif boteh and this kani shawl is
probably one of the finest examples of its genre. The
yellow vase, with trefoil-cross marking, containing a
radial spray of flower buds, is exceptionally well drawn.
The vase stands on a tripartite flower cluster which
reflects a similar one between the botehs. Despite the
usual compactness of the boteh a great effort has been
made to retain botanical reality. It is interesting to note
that rarely do vertical and horizontal hashias share the
same style, especially during the end of the 18th century.
Colour Plate 171 is no exception to the rule. It can be
seen, however, that the flowers are basically the same
and in many cases it may be that the vertical hashia is
simply a compressed version of the horizontal one. This is
due in part to the silk warps of the former and especially
to the vertical weaving angle. Among the delightful
multi-coloured hues of this piece are the dominating blue
and yellow flowers outlined mostly in black which
combine to form a pattern of handsome botehs
illuminated by a brilliant mauve ground.

COLOUR PLATE 173.
*Shoulder mantle. Afghan Period,
c.1805. 137cm x 304cm (54 x
119in.).*
*The boteh's chromatic scheme is
distinguished by a profusion of
pale green or greyish flowers on a
deep indigo blue ground.
Featured above the vibrant radial
flower is again the design device
of a small serrated-edge boteh
which belies the strong 18th
century aspect of this conservative
shawl. The twin branch
connection drawn vertically in
the top hashia's floral interstices
are indeed unusual.*

307

COLOUR PLATE 174.
*Shoulder mantle.
Afghan Period,
c.1800. 135cm. x
382cm (53 x 150in.).
The prevailing theme
of this piece relies
heavily on the play of
contrast. This is
achieved by the heavy
outlining of the
flowers against a
dark Bordeaux
ground in white or
light yellow.*

COLOUR PLATE 175.
*Shoulder mantle.
Afghan Period,
c.1800.
These wonderful buti
are finely drawn in
the Mughal style and
one can clearly
identify the freely
spaced flowers: the
rose bud, iris,
carnation and the
crocus. The bird is a
type of mynah bird
prevalent in Northern
India and especially
in Kashmir where they
are known as 'Hura'.*

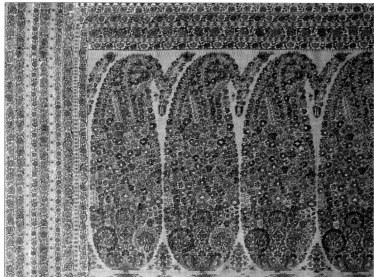

COLOUR PLATE 177.
*Shoulder mantle (fragment). Afghan Period,
c.1800. 91cm x 152cm (36 x 60in.).
A very fine kani weave of the turn of the century.
These exquisite botehs display a stunning tour-de-
force in design creativity. Taking advantage of
the flexible morphology of the boteh's base
elements, the naqqash has artfully combined
three distinct schools of shawl draftsmanship.
Starting with the mound and its bifurcated two-
tone fronds, we have an interesting revival of a
mid-18th century Mughal theme. The exaggerated
curling of these scalloped-edge fronds signals the
beginning of a design device which later on
enveloped the whole boteh. But the exciting
nature of this predominantly Afghan boteh lies in
the use of the 'radial-flower' technique. This
dochalla in its original form probably displayed
three horizontal and two vertical hashia strips. In
the second strip of the latter, notice the trilobed
flower within the repeating red roses.*

COLOUR PLATE 178.
*Kani shawl fragment. Afghan Period, late 18th
century.*

309

COLOUR PLATE 179.
'Millefleurs' kani prayer hanging or mat. Mughal Period, mid-18th century.
An extremely rare and exquisite piece illustrating a synthesis of Mughal and Central Asian styles.

COLOUR PLATE 180.
'Millefleurs' kani prayer hanging or mat. Afghan Period, mid-18th century. 81cm x 112cm (32 x 44in.). Woven all in one piece, this prayer mat contains a beautiful array of finely drawn flowers on an ecru ground. The spandrels of the arch are formed by serrated and cupped leaves which rise from partly visible capitals to the right and left. An imposing and ornate vase is flanked by sprays of multicoloured racemes rising up from a large dish. The field itself, beautifully executed by a master artist, with its riot of curving branches and flowers, appears to generate a continuous meandering energy as in the eddy currents of a magnetic field.

COLOUR PLATE 181.
'Millefleurs' prayer hanging or mat. Sikh Period, first half of the 19th century.

Colour Plate 182.
'Moon' shawl. Afghan Period, c.1800. 200cm x 190cm (79 x 75in.).
This piece with its intense cosmic image and direct appeal illustrates a fine example of one of the most difficult kani weaves and a moon shawl whose curves are exceptionally smooth and unbroken. The weaver is forced to make many corrections to oppose the warp twist which tends constantly to distort the curvilinear pattern with every weft shot. An exquisite richness of colour and delicacy of design is exhibited by the large and uncommon khatraaz (stripe) border in this example.

COLOUR PLATE 183.
'Moon' shawl. Afghan Period, c.1815. 160cm x 160cm (63 x 63in.).
In the moon shawls of this period we come across another distinct design pattern which enjoyed a large popularity. The 'cosmic' central medallion is composed of rosettes in the form of flattened flowers in an orbiting fashion around a large central flower. It is particularly interesting to see how the idea of a 'transparent' central medallion on a colourful khatraaz background creates the illusion of a moon in free suspension. The beautiful colours, the rich rose, dark indigo, and the bright cochineal virtually disappeared after the early Sikh Period.

COLOUR PLATE 184.
*Moon shawl. Afghan Period.
c.1815, 163cm x 163cm (64
x 64in.).*
*In this continuing theme of a
cosmic central medallion
with 'orbiting' flower
blossoms we find a finely
drawn khatraaz (striped)
field. The atypical feature of
this lunar shawl is the
narrowness of the stripes and
the wavy circumference of
the central medallion.*

COLOUR PLATE 184a.
*'Moon' shawl. Afghan Period,
c.1815. 149cm x 140cm (58
x 55in.).*
*A distinct transitional style
underlies the basic concept of
this fine moon shawl. Its style
departs from the 'Afghan
compression' of compact and
minute flower buds, racemes,
etc., to create a freedom of
botanical movement
recalling a style reminiscent
of the contemporary Norwich
drawloom shawl. The
meticulous detail applied to
the chandar's scalloped
circumference suggests a
shawl made by a master
weaver. (See Plate 130 for
corner detail.)*

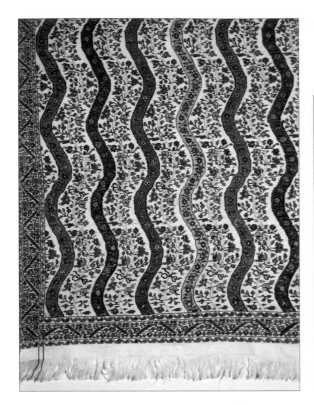

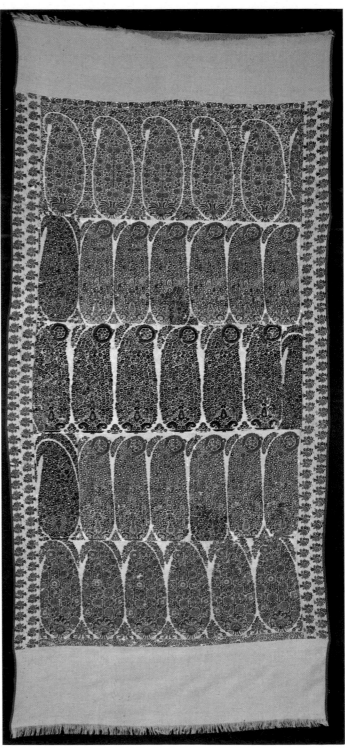

COLOUR PLATE 185.
Shoulder mantle. Sikh Period. c.1820. 135cm x 310cm (53 x 122in.).Only a small corner detail of this fabulous jamawar is illustrated here in order to provide a close inspection of the beauty of the colours and fine weave execution.

COLOUR PLATE 186.
Shoulder mantle (fragments). Afghan Period, c.1800. 92cm x 156cm (36 x 61in.).
This piece is a collection of palla fragments joined together to form a modern shoulder mantle. They illustrate botehs on a saffron ground – a popular colour at the turn of the 18th century. Those of both the bottom and the top rows share the same theme of rosettes growing from stiff vertical branches. The stiff branches suggest the beginnings of the 'tree' boteh. In the second and third rows from the top, the cone botehs are basically identical except for slight variations in detail. For example, the appearance of the small serrated-edge boteh is absent in the third row.

316

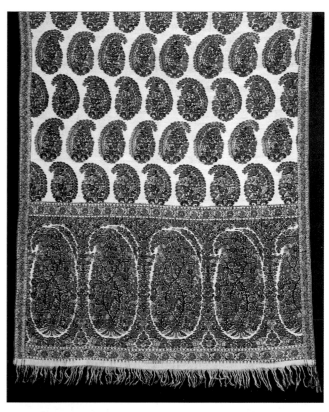

COLOUR PLATE 187.
Shoulder mantle (reduced).
Afghan Period, c.1815. 64cm x
270cm (25 x 106in.)
The importance of this piece is
that it represents one of the
earliest developments of full
ground ornamentation. The
boteh's infill with the criss-
crossing of the branches is
perhaps one of the beginning
steps toward the development of
the hooked vine.

COLOUR PLATE 188.
Shoulder mantle. Sikh Period,
c.1820.
In India, long and decorative
shawls are commonly known as
'jamawars'. This fine showy
kani weaving contains a
magnificently worked teal field
with complementary mosaic
botehs in the pallas.

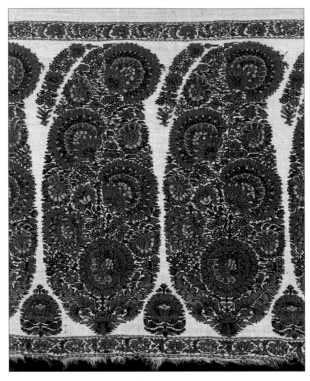

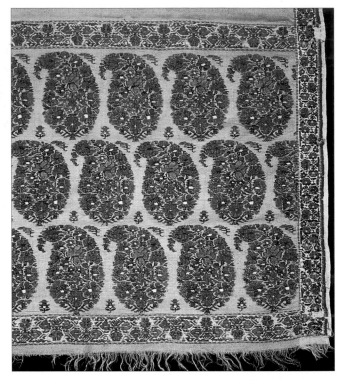

COLOUR PLATE 189.
Shoulder mantle. Afghan Period, c.1815. 135cm x 304cm (53 x 119in.).
Every once in a while one encounters a pattern which takes one by surprise and leaves one in awe. The novel use of large circular roses in bright reds, yellows and blues endows this exceptionally fine shawl with a wonderful cheerfulness.

COLOUR PLATE 190.
Shoulder mantle. Afghan, c.1815. 129cm x 300cm (51 x 118in.).
A saffron ground and pastel flowers provide a warm illuminating aspect to this handsome buti shawl. The style of the hashia's green serrated leaves and red, blue and rose coloured flowers follow a particular school of design. The idea of these flowers, set at right angles, may have been taken from the popular vase decoration of flowers set in the form of a cross.

COLOUR PLATE 191.
Shoulder mantle. Afghan Period, c.1815.

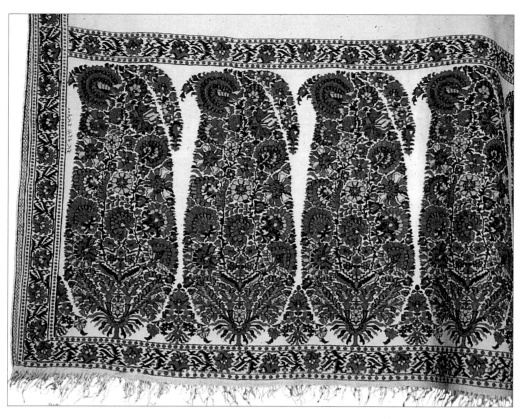

COLOUR PLATE 192.
Shoulder mantle. Afghan Period, c.1815. 136cm x 316cm (53 x 124in.).
In this superb pattern we can see the stamp of the same draughtsman's hand throughout the hashia and the boteh, indicating that we are dealing with an original design. What often happens is that in successive shawl copies the talims contained only the boteh pattern weaving code. As a result boteh patterns became crossbred with the displaced hashia talims. The distinctive draughtsmanship of this shawl pattern appears from time to time in other shawls and leads one to believe that artists coming from various back-grounds had been patronised. For example, it is quite possible that this piece may have been created by a papier mâché artist.

COLOUR PLATE *193.*
Shoulder mantle (fragment). Afghan Period.c.1815.
It is obvious that the style of this pattern relates very closely to that in Colour Plate 192.

COLOUR PLATE 194.
Boteh detail from Colour Plate 196.

COLOUR PLATE 195.
Shoulder mantle. Afghan Period, c.1815. 131cm x 307cm (51 x 121in.).

COLOUR PLATE 196.
Shoulder mantle. Sikh Period, c.1820 134cm x 314cm (53 x 123in.). At the time of Maharaja Runjit Singh and in France the fashion for the 'harlequin' shawl, such as this one with its multicoloured compartments, was becoming popular. Exceptional attention was devoted to highlighting the cochineal field (matan) with an elegant all-kani woven, floral trellis pattern. Adding a graceful movement to the delicate draughtsmanship of the boteh is the ogival pattern formed by the rising meander which falls gracefully at the cone's vertex. Within each compartment can be seen the ubiquitous fool's cap, an identifying Sikh Period characteristic. The high quality pashmina, vegetal dyes and pattern suggest that perhaps the shawl was woven at one of the court ateliers.

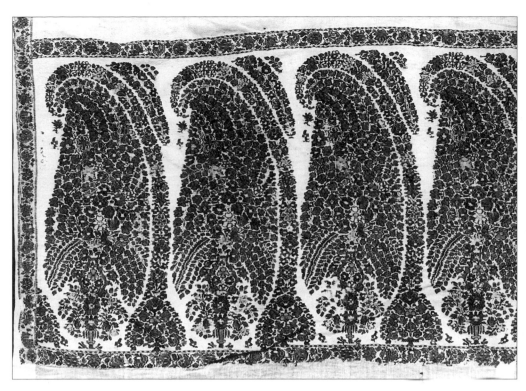

PLATE 132.
Shoulder mantle. Afghan Period. c.1815.

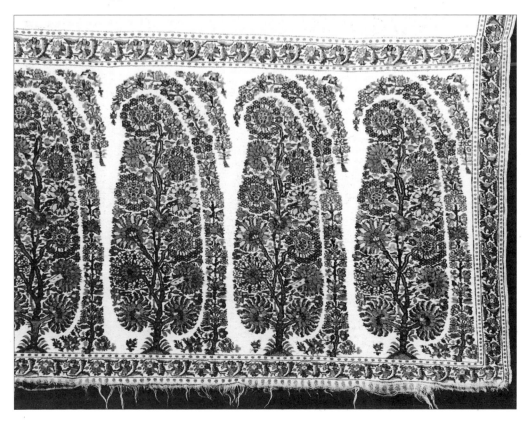

PLATE 133 (below).
*Shoulder mantle.
Afghan Period,
c.1815. 127cm x
330cm (50 x 130in.).
Although botanically
of an entirely different
nature, these two
pieces share a similar
pattern by the large
encircling coif branch
of flowers which rises
from between the
botehs. Plate 133 from
the Victoria and Albert
Museum is a
masterpiece of kani
weaving. The boteh's
well-proportioned style
draws much of its
influence from the
traditional school of
the 18th century shawl
artists as shown, for
example, by the radial
flower. (See Plate 60a
for an almost exact
European imitation of
this boteh.) The
ponderous branches
are probably
descendants of the
stiff-branch boteh seen
in Colour Plate 187,
which perhaps
provided the initial
impulse for the
development of the
'tree' boteh. Notice the
identical
draftsmanship of
Colour Plate 192 and
Plate 132, especially in
the hashias, also the
corner branch
ornaments of Plate
140, although in the
former the foliate
meander was given
exceptional design
emphasis. Another
'tree' boteh is
conserved in the
Bharat Kala Bhawan
which indicates that
this style may have
enjoyed a considerable
popularity.*

321

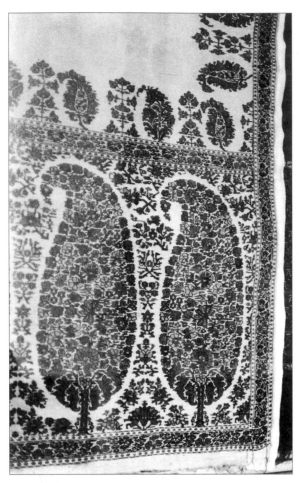

PLATE 134.
Shoulder mantle. Afghan Period, c.1815. 135cm x 315cm (53 x 124in.).

These examples are similar to the previous two pieces in the large supporting trunks of the botehs. They remain true to the excellence of late Afghan weaving by their crisp floral detail. It is always interesting to come across two Kashmir shawls which share almost 'word for word' the same weaving pattern. This is the case of the two pallas here except that the boteh outline in Plate 135 shows leaves instead of flowers. Similarities end here; the richly woven hashius of Plate 135 retain some of the most beautiful remnants of earlier Mughal weaving. The matan of this piece is perhaps of a slightly later date.

PLATE 135.
Waistband. Afghan Period, c.1815. 50cm x 308cm (19 x 121in.).

322

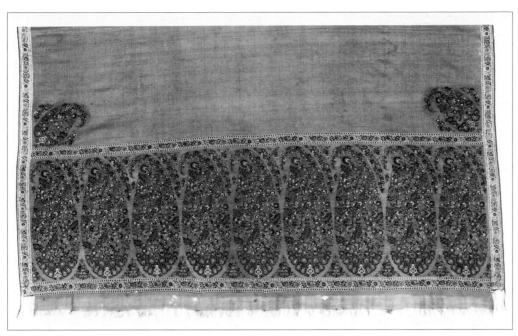

PLATE 136.
Shoulder mantle. Afghan Period c.1815. 322cm x 135cm (126 x 53in.).

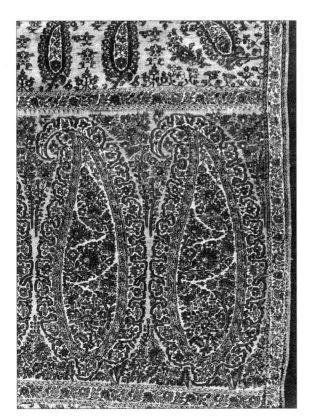

PLATE 137.
Shoulder mantle. Afghan Period, c.1815. 55cm x 135cm (21 x 53in.).

PLATE 138.
Shoulder mantle. Afghan Period, c.1815. 292cm x 135cm (115 x 53in.).
Grouping these three Kashmir shawls together is their common particularity: the boteh's scalloped outlining. This develops initially from the boteh's base foliage in the form of stylised leaves as seen in the khaki ground shawl of Plate 136. This design device, by extension, was further elaborated upon and becomes the highlight of Plates 137 and 138. These also relate to each other by their similar style of 'flattened' roses and thick stems. The treatment of their hashias is especially well finished and thought out.

323

PLATE 139.
Shoulder mantles. Afghan Period, c.1815.
309cm x 137cm (121 x 54in.).
The pallas of this identical pair (dochalla) of
indigo blue shawls, conserved by the Boston
Museum of Fine Arts, have been placed side
by side to illustrate their slight differences in
weaving. This is due to the different looms
which made them. The boteh's design, which
was coded on the talim card, remains the
same. However, variations in the weft thread
and the beat of the loom's comb are enough
to alter significantly the shape of the pattern.
For style, compare the large radial flower
enveloped by intertwining branches with
Plate 127. The complete floral style too seems
to have taken on a slightly new development,
the succession of which may be seen
somewhat in Moorcroft's drawing (Plate
38c) but without the racemes.

PLATE 140.
Shoulder mantle. Afghan Period, c.1815.
130cm x 315cm (51 x 124in.).

PLATE 141.

Shoulder mantle. Afghan Period, c.1815.

The patterns in Plates 140 to 142 illustrate design impulses from a variety of sources. Kashmir's early 19th century exposure to European decorative arts is suggested by the tassel and ribbon theme found in these three pieces – a theme most likely borrowed, in turn, from the Chinese. However, the corner ornament in Plate 140, in the form of a tree with two trunks, pays a Mughal respect to the influence of Persian miniature painting. Maybe this is why, in comparing the uneven ribbons in Plate 140 with the perfect ones in Colour Plate 195, one feels inclined to believe that the hashia border of the former is more of an interpretation than an actual copy. The ribbon or bow-tie theme is continued in the khatraaz piece of Plate 141. The collection AEDTA, Paris, contains an identical shawl to Colour Plate 195.

PLATE 142.

Shoulder mantle. Afghan Period, c.1815. 133cm x 262cm (52 x 103in.).

A simple yet dignified tall boteh pattern consisting of green, pale green, light rose, saffron and light blue flowers, enclosed by the boteh's shell of crenellated flowers aligned in three layers. A significant increase in boteh height is apparent here.

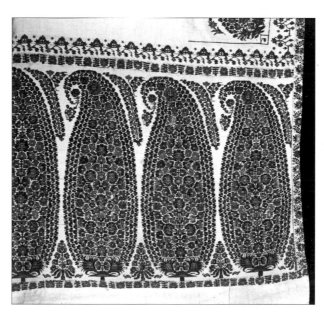

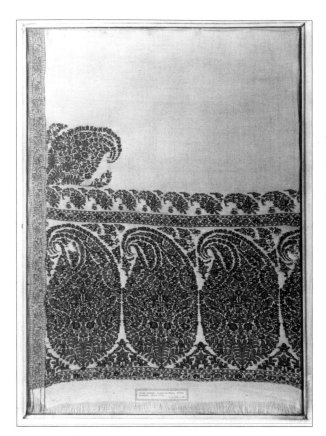

PLATE 143.
Shoulder mantle, Afghan Period, c.1815.

PLATE 144.
Shoulder mantle, Afghan Period, c.1815. 133cm x 310cm (52 x 122in.).
This 'feathered-coif' boteh shares, in a way, a very similar style to the tree trunk boteh of Plate 135 except that here the boteh is detached from its foliate shell. The shawl's draughtsmanship is excellent, although its foliage defies botanical identification.

PLATE 145.
Shoulder mantle (detail of fragment). Sikh Period. c.1825, 48cm x 132cm (19 x 52in.).
In this finely drawn kani weaving we find an extension of the encircling coif branch as in Plates 132 and 133, only here we also encounter the fool's cap flower which can be seen at the centre of the boteh.

PLATE 146.
Shoulder mantle. Sikh Period, c.1825. 133cm x 306cm (52 x 120in.).

PLATE 147.
Shoulder mantle. Sikh Period, c.1825. 135cm. x 270cm (53 x 106in.).

A similar boteh style provides the common ground for the grouping together of these three exotic shawl patterns. It has been found that almost all the botehs whose vertices end in curling and in split layers resemble each other rather closely. The tiny buti which 'pops out' from under the top of the botehs is also a noticeable common factor. In each case the hooked vine plays a strong role.

The hooked vine overlaid with small flower petals in the form of lunar crescents forms a very novel hashia meander in Plate 146. In Plate 147 the inner cone's chequered pattern offers a gay harlequin aspect to the shawl.

PLATE 148.
Shoulder mantle. Sikh Period, c.1825.

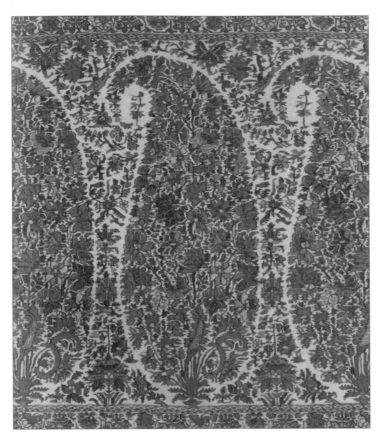

PLATE 149.
Shoulder mantle (fragment). Sikh Period c.1820.
35cm x 130cm (14 x 51in.).
Kani and European tapestry weaving are very
similar. What differentiates them significantly is
the lack of shading techniques in the former.
This example and Colour Plate 196 are unusual
in as much as they show a departure from the
traditionally flat two-dimensional effects
exhibited by earlier shawl designs. This is
achieved not exactly by shading in the strict
sense of the term, but by the subtle use of dark
thread outlining as opposed to lighter colours
traditionally employed on earlier pieces. Also,
the naqqash has carefully avoided the flattened
flower style by illustrating leaves which overlap.

PLATE 150.
'Moon' shawl. Sikh Period, c.1825. 174cm x
188cm (68 x 74in.).

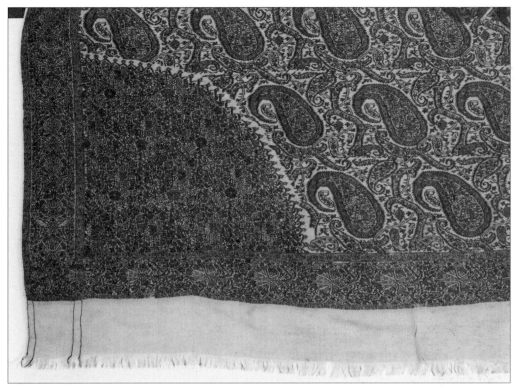

PLATE 151.
'Moon' shawl. Sikh Period, c.1825. 168cm x 173cm (66 x .68in.).

PLATE 152.
'Moon' shawl (fragment). Sikh Period, c.1825. 16cm x 48cm (6 x 19in.).
The salient characteristic of this chandar group (Plates 150-152) is, of course, the dense mosaic-like foliate nature that composes the medallions. In all three we find a sawtooth style in the field's design elements. Plate 152 shows an interesting trellis pattern which covers the field of leaning 'bent-tip' botehs. In the hashia of Plate 150 we see a novel variation of the fool's cap which bifurcates a repeating medallion-like device.

COLOUR PLATE 197. *Shoulder mantle. Sikh Period, c.1825, 128cm x 286cm (50 x 112in.).*
In this rich and colourfully patterned jamawar we find a graceful synthesis of Hindu-Islamic design elements. This can be seen in the three design themes which overlap, beginning with the striped field of botehs and floral sprigs, then the ogival trellis whose intersections are secured with lunar crescents and finally the hooked vine that runs diagonally across the shawl's surface. These themes are brought into stunning contrast by the brilliant dyes of deep indigo blue, saffron and mustard yellow and the soft blues and teals.

COLOUR PLATE 198. *Moon shawl. Sikh Period, c.1830, 168cm x 170cm (66 x 67in.).*
Fine draughtsmanship, careful attention to the symbolic forms and the unique pale-blue ground colour make this a fine example of Sikh Period weaving. The freely-spaced motifs hovering against the pale-blue field appear to enjoy a celestial movement all of their own. The large hashias (borders) with their unusually large guard borders reflect the same motifs found in the field, a characteristic of finely woven pieces.

COLOUR PLATE 199.
Shoulder mantle. Sikh Period, c.1825.
In this complex and sophisticated pattern of foliage and sharply hooked vines we discover what may be the quintessential Sikh patterned kani weave. In particular we note, not without a small degree of excitement, the large pairs of daggers placed in the lower register of the pattern as well as the smaller pairs located in the pattern surrounding the white field. The dagger expressed the militancy of the Sikh Brotherhood. See Colour Plate 20b for detail.

331

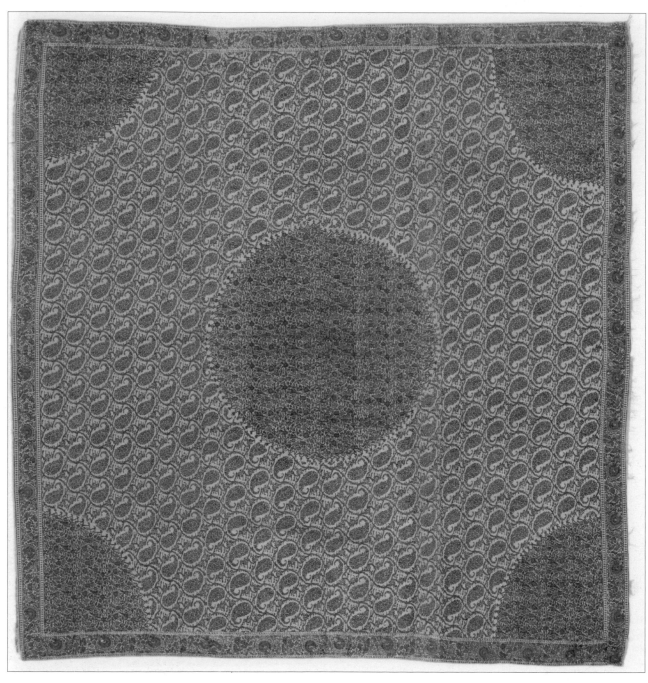

PLATE 153.
'Moon' shawl. Sikh Period, c.1825. 162cm x 162cm (64 x 64in.)
Usually found as decoration of the long shawl's dhoor, the small leaning butis here provide the overall field pattern. The central medallion and corners retain the popular theme of dense foliage that characterise nearly 80% of all chandars of this period. Four separate panels join to make this moon shawl – a fact which probably led to the misalignment of the central medallion's circumference. The flattened roses of the matching hashias recall the late Afghan style as seen, for example, in the moon shawl of Plate 128.

PLATE 154.
'Moon' shawl. Sikh Period, c.1830. 165cm x 166cm (65 x 65in.).
In this rare and very unusual moon shawl we find 'arrow-head' medallions arranged in
staggered rectilinear rows. The central moon's circumference of interlacing lines encircling the
eight pointed buti star pattern provides for a powerful and very graphic image.

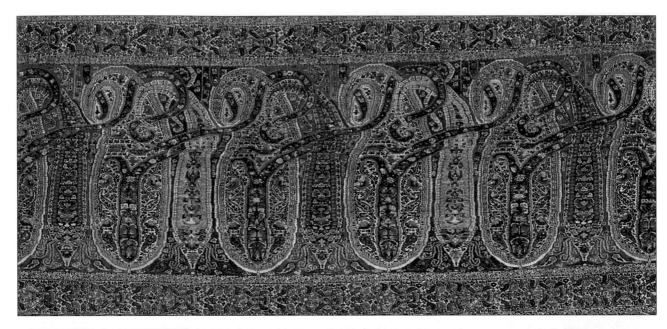

Colour Plate 199, a and b.
Shoulder mantle (fragments). Sikh Period, c.1820. 46cm x 132cm (18 x 52in.).
These pieces are 'Lahore' or 'Lahore-type' shawls. The colours have been extensively penned in.
The botehs appear hooked on the chimerical vines as they alternate in contrasting colours.
Flowers are almost completely absent and the design theme is dominated by a juxtaposition of
almost pure symbolic forms. Compare to Plate 162.

An identical chromatic range of rich rainbow-like colours and similar design features pair these two rare Sikh pieces. The repeat which patterns Colour Plate 200 is composed of a large spearhead placed upon a sturdy block-like pedestal the face of which contains a vase of flowers framed by a mihrab. Hanging from each side of the pedestal are two pendants in the form of long cones. The spearhead's base splits in two and each end curls upward, terminating in a cornucopia shape from which spills a small boteh. Flanking the spearhead's point, which is surmounted by a crescent moon pierced by the thin stem of a fan-like object, are two minarets.

Superimposed across all of the above, by its outlined form only, is a tall bent-tip boteh. Adjacent to the boteh and rising vertically above a mound to an equal height is a spray of fern-like leaves, the central stem of which is constructed of stacked, multicoloured chevrons. On the saffron coloured matan is a kani woven repeat of floral bedecked pavilions separated by fern-like plants. The lateral hashias are particularly interesting for their archetypal meander. The vertical hashias, although contemporary, are not original to the shawl.

The palla of Colour Plate 201 contains three pairs of opposing, bent-tip botehs, each pair intersected by a large cone throwing off on either side a spray of fern-like leaves. The cone's centre is decorated by a kind of totem pole of various shapes typical of the Sikh Period. Above the top lateral hashia's fine prototypal pattern is a continuation of the same design as the palla. As in Colour Plate 200, the vertical hashias here are probably not original to the piece.

COLOUR PLATE 200.
Shoulder mantle. Sikh Period, c.1830.
137cm x 300cm (54 x 118in.)

COLOUR PLATE 201.
Shoulder mantle. Sikh Period, c.1830.
146cm x 320cm (57 x 126in.).

PLATE 155.

*'Moon' shawl. Sikh Period, c.1830. 160cm x 160cm (63 x 63in.).
One of the prettiest pieces among all the chandar styles is the one
with the khatraaz field. Here again, as in Colour Plate 183, we
witness the aesthetic transparency of the medallions which is
created by the polychrome warp threads.*

PLATE 156.

*Shoulder mantle (detail). Sikh Period, c.1830. 101cm x 201cm
(40 x 79in.).
By 1820, quick imitations of the kani shawl were made by
embroidery as opposed to the time-consuming loom-woven
patterns. This led to the appearance of a host of human and
animal figures. Being simpler and less eye-exhausting,
embroidered shawls did not require the strict surveillance which
reigned within the crowded kharkandars, or weaving ateliers.
Instead they developed a folk style all of their own as they slowly
began to bear the personal household stamp of the Kashmir
families that designed them. On this particular shawl only the
matan's corners are embroidered, showing two courting couples
with the women admiring a flower offered as a gift and peacocks
(the peacock is northern India's national emblem but here it is
more likely a symbol of romance). The embroidered botehs echo
the palla's boteh style of concentric and snake-like decoration.*

336

PLATE 157.
Shoulder mantle (embroidered). Sikh Period, c.1820. 130cm x 310cm (51 x 122in.).
'Amli' or embroidered shawls frequently imitated the kani ones by abstracting their essential design features. The reverse effect was no less of a phenomenon. This example contains a well thought out pattern in fine style and opposing contrasts. The hooked vine's meander sweeps in and out of the cone. Upon re-entering it splits in two and suspends a fool's cap within the boteh's lance-like tip and centre. The remaining ground decoration is gracefully enhanced by leafy fronds.

PLATE 158.
Shoulder mantle. Sikh Period, c.1830. 121cm x 277cm (47 x 109in.).
There is no doubt that this style shares similar features with the moon shawl in Plate 154. The botehs are separated into compartments by the vertical line of 'stringed' symbolic forms which may be compared to the 'arrowhead' shapes of Plate 154.

PLATE 159.
Shoulder mantle (fragment). Sikh Period, c.1830. 46cm x 50cm (18 x 19½in.).

COLOUR PLATE 202.
Shoulder mantle.
Sikh Period, c.1825.
144cm x 314cm (56 x 123in.).
The unique pattern of this shawl arouses one's curiosity. The trilobed scalloped spandrel, the ends of which terminate in cornucopias, illuminates a 'sacred mountain' of pointed cypress trees all reaching up towards a large central spear, a phallic symbol. Indeed, the subjects have a symbolic and mystical ring to them.

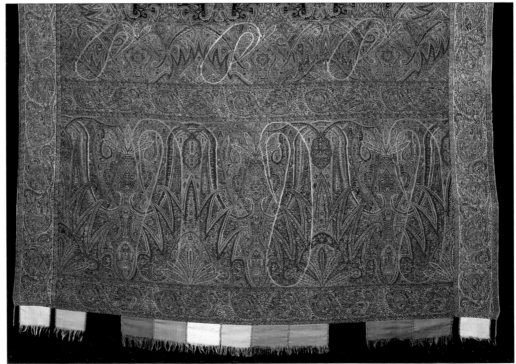

COLOUR PLATE 203.
Shoulder mantle.
Sikh Period, c.1830.
138cm x 308cm (54 x 121in.).
This piece is similar in style to Colour Plate 54. Again the Sacred Mountain features among the design elements. A similar idea is very often seen on early Chinese robes in the form of stylised mountains which loom up from a churning ocean, and are topped by crashing waves.

338

COLOUR PLATE 204.
Shoulder mantle. Sikh Period, c.1840. 142cm x 312cm (56 x 123in.).

COLOUR PLATE 205.
Shoulder mantle (detail). Sikh Period, c.1825.
The bold intertwining curves, arches, niches, large eight-pointed stars, all combine to camouflage the large hooked-cone botehs. The hashia's meander consists of oval emblems joined by a heavy vine. The emblems are further separated by leaning cone botehs. The weaving is very fine and the colours are most attractive: mustard yellow, sky blue, blue grey, navy blue, pink, cream, forest green, light green, cochineal and black. An embroidered inscription on the shawl reads 'Ordered by the royal [one] a novel and unique shawl – a thing of heavenly beauty studded with variegated, floral pattern, a delight to the eye was made'. This shawl relates remarkably well to Chavant's shawl patterns which were published in Paris in 1837.

339

PLATE 160.
Shoulder mantle. Sikh Period, c.1830. 135cm x 315cm (53 x 124in.).
These two pieces (plates 159 to 160) belong to the same design family; the sharply serrated boteh, the arching U-shaped form and the moon crescents being the main unifying features. However, the pervading style consists of the angularity with which the flower petals are drawn and systematically arranged in a linear fashion. As a result these distinct symbolic elements combine to provide a sweeping sinuous movement. Plate 159 is an exceptional piece. The fool's cap hashia lends a feeling of fantasy to an already wild palla design. A tiny lantern-like object appears balanced at each end of the arching U-shaped element, while the base of each boteh and mound is joined by a thick sinuous vine. The dhoor pattern cleverly imitates the palla; notice how the cypress tree is looped about itself, thereby maintaining volume and symmetry. In Plate 160 the sharp bristled aspect of the concentric cones is nicely softened by the hashia's winding hooked vine. These three pieces may be compared to their antecedents in Plates 150, 151 and 152.

PLATE 161.
'Moon' shawl. Sikh Period, c.1830. 175cm x 180cm. (69 x 71in.).
The same theme continues here as in Plates 159 and 160, lending itself well to the smaller repeat of leaning, hooked-tip botehs. The pattern is novel, innovative and rather lively.

PLATE 162.
Shoulder mantle (fragment). Sikh Period, c.1820. 53cm x 74cm (21 x 29in.).
This bizarre piece is of a type only very occasionally found in Western markets. However, similar pieces are quite commonly seen in Northern India and more especially in Lahore, Pakistan, which had once been the Sikh capital of the Punjab. For this reason we may label them 'Lahore' or 'Lahore-type' shawls. Besides their coarse yarn, which may be a mixture of sheep's or ordinary goat's wool, their generally sombre dyes were not very fast.

PLATE 163.
Shoulder mantle. Sikh Period, c.1820. 145cm x 305cm (57 x 120in.).
No shawl has captured so well, in visual form and pattern, the riotous undercurrents of an Islamic culture in full revolution. A tumultuous inner-cone movement appears to challenge the confining traditions of the boteh's classic curves. Within this frenzy of contorted shapes a new dynamic, if not radical, form of artistic expression finds its full growth potential. Each of the sweeping design elements interacts in such a way as to disintegrate the staunch notion of Kashmir's ubiquitous emblem, the boteh.

COLOUR PLATE 206.
Shoulder mantle. Sikh Period, c.1840. 140cm x 300cm (55 x 118in.)
The leafy frond vines join with the central field to run clear across the whole shawl. This is an unusual feature in shawls of this type which have a plain, round central field. Its also curious how some of the branches end in palm trees as they fall into the central field.

342

COLOUR PLATE 207.
*Shoulder mantle. Sikh Dogra
Period (Transitional). c.1845.
140cm x 320cm (55 x 126in.).*
One of the great masterpieces of
the mid-19th century, this
spectacular pattern epitomises the
great artistic heights that had been
sustained by the Kashmiri weavers
despite the growing influx of
European designs and the West's
ever increasing demands for the
Kashmir shawl.

Rare are shawl designs that fuse
pattern movements of both the
central field and end panels to
create a complete overall design.
The completeness found here is
expressed with explosive power
through the cosmic-like mandala
of the shawl's stunning and
unique central field, a field that
reflects the strong contiguous
cultures which surround the Valley
of Kashmir: Hinduism, Islam, and
Buddhism.

The 'dance' of leaning botehs
illuminated by a white ground
and intertwined with the sinuous
flow of vines and mihrabs
converging towards the centre,
and the special feature of the
flaming nimbus within the mihrab
spandrels, all fuse together to form
perhaps one of the most striking
shawls of this period. As the vines
flow into the end panels they form
a trellis pattern over a field of tall
stately botehs at the base of which
can be found three large mihrabs
whose scalloped spandrels all point
toward the central field in saph
(multiple prayer rug) formation.

343

*These two tapestry shawls are
monuments of design composition.
Because of the festive floral nature
of their fancy patterns they are
called 'celebration shawls'. In both
pieces the sweeping botehs invade
the lateral hashias – an idea which
influenced, to a large degree, the
Jacquard shawls. The swaying fan-
like flowers in Plate 164 are
descendants of the flattened rose.
The outlined sweeping botehs of
Plate 165 in pink, yellow, blue and
white alternating on various ground
colours of green, vermilion and
black might be a burst of fireworks
illuminating the sky.*

PLATE 166.
Rumal, shoulder mantle, Dogra Period, c.1870. 180cm x 180cm (71 x 71in.).
From a standpoint of colour range and weave execution this shawl was found to be a
particularly fine example of a late rumal. The number of patchwork pieces has been kept to a
strict minimum and the inserted black and white strips which form the large fleur-de-lis and
scalloped lobed pattern have been scrupulously joined.

345

COLOUR PLATE 208.
Shoulder mantle. Dogra Period, c.1860. l46cm x 310cm (57 x 122in.).
The complete absence of the boteh is rare but in this fine 'four season' shawl the artist has managed to avoid it through the ingenious use of cypress trees and sprays of fronds. The three prayer niches or 'mihrabs' along with their Mughal style supporting columns express a well-defined Islamic statement to what would normally be during this time frame a mostly western consumer market. The most pleasant feature of this colourful piece is the wide areas of plain colour which provide plenty of room for the flowers to blossom.

346

COLOUR PLATE 209.
Shoulder mantle. Dogra Period c.1865, 140cm x 320cm (55 x 126in.).
Brilliant dyes and crisp execution of weave combine here to form a dramatic zoomorphic pattern. The rising and strongly serrated botehs, snakes and other exotic plant life under each of the three mihrabs create a jungle atmosphere reminiscent of the designs made by the well-known French shawl artist, Antony Berrus, during the period 1848-1850. The red centre is elegantly rendered by the use of fine scalloped-edge kani work of cypress trees and pineapple-leaf sprays.

347

PLATE 167.
Rumal, shoulder mantle. Dogra, c.1870. 175cm x 175cm (69 x 69in.).
This curious rococo and densely ornate, cursive leaf design is of a type which falls into a
standard pattern which achieved an enormous popularity. Many of these what we call 'vase'
shawls have been found in private collections of Iranian exiles after the fall of the late Shah
Phalavi. Indeed, it is not impossible that most of them were actually woven in Iran. Hundreds of
little woven kani pieces had to be assembled, much like a jigsaw puzzle, in order to obtain the
full rumal. Equally, the intricately embroidered fringes are achieved through a careful process of
assembling tiny pieces of pashmina, much like a crazy quilt and then embellishing them
profusely with embroidery.

PLATE 168.
Shoulder mantle. Sikh Period, c.1830. 144cm x 327cm (56 x 129in.).
Here we see in a stylised form, the Sacred Mountain, which can be seen in less abstracted form
in Colour Plate 202. Apart from the three laurel wreaths the design similarities, except for the
dhoor and hashia patterns, are noticeable upon brief inspection. The long hashias in this plate
are not of the same design as the inner ones, and therefore they would have been replaced. Once
again, as in Colour Plate 202, we have an almost superfluous role played by the botehs.

COLOUR PLATE 210.
*Shoulder mantle Dogra Period
c.1875, 152cm x 325cm (60 x
128in.).*
*The extraordinary delicacy and
vitality of this shawl sets it in a class
of its own. The spectacular
Rorschach-type central field pattern
is created by the long and thin-
stemmed leafy fronds which
sinuously converge in opposing
colours of black and white from the
fringe ends toward the centre. With
peace and serenity these fronds
appear to navigate through a
churning sea of swirling mauve
flames recalling the Chinese cloud-
band forms of early Mughal art.
Besides the embroidered fringes
being the largest and most elaborate
ever encountered, the high warp/weft
density makes this one of the finest
pieces of Kashmir weaving.*

COLOUR PLATE 211.
Shoulder mantle Dogra Period, c.1875. 140cm x 320cm (55 x 126in.). Exemplified in this chef d'oeuvre of kani weaving is the beautiful synthesis of Hindu-Islamic styles. The serpent, symbol of procreative male force, is given particular attention by the Kashmiri artist. The large flame-tipped, serrated-edge botehs, the heads of which brush up against the mihrab spandrels, are held by truncated, stubby branches. The criss-crossing of long serpents across the whole palla renders a marvellous zoomorphic aspect to this picture of jungle morphology. A perfect contrast of changing ground colours is achieved through the use of conservative ground embellishment to enhance the shawl pattern's turbulent and almost nightmarish impact.

351

PLATE 169.
*Shoulder mantle.
Dogra Period,
c.1850. 132cm x
306cm (52 x
120in.).
Stylistically this
shawl shares
common features
with Colour Plate
208 in that there are
wide areas of plain
colour left
unembellished,
except that here of
course the boteh is
the star motif.*

PLATE 170.
Shoulder mantle. Sikh Period, c.1840. 135cm x 310cm (53 x 122in.).

COLOUR PLATE 212.
*Shoulder mantle. Dogra Period.
Dated 1875, 144cm x 344cm (56 x
135in.).*
*This shawl demonstrates the
Kashmiri's continued and freely
expressed exploration into the avant
garde effects of colour and design.
The kaleidoscopic colour palette
chosen for this eye dazzling shawl
must have certainly run counter to
the more sedate European taste for
those shawls coming off the jacquard
looms in 1875. However, it is well
known that a phenomenal demand
for shawls of unusual designs
continued in France throughout
most of the 19th century. And, as to
the question of any loss of creativity
in Kashmir toward the latter part of
the 19th century, this example
certainly lays that to rest. There is a
fine and delicate calligraphic trellis
pattern that runs well over the tall
and stately botehs and into the
central field of burnt saffron to form
a very unusual eight-lobed
medallion; a stained-glass effect is
created on the signed and dated
field. Observing carefully the end
panel designs, small and bizarre
human figures, animals, birds, and
gazebos can be seen interwoven
almost secretly within the design,
adding a mysterious aura to the
shawl. In several of the tiny scenes,
couples appear to be dallying.
Perhaps this had been a special
marriage shawl. But by far the most
unique feature of this rare shawl is
the changing direction of the tall
botehs from one palla to the other. In
one, they oppose, in the other, they
face the same direction. And as if
that was not enough, this gifted artist
chose to change the ground pattern
at each end of the shawl from a
chevron to a cascading diagonal
design.*

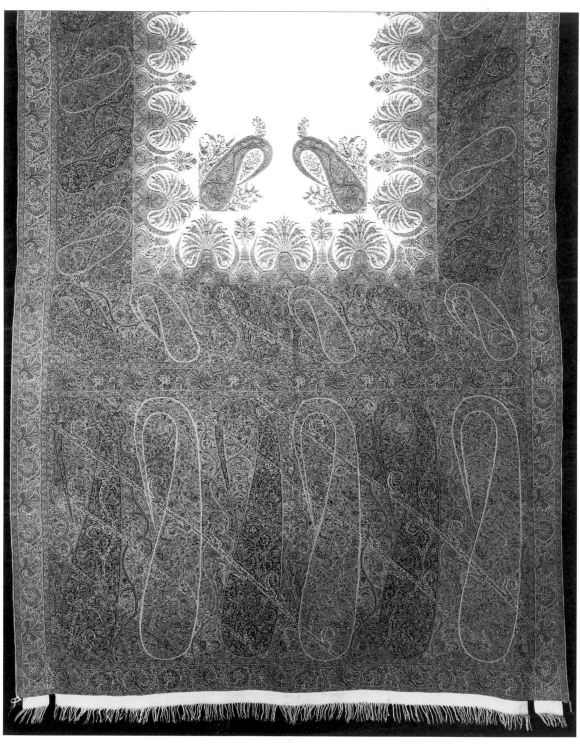

PLATE 171.
Shoulder mantle. Sikh Period, c.1840. 139cm x 328cm (55 x 129in.).
Exemplified by these two shawls is the incredible and inexhaustible virtuosity of the Kashmiri
artist in his use of the hooked vine motif. In Plate 170, each tall boteh is overlaid by two vertically
rising, interlaced hooked vines and a snaking floral meander. They cross the top hashia to end in
a swirling riot of leaning botehs and pineapple cone leaves located in the field.

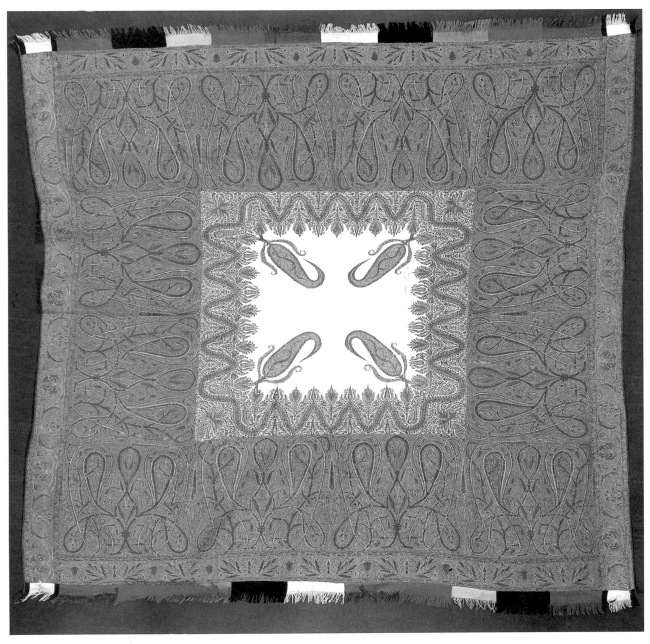

PLATE 172.
Shoulder mantle. Sikh Period, c.1840. 165cm x 165cm (65 x 65in.).
Fine square shawls with graphic patterns and a white sinuous centre with intricate kani work
are rare from this period. The four kunj botehs presented here, mounted on a lyre-like base,
show a certain European influence while the main border pattern of looping botehs is well
characteristic of the Sikh repertoire of patterns.

GLOSSARY

amli: embroidered; an embroidered shawl from Kashmir.

banian: banker, money lender.

battant brocheur espoulineur: an obscure loom which was capable of imitating the **kani** weave.

bedris: a tightly packed bale of woven goods for transport by caravan.

bent-tip strawberry: expression for a popular rose-type flower often seen in the **hashias** of the 17th and 18th century and sometimes in the **botchs** of the 17th century. It usually formed a repeat with the pinwheel flower.

boteh: Paisley, pine cone or mango shape; a western adaptation of the word buta.

broché: brocaded. A weave whereby the weft does not travel the full width of the cloth but forms the pattern only when its colour is required.

buta: flower in Indian. See **boteh.**

buti: small flower.

caillouté: early French word meaning pebbly. It denotes a particular floral style of the late Afghan shawls: compact flowers resembling a mosaic.

celebration shawls: refers to those exuberant and rare patterns mainly of the Sikh period whose effusively woven flora often appear like exploding fireworks.

chandar: the moon shawl. A square shawl containing a central medallion and quarter medallions at each corner of the field.

coif boteh: a boteh whose arching apex is highlighted by a detached **raceme.**

cone: see **boteh.**

counterfeit shawl: European kani shawl which was often passed off as a genuine Kashmir shawl.

dagshawl: a severe system of excise tax imposed during the Afghan period.

dhor: a running motif which borders the **matan.**

diapered field: allover pattern of diamond-shaped figures.

dochalla: one of two long shawls woven exactly alike. Literally a 'double' shawl.

doruka: literally 'two-sided'. Reversible **kani** shawl from Kashmir.

dorunga: a 'doruka' whose ground colour on one side differs from that of the other, due to a very intricate couching stitch.

drawloom: loom whose warps are attached to vertical cords called simples, which in turn are raised by a drawboy.

espouliné: French term for **kani** woven.

espoulins: see **tojis.**

exact imitation shawl: see **counterfeit shawl.**

foldover shawl: square shawl which when diagonally folded in half displays its full design. Also, turnover shawl.

fool's cap: a floral device of the Sikh period which looks like a hat.

fringe gates: the different coloured bands of wool which, often embroidered with **mihrabs,** composed the fringe of the **kani** shawl. Fringe gates began about mid-19th century.

garden shawl: a shawl whose design imitates running water in the Mughal fashion by a chevron pattern.

grenadine: a yarn composed of two silk strands slightly twisted but given a high torsion when combined together.

harlequin shawl: type of long shawl popular around the 1820s, each **boteh** of the **palla** is highlighted by a different ground colour. Thus a compartmentalised effect is achieved.

hashia: the narrow lateral borders which run the length of the shawl, the pattern of which is usually composed of a floral meander.

ideogram root: expression coined for a 17th century Mughal style in which the **boteh's** roots were secured with a device resembling a Chinese ideogram.

ikat: a resist dye process in which designs are dyed in yarns by tightly wrapping bundles of yarn to prevent dye penetration.

Jacquard loom: a loom whose **warps** are raised by a system of hooks controlled by a series of punched cards.

jamawar: gown piece. Usually a long decorative shawl.

kani: woven. The Kashmir weave: **twill** tapestry weave with interlocked **wefts.**

karkhana: the building in which the shawls were woven.

karkhandar: proprietor of a weaving factory.

khatraaz: striped shawl pattern.

lancé: weaving method whereby the **weft** crosses the full width of the cloth and appears on the surface only where the design calls for its colour; otherwise the weft remains floating on the reverse side or is trimmed off once the cloth leaves the loom.

lena: goat's fleece from Ladakh.

matan: the unworked central field of the shawl.

mihrab: prayer niche in a mosque oriented toward Mecca, the holy city of Islam. This architectural form is found often in Islamic decorative arts.

millefleurs: thousands of flowers. Often used for a type of prayer rug whose mihrab is completely filled with flowers.

mise-en-carte: the setting up of a given weaving pattern on special grid paper.

moon shawl: see **chandar.**

mugim: shawl appraiser.

naqqash: pattern maker.

paisley: see **boteh.** Also a town near Glasgow, Scotland, where large numbers of cheap 'Kashmir' shawls were woven.

palla: the patterned borders at each end of the shawl.

palme: early French equivalent for **boteh.**

papier briqueté: gridpaper whose pattern resembles that of a brick wall, on which the shawl pattern was drawn.

pashm: goat fleece.

pashmina: woven goat fleece.

patchwork shawl: shawls of the late 19th century composed of many separately woven pieces then joined together by the **rafugar.**

patka: waistband. A very long and narrow Kashmir shawl wrapped several times around the waist. It could also be used as a turban.

perfoliate leaves: botanical. Leaves that completely clasp the stem and are apparently pierced by it.

pin-wheel flower: expression for a particular yellow flower whose pointed petals appear arranged radially around a central axis. A flower often seen in 17th century Mughal textiles and rugs.

pricked-in colours: a process by which faded colours are enhanced by painting in new or fresh colours directly by brush on the wool.

putto: crudely woven Ladakhi sheep-wool.

Qajar boteh: a coined term for bulbous, 18th century style of curvilinear **boteh,** the apex of which is composed of arching **racemes.**

raceme: botanical. Stalked flowers arranged singly along a common main axis.

radial flowers: flowers whose petals or buds are arranged in a precise circular fashion around a central axis; a style developed in the third quarter of the 18th century under the Afghans.

rafle: machine spun wool derived from merino sheep.

rafugar: shawl tailor or seamster.

raised boteh: a style popular about 1815 where the **boteh** was often shown raised on a mound or other type of ornament.

rank shawl: an early Mughal shawl which may have indicated military rank because of the symmetrically arranged rows of leaves.

renaissance shawls: shawl patterns popular in Europe during the 1830s in which neo-gothic architecture was in vogue.

reversible shawl: shawl with the same pattern on both sides and which can be worn either way round.

ring shawl: a **shah tus** shawl whose extreme fineness may be demonstrated by slipping it through a finger ring.

rumal: square shawl.

sash: see **patka.**

shah tus: literally king's wool. The fleece comes from the ibex, a wild Himalayan goat of the genus capra, which grazes at very high altitudes. The rarest and most expensive fleece in the world.

shikarga: a shawl pattern depicting a hunting scene with animals.

shuttle: wooden bobbin with pointed ends which is slid back and forth across the loom to insert the **weft.**

talim: cards coded in the Kashmiri language on which the shawl pattern, according to **warp** number and its associated colour is indicated.

tanjir: the horizontal border which lies above and below the **palla.** Normally it is identical to the **hashia,** which is why in the text the word **hashia** is often used to denote both.

tarah guru: colour caller.

technique of characterisation: a coined term for an early Mughal style of mimicking nature in which case the **boteh's** flora, cartoon-like in quality. display a certain novel caricature effect.

tojis: needle-like wooden sticks used in the **kani** weave and around which the various dyed yarns are wrapped.

toshakhana: imperial wardrobe.

tree boteh: a boteh style popular around 1815 whose tall thick central branch is drawn like a tree trunk.

tus or tooch: literally wool, but generally refers to **shah tus.**

twill weave: a cloth texture of oblique ribs formed by the **warp** and **weft.**

umbrella-handle stem: a type of stem that terminates in a slight hook and usually found in the **buti.**

ustad: master weaver.

vase shawl: square **kani** shawl, the design of which is composed of vases in the form of leafy scrolls which approach the centre from each corner. The ground is usually heavily overfilled with other nondescript flora.

warp: the yarns which are stretched on the loom to form the underlying structure of the cloth.

weft: thread which crosses the cloth at right angles to the **warp;** the thread which forms the pattern.

winged-leaf buti: a type of small **buti,** the stem of which supports a lateral projection of a serrated leaf or flower or both. It is usually seen on late 18th century shawls patterned with a trellis, chevron or checkerboard design.

BIBLIOGRAPHY

General

Anonymous
Ouvriers de deux mondes. La société d'économie sociale, vol. 1, Paris, 1857.
Kashmeer and its Shawls, London, 1875.
The History of the Sikhs, Calcutta, 1846.
Aijazuddin, F.S.
Sikh Portraits by European Artists, London, 1979.
Alcan, Michel
Essai sur l'industrie des matières textiles, Paris, 1847.
Traité du travail des laines, Paris, 1866.
Les inventions et les perfectionnements apportés à la fabrication des châles par M. Eck, Paris 1848.
Ames, Frank
'The Fashion of the Kashmir Shawl in France', *Hali,* London, Vol.5, No.1, 1982.
'Le châle cachemire en France au 19ème siècle', *Hali,* Vol.6, No.2, 1984.
'Lost Horizons: The Stylistic Development of the Kashmir Shawl', *Hali,* Vol.6, No.4, 1984.
'The Development of Early Kashmir Shawl Motifs', *Art Textrina,* Vol. 22, June 1994
Baden-Powell, B.H.
Handbook of the Manufacturers and Arts of the Punjab, vol.2, Lahore, 1872.
Bamzai, Prithivi Nath Kaul
A History of. Kashmir, New Delhi, 1973.
Barret, Douglas, and Gray, Basil
Indian Painting, New York, 1963.
Bell, T.F.
Jacquard Weaving and Designing, London, 1895.
Bernier, François
Travels in the Mogul Empire, 1656-1668, 2 vols., London, 1891.
Biétry, Laurent
Reponse à une brochure d'un fabricant de châles, le châle cachemire français, le châle des Indes et la marque de fabrique, Paris, 1849.
Lettre adressée à Messieurs les Membres du Jury de la 20ème Classe à l'Exposition Universelle de 1855, Paris.
Birdwood, George C.M.
The Industrial Arts of India, London, 1880.
Blair, Mathew
The Paisley Shawl, Glasgow, 1904.
Blanqui, Jérôme-Adolphe
Conservatoir des Arts et Métiers, Cours d'économie industrielle, Paris, 1837-38.
Histoire de l'exposition des produits de l'industrie française en 1827, Paris.
Bogle, G.
Voyages au Thibet par Bogle, Turner et Pourungir., Paris, 1806.
Burnes, Alexander
Travels into Bokhara, 2 vols., London, 1834.
Chandra, Moti
'Kashmir Shawls', *Bulletin of the Prince of Wales Museum,* No.3, pp.1-24 Bombay, 1954.
Chassagne. Serge
Oberkampf, Paris, 1980.
Chattopadhaya, K.
Carpets of India and Floor Coverings, D.B. Taraporevala Sons and Co., private edition, 1969.
Clabburn, Pamela
The Norwich Shawl, London, HMSO, 1995.
Coffinet, Julien.
Arochiné ou l'art de la tapisserie, 1971.
Couder, Amédée
Analyse du dessin des cachemires et moyens de Vendre les schalls français supérieurs à ceux des Indes, Paris, 1834.
Description des dessins exposé en 1849, Paris.
Quelques idées sur l'Exposition Universelle en France, Paris, 1854.
Projects d'academie royale de musique et de réunion du Louvre aux Tuileries, 1845.
Exposition française à Londres. Description des Dessins exposes par Amédée Couder dessinateur pour l'industrie et architecture, 1849.
L'Architecture et l'Industrie comme moyen de perfection sociale. 8 plates, Paris 1842 2nd ed. with 9 folding plates 4, Paris, 1844.
Couder, Louis-Charles Auguste *Considérations pour le but morale des beaux arts,* Paris.
Cunningham, Alexander
Ladak, Physical, Statistical, and Historical, London, 1854.
Cuvillier-Fleury, A.A.
Notes historiques sur le Général Allard et sur le Royaume de Lahore, Paris, 1836.
Voyages et voyageurs, Paris, 1834.
Daclin, C.
Table générale analytique et raisonnée, etc., Paris 1838.

Deloche, Jean
> *Voyage en Inde du Comte de Modave, 1773-1776,* Paris, 1971.

Deneirouse Eugène
> *Traité sur la fabrication de châles des Indes,* Paris, 1851
> *Notes sur la situation de la fabrique de châles etc.,* Corbeil, 1849
> *Notice sur la nécessité de remplacer par un tissage mécanique les brochés à la main,* Paris, 1863.

Deslandres, Y.
> 'Josephine and the Arts', *Apollo,* July, 1977.

Dow, George Francis
> 'The Paisley Shawl with Some Account of the Shawl Made in Kashmir', *Old-Time England,* vol.2, pp.113-121, Boston, 1921.

Duprès, Adrien
> *Voyages en Perse faits dans les années 1807, 1808. 1809,* 2 vols., Paris, 1819.

Elphinstone, Baron Mountstuart
> *An Account of the Kingdom of Caubul,* London, 1815.

Eymard, Paul
> *Historique du métier Jacquard,* Lyon, 1863.

Falcot, P.
> *Traité de la fabrication de tissus,* 2 vols., Paris, 1852.

Falk, S.J.
> *Qajar Painting,* London, 1972.

Fichel, P.
> *Un mot sur le cachemire des Indes et le cachemire français,* Paris, 1834.

Flachat, Jean Claude
> *Observation sur le commerce et sur les arts etc.,* 2 vols., Paris, 1766.

Forster, George
> *Journey from Bengal to England,* London, 1798.

Fraser, James B.
> *Narrative of Journey into Khorasan in the Years 1821 and 1822 etc.,* London, 1825.
> *Journey of a Tour Through Part of the Snowy Range of the Himalayan Mountains, etc.,* London, 1820.
> *Travels and Adventures in the Persian Provinces etc., 1821-1822,* London, 1826.

French, C.J.
> *Journal of a Tour in Upper Hindustan etc., 1838-1839,* Simla, 1872.

Ganju, M.
> *Textile Industries in Kashmir, Delhi,* 1945.

Geijer. Agnus
> *A History of Textile Art,* England, 1979.

Grandsard, A.
> *Jacquard, Sa Vie,* Paris, n.d.

Grose, J.H.
> *Voyage to the East-Indies,* London, 1757.

Hanway, Jonas
> An Historical Account of the British Trade over the Caspian Sea, 4 vols., London, 1753.

Honigsberger, J.
> *33 Years in the East,* London, 1852.

Hunter, J
> 'The Paisley Textile Industry 1695-1830', *Costume,* No. 10, pp.1-15, 1976.

Ireland, John B.
> *Wall-Street to Cashmere,* New York, 1859.

Jacquard, Joseph Marie
> *Biographie universelle,* Paris, 1834.

Jacquemont, Victor
> *Voyages dans l'Inde pendant les années 1828 à 1832,* 4 vols., Paris, 1841.

Jehangir
> *The Tuzuk-i-Jehangiri; or the memoirs of Jehangir,* Trans. Alexander Rogers, Delhi, 1968.

Jaubert, P. Amédée
> *Voyages en Arménie et en Perse faits dans les années 1805 et 1806,* Paris, 1821.

Kahlenherg, Mary Hunt
> 'A Study of the Development and Use of the Mughal Patka (Sash) etc.' *Aspect of Indian Art,* Brill Pub., 1971, pp.153-166

Kaul, S.N.
> *Kashmir Economics,* Srinagar, 1954.

King, Margaret R.
> 'Cashmere Shawls', *Cincinatti Museum Review,* No. 5, Oct. 1892.

Klaproth, Heinrich Julius von
> *Voyage dans les steppes d'Astrakhan et de Caucase par le Comte Jean Potocki,* 2 vols., Paris, 1829.
> *Tableau historique, géographique... entre La Russie et La Perse,* Paris, 1827.

Koul, Anand
> 'The Kashmir Shawl Trade', *The East and West,* Srinagar. vol. XIV. Jan., 1915, No. 159, pp.28-42.

Leavitt, Thomas W.
> 'Fashion, Commerce and Technology in the 19th Century: The Shawl Trade', *Textile History,* Dec. 1972, vol.3, pp.51-64.

Legoux de Flaix
> *Essai historique, géographique et politique sur l'Hindustan,* 2 vols., Paris, 1807.

Leitner. G.W.
> *An Account of Shawl Weaving... from Linguistic Fragments Discovered in 1870, 1872 and 1879,* Lahore, 1882.

Lomüller, Louis M.
> *Guillaume Ternaux 1763-1833,* Paris, 1979.

Martin, Henri
> *Histoire de France.* 9 vols., Paris, 1875.

Niclausse, Juliette
> *Tapisseries et tapis de la ville de Paris,* 1948.

Oliver. Guillaume. Antoine
> *Voyages dans l'Empire Ottoman, l'Egypte et la Perse etc.,* 4 vols., Paris, 1804.

Pearse, Major Hugh
Memoirs of Alexander Gardner, Soldier and Traveller, Colonel of Artillery in the Service of Maharaja Runjit Singh, 1898.

Perleberg, H.C.
Persian Textiles, Newark Museum Association, 1919.

Picard, Charles
Saint-Quentin, de son Commerce et de ses Industries, 2 vols., Paris, 1867.

Posselt, E.A.
The Jacquard Machine Analysed and Explained, Philadelphia, 1893.

Prat, D. de
Traité de tissage au Jacquard, Paris, 1921.

Reath, Nancy Andrews, and Sachs, Eleanor B.
Persian Textiles and their Technique from the 6th to the 18th Century, Yale University Press, 1937.

Rey, Jean
Etude pour servir à l'histoire des châles, Paris, 1823.

Ruppert, Jacques, *Le Costume,* 5 vols., Paris 1930

Schürmann, Ulrich
Caucasian Rugs, London, 1974.

Sée, Henri
Esquisse de l'evolution industrielle de la France de 1815 à 1818, Paris, 1923.

Shah, Hajji Mukhtar
A Treatise on the Art of Shawl Weaving. Koh-i-Nor Press, Lahore, 1887. Translated from the Persian by Prof. Bashir Ahmad Dar, Srinagar, 1981.

Simpson, W.
India Ancient and Modern, London, 1867.

Singh, Ganda
Early European Accounts of the Sikhs, Calcutta, 1862.

Skelton, Robert
A Decorative Motif in Mughal Art, Aspects of Indian Art, Brill pub., 1971.

Soltykoff, Prince Alexis
Voyages dans l'Inde et en Perse, Paris, 1853.

Sonnerat
Voyages aux Indes Orientales et en Chine depuis 1774 jusqu'au 1781, 2 vols., Paris 1782.

Stewart, A.M.
The History and Romance of the Paisley Shawl, Paisley, 1922.

Sufi, Dr. G.M. (AL-Hajj)
A history of Kashmir, 2 vols., New Delhi, 1974.

Tavernier, Jean Baptiste
Les six Voyages en Turquie et en Perse, 2 vols., Paris, 1981.

Tessier, M.
Mémoire sur l'importation en France des chèvres à duvet de Cachemire, Paris, 1819.

Torrens, Lieut.-Col.
Travels in Ladak, Tartary and Kashmir, London, 1862.

Turner, Samuel M.
Ambassade au Thibet et au Boutan, Trans. into French by J. Castéra, Paris, 1800.

Vigne, G.T.
Travels in Kashmir, 2 vols., London, 1842.

Waheeduddin, Fakir Syed
The Real Runjit Singh, New Delhi, 1976.

Watson, J. Forbes
The Textile Manufacturers and the Costumes of the People of India, London, 1866.
Textile Fabrics of India, 18 vols., London, 1977.

Watt, Sir George
Indian Art at Delhi, London, 1904.
The Commercial Products of India, London, 1908.

Whiteley, J.
Ingres, London, 1977.

Whyte, Dorothy
'Edinburgh Shawls and their makers', *Costume,* No.10, London, 1976.

Whyte, Dorothy, and Swain, M.H.
'Edinburgh Shawls', *Old Edinburgh Club,* vol.31, 1962.

Wilson, H.H.
Travels in the Himalayan Provinces by Moorcroft and G. Trebeck, 1819 to 1825. 2 vols., London, 1841.

Museum Publications and Exhibition Catalogues

Archer W.G.
Painting of the Sikhs, Victoria and Albert Museum, London, 1966.

Irwin, John
Shawls, Victoria and Albert Museum, London, 1955.
The Kashmir Shawl, Victoria and Albert Museum, London, 1973.

Lévis-Strauss, Monique
Le tissage des châles au Cachemire et en France, exhibition catalogue: 'La mode du châle cachemire en France', Paris, 1982.
Les châles tissées en Inde et en France, exhibition catalogue: 'Le Châle Cachemire en France au XIX siècle', Lyon, 1983.

Nîmes et le Châle, la collection du musée du Vieux Nîmes, 1988.

Rothstein Natalie
Introduction of the Jacquard loom into England, Studies in Textile History, Royal Ontario Museum.

Singh, Chandrmani and Ahivasi, Devaki
Woollen Textiles and Costumes from Bharat Kala Bhavan, Benares Hindu University, 1981.

Vial, Gabriel
La technique du châle, catalogue of the exhibition: 'Le Châle Cachemire en France au XIX siècle', Lyon. 1983.

Yale University Art Gallery
The Kashmir Shawl, Connecticut, 1975.
West Surrey College of Art and Design
The Art of the Shawl, England, 1977.
Conservatoire National des Arts and Métiers
Catalogue de musée, section I (industries textiles. teintures et apprêts). Paris, 1942.
The Oriental Rug Collection of Mary Jane and Jerome Straka, New York, 1978.

French National and Universal Exhibitions

1798	Première exposition des produits de l'industrie Française (abbr. E.P.I.F.)
1801	Seconde E.P.I.F.
	Procès verbal, E.P.I.F.
1802	Troisième E.P.I.F.
	Procès verbal, E.P.I.F.
1806	Catalogue des produits de l'E.P.I.F.
	Rapport du jury presente par M. De Champagny of l'E.P.I.F.
1819	Rapport du jury central sur les E.P.I.F. présenté par Decazes et L. Costaz.
	Rapport du jury d'admission sur l'exposition des produits des manu factures du Dept. de la Seine.
1823	Rapport du jury d'admission, Louvre, présenté par L. Héricart de Thury.
	Rapport sur les E P.I.F., au nom du jury central, rédigé par M. le Vicomte Héricart de Thury et par M. Migneron.
1827	Rapport sur les E.P.I.F., par Héricart et Migneron.
	Rapport du jury départemental de la Seine sur les produits de l'industrie admis au concours de l'exposition public par M. Payen, vols. 1 et 2, 1829 et 1832.
	Compte-rendu des E.P.I.F.
	Histoire de l'E.P.I.F. par Jean Adolphe Blanqui.
1834	Musée industriel.
	Notice des E.P.I.F.
	Rapport du jury central sur des E.P.I.F. , par le Baron Charles Dupin, 3 vols.
	l'Industrie par Stéphane Flachat, Paris.
1839	E.P.I.F., 3 vols., 1839.
1844	Musée Challamel par Jules Burat.
	Rapport du jury central, Vol.3.
	Vol.I, reporteurs: Deneirouse et Legentil.
	Vol.II, reporteur: Théodore Olivier.
	Catalogue Officiel des produits de l'industrie.
1819	Exposition française à Londres, description des dessins exposés par Amédée Couder.
1851	Travaux de la commission française, 13 vols. sur l'industrie des nations. Vol. 4: industrie des Châles etc., rapport de Maxime Gaussen.
1855	Rapport du jury mixte international, Vol. 1, et 3.

Visite à l'Exposition Universelle de Paris, Tresca.

Paris Universal Exhibition 1855, Committee reports Part I., Great Britain: Huddersfield Chamber of Commerce.

Catalogue spécial des envois d'Autriche.

Catalogue de l'Exposition de 1855.

1862	Rapport du jury international publié sous la direction de Michel Chevalier.
	Catalogue Officiel.
1867	Rapports des delegations ouvrières, 3 vols.
	Rapports du jury international, 13 vols.
	'Châles' par David Gerson.
	Catalogue Général publié par le commission imperiale.
	Exposition Universelle de 1867, illustré par Prosper Poitevin.
1878	Exposition Universelle Internationale de 1878, rapport sur les châles par M. Gaussen, Paris.

Dictionaries

Nouveau Larousse Illustré, 7 vols., Paris, 1900.
Dictionnaire technologique ou nouveau dictionnaire universel des arts et métiers, 22 vols., Paris, 1823.
Dictionnaire universel du commerce de la banque et des manufactures, Pillet Imprimeur-Libraire, 2 vols., Paris, 1838, 1841.
Dictionnaire universel de commerce, banque, manufacture, douane, etc., 2 vols., Paris, 1805.

Kashmir Design Albums

Musée des Arts Décoratifs, Paris:
Oberkampf
Dessins Copiés sur d 'anciens châles et écharpes de Cachemire, frontispiece reads: 'La plupart ont été copiés sur les premiers châles et écharpes qui furent introduits en France au commencement de ce siècle par les officiers de l'armée d'Egypte, Fabrique de Jouy.'
Recueil des premières empreintes de dessins pour la fabrication d'étoffes imprimés, Jouy. 1804-1811.
Dessins copiés d'après des anciennes toiles peintes de la Perse et de l'Inde, Jouy, 1760-1790.
Empreintes et dessins pour toiles imprimées, mouchoirs et fichus, manufacture d'Indiennes à Nantes, vols. I et II, 1770-1822.
Petitpierre
Manufacture d'Indiennes à Nantes, mouchoirs et fichus, 1770-1822.
Fay and Brulé
Dessins pour dentelle, 1809-1902. (It is felt that these designs were not reserved for lace only but were employed for embroidery and weavings also.)

Gonelle Frères

Dessins pour cachemire. (Inside label reads 'Dessaigne, successeur de Chavant 1854-1862'.)

Berrus

Dessins de châles fonds pleins. 5 albums. (Album I dated 1848-50. album II dated 1849-50.)

Pochades Longues, 6 vols., 1858-60.

Dessins de châles longs, 7 albums.

Pochades carrées. 3 albums, 1865-66.

Dessins de châles carrés, 22 albums. (Album I dated 1851-53.)

Bibliothèque Nationale, Paris (departement des estampes):

Chavant, F.

Souvenir de l'exposition des produits de l'industrie française de 1839. 'Reproduction exacte des principales étoffes faconnées et imprimées, 350 dessins réunis en 50 feuilles.'

Album du Cachemirien. 'Reproduction exacte de tous les beaux châles des Indes et de la Perse fabriqués à Lahore, Ispahan, Teheran, Caboul, Kashmir, et Candahar qui arrivent en Europe calqués fidèlement et dessinés aux traits simples dans leurs grandeurs naturelles Ouvrages précieux pour servir de matériaux aux dessinateurs de manufactures.' Paris et Kashmir, 1837.

Journal du fabricant d'étoffes façonnées, 1837.

Guide du dessinateur de l'industrie, 1837.

Le dessinateur de Cachemire. 'Recueil de motifs et matériaux pour les dessinateurs de manufactures, composeés sur pierres par des artists spéciaux.' Paris, 1837.

Delaye, V.

Indo-Parisien (1850-69).

Costumes féminins (albums from 1792-1803, 1804-13. 1814-21).

Dessins de Cachemire, 2 vols. (mid-19th century).

Costumes of Turkey, printed for William Miller, London, 1804.

Archives

National Archives, Paris:

Carton

F12-2199, Métier Jacquard.

F12-2414, Châles.

F12-2175, Vingtième extrait de divers avis sur le commerce fasicule, Fev. 1822.

F12-254, Recettes et dépenses faites par les Sieurs Fourcade à l'établissement des Indiens à Thieux, 1785.

F12-1004, F12-1005A (contain documents relating to patents delivered to Ternaux).

F12-600-603 (contain important documents on the raising of fleece goats and Ternaux's expedition to Russia to bring back the Kashmir goat).

Chambre de Commerce, Paris:

Registre de Correspondance, T4, 'Rapport de Ternaux et de Ballenger sur l'industrie parisienne de châles et de gazes.' Séance du 17 Juillet, 1822.

Indian Office Library. London:

Strachey. R.

'Memoire on the Revenue and trade of Cabul, etc., with other points of information relative to that Kingdom. (Contains interesting report on 'shawl manufactory'.) Unpublished, 1812.

INDEX

The index covers the first eight chapters of the book
onlyPage numbers in bold type refer to pictures and captions.

BY
D. H. LAWRENCE

THE LATER D. H. LAWRENCE
The Best Novels, Stories, and Essays, 1925–1930
Selected, with Introductions, by
WILLIAM YORK TINDALL
(*St. Mawr; The Man Who Died; The Woman Who
Rode Away; Sun;* selections, complete in themselves,
from *Mornings in Mexico, Assorted Articles,* and *Reflections on the Death of a Porcupine*)

THE PLUMED SERPENT
with an Introduction by
WILLIAM YORK TINDALL

THESE ARE *Borzoi Books*
PUBLISHED IN NEW YORK BY *Alfred A. Knopf*

THE
PLUMED SERPENT

THE
PLUMED SERPENT

THE
PLUMED SERPENT
[QUETZALCOATL]

By
D. H. LAWRENCE

INTRODUCTION BY
WILLIAM YORK TINDALL

19 66

NEW YORK: ALFRED·A·KNOPF

04220

THIS IS A BORZOI BOOK,
PUBLISHED BY ALFRED A. KNOPF, INC.

Published January 15, 1926
Reprinted Twice
Fourth Printing, with Introduction, April 1951
Fifth Printing, February 1952
Sixth Printing, June 1959
Seventh Printing, August 1963
Eighth Printing, November 1966

INTRODUCTION

THIS glowing landscape, where flat figures move in ritual patterns, is one of the great creations of our time. Places, people, and actions come from Mexico and New Mexico but, whatever the vividness and actuality of these elements, the whole is far from photographic. Comparable in splendor to "Kubla Khan" or *Salammbô*, or, better perhaps, to the paintings of Gauguin, *The Plumed Serpent* is at once design and vision. In the design Lawrence found expression for his feelings and desires. By the design he creates for us not only a vision of reality but a sense of its wonder. "Strangeness added to beauty," Pater's apprehension of romantic art and its value, describes this wonderful book.

Lawrence's years in New Mexico and Mexico were on the whole his happiest and his most productive. *The Plumed Serpent*, written during this period after many preliminary sketches and studies, is his complete expression. Lawrence had spent his life in quest of a place that should be at once a home and his symbol of unity. Italy had always seemed good; but for a while in the 1920's Spanish and Indian America seemed better. He knew of course that place alone could not give him what he wanted. He knew that Mexico, however enchanting it might be, could provide no more than excitement and the materials for something he must make. That place, with its sterility and color, its horror and loveliness, its immediate sense of life and death, approximated his needs. Not Mexico, however, but his book became the adequate symbol, and like many writers before him Lawrence found in art the peace that life denied.

His quest for a suitable place provides the theme for *St. Mawr*, one of the earliest and most elaborate studies for *The Plumed Serpent*. The seeker, a girl named Lou, is married to an ineffectual baron. In her stable, however, St. Mawr, a stallion, emanates a

dark fire that awes her a little.   This beast is the first noble, dangerous thing she has known; and the black-bearded Welsh groom who
goes with him is not unattractive.   But Phoenix, the redskinned
groom, seems even more possible.   "Flooded with ancient understanding," she feels that her husband is unreal.   Therefore with
horse, grooms, and her groom-loving mother she leaves England in
search of another place—which she finds in the mountains near
Taos, New Mexico.   Somewhat surprisingly neglecting her willing
and able groom, she establishes herself in Lawrence's ranch and
finds her center there.

Although this story is not without narrative interest, the significant progress is from symbol to symbol.   In the first half the horse
and his grooms stand out against a background of meaningless society, with its tea and mental loves.   The ranch is the dominant
symbol of the second half.   That the story falls into two parts might
seem no more than fitting for a journey from a bad place to a good
one.   But Lawrence does nothing to connect his symbols.   Horse
and ranch may signify more or less the same thing, or parallel things,
but think what we may, a ranch cannot take the place of a horse.
As our feelings decline this substitution, the structure collapses.

To Lou, who has forgotten the horse entirely, the ranch is a
substitute for man, whether groom or husband.   Full of "meaning
and mystery," like any symbol, her chosen landscape is not only
bigger than man but bigger than spirit.   As soon as she sets eye
upon it she cries, as Lawrence, advancing in his flivver, must have
done before her: *"This is the place."*   The moving and beautiful
description that occupies the last quarter of the book elaborates
their symbol.   Something concrete, it immediately presents what
Lou and Lawrence have been tediously talking about.   Their symbolic place, like the disappearing horse, is both devilish and benign.
A sordid place of pack-rats and sick goats, it is filled nevertheless
with an awful holiness.   The lovely flowers are fierce.   Nothing so
blameless as Wordsworth's more than simple primrose could em-
body Lawrence's vision of life and the passing tranquillity he found
in the balance between attraction and repulsion.

It is not surprising that the character who undertakes Lawrence's
quest should be a woman; for the seeker in the later novels at least
is commonly a woman.   Not only Ursula of *Women in Love* but

Lady Chatterley herself follows this pattern. A reasonable explanation, but not the only one perhaps, is that Lawrence, like Jung or indeed like Joyce, thought the creative principle feminine. If that is so, his questing girl becomes the artist's deepest self in search of a subject and a place.

Having preceded Lou to that New Mexican ranch, Lawrence made further studies for the great book that the place demanded. Most of these preliminaries took the form of reflections or traveller's sketches. Essays in *Reflections on the Death of a Porcupine,* a little known but fascinating volume, draw philosophical conclusions from life at Taos among the animals and the pine trees. In harmony with their potencies, both attractive and dangerous, he felt that one could be almost happy there.

Mornings in Mexico exploits again what he called "the spirit of place." These essays, written during his last days in Taos and his first in Mexico, compose one of the most brilliant and sensitive books of travel in the language, rivaled most nearly perhaps by his earlier essays on Italy. Whether he describes his parrot and his Indian servant, a Sunday picnic in Mexico or the snake-dancers of Arizona, the colors are clear and the movement vital. Having passed through his temperament, colors already bright become brighter and assume a mysterious significance. Seeming to reproduce reality, Lawrence creates it.

Anthropologists admire his dancing Indians. This is not unnatural since it was partly by their aid that he interpreted what he saw. He is more than authentic and orthodox however. His bird-treading dancers, like other animists, may try to placate or conquer the potencies of the living universe. Their pious concentration over drums and their ejaculations may call sun, rain, wind, and earth into the service of the sprouting corn. But these more or less familiar ideas and this popular spectacle, so often described, draw their strange power from what they meant to Lawrence. In these barbaric exercises he found an image for what he had been trying to state. No longer a cultural curiosity, the dances became in his hands a form for presenting feelings and ideas. What Lawrence says of his dancers is true of his essays on them: "They are not representing something. . . . It is a soft, subtle *being* something."

Even the interpretations that interrupt the dance fail to distract us from it. What might have been tiresome is intense. Even his remarks about vitality are vital; for Lawrence had found ways to transform prose from a means of discourse to a means of immediate presentation. Heavy, repetitious, and hypnotic, his words dance the dance they are interpreting. By a kind of ritual of rhythm, sound, and tone he presents while explaining the ritual movements of the dancers. As his Indians win from the reluctant powers their "unspeakable renewal," his words convey what cannot be spoken. And as he goes monotonously on, "the mind bows down before the creative mystery," acknowledging the wonder.

At first glance the later narratives seem little more than rearrangements of materials from these sketches. In "The Woman Who Rode Away" matters of New Mexico combine with those of Mexico to produce an original landscape. Ritual prose, which Lawrence perfected in the essays, reappears in *The Plumed Serpent,* together with dreams of drum, dance, snake, and eagle, and theories of uniting opposites. Many or maybe most of its parts come from the sketches and studies, but Lawrence's great novel, like any aesthetic organization is more than the sum of its parts. New relationships among them compose a form expressing all he thought and felt. His quest for a symbol to unify himself and to communicate with others might have rested here.

The Plumed Serpent differs from novels in which character is central—from most of them in fact. When we think of a novel we think of characters—Elizabeth Bennett, Mr. Pickwick, or Mrs. Bloom—but in Lawrence's novel, characters are less important than pattern. If we compare Kate, Lawrence's heroine, with heroines of other novels, she is not there at all. She is complex enough in origin, to be sure, part of her projected from Lawrence's idea of Lawrence and part from his idea of Mrs. Lawrence, but she has not emerged far enough from her origins to have independence. Don Ramón, for all his exercises and theories, is more the allegorical image of a savior than a character. And as for Don Cipriano, the assistant savior, although we are told he is both goatish and cocky, he is no more substantial than something out of melodrama. "The things he said were hardly interesting at all," says Lawrence, "Only what he *was.*" A character does not necessarily come to life, how-

ever, when the author says he does. Yet, in spite of such cavils, it is plain that Lawrence composed an uncommonly good novel. More like a tapestry or a painted window than like the novels we are used to, it triumphs by arrangements of shape and color. Not people but functions, the characters exist like figures in the carpet only by relationship with other parts of the great design.

Lady Chatterley and her famous lover, even more functional than these figures, are less memorable than their relations with one another. Their profound inhumanity might argue the inhumanity of their creator or at least his indifference to mankind. Certainly Kate, who seems most nearly to share Lawrence's attitudes, regards ordinary people with disgust. Nothing approaching charity or compassion is apparent in the great design. Indeed, Don Ramón particularly condemns them. "You must hate people and humanity," he observes, and in order to escape horror of mankind, you must go beyond it to the "greater life." Lawrence's saviors are opposite to Jesus, and Lawrence himself seems to have regarded human beings with dislike, impatience, or missionary zeal. "The individual hardly counted," says Kate, thinking of the mystery of sex, "a mystery greater than the individual." It seems to her that the highest thing is "some powerful relationship of man to man." She speaks for Lawrence. Forces, ideas, and relationships, supplanting people, make and resolve the tensions of his novel as of a play by Shaw. But symbols and plot give body, mystery, and movement to these abstractions.

The narrative line is another quest. Seeking reality, Kate finds or almost finds it in Sayula, at the lake, through the advice and example of Don Ramón and Don Cipriano, especially the latter. The obstacle to her salvation is that personal independence which she seems to lack. Like other emancipated intellectuals and middle-aged widows of means, she prides herself on herself. But before she can be saved, they tell her, she must abandon herself to the "gentle reciprocal giving" of unintimate intimacy. That is not easy—as Lawrence's other novels prove; and the present story faithfully follows the ups and downs of a difficult conversion. Fascinated and repelled by Cipriano, her "demon lover," and somewhat confused, she reluctantly bids common intimacy good-by. But impersonal balance is easily disturbed. Sometimes she calls his

ritual childish and his theology "high-flown bunk." Sometimes she feels for his hand—and "All was so dark. But oh, so deep, so deep and beyond her, the vast, soft, living heat! So beyond her!" At such times she allows herself to follow the masters and even to occupy a chair in their pantheon. Even after her marriage to Cipriano, troubles recur; and although officially transfigured, she remains a little doubtful.

As Kate is reborn, so is Mexico. Under the direction of the saviors, rebirth occurs simultaneously on several levels: sexual, religious, and political. When the rains come to end the drought, it is impossible to tell whether these waters promise sexual, religious, or political regeneration, or all three at once, along with vegetable awakening. The language is consistently ambiguous. When Don Ramón says "I am not with you till my serpent has coiled his circle of rest in your belly," he confuses the sexual with the religious; but when, welcoming the downpour, he delivers a sermon on "the milk of the maize bud among its hair," there is greater confusion.

Lawrence devotes the opening chapters to a description of the wasteland, waiting for rain. The bullfight, with its martyred male or female horses, shows how far citified Mexicans have degenerated under the influence of democracy, machines, and "the insidious modern disease of tolerance." While saving the stomach, Mexican socialism has ignored the genitals and the soul. To Kate, the cruel, jeering, down-dragging Indians in the country, unawakened by their alien religion and politics, represent indifference if not death. Dona Carlota, Don Ramón's malevolent Catholic wife, establishes marital incapacity. Kate herself is only half alive as she pauses between husbands.

Ramón and Cipriano awaken the sleepers, the jeerers, and the dead ones, or liquidate them when they fail to hear. Dictators now as well as saviors, they secure political rebirth by revolution. Cipriano's storm troopers, occupying the strong points and the churches, easily defeat mobs led by fanatical Roman priests, reluctant to be saved. Meanwhile religious rebirth, which cannot be separated from political, is accomplished by sermon, dance, and song. Sexual rebirth, which cannot be separated from religious, is managed not

only by advice but by ritual. Sex, politics, and religion, gaining strength through joy, become a singular thing.

The theme of rebirth is supported by symbols so central and impressive that it would be more accurate to say that theme and narrative serve them. Of these symbols Quetzalcoatl, who gives his name to the book, is the most apparent. Bird and snake together, this Aztec god expresses not only a Freudian vision but that connection of earth and sky, matter and spirit, above and below which thrice-great Hermes commended. Convinced that he is Quetzalcoatl, with the serpent of middle-earth in his loins and the bird of the outer air on his brow, Don Ramón says: "I am lord of two ways. I am master of up and down." Lawrence makes his feathered snake not only a sign of unity but of those dying and reviving gods he learned about from Frazer. Like Attis, Osiris, and Adonis, Quetzalcoatl has died in order to live. His return from the waters of resurrection coincides with the departure of Jesus, who, exiled by Don Ramón, goes back for a long immersion and ultimate renewal. But Quetzalcoatl, unlike Jesus, is "only the symbol of the best a man may be." Identifying this symbol with another, Don Ramón exclaims: "The universe is a nest of dragons, with a perfectly unfathomable mystery at the centre of it. If I call the mystery the Morning Star, surely it doesn't matter!"

That star, the "ultimate clue," hovers like a bird-snake in tranquil suspense between the energies of the cosmos, between day and night, earth and sky, reconciling these opposites. That star of twilight suggests marriage and peace. Rising between heart and loins, it is womanhood for woman and manhood for man. ("My manhood," says Don Ramón, "is like a demon howling inside me.") It becomes plain that star and feathered serpent have many meanings, only some of which can be reduced to propositions. This pleases Kate, who, "weary to death of definite meanings, and a God of one fixed purport," loves to lose herself in a mystery.

More mysterious than star or god, the lake, which contains them both, is the central and most potent symbol of the book. A "pool of peace," it is the place where gods sink for renewal and the place whence they emerge. But it is not only for convenience that Don Ramón establishes his center there. Rather it is for the nameless

things the lake evokes with its spermy waters. Full of stars, flowers, and gods, these pale filmy waters, uniting all incompatibles, are indefinitely suggestive. At one time they seem "like some frail milk of thunder," and at another like clotted electricity, thick as "fish-milk." Pale and unreal, the lake extends into nowhere. Kate is profoundly moved; and as Lawrence improves reality, the reader shares her experience and something of her knowledge. It was the possibility of such improvements and such expansions of awareness that drew Lawrence to Mexico and kept him balanced between thunder above and volcanic potency below in the significant landscape.

The rituals of Don Ramón that occupy a large part of the book may seem monotonous and overlong. But ritual, like landscape, is a symbolic form for knowledge. By rhythmic incantation, as Lawrence presents the throbbing of the imported drum and the pressures of the imported dance, he extends our insight. But his ceremonies differ in some particulars from those he found expressive in New Mexico. Consisting partly of sermons and hymns, which, however incantatory, are conceptual, Don Ramon's religion unites the European and the Asiatic with the Indian. The manager of the local hotel, exposed by Kate as a cynic, finds a hint of national socialism in the ceremonies of his neighbor. Kate herself irreverently detects an element of the revival meeting, of the Salvation Army too; and if she had known about it, she could have detected yoga in those postures by which Don Ramón restores his soul and inducts Don Cipriano.

Incidental symbols of birds, beasts, and flowers, together with suns behind suns, the womb-like patio, and the primary colors, maintain the flickering interplay of meanings. The catalogue of Aztec gods invokes the magic of sound. Descriptions, never literal, cannot be received in the common light of day. When the hard green fruits of the mango, "curiously heavy with life," become the organs of some animal, Lawrence is illustrating the poetic analogies from which he constructs his vision.

Analogy is the important literary method of our time. Before science had established the world of fact, analogy had been the way of knowing reality. Dante's four-leveled allegory and Donne's conceits, which compare the physical with the metaphysical, are exam-

ples of this metaphorical way to value and meaning. Preserved through the enlightenment only by the occultists, analogy emerged again during the romantic revival. The occult studies of Blake, Rimbaud, and Yeats made correspondence, as Baudelaire called it, the central preoccupation of the symbolist movement. Conrad, Joyce, and Virginia Woolf are among the novelists who followed poets away from the external, the literal, and the discursive into imagistic and rhythmic suggestion. Lawrence is one of this great company.

The symbol, says Lawrence in one of his essays, is "a complex of emotional experience. And the power of the symbol is to arouse the deep emotional self . . . beyond comprehension." Myth, which is composed of symbols, narrates "a whole human experience, of which the purpose is too deep, going too deep in the blood and soul, for mental explanation or description." Whether we agree with him that myth is non-discursive presentation, with the anthropologists that it is cultural sanction, or with the psychoanalysts that it is Oedipal dream, *The Plumed Serpent* is plainly mythical. It owes this character not to the employment of Aztec myths or patterns from Frazer or hints of Joachim and Salomé, but to a recovery of the way of knowing that produced the myths.

Like ritual or music, myth is a significant form through which we may conceive reality. The elements of the form that Lawrence composed are not only his figures and narrative, and his symbols of god, star, or lake but his structure and his style. Expanding and contracting in scenes of alternate intensity and depression, of movement and rumination, the emotional rhythm accompanies the thematic. The didactic elements that in some of Lawrence's earlier novels almost overwhelm the symbolic narrative they were designed to support are sufficiently incantatory to be non-discursive in effect. The stiff, awkward, and even ungrammatical prose of the opening chapter, whether intentional or not, is a happy device for expressing discouragement. The gradual transfiguration of style from chapter to chapter conveys the growth of hope, and, at its poetic climax, the very sensation of life. Structure, style, and incidental symbols compose an elaborate symbol or the work of art itself. Although it contains political and religious elements, its total significance is neither political nor religious. Although it contains nonsense and

cruelty, the value is neither rational nor moral but what arises from a relationship of part to part in which the inhuman and awkward elements dissonantly combine with the imaginative and the human. *The Plumed Serpent* is a great metaphor for a feeling about reality. Conditioned by place and contemporary politics (of which on one level the book is a nightmare vision), that feeling is the wonder of all things—even of such politics. Kate is always calling for the return of magic and wonder. Her story brings them back.

But neither she nor Lawrence was satisfied for long. Although providing temporary peace, the metaphor became inadequate and the quest went on. Lawrence was not fooled by his mummery, nor was he altogether an enthusiast. The ending of *The Plumed Serpent* is as inconclusive as the ending of *St. Mawr* is ironic. Kate is aware of death as a figure in her design, but the questing lady of "The Woman Who Rode Away" finds only death in the ambiguous landscape. Even the sun, which her sacrifice promises to revive, shines on the altar through a screen of ice. It was time for Lawrence to go away and find another place and another symbol.

Returning for renewal to the Mediterranean, he exchanged Quetzalcoatl for Jesus and the synthetic rituals of Don Ramón for the less extravagant ceremony of Isis. But the pattern remained almost the same. Maybe the ritual of *The Man Who Died* is more Egyptian than Indian, but the dancing Indians of *Mornings in Mexico* had reminded Lawrence of Egyptians. The disappearing horse of *St. Mawr* reappears as the escaped but forgotten cock. Isis, the divinity adored by the lonesome priestess and identified with her, although searching for dismembered Osiris, is only the last of many questing girls. It is not always easy to tell Lawrence's Jesus apart from the living Quetzalcoatl except that Jesus, as the reassembled Osiris, is disenchanted. It is sometimes hard to tell him from Kate. The difference between *The Plumed Serpent* and *The Man Who Died* is that the latter is shorter, more public, and less magical. Lawrence's Mexican dream, alone of the later novels, takes its place beside *Sons and Lovers,* the great work of his youth.

WILLIAM YORK TINDALL

CONTENTS

THE
PLUMED SERPENT

CHAPTER I

BEGINNINGS OF A BULL-FIGHT

IT was the Sunday after Easter, and the last bull-fight of the season in Mexico City. Four special bulls had been brought over from Spain for the occasion, since Spanish bulls are more fiery than Mexican. Perhaps it is the altitude, perhaps just the spirit of the western Continent which is to blame for the lack of "pep," as Owen put it, in the native animal.

Although Owen, who was a great socialist, disapproved of bull-fights, "We have never seen one. We shall have to go," he said.

"Oh yes, I think we must see it," said Kate.

"And it's our last chance," said Owen.

Away he rushed to the place where they sold tickets, to book seats, and Kate went with him. As she came into the street, her heart sank. It was as if some little person inside her were sulking and resisting. Neither she nor Owen spoke much Spanish, there was a fluster at the ticket place, and an unpleasant individual came forward to talk American for them.

It was obvious they ought to buy tickets for the "Shade." But they wanted to economise, and Owen said he preferred to sit among the crowd, therefore, against the resistance of the ticket man and the onlookers, they reserved seats in the "Sun."

The show was on Sunday afternoon. All the tram-cars and the frightful little Ford omnibuses called *Camions* were labelled *Torero*, and were surging away towards Chapultepec. Kate felt that sudden dark feeling, that she didn't want to go.

"I'm not very keen on going," she said to Owen.

"Oh, but why not? I don't believe in them on principle, but we've never seen one, so we shall *have* to go."

Owen was an American, Kate was Irish. "Never having seen one" meant "having to go." But it was American logic rather than Irish, and Kate only let herself be overcome.

Villiers of course was keen. But then he too was American, and he too had never seen one, and being younger, more than anybody he *had* to go.

1

They got into a Ford taxi and went. The busted car careered away down the wide dismal street of asphalt and stone and Sunday dreariness. Stone buildings in Mexico have a peculiar hard, dry dreariness.

The taxi drew up in a side street under the big iron scaffolding of the stadium. In the gutters, rather lousy men were selling pulque and sweets, cakes, fruit, and greasy food. Crazy motor-cars rushed up and hobbled away. Little soldiers in washed-out cotton uniforms, pinky drab, hung around an entrance. Above all loomed the network iron frame of the huge, ugly stadium.

Kate felt she was going to prison. But Owen excitedly surged to the entrance that corresponded to his ticket. In the depths of him, he too didn't want to go. But he was a born American, and if anything was on show, he had to see it. That was "Life."

The man who took the tickets at the entrance, suddenly, as they were passing in, stood in front of Owen, put both his hands on Owen's chest and pawed down the front of Owen's body. Owen started, bridled, transfixed for a moment. The fellow stood aside. Kate remained petrified.

Then Owen jerked into a smiling composure as the man waved them on. "Feeling for fire-arms!" he said, rolling his eyes with pleased excitement at Kate.

But she had not got over the shock of horror, fearing the fellow might paw her.

They emerged out of a tunnel in the hollow of the concrete-and-iron amphitheatre. A real gutter-lout came to look at their counterslips, to see which seats they had booked. He jerked his head downwards, and slouched off. Now Kate knew she was in a trap—a big concrete beetle trap.

They dropped down the concrete steps till they were only three tiers from the bottom. That was their row. They were to sit on the concrete, with a loop of thick iron between each numbered seat. This was a reserved place in the "Sun."

Kate sat gingerly between her two iron loops, and looked vaguely around.

"I think it's thrilling!" she said.

Like most modern people, she had a will-to-happiness.

"Isn't it thrilling!" cried Owen, whose will-to-happiness was almost a mania. "Don't you think so, Bud?"

"Why, yes, I think it may be," said Villiers, non-committal.

But then Villiers was young, he was only over twenty, while

Owen was over forty. The younger generation calculates its "happiness" in a more business-like fashion. Villiers was out after a thrill, but he wasn't going to say he'd got one till he'd got it. Kate and Owen—Kate was also nearly forty—must enthuse a thrill, out of a sort of politeness to the great Show-man, Providence.

"Look here!" said Owen. "Supposing we try to protect our extremity on this concrete—" and thoughtfully he folded his rain-coat and laid it along the concrete ledge so that both he and Kate could sit on it.

They sat and gazed around. They were early. Patches of people mottled the concrete slope opposite, like eruptions. The ring just below was vacant, neatly sanded; and above the ring, on the encircling concrete, great advertisements for hats, with a picture of a city-man's straw hat, and advertisements for spectacles, with a pair of spectacles supinely folded, glared and shouted.

"Where is the 'Shade' then?" said Owen, twisting his neck.

At the top of the amphitheatre, near the sky, were concrete boxes. This was the "Shade," where anybody who was anything sat.

"Oh but," said Kate, "I don't want to be perched right up there, so far away."

"Why no!" said Owen. "We're much better where we are, in our 'Sun,' which isn't going to shine a great deal after all."

The sky was cloudy, preparing for the rainy season.

It was nearly three o'clock in the afternoon, and the crowd was filling in, but still only occupied patches of the bare concrete. The lower tiers were reserved, so the bulk of the people sat in the mid-way levels, and gentry like our trio were more or less isolated.

But the audience was already a mob, mostly of fattish town men in black tight suits and little straw hats, and a mixing-in of the dark-faced labourers in big hats. The men in black suits were probably employees and clerks and factory hands. Some had brought their women, in sky-blue chiffon with brown chiffon hats and faces powdered to look like white marshmallows. Some were families with two or three children.

The fun began. The game was to snatch the hard straw hat off some fellow's head, and send it skimming away down the slope of humanity, where some smart bounder down below would catch it and send it skimming across in another direction. There were shouts of jeering pleasure from the mass, which rose almost to

a yell as seven straw hats were skimming, meteor-like, at one moment across the slope of people.

"Look at that!" said Owen. "Isn't that fun!"

"No," said Kate, her little *alter ego* speaking out for once, in spite of her will-to-happiness. "No, I don't like it. I really hate common people."

As a socialist, Owen disapproved, and as a happy man, he was disconcerted. Because his own real self, as far as he had any left, hated common rowdiness just as much as Kate did.

"It's awfully smart though!" he said, trying to laugh in sympathy with the mob. "There now, see that!"

"Yes, it's quite smart, but I'm glad it's not my hat," said Villiers.

"Oh, it's all in the game," said Owen largely.

But he was uneasy. He was wearing a big straw hat of native make, conspicuous in the comparative isolation of the lower tiers. After a lot of fidgeting, he took off this hat and put it on his knees. But unfortunately he had a very definitely bald spot on a sunburnt head.

Behind, above, sat a dense patch of people in the unreserved section. Already they were throwing things. *Bum!* came an orange, aimed at Owen's bald spot, and hitting him on the shoulder. He glared round rather ineffectually through his big shell spectacles.

"I'd keep my hat on if I were you," said the cold voice of Villiers.

"Yes, I think perhaps it's wiser," said Owen, with assumed nonchalance, putting on his hat again.

Whereupon a banana skin rattled on Villiers' tidy and ladylike little panama. He glared round coldly, like a bird that would stab with its beak if it got the chance, but which would fly away at the first real menace.

"How I detest them!" said Kate.

A diversion was created by the entrance, opposite, of the military bands, with their silver and brass instruments under their arms. There were three sets. The chief band climbed and sat on the right, in the big bare tract of concrete reserved for the Authorities. These musicians wore dark grey uniforms trimmed with rose colour, and made Kate feel almost reassured, as if it were Italy and not Mexico City. A silver band in pale buff uniforms sat opposite our party, high up across the hollow distance, and still a

third "musica" threaded away to the left, on the remote scattered hillside of the amphitheatre. The newspapers had said that the President would attend. But the Presidents are scarce at bull-fights in Mexico, nowadays.

There sat the bands, in as much pomp as they could muster, but they did not begin to play. Great crowds now patched the slopes, but there were still bare tracts, especially in the Authorities' section. Only a little distance above Kate's row was a mass of people, as it were impending; a very uncomfortable sensation.

It was three o'clock, and the crowds had a new diversion. The bands, due to strike up at three, still sat there in lordly fashion, sounding not a note.

"La musica! La musica!" shouted the mob, with the voice of mob authority. They were the People, and the revolutions had been their revolutions, and they had won them all. The bands were their bands, present for their amusement.

But the bands were military bands, and it was the army which had won all the revolutions. So the revolutions were *their* revolutions, and they were present for their own glory alone.

Musica pagada toca mal tono.

Spasmodically, the insolent yelling of the mob rose and subsided. *La musica! La musica!* The shout became brutal and violent. Kate always remembered it. *La musica!* The band peacocked its nonchalance. The shouting was a great yell: the degenerate mob of Mexico City!

At length, at its own leisure, the band in grey with dark rose facings struck up: crisp, martial, smart.

"That's fine!" said Owen. "But that's really good! And it's the first time I've heard a good band in Mexico, a band with any backbone."

The music was smart, but it was brief. The band seemed scarcely to have started, when the piece was over. The musicians took their instruments from their mouths with a gesture of dismissal. They played just to say they'd played, making it as short as possible.

Musica pagada toca mal tono.

There was a ragged interval, then the silver band piped up. And at last it was half-past three, or more.

Whereupon, at some given signal, the masses in the middle, unreserved seats, suddenly burst and rushed down on to the lowest, reserved seats. It was a crash like a burst reservoir, and the

populace in black Sunday suits poured down round and about our astonished, frightened trio. And in two minutes it was over. Without any pushing or shoving. Everybody careful, as far as possible, not to touch anybody else. You don't elbow your neighbour if he's got a pistol on his hip and a knife at his belly. So all the seats in the lower tiers filled in one rush, like the flowing of water.

Kate now sat among the crowd. But her seat, fortunately, was above one of the track-ways that went round the arena, so at least she would not have anybody sitting between her knees.

Men went uneasily back and forth along this gangway past the feet, wanting to get in next their friends, but never venturing to ask. Three seats away, on the same row, sat a Polish bolshevist fellow who had met Owen. He leaned over and asked the Mexican next to Owen if he might change seats with him. "No," said the Mexican. "I'll sit in my own seat."

"*Muy bien, Señor, muy bien!*" said the Pole.

The show did not begin, and men like lost mongrels still prowled back and forth on the track that was next step down from Kate's feet. They began to take advantage of the ledge on which rested the feet of our party, to squat there.

Down sat a heavy fellow, plumb between Owen's knees.

"I hope they won't sit on *my* feet," said Kate anxiously.

"We won't let them," said Villiers, with bird-like decision. "Why don't you shove him off, Owen? Shove him off."

And Villiers glared at the Mexican fellow ensconced between Owen's legs. Owen flushed, and laughed uncomfortably. He was not good at shoving people off. The Mexican began to look round at the three angry white people.

And in another moment, another fat Mexican in a black suit and a little black hat was lowering himself into Villiers' foot-space. But Villiers was too quick for him. He quickly brought his feet together under the man's sinking posterior, so the individual subsided uncomfortably on to a pair of boots, and at the same time felt a hand shoving him quietly but determinedly on the shoulder.

"No!" Villiers was saying in good American. "This place is for my *feet!* Get off! You get off!"

And he continued, quietly but very emphatically, to push the Mexican's shoulder, to remove him.

The Mexican half raised himself, and looked round murderously at Villiers. Physical violence was being offered, and the only retort was death. But the young American's face was so cold and abstract, only the eyes showing a primitive, bird-like fire, that the Mexican was nonplussed. And Kate's eyes were blazing with Irish contempt.

The fellow struggled with his Mexican city-bred inferiority complex. He muttered an explanation in Spanish that he was only sitting there for a moment, till he could join his friends —waving his hand towards a lower tier. Villiers did not understand a word, but he reiterated:

"I don't care what it is. This place is for my *feet,* and you don't sit there."

Oh, home of liberty! Oh, land of the free! Which of these two men was to win in the struggle for conflicting liberty? Was the fat fellow free to sit between Villiers' feet, or was Villiers free to keep his foot-space?

There are all sorts of inferiority complex, and the city Mexican has a very strong sort, that makes him all the more aggressive, once it is roused. Therefore the intruder lowered his posterior with a heavy, sudden bounce on Villiers' feet, and Villiers, out of very distaste, had had to extricate his feet from such a compression. The young man's face went white at the nostrils, and his eyes took on that bright abstract look of pure democratic anger. He pushed the fat shoulders more decisively, repeating:

"Go away! Go away! You're not to *sit* there."

The Mexican, on his own ground, and heavy on his own base, let himself be shoved, oblivious.

"Insolence!" said Kate loudly. "Insolence!"

She glared at the fat back in the shoddily-fitting black coat, which looked as if a woman dressmaker had made it, with loathing. How could any man's coat-collar look so home-made, so *en famille!*

Villiers remained with a fixed, abstract look on his thin face, rather like a death's head. All his American will was summoned up, the bald eagle of the north bristling in every feather. The fellow *should not* sit there.—But how to remove him?

The young man sat tense with will to annihilate his beetle-like intruder, and Kate used all her Irish malice to help him.

"Don't you wonder who was his tailor?" she asked, with a flicker in her voice.

Villiers looked at the femalish black coat of the Mexican, and made an arch grimace at Kate.

"I should say he hadn't one. Perhaps did it himself."

"Very likely!" Kate laughed venomously.

It was too much. The man got up and betook himself, rather diminished, to another spot.

"Triumph!" said Kate. "Can't you do the same, Owen?"

Owen laughed uncomfortably, glancing down at the man between his knees as he might glance at a dog with rabies, when it had its back to him.

"Apparently not yet, unfortunately," he said, with some constraint, turning his nose away again from the Mexican, who was using him as a sort of chair-back.

There was an exclamation. Two horsemen in gay uniforms and bearing long staffs had suddenly ridden into the ring. They went round the arena, then took up their posts, sentry-wise, on either side the tunnel entrance through which they had come in.

In marched a little column of four toreadors wearing tight uniforms plastered with silver embroidery. They divided, and marched smartly in opposite directions, two and two, around the ring, till they came to the place facing the section of the Authorities, where they made their salute.

So this was a bull-fight! Kate already felt a chill of disgust.

In the seats of the Authorities were very few people, and certainly no sparkling ladies in high tortoise-shell combs and lace mantillas. A few common-looking people, bourgeois with not much taste, and a couple of officers in uniform. The President had not come.

There was no glamour, no charm. A few commonplace people in an expanse of concrete were the elect, and below, four grotesque and effeminate looking fellows in tight, ornate clothes were the heroes. With their rather fat posteriors and their squiffs of pigtails and their clean-shaven faces, they looked like eunuchs, or women in tight pants, these precious toreadors.

The last of Kate's illusions concerning bull-fights came down with a flop. These were the darlings of the mob? These were the gallant toreadors! Gallant? Just about as gallant as assistants in a butcher's shop. Lady-killers? Ugh!

There was an Ah! of satisfaction from the mob. Into the

ring suddenly rushed a smallish, dun-coloured bull with long flourishing horns. He ran out, blindly, as if from the dark, probably thinking that now he was free. Then he stopped short, seeing he was not free, but surrounded in an unknown way. He was utterly at a loss.

A toreador came forward and switched out a pink cloak like a fan not far from the bull's nose. The bull gave a playful little prance, neat and pretty, and charged mildly on the cloak. The toreador switched the cloak over the animal's head, and the neat little bull trotted on round the ring, looking for a way to get out.

Seeing the wooden barrier around the arena, finding he was able to look over it, he thought he might as well take the leap. So over he went into the corridor or passage-way which circled the ring, and in which stood the servants of the arena.

Just as nimbly, these servants vaulted over the barrier into the arena, that was now bull-less.

The bull in the gangway trotted inquiringly round till he came to an opening on to the arena again. So back he trotted into the ring.

And back into the gangway vaulted the servants, where they stood again to look on.

The bull trotted waveringly and somewhat irritated. The toreadors waved their cloaks at him, and he swerved on. Till his vague course took him to where one of the horsemen with lances sat motionless on his horse.

Instantly, in a pang of alarm, Kate noticed that the horse was thickly blindfolded with a black cloth. Yes, and so was the horse on which sat the other picador.

The bull trotted suspiciously up to the motionless horse bearing the rider with the long pole; a lean old horse that would never move till Doomsday, unless someone shoved it.

O shades of Don Quixote! O four Spanish horsemen of the Apocalypse! This was surely one of them.

The picador pulled his feeble horse round slowly, to face the bull, and slowly he leaned forward and shoved his lance-point into the bull's shoulder. The bull, as if the horse were a great wasp that had stung him deep, suddenly lowered his head in a jerk of surprise and lifted his horns straight up into the horse's abdomen. And without more ado, over went horse and rider, like a tottering monument upset.

The rider scrambled from under the horse and went running

away with his lance. The old horse, in complete dazed amazement, struggled to rise, as if overcome with dumb incomprehension. And the bull, with a red place on his shoulder welling a trickle of dark blood, stood looking around in equally hopeless amazement.

But the wound was hurting. He saw the queer sight of the horse half reared from the ground, trying to get to its feet. And he smelled blood and bowels.

So rather vaguely, as if not quite knowing what he ought to do, the bull once more lowered his head and pushed his sharp, flourishing horns in the horse's belly, working them up and down inside there with a sort of vague satisfaction.

Kate had never been taken so completely by surprise in all her life. She had still cherished some idea of a gallant show. And before she knew where she was, she was watching a bull whose shoulders trickled blood goring his horns up and down inside the belly of a prostrate and feebly plunging old horse.

The shock almost overpowered her. She had come for a gallant show. This she had paid to see. Human cowardice and beastliness, a smell of blood, a nauseous whiff of bursten bowels! She turned her face away.

When she looked again, it was to see the horse feebly and dazedly walking out of the ring, with a great ball of its own entrails hanging out of its abdomen and swinging reddish against its own legs as it automatically moved.

And once more, the shock of amazement almost made her lose consciousness. She heard the confused small applause of amusement from the mob. And that Pole, to whom Owen had introduced her, leaned over and said to her, in horrible English:

"Now, Miss Leslie, you are seeing Life! Now you will have something to write about, in your letters to England."

She looked at his unwholesome face in complete repulsion, and wished Owen would not introduce her to such sordid individuals.

She looked at Owen. His nose had a sharp look, like a little boy who may make himself sick, but who is watching at the shambles with all his eyes, knowing it is forbidden.

Villiers, the younger generation, looked intense and abstract, getting the sensation. He would not even feel sick. He was just getting the thrill of it, without emotion, coldly and scientifically, but very intent.

And Kate felt a real pang of hatred against this Americanism which is coldly and unscrupulously sensational.

"Why doesn't the horse move? Why doesn't it run away from the bull?" she asked in repelled amazement, of Owen.

Owen cleared his throat.

"Didn't you see? It was blindfolded," he said.

"But can't it *smell* the bull?" she asked.

"Apparently not.—They bring the old wrecks here to finish them off.—I know it's awful, but it's part of the game."

How Kate hated phrases like "part of the game." What do they mean, anyhow! She felt utterly humiliated, crushed by a sense of human indecency, cowardice of two-legged humanity. In this "brave" show she felt nothing but reeking cowardice. Her breeding and her natural pride were outraged.

The ring servants had cleaned away the mess and spread new sand. The toreadors were playing with the bull, unfurling their foolish cloaks at arm's length. And the animal, with the red sore running on his shoulder, foolishly capered and ran from one rag to the other, here and there.

For the first time, a bull seemed to her a fool. She had always been afraid of bulls, fear tempered with reverence of the great Mithraic beast. And now she saw how stupid he was, in spite of his long horns and his massive maleness. Blindly and stupidly he ran at the rag, each time, and the toreadors skipped like fat-hipped girls showing off. Probably it needed skill and courage, but it *looked* silly.

Blindly and foolishly the bull ran ducking its horns each time at the rag, just because the rag fluttered.

"Run at the *men*, idiot!" said Kate aloud, in her overwrought impatience. "Run at the men, not at the cloaks."

"They never do, isn't it curious!" replied Villiers, with cool scientific interest. "They say no toreador will face a cow, because a cow always goes for *him* instead of the cloak. If a bull did that there'd be no bull-fights. Imagine it!"

She was bored now. The nimbleness of the skipping tricks of the toreador bored her. Even when one of the banderilleros reared himself on tiptoe, his plump posterior much in evidence, and from his erectness pushed two razor-sharp darts with frills at the top into the bull's shoulder, neatly and smartly, Kate felt no admiration. One of the darts fell out, anyway, and the bull

ran on with the other swinging and waggling in another bleeding place.

The bull now wanted to get away, really. He leaped the fence again, quickly, into the attendants' gangway. The attendants vaulted over into the arena. The bull trotted in the corridor, then nicely leaped back. The attendants vaulted once more into the corridor. The bull trotted round the arena, ignoring the toreadors, and leaped once more into the gangway. Over vaulted the attendants.

Kate was beginning to be amused, now that the mongrel men were skipping for safety.

The bull was in the ring again, running from cloak to cloak, foolishly. A banderillero was getting ready with two more darts. But first another picador put nobly forward on his blindfolded old horse. The bull ignored this little lot too, and trotted away again, as if all the time looking for something, excitedly looking for something. He stood still and excitedly pawed the ground, as if he wanted something. A toreador advanced and swung a cloak. Up pranced the bull, tail in air, and with a prancing bound charged—upon the rag, of course. The toreador skipped round with a ladylike skip, then tripped to another point. Very pretty!

The bull, in the course of his trotting and prancing and pawing, had once more come near the bold picador. The bold picador shoved forward his ancient steed, leaned forwards, and pushed the point of his lance in the bull's shoulder. The bull looked up, irritated and arrested. What the devil!

He saw the horse and rider. The horse stood with that feeble monumentality of a milk horse, patient as if between the shafts, waiting while his master delivered the milk. How strange it must have been to him when the bull, giving a little bound like a dog, ducked its head and dived its horns upwards into his belly, rolling him over with his rider as one might push over a hat-stand.

The bull looked with irritable wonder at the incomprehensible medley of horse and rider kicking on the ground a few yards away from him. He drew near to investigate. The rider scrambled out and bolted. And the toreadors running up with their cloaks, drew off the bull. He went caracoling round, charging at more silk-lined rags.

Meanwhile an attendant had got the horse on its feet again, and was leading it totteringly into the gangway and round to

the exit, under the Authorities. The horse crawled slowly. The bull, running from pink cloak to red cloak, rag to rag, and never catching anything, was getting excited, impatient of the rag game. He jumped once more into the gangway and started running, alas, on towards where the wounded horse was still limping its way to the exit.

Kate knew what was coming. Before she could look away, the bull had charged on the limping horse from behind, the attendants had fled, the horse was up-ended absurdly, one of the bull's horns between his hind legs and deep in his inside. Down went the horse, collapsing in front, but his rear was still heaved up, with the bull's horn working vigorously up and down inside him, while he lay on his neck all twisted. And a huge heap of bowels coming out. And a nauseous stench. And the cries of pleased amusement among the crowd.

This pretty event took place on Kate's side of the ring, and not far from where she sat, below her. Most of the people were on their feet craning to look down over the edge to watch the conclusion of this delightful spectacle.

Kate knew if she saw any more she would go into hysterics. She was getting beside herself.

She looked swiftly at Owen, who looked like a guilty boy spellbound.

"I'm going!" she said, rising.

"Going!" he cried, in wonder and dismay, his flushed face and his bald flushed forehead a picture, looking up at her.

But she had already turned, and was hurrying away towards the mouth of the exit-tunnel.

Owen came running after her, flustered, and drawn in all directions.

"Really going!" he said in chagrin, as she came to the high, vaulted exit-tunnel.

"I must. I've got to get out," she cried. "Don't you come."

"Really!" he echoed, torn all ways.

The scene was creating a very hostile attitude in the audience. To leave the bull-fight is a national insult.

"Don't come! Really! I shall take a tram-car," she said hurriedly.

"Really! Do you really think you'll be all right?"

"Perfectly. You stay. Goodbye! I can't smell any more of this stink."

He turned like Orpheus looking back into hell, and wavering made towards his seat again.

It was not so easy, because many people were now on their feet and crowding to the exit vault. The rain which had sputtered a few drops suddenly fell in a downward splash. People were crowding to shelter; but Owen, unheeding, fought his way back to his seat, and sat in his rain-coat with the rain pouring on his bald head. He was as nearly in hysterics as Kate. But he was convinced that this was life. He was seeing LIFE, and what can an American do more!

"They might just as well sit and enjoy somebody else's diarrhœa," was the thought that passed through Kate's distracted but still Irish mind.

There she was in the great concrete archway under the stadium, with the lousy press of the audience crowding in after her. Facing outwards, she saw the straight downpour of the rain, and a little beyond, the great wooden gates that opened to the free street. Oh to be out, to be out of this, to be free!

But it was pouring tropical rain. The little shoddy soldiers were pressing back under the brick gateway, for shelter. And the gates were almost shut. Perhaps they would not let her out. Oh horror!

She stood hovering in front of the straight downpour. She would have dashed out, but for the restraining thought of what she would look like when her thin gauze dress was plastered to her body by drenching rain. On the brink she hovered.

Behind her, from the inner end of the stadium tunnel, the people were surging in in waves. She stood horrified and alone, looking always out to freedom. The crowd was in a state of excitement, cut off in its sport, on tenterhooks lest it should miss anything. Thank goodness the bulk stayed near the inner end of the vault. She hovered near the outer end, ready to bolt at any moment.

The rain crashed steadily down.

She waited on the outer verge, as far from the people as possible. Her face had that drawn, blank look of a woman near hysterics. She could not get out of her eyes the last picture of the horse lying twisted on its neck with its hind-quarters hitched up and the horn of the bull goring slowly and rhythmically in its vitals. The horse so utterly passive and grotesque. And all its bowels slipping on to the ground.

But a new terror was the throng inside the tunnel entrance. The big arched place was filling up, but still the crowd did not come very near her. They pressed towards the inner exit.

They were mostly loutish men in city clothes, the mongrel men of a mongrel city. Two men stood making water against the wall, in the interval of their excitement. One father had kindly brought his little boys to the show, and stood in fat, sloppy paternal benevolence above them. They were pale mites, the elder about ten years old, highly dressed up in Sunday clothes. And badly they needed protecting from that paternal benevolence, for they were oppressed, peaked and a bit wan from the horrors. To those children at least bull-fights did not come natural, but would be an acquired taste. There were other children, however, and fat mammas in black satin that was greasy and grey at the edges with an overflow of face-powder. These fat mammas had a pleased, excited look in their eyes, almost sexual, and very distasteful in contrast to their soft passive bodies.

Kate shivered a little in her thin frock, for the ponderous rain had a touch of ice. She stared through the curtain of water at the big rickety gates of the enclosure surrounding the amphitheatre, at the midget soldiers cowering in their shoddy, pink-white cotton uniforms, and at the glimpse of the squalid street outside, now running with dirty brown streams. The vendors had all taken refuge, in dirty-white clusters, in the pulque shops, one of which was sinisterly named: *A Ver que Sale.*

She was afraid more of the repulsiveness than of anything. She had been in many cities of the world, but Mexico had an underlying ugliness, a sort of squalid evil, which made Naples seem debonair in comparison. She was afraid, she dreaded the thought that anything might really touch her in this town, and give her the contagion of its crawling sort of evil. But she knew that the one thing she must do was to keep her head.

A little officer in uniform, wearing a big, pale-blue cape, made his way through the crowd. He was short, dark, and had a little black beard like an imperial. He came through the people from the inner entrance, and cleared his way with a quiet, silent unobtrusiveness, yet with the peculiar heavy Indian momentum. Even touching the crowd delicately with his gloved hand, and murmuring almost inaudibly the *Con permiso!* formula, he seemed to be keeping himself miles away from contact. He was brave too: because there was just the chance some lout might shoot him

because of his uniform. The people knew him too. Kate could tell that by the flicker of a jeering, self-conscious smile that passed across many faces, and the exclamation: "General Viedma! Don Cipriano!"

He came towards Kate, saluting and bowing with a brittle shyness.

"I am General Viedma. Did you wish to leave? Let me get you an automobile," he said, in very English English, that sounded strange from his dark face, and a little stiff on his soft tongue.

His eyes were dark, quick, with the glassy darkness that she found so wearying. But they were titled up with a curious slant, under arched black brows. It gave him an odd look of detachment, as if he looked at life with raised brows. His manner was superficially assured, underneath perhaps half-savage, shy and farouche, and deprecating.

"Thank you so much," she said.

He called to a soldier in the gateway.

"I will send you in the automobile of my friend," he said. "It will be better than a taxi. You don't like the bull-fight?"

"No! Horrible!" said Kate. "But do get me a yellow taxi. That is quite safe."

"Well, the man has gone for the automobile. You are English, yes?"

"Irish," said Kate.

"Ah Irish!" he replied, with the flicker of a smile.

"You speak English awfully well," she said.

"Yes! I was educated there. I was in England seven years."

"Were you! My name is Mrs Leslie."

"Ah Leslie! I knew James Leslie in Oxford. He was killed in the war."

"Yes. That was my husband's brother."

"Oh really!"

"How small the world is!" said Kate.

"Yes indeed!" said the general.

There was a pause.

"And the gentlemen who are with you, they are—?"

"American," said Kate.

"Ah Americans! Ah yes!"

"The older one is my cousin—Owen Rhys."

"Owen Rhys! Ah yes! I think I saw in the newspaper you were here in town—visiting Mexico."

He spoke in a peculiar quiet voice, rather suppressed, and his quick eyes glanced at her, and at his surroundings, like those of a man perpetually suspecting an ambush. But his face had a certain silent hostility, under his kindness. He was saving his nation's reputation.

"They did put in a not very complimentary note," said Kate. "I think they don't like it that we stay in the Hotel San Remo. It is too poor and foreign. But we are none of us rich, and we like it better than those other places."

"The Hotel San Remo? Where is that?"

"In the Avenida del Peru. Won't you come and see us there, and meet my cousin and Mr Thompson?"

"Thank you! Thank you! I hardly ever go out. But I will call if I may, and then perhaps you will all come to see me at the house of my friend, Señor Ramón Carrasco."

"We should like to," said Kate.

"Very well. And shall I call, then?"

She told him a time, and added:

"You mustn't be surprised at the hotel. It *is* small, and nearly all Italians. But we tried some of the big ones, and there is such a feeling of lowness about them, awful! I can't stand the feeling of prostitution. And then the cheap insolence of the servants. No, my little San Remo may be rough, but it's kindly and human, and it's not rotten. It is like Italy as I always knew it, decent, and with a bit of human generosity. I do think Mexico City is evil, underneath."

"Well," he said, "the hotels are bad. It is unfortunate, but the foreigners seem to make the Mexicans worse than they are, naturally. And Mexico, or something in it, certainly makes the foreigners worse than they are at home."

He spoke with a certain bitterness.

"Perhaps we should all stay away," she said.

"Perhaps!" he said, lifting his shoulders a little. "But I don't think so."

He relapsed into a slightly blank silence. Peculiar how his feelings flushed over him, anger, diffidence, wistfulness, assurance, and an anger again, all in little flushes, and somewhat naïve.

"It doesn't rain so much," said Kate. "When will the car come?"

"It is here now. It has been waiting some time," he replied.

"Then I'll go," she said.

"Well," he replied, looking at the sky. "It is still raining, and your dress is very thin. You must take my cloak."

"Oh!" she said, shrinking, "It is only two yards."

"It is still raining fairly fast. Better either wait, or let me lend you my cloak."

He swung out of his cloak with a quick little movement, and held it up to her. Almost without realising, she turned her shoulders to him, and he put the cape on her. She caught it round her, and ran out to the gate, as if escaping. He followed, with a light yet military stride. The soldiers saluted rather slovenly, and he responded briefly.

A not very new Fiat stood at the gate, with a chauffeur in a short red-and-black check coat. The chauffeur opened the door. Kate slipped off the cloak as she got in, and handed it back. He stood with it over his arm.

"Goodbye!" she said. "Thank you ever so much. And we shall see you on Tuesday. Do put your cape on."

"On Tuesday, yes. Hotel San Remo. Calle de Peru," he added to the chauffeur. Then turning again to Kate: "The hotel, no?"

"Yes," she said, and instantly changed. "No, take me to Sanborn's, where I can sit in a corner and drink tea to comfort me."

"To comfort you after the bull-fight?" he said, with another quick smile. "To Sanborn's, Gonzalez."

He saluted and bowed and closed the door. The car started.

Kate sat back, breathing relief. Relief to get away from that beastly place. Relief even to get away from that nice man. He was awfully nice. But he made her feel she wanted to get away from him too. There was that heavy, black Mexican fatality about him, that put a burden on her. His quietness, and his peculiar assurance, almost aggressive; and at the same time, a nervousness, an uncertainty. His heavy sort of gloom, and yet his quick, naïve, childish smile. Those black eyes, like black jewels, that you couldn't look into, and which were so watchful; yet which, perhaps, were waiting for some sign of recognition and of warmth! Perhaps!

She felt again, as she felt before, that Mexico lay in her destiny almost as a doom. Something so heavy, so oppressive, like the

folds of some huge serpent that seemed as if it could hardly raise itself.

She was glad to get to her corner in the tea-house, to feel herself in the cosmopolitan world once more, to drink her tea and eat strawberry shortcake and try to forget.

CHAPTER II

TEA-PARTY IN TLACOLULA

OWEN came back to the hotel at about half-past six, tired, excited, a little guilty, and a good deal distressed at having let Kate go alone. And now the whole thing was over, rather dreary in spirit.

"Oh, how did you get on?" he cried, the moment he saw her, afraid almost like a boy of his own sin of omission.

"I got on perfectly. Went to Sanborn's for tea, and had strawberry shortcake—so good!"

"Oh, good for you!" he laughed in relief. "Then you weren't *too* much overcome! I'm so glad. I had such awful qualms after I'd let you go. Imagined all the things that are supposed to happen in Mexico—chauffeur driving away with you into some horrible remote region, and robbing you and all that—but then I *knew* really you'd be all right. Oh, the time I had—the rain! —and the people throwing things at my bald patch—and those horses—wasn't that horrible?—I wonder I'm still alive." And he laughed with tired excitement, putting his hand over his stomach and rolling his eyes.

"Aren't you drenched?" she said.

"Drenched!" he replied. "Or at least I was. I've dried off quite a lot. My rain-coat is no good—I don't know why I don't buy another. Oh, but what a time! The rain *streaming* on my bald head, and the crowd behind throwing oranges at it. Then simply *gored* in my inside about letting you go alone. Yet it was the only bull-fight I shall *ever* see. I came then before it was over. Bud wouldn't come. I suppose he's still there."

"Was it as awful as the beginning?" she asked.

"No! No! It wasn't. The first was worst—that horse-shambles. Oh, they killed two more horses. And *five* bulls! Yes, a regular butchery. But some of it was very neat work; those toreadors did some very pretty feats. One stood on his cloak while a bull charged him."

"I think," interrupted Kate, "if I knew that some of those

20

toreadors were going to be tossed by the bull, I'd go to see another bull-fight. Ugh, how I detest them! The longer I live the more loathsome the human species becomes to me. *How* much nicer the bulls are!"

"Oh, quite!" said Owen vaguely. "Exactly. But still there was some very skilful work, very pretty. Really very plucky."

"Yah!" snarled Kate. "Plucky! They with all their knives and their spears and cloaks and darts—and they know just how a bull will behave. It's just a performance of human beings torturing animals, with those common fellows showing off, how smart they are at hurting a bull. Dirty little boys maiming flies—that's what they are. Only grown-up, they are bastards, not boys. Oh, *I* wish I could be a bull, just for five minutes. Bastard, that's what I call it!"

"Well!" laughed Owen uneasily, "It is rather."

"Call that manliness!" cried Kate. "Then thank God a million times that I'm a woman, and know poltroonery and dirty-mindedness when I see it."

Again Owen laughed uncomfortably.

"Go upstairs and change," she said. "You'll die."

"I think I'd better. I feel I might die any minute, as a matter of fact. Well, till dinner then. I'll tap at your door in half an hour."

Kate sat trying to sew, but her hand trembled. She could not get the bull-ring out of her mind, and something felt damaged in her inside.

She straightened herself, and sighed. She was really very angry, too, with Owen. He was naturally so sensitive, and so kind. But he had the insidious modern disease of tolerance. He must tolerate everything, even a thing that revolted him. He would call it Life! He would feel he had *lived* this afternoon. Greedy even for the most sordid sensations.

Whereas *she* felt as if she had eaten something which was giving her ptomaine poisoning. If *that* was life!

Ah men, men! They all had this soft rottenness of the soul, a strange perversity which made even the squalid, repulsive things seem part of *life* to them. Life! And what is life? A louse lying on its back and kicking? Ugh!

At about seven o'clock Villiers came tapping. He looked wan, peaked, but like a bird that had successfully pecked a bellyfull of garbage.

"Oh it was GREAT!" he said, lounging on one hip.   "GREAT! They killed *seven* BULLS."

"No calves, unfortunately," said Kate, suddenly furious again.

He paused to consider the point, then laughed.   Her anger was another slight sensational amusement to him.

"No, no calves," he said.   "The calves have gone home to be fattened.   But several more horses after you'd gone."

"I don't want to hear," she said coldly.

He laughed, feeling rather heroic.   After all, one must be able to look on blood and bursten bowels calmly: even with a certain thrill.   The young hero!   But there were dark rings round his eyes, like a debauch.

"Oh but!" he began, making a rather coy face.   "Don't you want to hear what I did after!   I went to the hotel of the chief toreador, and saw him lying on his bed all dressed up, smoking a fat cigar.   Rather like a male Venus who is never undressed. So funny!"

"Who took you there?" she said.

"That Pole, you remember?—and a Spaniard who talked English.   The toreador was great, lying on his bed in all his get-up, except his shoes, and quite a crowd of men going over it all again —wawawawawawa! you never heard such a row!"

"Aren't you wet?" said Kate.

"No, not at all.   I'm perfectly dry.   You see I had my coat. Only my head, of course.   My poor hair was all streaked down my face like streaks of dye."   He wiped his thin hair across his head with rather self-conscious humour.   "Hasn't Owen come in?" he asked.

"Yes, he's changing."

"Well I'll go up.   I suppose it's nearly supper time.   Oh yes, it's *after!*"   At which discovery he brightened as if he'd received a gift.

"Oh by the way, how did you get on?   Rather mean of us to let you go all alone like that," he said, as he hung poised in the open doorway.

"Not at all," she said.   "You wanted to stay.   And I can look after myself, at my time of life."

"We-ell!" he said, with an American drawl.   "Maybe you can!"   Then he gave a little laugh.   "But you *should* have seen all those men rehearsing in that bedroom, throwing their arms

about, and the toreador lying on the bed like Venus with a fat cigar, listening to her lovers."

"I'm glad I didn't," said Kate.

Villiers disappeared with a wicked little laugh.

And as she sat her hands trembled with outrage and passion. A-moral! How could one be a-moral, or non-moral, when one's soul was revolted! How could one be like these Americans, picking over the garbage of sensations, and gobbling it up like carrion birds. At the moment, both Owen and Villiers seemed to her like carrion birds, repulsive.

She felt, moreover, that they both hated her first because she was a woman. It was all right so long as she fell in with them in every way. But the moment she stood out against them in the least, they hated her mechanically for the very fact that she was a woman. They hated her womanness.

And in this Mexico, with its great under-drift of squalor and heavy reptile-like evil, it was hard for her to bear up.

She was really fond of Owen. But how could she respect him? So empty, and waiting for circumstance to fill him up. Swept with an American despair of having lived in vain, or of not having *really* lived. Having missed something. Which fearful misgiving would make him rush like mechanical steel filings to a magnet, towards any crowd in the street. And then all his poetry and philosophy gone with the cigarette-end he threw away, he would stand craning his neck in one more frantic effort to *see* —just to *see*. Whatever it was, he must see it. Or he might miss something. And then, after he'd seen an old ragged woman run over by a motor-car and bleeding on the floor, he'd come back to Kate pale at the gills, sick, bewildered, daunted, and yet, yes, glad he'd seen it. It was Life!

"Well," said Kate, "I always thank God I'm not Argus. Two eyes are often two too many for me, in all the horrors. I don't feed myself on street-accidents."

At dinner they tried to talk of pleasanter things than bull-fights. Villiers was neat and tidy and very nicely mannered, but she knew he was keeping a little mocking laugh up his sleeve, because she could not stomach the afternoon's garbage. He himself had black rings under his eyes, but that was because he had "lived."

The climax came with the dessert. In walked the Pole and that

Spaniard who spoke American. The Pole was unhealthy and unclean-looking. She heard him saying to Owen, who of course had risen with automatic cordiality:

"We thought we'd come here to dinner. Well, how are you?"

Kate's skin was already goose-flesh. But the next instant she heard that dingy voice, that spoke so many languages dingily, assailing her with familiarity:

"Ah, Miss Leslie, you missed the best part of it. You missed all the fun! Oh, I say——"

Rage flew into her heart and fire into her eyes. She got up suddenly from her chair, and faced the fellow behind her.

"Thank you!" she said. "I don't want to hear. I don't want you to speak to me. I don't want to know you."

She looked at him once, then turned her back, sat down again, and took a pitahaya from the fruit plate.

The fellow went green, and stood a moment speechless.

"Oh, all right!" he said mechanically, turning away to the Spaniard who spoke American.

"Well—see you later!" said Owen rather hurriedly, and he went back to his seat at Kate's table.

The two strange fellows sat at another table. Kate ate her cactus fruit in silence, and waited for her coffee. By this time she was not so angry, she was quite calm. And even Villiers hid his joy in a new sensation under a manner of complete quiet composure.

When coffee came she looked at the two men at the other table, and at the two men at her own table.

"I've had enough of *canaille,* of any sort," she said.

"Oh, I understand, perfectly," said Owen.

After dinner, she went to her room. And through the night she could not sleep, but lay listening to the noises of Mexico City, then to the silence and the strange, grisly fear that so often creeps out on to the darkness of a Mexican night. Away inside her, she loathed Mexico City. She even feared it. In the daytime it had a certain spell—but at night, the underneath grisliness and evil came forth.

In the morning Owen also announced that he had not slept at all.

"Oh, I never slept so well since I was in Mexico," said Villiers, with a triumphant look of a bird that has just pecked a good morsel from the garbage-heap.

"Look at the frail aesthetic youth!" said Owen, in a hollow voice.

"His frailty and his aestheticism are both bad signs, to me," said Kate ominously.

"And the youth. Surely that's another!" said Owen, with a dead laugh.

But Villiers only gave a little snort of cold, pleased amusement.

Someone was calling Miss Leslie on the telephone, said the Mexican chambermaid. It was the only person Kate knew in the capital—or in the Distrito Federal—a Mrs Norris, widow of an English embassador of thirty years ago. She had a big, ponderous old house out in the village of Tlacolula.

"Yes! Yes! This is Mrs Norris. How are you? That's right, that's right. Now, Mrs Leslie, won't you come out to tea this afternoon and see the garden? I wish you would. Two friends are coming in to see me, two Mexicans: Don Ramón Carrasco and General Viedma. They are both *charming* men, and Don Ramón is a great scholar. I assure you, they are both entirely the exception among Mexicans. Oh, but *entirely* the exception! So now, my *dear* Mrs Leslie, won't you come with your cousin? I wish you would."

Kate remembered the little general; he was a good deal smaller than herself. She remembered his erect, alert little figure, something birdlike, and the face with eyes slanting under arched eyebrows, and the little black tuft of an imperial on the chin: a face with a peculiar Chinese suggestion, without being Chinese in the least, really. An odd, detached, yet cocky little man, a true little Indian, speaking Oxford English in a rapid, low, musical voice, with extraordinarily gentle intonation. Yet those black, inhuman eyes!

Till this minute she had not really been able to recall him to herself, to get any sharp impression. Now she had it. He was an Indian pure and simple. And in Mexico, she knew, there were more generals than soldiers. There had been three generals in the Pullman coming down from El Paso, two, more or less educated, in the "drawing-room," and the third, a real peasant Indian, travelling with a frizzy half-white woman who looked as if she had fallen into a flour-sack, her face was so deep in powder, and her frizzy hair and her brown silk dress so douched with the white dust of it. Neither this "general" nor this woman had ever been in a Pullman before. But the general was sharper

than the woman. He was a tall wiry fellow with a reddened pock-marked face and sharp little black eyes. He followed Owen to the smoking room, and watched with sharp eyes, to see how everything was done. And soon he knew. And he would wipe his wash-bowl dry as neatly as anybody. There was something of a real man about him. But the poor, half-white woman, when she wanted the ladies' toilet, got lost in the passage and wailed aloud: *I don't know where to go! No sé adonde! No sé adonde!*—until the general sent the Pullman boy to direct her.

But it had annoyed Kate to see this general and this woman eating chicken and asparagus and jelly in the Pullman, paying fifteen pesos for a rather poor dinner, when for a peso-and-a-half apiece they could have eaten a better meal, and real Mexican, at the meal-stop station. And all the poor, barefoot people clamouring on the platform, while the "general," who was a man of their own sort, nobly swallowed his asparagus on the other side of the window-pane.

But this is how they save the people, in Mexico and elsewhere. Some tough individual scrambles up out of the squalor and proceeds to save himself. Who pays for the asparagus and jelly and face-powder, nobody asks, because everybody knows.

And so much for Mexican generals: as a rule, a class to be strictly avoided.

Kate was aware of all this. She wasn't much interested in any sort of Mexican in office. There is so much in the world that one wants to avoid, as one wants to avoid the lice that creep on the unwashed crowd.

Being rather late, Owen and Kate bumped out to Tlacolula in a Ford taxi. It was a long way, a long way through the peculiar squalid endings of the town, then along the straight road between trees, into the valley. The sun of April was brilliant, there were piles of cloud about the sky, where the volcanoes would be. The valley stretched away to its sombre, atmospheric hills, in a flat dry bed, parched except where there was some crop being irrigated. The soil seemed strange, dry, blackish, artificially wetted, and old. The trees rose high, and hung bare boughs, or withered shade. The buildings were either new and alien, like the Country Club, or cracked and dilapidated, with all the plaster falling off. The falling of thick plaster from cracked buildings —one could almost hear it!

Yellow tram-cars rushed at express speed away down the

fenced-in car-lines, rushing round towards Xochimilco or Tlalpam The asphalt road ran outside these lines, and on the asphalt rushed incredibly dilapidated Ford omnibuses, crowded with blank dark natives in dirty cotton clothes and big straw hats. At the far edge of the road, on the dust-tracks under the trees, little donkeys under huge loads loitered towards the city, driven by men with blackened faces and bare, blackened legs. Three-fold went the traffic; the roar of the tram-trains, the clatter of the automobiles, the straggle of asses and of outside-seeming individuals.

Occasional flowers would splash out in colour from a ruin of falling plaster. Occasional women with strong, dark-brown arms would be washing rags in a drain. An occasional horseman would ride across to the herd of motionless black-and-white cattle on the field. Occasional maize fields were already coming green. And the pillars that mark the water conduits passed one by one.

They went through the tree-filled plaza of Tlacolula, where natives were squatting on the ground, selling fruits or sweets, then down a road between high walls. They pulled up at last at big gate-doors, beyond which was a heavy pink-and-yellow house, and beyond the house, high, dark cypress trees.

In the road two motor-cars were already standing. That meant other visitors. Owen knocked on the studded fortress doors: there was an imbecile barking of dogs. At last a little footman with a little black moustache opened silently.

The square, inner patio, dark, with sun lying on the heavy arches of one side, had pots of red and white flowers, but was ponderous, as if dead for centuries. A certain dead, heavy strength and beauty seemed there, unable to pass away, unable to liberate itself and decompose. There was a stone basin of clear but motionless water, and the heavy reddish-and-yellow arches went round the courtyard with warrior-like fatality, their bases in dark shadow. Dead, massive house of the Conquistadores, with a glimpse of tall-grown garden beyond, and further Aztec cypresses rising to strange dark heights. And dead silence, like the black, porous, absorptive lava rock. Save when the tram-cars battered past outside the solid wall.

Kate went up the jet-like stone staircase, through the leather doors. Mrs Norris came forward on the terrace of the upper patio to receive her guests.

"I'm so glad, my dear, that you came. I should have rung you

up before, but I've had such trouble with my heart. And the doctor wanting to send me down to a lower altitude! I said to him, I've no patience! If you're going to cure me, cure me at an altitude of seven thousand feet or else admit your incompetence at once. Ridiculous, this rushing up and down from one altitude to another. I've lived at this height all these years. I simply refuse to be bundled down to Cuernavaca or some other place where I don't want to go. Well, my dear, and how are you?"

Mrs Norris was an elderly woman, rather like a conquistador herself in her black silk dress and her little black shoulder-shawl of fine cashmere, with a short silk fringe, and her ornaments of black enamel. Her face had gone slightly grey, her nose was sharp and dusky, and her voice hammered almost like metal, a slow, distinct, peculiar hard music of its own. She was an archaeologist, and she had studied the Aztec remains so long, that now some of the black-grey look of the lava rock, and some of the experience of the Aztec idols, with sharp nose and slightly prominent eyes and an expression of tomb-like mockery, had passed into her face. A lonely daughter of culture, with a strong mind and a dense will, she had browsed all her life on the hard stones of archaeological remains, and at the same time she had retained a strong sense of humanity, and a slightly fantastic humorous vision of her fellow men.

From the first instant, Kate respected her for her isolation and her dauntlessness. The world is made up of a mass of people and a few individuals. Mrs Norris was one of the few individuals. True, she played her social game all the time. But she was an odd number; and all alone, she could give the even numbers a bad time.

"But come in. Do come in!" she said, after keeping her two guests out on the terrace that was lined with black idols and dusty native baskets and shields and arrows and tapa, like a museum.

In the dark sitting-room that opened on to the terrace were visitors: an old man in a black morning coat and white hair and beard, and a woman in black crêpe-de-chine, with the inevitable hat of her sort upon her grey hair: a stiff satin turned up on three sides and with black ospreys underneath. She had the baby face and the faded blue eyes and the middle-west accent inevitable.

"Judge and Mrs Burlap."

The third visitor was a youngish man, very correct and not

quite sure. He was Major Law, American military attaché at the moment.

The three people eyed the newcomers with cautious suspicion. They might be shady. There are indeed so many shady people in Mexico that it is taken for granted, if you arrive unannounced and unexpected in the capital, that you are probably under an assumed name, and have some dirty game up your sleeve.

"Been long in Mexico?" snapped the Judge; the police enquiry had begun.

"No!" said Owen, resonantly, his gorge rising. "About two weeks."

"You are an American?"

"I," said Owen, "am American. Mrs Leslie is English—or rather Irish."

"Been in the club yet?"

"No," said Owen, "I haven't. American clubs aren't much in my line. Though Garfield Spence gave me a letter of introduction."

"Who? Garfield Spence?" The Judge started as if he had been stung. "Why, the fellow's nothing better than a bolshevist. Why, he went to Russia!"

"I should rather like to go to Russia myself," said Owen. "It is probably the most interesting country in the world to-day."

"But weren't you telling me," put in Mrs Norris, in her clear metal-musical voice, "that you loved China so much, Mr Rhys?"

"I *did* like China *very* much," said Owen.

"And I'm sure you made some wonderful collections. Tell me now, what was your particular fancy?"

"Perhaps, after all," said Owen, "it was jade."

"Ah jade! Yes! Jade! Jade is beautiful! Those wonderful little fairy-lands they carve in jade!"

"And the stone itself! It was the delicate stone that fascinated me," said Owen. "The wonderful quality of it!"

"Ah wonderful, wonderful! Tell me now, dear Mrs Leslie, what you have been doing since I saw you?"

"We went to a bull-fight, and hated it," said Kate. "At least I did. We sat in the Sun, near the ring, and it was all horrible."

"Horrible, I am sure. I never went to a bull-fight in Mexico. Only in Spain, where there is wonderful colour. Did you ever try a bull-fight, Major?"

"Yes, I have been several times."

"You have! Then you know all about it. And how are you liking Mexico, Mrs Leslie?"

"Not much," said Kate. "It strikes me as evil."

"It does! It does!" said Mrs Norris. "Ah, if you had known it before! Mexico before the revolution! It was different then. What is the latest news, Major?"

"About the same," said the Major. "There is a rumour that the new President will be turned down by the army, a few days before he comes into office. But you never know."

"I think it would be a great shame not to let him have a try," put in Owen hotly. "He seems a sincere man, and just because he is honestly a Labour man, they want to shut him out."

"Ah, my dear Mr Rhys, they *all* talk so nobly beforehand. If only their deeds followed their words, Mexico would be heaven on earth."

"Instead of hell on earth," snapped the Judge.

A young man and his wife, also Americans, were introduced as Mr and Mrs Henry. The young man was fresh and lively.

"We were talking about the new President," said Mrs Norris.

"Well, why not!" said Mr Henry breezily. "I'm just back from Orizaba. And do you know what they've got pasted up on the walls?—*Hosanna! Hosanna! Hosanna! Viva el Jesús Cristo de Mexico, Socrates Tomas Montes!*"

"Why, did you ever hear of such a thing!" said Mrs Norris.

"*Hosanna! Hosanna! Hosanna!* To the new Labour President! I think it's rich," said Henry.

The Judge stamped his stick on the ground in a speechless access of irritability.

"They pasted on my luggage," said the Major, "when I came through Vera Cruz: *La degenerada media clasa, Sera regenerada, por mi, Montes.* The degenerate middle class shall be regenerated by me, Montes."

"Poor Montes!" said Kate. "He seems to have got his work cut out."

"He has indeed!" said Mrs Norris. "Poor man, I wish he might come in peacefully and put a strong hand on the country. But there's not much hope, I'm afraid."

There was a silence, during which Kate felt that bitter hopelessness that comes over people who know Mexico well. A bitter barren hopelessness.

"How can a man who comes in on a Labour vote, even a doctored one, put a strong hand on a country!" snapped the Judge. "Why he came in on the very cry of *Down with the strong hand!*" And again the old man stamped his stick in an access of extreme irritability.

This was another characteristic of the old residents of the city: A state of intense, though often suppressed irritation, an irritation amounting almost to rabies.

"Oh, but mayn't it be possible that he will change his views a little on coming into power?" said Mrs Norris. "So many Presidents have done so."

"I should say very probable, if ever he gets into power," said young Henry. "He'll have all his work cut out saving Socrates Tomas, he won't have much time left for saving Mexico."

"He's a dangerous fellow, and will turn out a scoundrel," said the Judge.

"Myself," said Owen, "as far as I have followed him, I believe he is sincere, and I admire him."

"I thought it was so nice," said Kate, "that they received him in New York with loud music by the Street Sweepers' Band. The Street Sweepers' Band they sent to receive him from the ship!"

"You see," said the Major, "no doubt the Labour people themselves wished to send that particular band."

"But to be President Elect, and to be received by the Street Sweepers' Band!" said Kate. "No, I can't believe it!"

"Oh, it actually was so," said the Major. "But that is Labour hailing Labour, surely."

"The latest rumour," said Henry, "is that the army will go over *en bloc* to General Angulo about the twenty-third, a week before the inauguration."

"But how is it possible?" said Kate, "when Montes is so popular?"

"Montes popular!" they all cried at once. "Why!" snapped the Judge, "he's the most unpopular man in Mexico."

"Not with the Labour Party!" said Owen, almost at bay.

"The Labour Party!" the Judge fairly spat like a cat. "There is no such thing. What is the Labour Party in Mexico? A bunch of isolated factory hands here and there, mostly in the State of Vera Cruz. The Labour Party! They've done what they could already. We know them."

"That's true," said Henry. "The Labourites have tried every

little game possible. When I was in Orizaba they marched to
the Hotel Francia to shoot all the gringoes and the Gachupines.
The hotel manager had pluck enough to harangue them, and they
went off to the next hotel. When the man came out there to
talk to them, they shot him before he got a word out. It's funny,
really! If you have to go to the Town Hall, you're dressed in
decent clothes, they let you sit on a hard bench for hours. But
if a street-sweeper comes in, or a fellow in dirty cotton drawers,
it is *Buenos Dias! Señor! Pase Usted! Quiere Usted algo?*—
while you sit there waiting their pleasure. Oh, it's quite funny."

The Judge trembled with irritation like an access of gout.
The party sat in gloomy silence, that sense of doom and despair
overcoming them as it seems to overcome all people who talk
seriously about Mexico. Even Owen was silent. He too had
come through Vera Cruz, and had had his fright; the porters
had charged him twenty pesos to carry his trunk from the ship
to the train. Twenty pesos is ten dollars, for ten minutes' work.
And when Owen had seen the man in front of him arrested and
actually sent to jail, a Mexican jail at that, for refusing to pay
the charge, "the legal charge," he himself had stumped up without a word.

"I walked into the National Museum the other day," said the
Major quietly. "Just into that room on the patio where the stones
are. It was rather a cold morning, with a Norte blowing. I'd
been there about ten minutes when somebody suddenly poked me
on the shoulder. I turned round, and it was a lout in tight boots.
You spik English? I said *yes!* Then he motioned me to take
my hat off: I'd got to take my hat off. *What for?* said I, and I
turned away and went on looking at their idols and things · ugliest
set of stuff in the world, I believe. Then up came the fellow
with the attendant—the attendant of course wearing his cap.
They began gabbling that this was the National Museum, and I
must take off my hat to their national monuments. Imagine it:
those dirty stones! I laughed at them and jammed my hat on
tighter and walked out. They are really only monkeys, when
it comes to nationalism."

"Exactly!" cried Henry. "When they forget all about the
Patria and Mexico and all that stuff, they're as nice a people as
you'd find. But as soon as they get national, they're just monkeys. A man up from Mixcoatl told me a nice story. Mixcoatl
is a capital way in the South, and they've got a sort of Labour

bureau there. Well, the Indians come in from the hills, as wild as rabbits. And they get them into that bureau, and the Laboristas, the agitator fellows, say to them: *Now Señores, have you anything to report from your native village? Haven't you anything for which you would like redress?* Then of course the Indians start complaining about one another, and the Secretary says: *Wait a minute, gentlemen! Let me ring up the Governor and report this.* So he goes to the telephone and starts ringing: ringing: *Ah! Is that the Palace? Is the Governor in? Tell him Señor Fulano wants to speak to him!* The Indians sit gaping with open mouths. To them it's a miracle. *Ah! Is that you, Governor! Good morning! How are you! Can I have your attention for a moment? Many thanks! Well I've got some gentlemen here down from Apaxtle, in the hills: José Garcia, Jesus Querido, etc.—and they wish to report so-and-so. Yes! Yes! That's it! Yes! What? You will see that justice is done and the thing is made right? Ah señor, many thanks! In the name of these gentlemen from the hills, from the village of Apaxtle, many thanks.*

"There sit the Indians staring as if heaven had opened and the Virgin of Guadalupe was standing tiptoe on their chins. And what do you expect? The telephone is a dummy. It isn't connected with anywhere. Isn't that rich? But it's Mexico."

The moment's fatal pause followed this funny story.

"Oh but!" said Kate, "it's wicked! It *is* wicked. I'm sure the Indians would be all right, if they were left alone."

"Well," said Mrs Norris. "Mexico isn't like any other place in the world."

But she spoke with fear and despair in her voice.

"They seem to *want* to betray everything," said Kate. "They seem to *love* criminals and ghastly things. They seem to want the ugly things to come up to the top. All the foulness that lies at the bottom, they want to stir up to the top. They seem to enjoy it. To enjoy making everything fouler. Isn't it curious!"

"It is curious," said Mrs Norris.

"But that's what it is," said the Judge. "They want to turn the country into one big crime. They don't like anything else. They don't like honesty and decency and cleanliness. They want to foster lies and crime. What they call liberty here is just freedom to commit crime. That's what Labour means, that's what they all mean. Free crime, nothing else."

"I wonder all the foreigners don't go away," said Kate.

"They have their occupations here," snapped the Judge.

"And the good people *are* all going away. They have nearly all gone, those that have anything left to go to," said Mrs Norris. "Some of us, who have our property here, and who have made our lives here, and who know the country, we stay out of a kind of tenacity. But we know it's hopeless. The more it changes, the worse it is.—Ah, here is Don Ramon and Don Cipriano. So pleased to see you. Let me introduce you."

Don Ramon Carrasco was a tall, big, handsome man who gave the effect of bigness. He was middle aged, with a large black moustache and large, rather haughty eyes under straight brows. The General was in civilian clothes, looking very small beside the other man, and very smartly built, almost cocky.

"Come," said Mrs Norris. "Let us go across and have tea."

The Major excused himself, and took his departure.

Mrs Norris gathered her little shawl round her shoulders and led through a sombre antechamber to a little terrace, where creepers and flowers bloomed thick on the low walls. There was a bell-flower, red and velvety, like blood that is drying: and clusters of white roses: and tufts of bougainvillea, papery magenta colour.

"How lovely it is here!" said Kate. "Having the great dark trees beyond."

But she stood in a kind of dread.

"Yes it *is* beautiful," said Mrs Norris, with the gratification of a possessor. "I have such a time trying to keep these apart." And going across in her little black shawl, she pushed the bougainvillea away from the rust-scarlet bell-flowers, stroking the little white roses to make them intervene."

"I think the two reds together interesting," said Owen.

"Do you really!" said Mrs Norris, automatically, paying no heed to such a remark.

The sky was blue overhead, but on the lower horizon was a thick, pearl haze. The clouds had gone.

"One never sees Popocatepetl nor Ixtaccihuatl," said Kate, disappointed.

"No, not at this season. But look, through the trees there, you see Ajusco!"

Kate looked at the sombre-seeming mountain, between the huge dark trees.

On the low stone parapet were Aztec things, obsidian knives, grimacing squatting idols in black lava, and a queer thickish stone stick, or bâton. Owen was balancing the latter: it felt murderous even to touch.

Kate turned to the general, who was near her, his face expressionless, yet alert.

"Aztec things oppress me," she said.

"They *are* oppressive," he answered, in his beautiful cultured English, that was nevertheless a tiny bit like a parrot talking.

"There is no hope in them," she said.

"Perhaps the Aztecs never asked for hope," he said, somewhat automatically.

"Surely it is hope that keeps one going?" she said.

"You, maybe. But not the Aztec, nor the Indian to-day."

He spoke like a man who has something in reserve, who is only half attending to what he hears, and even to his own answer.

"What do they have, if they don't have hope?" she said.

"They have some other strength, perhaps," he said evasively.

"I would like to give them hope," she said. "If they had hope, they wouldn't be so sad, and they would be cleaner, and not have vermin."

"That of course would be good," he said, with a little smile. "But I think they are not so very sad. They laugh a good deal and are gay."

"No," she said. "They oppress me, like a weight on my heart. They make me irritable, and I want to go away."

"From Mexico?"

"Yes. I feel I want to go away from it and never, never see it again. It is so oppressive and gruesome."

"Try it a little longer," he said. "Perhaps you will feel differently. But perhaps not," he ended vaguely, driftingly.

She could feel in him a sort of yearning towards her. As if a sort of appeal came to her from him, from his physical heart in his breast. As if the very heart gave out dark rays of seeking and yearning. She glimpsed this now for the first time, quite apart from the talking, and it made her shy.

"And does everything in Mexico oppress you?" he added, almost shyly, but with a touch of mockery, looking at her with a troubled naïve face that had its age heavy and resistant beneath the surface.

"Almost everything!" she said. "It *always* makes my heart sink. Like the eyes of the men in the big hats—I call them the

peons. Their eyes have no middle to them. Those big handsome men, under their big hats, they aren't really there. They have no centre, no real *I*. Their middle is a raging black hole, like the middle of a maelstrom."

She looked with her troubled grey eyes into the black, slanting, watchful, calculating eyes of the small man opposite her. He had a pained expression, puzzled, like a child. And at the same time something obstinate, and mature, a demonish maturity, opposing her in an animal way.

"You mean we aren't real people, we have nothing of our own, except killing and death," he said, quite matter of fact.

"I don't know," she said, startled by his interpretation. "I only say how it makes me feel."

"You are very clever, Mrs Leslie," came Don Ramón's quiet, but heavy teasing voice behind her. "It is quite true. Whenever a Mexican cries *Viva!* he ends up with *Muera!* When he says *Viva!* he really means *Death for Somebody or Other!* I think of all the Mexican revolutions, and I see a skeleton walking ahead of a great number of people, waving a black banner with *Viva la Muerte!* written in large white letters. *Long live Death!* Not *Viva Cristo Rey!* but *Viva Muerte Rey! Vamos! Viva!*"

Kate looked round. Don Ramón was flashing his knowing brown Spanish eyes, and a little sardonic smile lurked under his moustache. Instantly Kate and he, Europeans, in essence, understood one another. He was waving his arm to the last *Viva!*

"But," said Kate, "I don't want to say *Viva la Muerte!*"

"But when you are real Mexican—" he said, teasing.

"I *never* could be," she said hotly, and he laughed.

"I'm afraid *Viva la Muerte!* hits the nail on the head," said Mrs Norris, rather stonily. "But won't you come to tea! Do!"

She led the way in her black little shawl and neat grey hair, going ahead like a Conquistador herself, and turning to look with her Aztec eyes through her pince-nez, to see if the others were coming.

"We are following," said Don Ramón in Spanish, teasing her. Stately in his black suit, he walked behind her on the narrow terrace, and Kate followed, with the small, strutting Don Cipriano, also in a black suit, lingering oddly near her.

"Do I call you General or Don Cipriano?" she asked, turning to him.

An amused little smile quickly lit his face, though his eyes did not smile. They looked at her with a black, sharp look.

"As you wish," he said. "You know *General* is a term of disgrace in Mexico. Shall we say Don Cipriano?"

"Yes, I like that much the best," she said.

And he seemed pleased.

It was a round tea-table, with shiny silver tea-service, and silver kettle with a little flame, and pink and white oleanders. The little neat young footman carried the tea-cups, in white cotton gloves. Mrs Norris poured tea and cut cakes with a heavy hand.

Don Ramón sat on her right hand, the Judge on her left. Kate was between the Judge and Mr Henry. Everybody except Don Ramón and the Judge was a little nervous. Mrs Norris always put her visitors uncomfortably at their ease, as if they were captives and she the chieftainess who had captured them. She rather enjoyed it, heavily, archaeologically queening at the head of the table. But it was evident that Don Ramón, by far the most impressive person present, liked her. Cipriano, on the other hand, remained mute and disciplined, perfectly familiar with the tea-table routine, superficially quite at ease, but underneath remote and unconnected. He glanced from time to time at Kate.

She was a beautiful woman, in her own unconventional way, and with a certain richness. She was going to be forty next week. Used to all kinds of society, she watched people as one reads the pages of a novel, with a certain disinterested amusement. She was never *in* any society: too Irish, too wise.

"But of course nobody lives without hope," Mrs Norris was saying banteringly to Don Ramón. "If it's only the hope of a *real*, to buy a litre of pulque."

"Ah, Mrs Norris!" he replied in his quiet, yet curiously deep voice, like a violoncello: "If pulque is the highest happiness!"

"Then we are fortunate, because a tostón will buy paradise," she said.

"It is a *bon mot*, Señora mia," said Don Ramón, laughing and drinking his tea.

"Now won't you try these little native cakes with sesame seeds on them?" said Mrs Norris to the table at large. "My cook makes them, and her national feeling is flattered when anybody likes them. Mrs Leslie, do take one."

"I will," said Kate. "Does one say *Open Sesame!*"

"If one wishes," said Mrs Norris.

"Won't you have one?" said Kate, handing the plate to Judge Burlap.

"Don't want any," he snapped, turning his face away as if he had been offered a plate of Mexicans, and leaving Kate with the dish suspended.

Mrs Norris quickly but definitely took the plate, saying:

"Judge Burlap is afraid of *Sesame Seed,* he prefers the cave shut." And she handed the dish quietly to Cipriano, who was watching the old man's bad manners with black, snake-like eyes.

"Did you see that article by Willis Rice Hope, in the *Excelsior?*" suddenly snarled the Judge, to his hostess.

"I did. I thought it very sensible."

"The only sensible thing that's been said about these Agrarian Laws. Sensible! I should think so. Why, Rice Hope came to me, and I put him up to a few things. But his article says *everything,* doesn't miss an item of importance."

"Quite!" said Mrs Norris, with rather stony attention. "If only *saying* would alter things, Judge Burlap."   ..

"Saying the wrong thing has done all the mischief!" snapped the Judge. "Fellows like Garfield Spence coming down here and talking a lot of criminal talk. Why the town's full of Socialists and Sinvergüenzas from New York."

Mrs Norris adjusted her pince-nez.

"Fortunately," she said, "they don't come out to Tlacolula, so we needn't think about them. Mrs Henry, let me give you some more tea."

"Do you read *Spanish?*" the Judge spat out, at Owen. Owen, in his big shell spectacles, was evidently a red rag to his irritable fellow-countryman.

"No!" said Owen, round as a cannon-shot.

Mrs Norris once more adjusted her eye-glasses.

"It's such a relief to hear someone who is altogether innocent of Spanish, and altogether unashamed," she said. "My father had us all speaking four languages by the time we were twelve, and we have none of us ever quite recovered. My stockings were all dyed blue for me before I put my hair up. By the way! How have you been for walking, Judge? You heard of the time I had with my ankle?"

"Of course we heard!" cried Mrs Burlap, seeing dry land at

last. "I've been trying so hard to get out to see you, to ask about it. We were so *grieved* about it."

"What happened?" said Kate.

"Why I foolishly slipped on a piece of orange peel in town—just at the corner of San Juan de Letrán and Madero. And I fell right down. And of course, the first thing I did when I got up was to push the piece of orange peel into the gutter. And would you believe it, that lot of Mex—" she caught herself up—"that lot of fellows standing there at the corner laughed heartily at me, when they saw me doing it. They thought it an excellent joke."

"Of course they would," said the Judge. "They were waiting for the next person to come along and fall."

"Did nobody help you?" asked Kate.

"Oh no! If anyone has an accident in this country, you must never, *never* help. If you touch them even, you may be arrested for causing the accident."

"That's the law!" said the Judge. "If you touch them before the police arrive, you are arrested for complicity. Let them lie and bleed, is the motto."

"Is that true?" said Kate to Don Ramón.

"Fairly true," he replied. "Yes, it is true you must not touch the one who is hurt."

"How disgusting!" said Kate.

"Disgusting!" cried the Judge. "A great deal is disgusting in this country, as you'll learn if you stay here long. I nearly lost my life on a banana skin; lay in a darkened room for days, between life and death, and lame for life from it."

"How awful!" said Kate. "What did you do when you fell?"

"What did I do? Just smashed my hip."

It had truly been a terrible accident, and the man had suffered bitterly.

"You can hardly blame Mexico for a banana skin," said Owen, elated. "I fell on one in Lexington Avenue; but fortunately I only bruised myself on a soft spot."

"That wasn't your head, was it?" said Mrs Henry.

"No," laughed Owen. "The other extreme."

"We've got to add banana skins to the list of public menaces," said young Henry. "I'm an American, and I may any day turn bolshevist, to save my pesos, so I can repeat what I heard a man

saying yesterday.   He said there were only two great diseases in
the world to-day—Bolshevism and Americanism; and Americanism is the worst of the two, because Bolshevism only smashes your
house or your business or your skull, but Americanism smashes
your soul."

"Who was he?" snarled the Judge.

"I forget," said Henry, wickedly.

"One wonders," said Mrs Norris slowly, "what he meant by
Americanism."

"He didn't define it," said Henry.   "Cult of the dollar, I suppose."

"Well," said Mrs Norris.   "The cult of the dollar, in my experience, is far more intense in the countries that haven't got the
dollar, than in the United States."

Kate felt that the table was like a steel disc to which they were
all, as victims, magnetised and bound.

"Where *is* your garden, Mrs Norris?" she asked.

They trooped out, gasping with relief, to the terrace.   The
Judge hobbled behind, and Kate had to linger sympathetically to
keep him company.

They were on the little terrace.

"Isn't this strange stuff!" said Kate, picking up one of the
Aztec stone knives on the parapet.   "Is it a sort of jade?"

"Jade!" snarled the Judge.   "Jade's *green*, not black.   That's
obsidian."

"Jade *can* be black," said Kate.   "I've got a lovely little black
tortoise of jade from China."

"You can't have.   Jade's bright green."

"But there's white jade too.   I know there is."

The Judge was silent from exasperation for a few moments,
then he snapped:

"Jade's bright green."

Owen, who had the ears of a lynx, had heard.

"What's that?" he said.

"Surely there's more than green jade!" said Kate.

"What!" cried Owen.   "More!   Why there's every imaginable
tint—white, rose, lavender—"

"And black?" said Kate.

"Black?   Oh yes, quite common.   Why you should see my
collection.   The most beautiful range of colour!   *Only green
jade!*   Ha-ha-ha!"—and he laughed a rather stage laugh.

They had come to the stairs, which were old stone, waxed and polished in some way till they were a glittering black.

"I'll catch hold of your arm down here," said the Judge to young Henry. "This stair-case is a death-trap."

Mrs Norris heard without comment. She only tilted her pince-nez on her sharp nose.

In the archway downstairs, Don Ramón and the General took their leave. The rest trailed on into the garden.

Evening was falling. The garden was drawn up tall, under the huge dark trees on the one side, and the tall, reddish-and-yellow house on the other. It was like being at the bottom of some dusky, flowering garden down in Hades. Hibiscus hung scarlet from the bushes, putting out yellow bristling tongues. Some roses were scattering scentless petals on the twilight, and lonely-looking carnations hung on weak stalks. From a huge dense bush the mysterious white bells of the datura were suspended, large and silent, like the very ghosts of sound. And the datura scent was moving thick and noiseless from the tree, into the little alleys.

Mrs Burlap had hitched herself on to Kate, and from her silly, social baby-face was emitting searching questions.

"What hotel are you staying at?"

Kate told her.

"I don't know it. Where is it?"

"In the Avenida del Peru. You wouldn't know it, it is a little Italian hotel."

"Are you staying long?"

"We aren't certain."

"Is Mr Rhys on a newspaper?"

"No, he's a poet."

"Does he make a living by poetry?"

"No, he doesn't try to."

It was the sort of secret service investigation one is submitted to, in the capital of shady people, particularly shady foreigners.

Mrs Norris was lingering by a flowering arch of little white flowers.

Already a firefly was sparking. It was already night.

"Well, goodbye, Mrs Norris! *Won't* you come and lunch with us? I don't mean come out to our house. Only let me know, and lunch with me *anywhere you like,* in town."

"Thank you my dear! Thank you so much! Well! I'll see!"

Mrs Norris was almost regal, stonily, Aztec-regal.

At last they had all made their adieus, and the great doors were shut behind them.

"How did you come out!" Mrs Burlap asked, impertinent.

"In an old Ford taxi—but where is it?" said Kate, peering into the dark. It should have been under the *fresno* trees opposite, but it wasn't.

"What a curious thing!" said Owen, and he disappeared into the night.

"Which way do you go?" said Mrs Burlap.

"To the Zócalo," said Kate.

"We have to take a tram, the opposite way," said the baby-faced, withered woman from the Middle-West.

The Judge was hobbling along the pavement like a cat on hot bricks, to the corner. Across the road stood a group of natives in big hats and white calico clothes, all a little the worse for the pulque they had drunk. Nearer, on this side of the road, stood another little gang, of workmen in town clothes.

"There you have them," said the Judge, flourishing his stick with utter vindictiveness. "There's the two lots of 'em."

"What two lots?" said Kate, surprised.

"Those peon fellows and those obreros, all drunk, the lot of them. The lot of them!" And in a spasm of pure, frustrated hate, he turned his back on her.

At the same time they saw the lights of a tram-car rushing dragon-like up the dark road, between the high wall and the huge trees.

"Here's our car!" said the Judge, beginning to scramble excitedly with his stick.

"You go the other way," flung the baby-faced, faded woman in the three-cornered satin hat, also beginning to fluster as if she were going to swim off the pavement.

The couple clambered avidly into the brightly-lighted car, first class; hobbling up. The natives crowded into the second class.

Away whizzed the *tren*. The Burlap couple had not even said goodnight! They were terrified lest they might have to know somebody whom they might not want to know; whom it might not *pay* to know.

"You common-place little woman!" said Kate aloud, looking after the retreating tram-car. "You awful ill-bred little pair."

She was a bit afraid of the natives, not quite sober, who were waiting for the car in the opposite direction. But stronger than

her fear was a certain sympathy with these dark-faced silent men in their big straw hats and naïve little cotton blouses. Anyhow they had blood in their veins : they were columns of dark blood.

Whereas the other bloodless, acidulous couple from the Middle-West, with their nasty whiteness . . . !

She thought of the little tale the natives tell. When the Lord was making the first men, he made them of clay and put them into the oven to bake. They came out black. *They're baked too much!* said the Lord. So he made another batch, and put them in. They came out white. *They're baked too little!* He said. So He had a third try. These came out a good warm brown. *They're just right!* said the Lord.

The couple from the Middle-West, that withered baby-face and that limping Judge, they weren't baked. They were hardly baked at all.

Kate looked at the dark faces under the arc-lamp. They frightened her. They were a sort of menace to her. But she felt they were at least baked hot and to a certain satisfactory colour.

The taxi came lurching up, with Owen poking his head out and opening the door.

"I found the man in a *pulqueria*," he said. "But I don't think he's *quite* drunk. Will you risk driving back with him?"

"The *pulqueria* was called *La Flor de un Dia*—the Flower of a Day," said Owen, with an apprehensive laugh.

Kate hesitated, looking at her man.

"We may as well," she said.

Away gallivanted the Ford, full speed to Hell.

"Do tell him not so fast," said Kate.

"I don't know how," said Owen.

He shouted in good English :

"Hey! chauffeur! Not so fast! Don't drive so fast."

"No presto. Troppo presto. Va troppo presto!" said Kate.

The man looked at them with black, dilated eyes of fathomless incomprehension. Then he put his foot on the accelerator.

"He's only going faster!" laughed Owen nervously.

"Ah! Let him alone!" said Kate, with utter weariness.

The fellow drove like a devil incarnate, as if he had the devil in his body. But also, he drove with the devil's own nonchalant skill. There was nothing to do but let him rip.

"Wasn't that a ghastly tea party!" said Owen.

"Ghastly!" said Kate.

CHAPTER III

FORTIETH BIRTHDAY

KATE woke up one morning, aged forty. She did not hide the fact from herself, but she kept it dark from the others.

It was a blow, really. To be forty! One had to cross a dividing line. On this side there was youth and spontaneity and "happiness." On the other side something different: reserve, responsibility, a certain standing back from "fun."

She was a widow, and a lonely woman now. Having married young, her two children were grown up. The boy was twenty-one, and her daughter nineteen. They stayed chiefly with their father, from whom she had been divorced ten years before, in order to marry James Joachim Leslie. Now Leslie was dead, and all that half of life was over.

She climbed up to the flat roofs of the hotel. It was a brilliant morning, and for once, under the blue sky of the distance, Popocatepetl stood aloof, a heavy giant presence under heaven, with a cape of snow. And rolling a long dark roll of smoke like a serpent.

Ixtaccihuatl, the White Woman, glittered and seemed near, but the other mountain, Popocatepetl, stood further back, and in shadow, a pure cone of atmospheric shadow, with glinting flashes of snow. There they were, the two monsters, watching gigantically and terribly over their lofty, bloody cradle of men, the Valley of Mexico. Alien, ponderous, the white-hung mountains seemed to emit a deep purring sound, too deep for the ear to hear, and yet audible on the blood, a sound of dread. There was no soaring or uplift or exaltation, as there is in the snowy mountains of Europe. Rather a ponderous white-shouldered weight, pressing terribly on the earth, and murmuring like two watchful lions.

Superficially, Mexico might be all right: with its suburbs of villas, its central fine streets, its thousands of motor-cars, its tennis and its bridge-parties. The sun shone brilliantly every day, and big bright flowers stood out from the trees. It was a holiday.

44

Until you were alone with it. And then the undertone was like the low angry, snarling purring of some jaguar spotted with night. There was a ponderous, down-pressing weight upon the spirit: the great folds of the dragon of the Aztecs, the dragon of the Toltecs winding around one and weighing down the soul. And on the bright sunshine was a dark stream of an angry, impotent blood, and the flowers seemed to have their roots in spilt blood. The spirit of place was cruel, down-dragging, destructive.

Kate could so well understand the Mexican who had said to her: *El Grito mexicano es siempre el Grito del Odio*—The Mexicano shout is always a shout of hate. The famous revolutions, as Don Ramón said, began with *Viva!* but ended always with *Muera!* Death to this, death to the other, it was all death! death! death! as insistent as the Aztec sacrifices. Something for ever gruesome and macabre.

Why had she come to this high plateau of death? As a woman, she suffered even more than men suffer: and in the end, practically all men go under. Once, Mexico had had an elaborate ritual of death. Now it has death ragged, squalid, vulgar, without even the passion of its own mystery.

She sat on a parapet of the old roof. The street beyond was like a black abyss, but around her was the rough glare of uneven flat roofs, with loose telephone wires trailing across, and the sudden, deep, dark wells of the patios, showing flowers blooming in shade.

Just behind was a huge old church, its barred roof humping up like some crouching animal, and its domes, like bubbles inflated, glittering with yellow tiles, and blue and white tiles, against the intense blue heaven. Quiet native women in long skirts were moving on the roofs, hanging out washing or spreading it on the stones. Chickens perched here and there. An occasional bird soared huge overhead, trailing a shadow. And not far away stood the brownish tower-stumps of the Cathedral, the profound old bell trembling huge and deep, so soft as to be almost inaudible, upon the air.

It ought to have been all gay, allegro, allegretto, in that sparkle of bright air and old roof surfaces. But no! There was the dark undertone, the black, serpent-like fatality all the time.

It was no good Kate's wondering why she had come. Over in England, in Ireland, in Europe, she had heard the *consummatum est* of her own spirit. It was finished, in a kind of death agony.

But still this heavy continent of dark-souled death was more than she could bear.

She was forty: the first half of her life was over. The bright page with its flowers and its love and its stations of the Cross ended with a grave. Now she must turn over, and the page was black, black and empty.

The first half of her life had been written on the bright, smooth vellum of hope, with initial letters all gorgeous upon a field of gold. But the glamour had gone from station to station of the Cross, and the last illumination was the tomb.

Now the bright page was turned, and the dark page lay before her. How could one write on a page so profoundly black?

She went down, having promised to go and see the frescoes in the university and schools. Owen and Villiers and a young Mexican were waiting for her. They set off through the busy streets of the town, where automobiles and the little omnibuses called camions run wild, and where the natives in white cotton clothes and sandals and big hats linger like heavy ghosts in the street, among the bourgeoisie, the young ladies in pale pink crêpe de Chine and high heels, the men in little shoes and American straw hats. A continual bustle in the glitter of sunshine.

Crossing the great shadeless plaza in front of the Cathedral, where the tram-cars gather as in a corral, and slide away down their various streets, Kate lingered again to look at the things spread for sale on the pavement: the little toys, the painted gourd-shells, brilliant in a kind of lacquer, the *novedades* from Germany, the fruits, the flowers. And the natives squatting with their wares, large-limbed, silent, handsome men looking up with their black, centreless eyes, speaking so softly, and lifting with small sensitive brown hands the little toys they had so carefully made and painted. A strange gentle appeal and wistfulness, strange male voices, so deep, yet so quiet and gentle. Or the women, the small quick women in their blue rebozos, looking up quickly with dark eyes, and speaking in their quick, coaxing voices. The man just setting out his oranges, wiping them with a cloth so carefully, almost tenderly, and piling them in bright tiny pyramids, all neat and ex-quisite. A certain sensitive tenderness of the heavy blood, a certain chirping charm of the bird-like women, so still and tender with a bud-like femininity. And at the same time, the dirty clothes, and the unwashed skin, the lice, and the peculiar hollow glint of the black eyes, at once so fearsome and so appealing.

Kate knew the Italian fruit vendors, vigorously polishing their oranges on their coat-sleeves. Such a contrast, the big, handsome Indian, sitting so soft and as it were lonely by the kerb, softly, lingeringly polishing his yellow oranges to a clean gleam, and lingeringly, delicately arranging the little piles, the pyramids for two or three cents each.

Queer work, for a big, handsome, male-looking man. But they seem to prefer these childish jobs.

The University was a Spanish building that had been done up spick and span, and given over to the young artists to decorate. Since the revolutions, nowhere had authority and tradition been so finally overthrown as in the Mexican fields of science and art. Science and art are the sport of the young. Go ahead, my boys!

The boys had gone ahead. But even then, the one artist of distinction was no longer a boy, and he had served a long apprenticeship in Europe.

Kate had seen the reproductions of some of Rivera's frescoes. Now she went round the patios of the University, looking at the originals. They were interesting: the man knew his craft.

But the impulse was the impulse of the artist's hate. In the many frescoes of the Indians, there was sympathy with the Indian, but always from the ideal, social point of view. Never the spontaneous answer of the blood. These flat Indians were symbols in the great script of modern socialism, they were figures of the pathos of the victims of modern industry and capitalism. That was all they were used for: symbols in the weary script of socialism and anarchy.

Kate thought of the man polishing his oranges half-an-hour before: his peculiar beauty, a certain richness of physical being, a ponderous power of blood within him, and a helplessness, a profound unbelief that was fatal and demonish. And all the liberty, all the progress, all the socialism in the world would not help him. Nay, it would only help further to destroy him.

On the corridors of the University, young misses in bobbed hair and boys' jumpers were going around, their chins pushed forward with the characteristic, deliberate youth-and-eagerness of our day. Very much aware of their own youth and eagerness. And very American. Young professors were passing in soft amiability, young and apparently harmless.

The artists were at work on the frescoes, and Kate and Owen were introduced to them. But they were men—or boys—whose

very pigments seemed to exist only to *épater le bourgeois*. And Kate was weary of épatisme just as much as of the bourgeoisie. She wasn't interested in épatant le bourgeois. The épateurs were as boring as the bourgeois, two halves of one dreariness.

The little party passed on to the old Jesuit convent, now used as a secondary school. Here were more frescoes.

But they were by another man. And they were caricatures so crude and so ugly that Kate was merely repelled. They were meant to be shocking, but perhaps the very deliberateness prevents them from being so shocking as they might be. But they were ugly and vulgar. Strident caricatures of the Capitalist and the Church, and of the Rich Woman, and of Mammon painted life-size and as violently as possible, round the patios of the grey old building, where the young people are educated. To anyone with the spark of human balance, the things are a misdemeanour.

"Oh, but how wonderful!" cried Owen.

His susceptibilities were shocked, therefore, as at the bull-fight, he was rather pleased. He thought it was novel and stimulating to decorate your public buildings in this way.

The young Mexican who was accompanying the party was a professor in the University too: a rather short, soft young fellow of twenty-seven or eight, who wrote the inevitable poetry of sentiment, had been in the Government, even as a member of the House of Deputies, and was longing to go to New York. There was something fresh and soft, petulant about him. Kate liked him. He could laugh with real hot young amusement, and he was no fool.

Until it came to these maniacal ideas of socialism, politics, and La Patria. Then he was as mechanical as a mousetrap. Very tedious.

"Oh no!" said Kate in front of the caricatures. "They are too ugly. They defeat their own ends."

"But they are meant to be ugly," said young Garcia. "They must be ugly, no? Because capitalism is ugly, and Mammon is ugly, and the priest holding his hand to get the money from the poor Indians is ugly. No?" He laughed rather unpleasantly.

"But," said Kate, "these caricatures are too intentional. They are like vulgar abuse, not art at all."

"Isn't that true?" said Garcia, pointing to a hideous picture of a fat female in a tight short dress, with hips and breasts as protuberances, walking over the faces of the poor.

"That is how they are, no?"

"Who is like that?" said Kate. "It bores me. One must keep a certain balance."

"Not in Mexico!" said the young Mexican brightly, his plump cheeks flushing. "In Mexico you can't keep a balance, because things are so bad. In other countries, yes, perhaps you can remain balanced, because things are not so bad as they are here. But here they are so very bad, you can't be human. You have to be Mexican. You have to be more Mexican than human, no? You can't do no other. You have to hate the capitalist, you have to, in Mexico, or nobody can live. We can't live. Nobody can live. If you are Mexican you can't be human, it is impossible. You have to be a socialist Mexican, or you have to be a capitalist Mexican, and you hate. What else is there to be done? We hate the capitalist because he ruins the country and the people. We *must* hate him."

"But after all," said Kate, "what about the twelve million poor —mostly Indians—whom Montes talks about? You can't make them all rich, whatever you do. And they don't understand the very words, capital and socialism. They are Mexico, really, and nobody ever looks at them, except to make a *casus belli* of them. Humanly, they never exist for you."

"Humanly they can't exist, they are too ignorant!" cried Garcia. "But when we can kill all the capitalists, then—"

"You'll find somebody killing *you*," said Kate. "No, I don't like it. *You* aren't Mexico. You aren't even Mexican, really. You are just half Spaniards full of European ideas, and you care for asserting your own ideas and nothing else. You have no real bowels of compassion. You are no good."

The young man listened with round eyes, going rather yellow in the face. At the end he lifted his shoulders and spread his hands in a pseudo-Mediterranean gesture.

"Well! It may be!" he said, with a certain jeering flippancy. "Perhaps you know everything. Maybe! Foreigners, they usually know everything about Mexico." And he ended on a little cackling laugh.

"I know what I *feel*," said Kate. "And now I want a taxi, and I want to go home. I don't want to see any more stupid, ugly pictures."

Off she drove back to the hotel, once more in a towering rage. She was amazed at herself. Usually she was so good-tempered

and easy. But something about this country irritated her and put her into such a violent anger, she felt she would die. Burning, furious rage.

And perhaps, she thought to herself, the white and half-white Mexicans suffered some peculiar reaction in their blood which made them that they too were almost always in a state of suppressed irritation and anger, for which they *must* find a vent. They *must* spend their lives in a complicated game of frustration, frustration of life in its ebbing and flowing.

Perhaps something came out of the earth, the dragon of the earth, some effluence, some vibration which militated against the very composition of the blood and nerves in human beings. Perhaps it came from the volcanoes. Or perhaps even from the silent, serpent-like dark resistance of those masses of ponderous natives whose blood was principally the old, heavy, resistant Indian blood.

Who knows? But something there was, and something very potent. Kate lay on her bed and brooded her own organic rage. There was nothing to be done?

But young Garcia was really nice. He called in the afternoon and sent up his card. Kate, feeling sore, received him unwillingly.

"I came." he said, with a little stiff dignity, like an ambassador on a mission, "to tell you that I, too, don't like those caricatures. I, too, don't like them. I don't like the young people, boys and girls, no?—to be seeing them all the time. I, too, don't like. But I think, also, that here in Mexico, we can't help it. People are very bad, very greedy, no?—they only want to get money here, and they don't care. So we must hate them. Yes, we must. But I, too, I don't like it."

He held his hat in his two hands, and twisted his shoulders in a conflict of feelings.

Kate suddenly laughed, and he laughed too, with a certain pain and confusion in his laughter.

"That's awfully nice of you to come and say so," she said, warming to him.

"No, not nice," he said, frowning. "But I don't know what to *do*. Perhaps you think I am—different—I am not the thing that I am. And I don't want it."

He flushed and was uncomfortable. There was a curious naïve sincerity about him, since he was being sincere. If he had

chosen to play a game of sophistication, he could have played it better. But with Kate he wanted to be sincere.

"I know, really," laughed Kate, "you feel a good deal like I do about it. I know you only pretend to be fierce and hard."

"No!" he said, suddenly making solemn, flashing eyes. "I do also feel fierce. I do hate these men who take, only take everything from Mexico—money, and all—*everything!*" he spread his hands with finality. "I hate them because I *must,* no? But also, I am sorry—I am sorry I have to hate so much. Yes, I think I am sorry. I think so."

He knitted his brows rather tense. And over his plump, young, fresh face was a frown of resentment and hatred, quite sincere too.

Kate could see he wasn't really sorry. Only the two moods, of natural, soft, sensuous flow, and of heavy resentment and hate, alternated inside him like shadow and shine on a cloudy day, in swift, unavoidable succession. What was nice about him was his simplicity, in spite of the complication of his feelings, and the fact that his resentments were not personal, but beyond persons, even beyond himself.

She went out with him to tea, and while she was out, Don Ramón called and left cards with the corners turned down, and an invitation to dinner for her and Owen. There seemed an almost old-fashioned correctness in those cards.

Looking over the newspaper, she came on an odd little item. She could read Spanish without much difficulty. The trouble lay in talking it, when Italian got in her way and caused a continual stumble. She looked on the English page of the *Excelsior* or the *Universal* for the news—if there was any. Then she looked through the Spanish pages for bits of interest.

This little item was among the Spanish information, and was headed: The Gods of Antiquity Return to Mexico.

"There was a ferment in the village of Sayula, Jalisco, on the Lake of Sayula, owing to an incident of more or less comic nature, yesterday morning towards mid-day. The women who inhabit the shores of the lake are to be seen each day soon after sunrise descending to the water's edge with large bundles. They kneel on the rocks and stones, and in little groups, like water-fowl, they wash their dirty linen in the soft water of the lake, pausing at times as an old *canoa* sails by with large single sail. The scene

is little changed since the days of Montezuma, when the natives of the lake worshipped the spirit of the waters, and threw in little images and idols of baked clay, which the lake sometimes returns to the descendants of the dead idolaters, to keep them in mind of practices not yet altogether forgotten.

"As the hot sun rises in the sky, the women spread their washing on the sand and pebbles of the shore, and retire to the shade of the willow trees that grow so gracefully and retain their verdant hue through the dryest season of the year. While thus reposing after their labours, these humble and superstitious women were astonished to see a man of great stature rise naked from the lake and wade towards the shore. His face, they said, was dark and bearded, but his body shone like gold.

"As if unaware of any watchful eyes, he advanced calmly and majestically towards the shore. There he stood a moment, and selecting with his eye a pair of the loose cotton pants worn by the peasants in the fields, that was spread whitening in the sun, he stooped and proceeded to cover his nakedness with the said garment.

"The woman who thus saw her husband's apparel robbed beneath her eye, rose, calling to the man and summoning the other women. Whereupon the stranger turned his dark face upon them, and said in a quiet voice: 'Why are you crying? Be quiet! It will be given back to you. Your gods are ready to return to you. Quetzalcoatl and Tlaloc, the old gods, are minded to come back to you. Be quiet, don't let them find you crying and complaining. I have come from out of the lake to tell you the gods are coming back to Mexico, they are ready to return to their own home.'

"Little comforted by this speech, the woman who had lost her washing was overcome and said no more. The stranger then appropriated a cotton blouse, which he donned, and disappeared.

"After a while, the simple women gathered courage to return to their humble dwellings. The story thus reached the ears of the police, who at once set out to search for the thief.

"The story, however, is not yet concluded. The husband of the poor woman of the lake-shore, returning from his labours in the field, approached the gates of the village towards sunset, thinking, no doubt, of nothing but repose and the evening meal. A man in a black serape stepped towards him, from the shadows of a broken wall, and asked: Are you afraid to come with me? The

labourer, a man of spirit, promptly replied; No, señor! He therefore followed the unknown man through the broken wall and through the bushes of a deserted garden. In a dark room, or cellar, a small light was burning, revealing a great basin of gold, into which four little men, smaller than children, were pouring sweet-scented water. The astounded peasant was now told to wash and put on clean clothes, to be ready for the return of the gods. He was seated in the golden basin and washed with sweet-smelling soap, while the dwarfs poured water over him. *This, they said, is the bath of Quetzalcoatl. The bath of fire is yet to come.* They gave him clean clothing of pure white cotton, and a new hat with star embroidery, and sandals with straps of white leather. But beside this, a new blanket, white with bars of blue and black, and flowers like stars at the centre, and two pieces of silver money. *Go,* he was told. *And when they ask you, where did you get your blanket? answer that Quetzalcoatl is young again.* The poor fellow went home in sore fear, lest the police should arrest him for possessing stolen goods.

"The village is full of excitement, and Don Ramón Carrasco, our eminent historian and archaeologist, whose hacienda lies in the vicinity, has announced his intention of proceeding as soon as possible to the spot to examine the origin of this new legend. Meanwhile, the police are watching attentively the development of affairs, without taking any steps for the moment. Indeed, these little fantasies create a pleasant diversion in the regular order of banditry, murder, and outrage, which it is usually our duty to report."

Kate wondered what was at the back of this: if anything more than a story. Yet, strangely, a different light than the common light seemed to gleam out of the words of even this newspaper paragraph.

She wanted to go to Sayula. She wanted to see the big lake where the gods had once lived, and whence they were due to emerge. Amid all the bitterness that Mexico produced in her spirit, there was still a strange beam of wonder and mystery, almost like hope. A strange darkly-iridescent beam of wonder, of magic.

The name Quetzalcoatl, too, fascinated her. She had read bits about the god. Quetzal is the name of a bird that lives high up in the mists of tropical mountains, and has very beautiful tail-

feathers, precious to the Aztecs. Coatl is a serpent. Quetzalcoatl is the Plumed Serpent, so hideous in the fanged, feathered,
writhing stone of the National Museum.

But Quetzalcoatl was, she vaguely remembered, a sort of fair-
faced bearded god; the wind, the breath of life, the eyes that see
and are unseen, like the stars by day. The eyes that watch behind the wind, as the stars beyond the blue of day. And Quetzalcoatl must depart from Mexico to merge again into the deep bath
of life. He was old. He had gone eastwards, perhaps into the
sea, perhaps he had sailed into heaven, like a meteor returning,
from the top of the Volcano of Orizaba: gone back as a peacock
streaming into the night, or as a bird of Paradise, its tail gleaming
like the wake of a meteor. Quetzalcoatl! Who knows what
he meant to the dead Aztecs, and to the older Indians, who knew
him before the Aztecs raised their deity to heights of horror and
vindictiveness?

All a confusion of contradictory gleams of meaning, Quetzalcoatl. But why not? Her Irish spirit was weary to death of
definite meanings, and a God of one fixed purport. Gods should
be iridescent, like the rainbow in the storm. Man creates a God
in his own image, and the gods grow old along with the men that
made them. But storms sway in heaven, and the god-stuff sways
high and angry over our heads. Gods die with men who have
conceived them. But the god-stuff roars eternally, like the sea,
with too vast a sound to be heard. Like the sea in storm, that
beats against the rocks of living, stiffened men, slowly to destroy
them. Or like the sea of the glimmering, ethereal plasm of the
world, that bathes the feet and the knees of men as earth-sap
bathes the roots of trees. Ye must be born again. Even the
gods must be born again. We must be born again.

In her vague, woman's way, Kate knew this. She had lived
her life. She had had her lovers, her two husbands. She had
her children.

Joachim Leslie, her dead husband, she had loved as much as
a woman can love a man: that is, to the bounds of human love.
Then she had realised that human love has its limits, that there is
a beyond. And Joachim dead, willy nilly her spirit had passed
the bounds. She was no longer in love with love. She no longer
yearned for the love of a man, or the love even of her children.
Joachim had gone into eternity in death, and she had crossed
with him into a certain eternity in life. There, the yearning for

companionship and sympathy and human love had left her. Something infinitely intangible but infinitely blessed took its place: a peace that passes understanding.

At the same time, a wild and angry battle raged between her and the thing that *Owen* called life: such as the bull-fight, the tea-party, the enjoyments; like the arts in their modern aspect of hate effusion. The powerful, degenerate thing called life, wrapping one or other of its tentacles round her.

And then, when she could escape into her true loneliness, the influx of peace and soft, flower-like potency which was beyond understanding. It disappeared even if you thought about it, so delicate, so fine. And yet, the only reality.

Ye must be born again. Out of the fight with the octopus of life, the dragon of degenerate or of incomplete existence, one must win this soft bloom of being, that is damaged by a touch.

No, she no longer wanted love, excitement, and something to fill her life. She was forty, and in the rare, lingering dawn of maturity, the flower of her soul was opening. Above all things, she must preserve herself from worldly contacts. Only she wanted the silence of other unfolded souls around her, like a perfume. The presence of that which is forever unsaid.

And in the horror and climax of death-rattles, which is Mexico, she thought she could see it in the black eyes of the Indians. She felt that Don Ramón and Don Cipriano both had heard the soundless call, across all the hideous choking.

Perhaps this had brought her to Mexico: away from England and her mother, away from her children, away from everybody. To be alone with the unfolding flower of her own soul, in the delicate, chiming silence that is at the midst of things.

The thing called "Life" is just a mistake we have made in our own minds. Why persist in the mistake any further?

Owen was the mistake itself: so was Villiers: so was that Mexico City.

She wanted to get out, to disentangle herself again.

They had promised to go out to dinner to the house of Don Ramón. His wife was away in the United States with her two boys, one of whom had been ill, not seriously, at his school in California. But Don Ramón's aunt would be hostess.

The house was out at Tlalpam. It was May, the weather was hot, the rains were not yet started. The shower at the bull-fight had been a sort of accident.

"I wonder," said Owen, "whether I ought to put on a dinner ⸴ coat. Really, I feel humiliated to the earth every time I put on evening dress."

"Then don't do it!" said Kate, who was impatient of Owen's kicking at these very little social pricks, and swallowing the whole porcupine.

She herself came down in a simple gown with a black velvet top and a loose skirt of delicate brocaded chiffon, of a glimmering green and yellow and black. She also wore a long string of jade and crystal.

It was a gift she had, of looking like an Ossianic goddess, a certain feminine strength and softness glowing in the very material of her dress. But she was never "smart."

"Why you're dressed up to the eyes!" cried Owen in chagrin, pulling at his soft collar. "Bare shoulders notwithstanding!"

They went out to the distant suburb in the tram-car, swift in the night, with big clear stars overhead, dropping and hanging with a certain gleam of menace. In Tlalpam there was a heavy scent of nightflowers, a feeling of ponderous darkness, with a few sparks of intermittent fireflies. And always the heavy calling of nightflower scents. To Kate, there seemed a faint whiff of blood in all tropical-scented flowers: of blood or sweat.

It was a hot night. They banged on the iron doors of the entrance, dogs barked, and a mozo opened to them, warily, closing fast again the moment they had entered the dark garden of trees.

Don Ramón was in white, a white dinner-jacket: Don Cipriano the same. But there were other guests, young Garcia, another pale young man called Mirabal, and an elderly man in a black cravat, named Toussaint. The only other woman was Doña Isabel, aunt to Don Ramón. She wore a black dress with a high collar of black lace, and some strings of pearls, and seemed shy, frightened, absent as a nun before all these men. But to Kate she was very kind, caressive, speaking English in a plaintive faded voice. This dinner was a sort of ordeal and ritual combined, to the cloistered, elderly soul.

But it was soon evident that she was trembling with fearful joy. She adored Ramón with an uncritical, nun-like adoration. It was obvious she hardly heard the things that were said. Words skimmed the surface of her consciousness without ever penetrating. Underneath, she was trembling in nun-like awareness of so

many men, and in almost sacred excitement at facing Don Ramón as hostess.

The house was a fairly large villa, quietly and simply furnished, with natural taste.

"Do you always live here?" said Kate to Don Ramón. "Never at your hacienda?"

"How do you know I have a hacienda?" he asked.

"I saw it in a newspaper—near Sayula."

"Ah!" he said, laughing at her with his eyes. "You saw about the returning of the Gods of Antiquity."

"Yes," she said. "Don't you think it is interesting?"

"I think so," he said.

"I love the *word* Quetzalcoatl."

"The *word!*" he repeated.

His eyes laughed at her teasingly all the time.

"What do you think, Mrs Leslie," cried the pale-faced young Mirabal, in curiously resonant English, with a French accent. "Don't you think it would be wonderful if the gods came back to Mexico? our own gods?" He sat in intense expectation, his blue eyes fixed on Kate's face, his soup-spoon suspended.

Kate's face was baffled with incomprehension.

"Not those Aztec horrors!" she said.

"The Aztec horrors! The Aztec horrors! Well, perhaps they were not so horrible after all. But if they were, it was because the Aztecs were all tied up. They were in a cul de sac, so they saw nothing but death. Don't you think so?"

"I don't know enough!" said Kate.

"Nobody knows any more. But if you like the *word* Quetzal-coatl, don't you think it would be wonderful if he came back again? Ah, the *names* of the gods! Don't you think *the names* are like seeds, so full of magic, of the unexplored magic? Huitzilopochtli! —how wonderful! And Tlaloc! Ah! I love them! I say them over and over, like they say *Mani padma Om!* in Thibet. I believe in the fertility of sound. *Itzpapalotl*—the Obsidian Butterfly! Itzpapalotl! But say it, and you will see it does good to your soul. Itzpapalotl! Tezcatlipocá! They were old when the Spaniards came, they needed the bath of life again. But now, re-bathed in youth, how wonderful they must be! Think of *Jehovah! Jehovah!* Think of *Jesus Christ!* How thin and poor they sound! Or *Jesús Cristo!* They are dead names, all the life withered out of them. Ah, it is time now

for Jesus to go back to the place of the death of the gods, and take the long bath of being made young again. He is an old-old young god, don't you think?" He looked long at Kate, then dived for his soup.

Kate widened her eyes in amazement at this torrent from the young Mirabal. Then she laughed.

"I think it's a bit overwhelming!" she said, non-committal.

"Ah! Yes! Exactly! Exactly! But how good to be overwhelmed! How splendid if something will overwhelm me! Ah, I am so glad!"

The last word came with a clapping French resonance, and the young man dived for his soup again. He was lean and pale, but burning with an intense, crazy energy.

"You see," said young Garcia, raising his full, bright dark eyes to Kate, half aggressive and half-bashful: "we must do something for Mexico. If we don't, it will go under, no? You say you don't like socialism. I don't think I do either. But if there is nothing else but socialism, we will have socialism. If there is nothing better. But perhaps there is."

"Why should Mexico go under?" said Kate. "There are lots of children everywhere."

"Yes. But the last census of Porfirio Diaz gave seventeen million people in Mexico, and the census of last year gave only thirteen millions. Maybe the count was not quite right. But you count four million people fewer, in twenty years, then in sixty years there will be no Mexicans: only foreigners, who don't die."

"Oh, but figures always lie!" said Kate. "Statistics are always misleading."

"Maybe two and two don't make four," said Garcia. "I don't know if they do. But I know, if you take two away from two, it leaves none."

"Do you think Mexico might die out?" she said to Don Ramón.

"Why!" he replied. "It might. Die out and become Americanised."

"I quite see the danger of Americanisation," said Owen. "That *would* be ghastly. Almost better die out."

Owen was so American, he invariably said these things.

"But!" said Kate. "The Mexicans look so strong!"

"They are strong to carry heavy loads," said Don Ramón. "But they die easily. They eat all the wrong things, they drink

the wrong things, and they don't mind dying. They have many children, and they like their children very much. But when the child dies, the parents say: *Ah, he will be an angelito!* So they cheer up and feel as if they had been given a present. Sometimes I think they enjoy it when their children die. Sometimes I think they would like to transfer Mexico *en bloc* into Paradise, or whatever lies behind the walls of death. It would be better there!"

There was a silence.

"But how sad you are!" said Kate, afraid.

Doña Isabel was giving hurried orders to the manservant.

"Whoever knows Mexico below the surface, is sad!" said Julio Toussaint, rather sententiously, over his black cravat.

"Well," said Owen, "it seems to me, on the contrary, a gay country. A country of gay, irrresponsible children. Or rather, they *would* be gay, if they were properly treated. If they had comfortable homes, and a sense of real freedom. If they felt that they could control their lives and their own country. But being in the grip of outsiders, as they have been for hundreds of years, life of course seems hardly worth while to them. Naturally, they don't care if they live or die. They don't feel *free*."

"Free for what?" asked Toussaint.

"To make Mexico their own. Not to be so poor and at the mercy of outsiders."

"They are at the mercy of something worse than outsiders," said Toussaint. "Let me tell you. They are at the mercy of their own natures. It is this way. Fifty per cent. of the people in Mexico are pure Indian: more or less. Of the rest, a small proportion are foreigners or Spaniard. You have then the mass which is on top, of mixed blood, Indian and Spaniard mixed, chiefly. These are the Mexicans, those with the mixed blood. Now, you take us at this table. Don Cipriano is pure Indian. Don Ramón is almost pure Spaniard, but most probably he has the blood of Tlaxcalan Indians in his veins as well. Señor Mirabal is mixed French and Spanish. Señor Garcia most probably has a mixture of Indian blood with Spanish. I myself, have French, Spanish, Austrian and Indian blood. Very well! Now you mix blood of the same race, and it may be all right. Europeans are all Aryan stock, the race is the same. But when you mix European and American Indian, you mix different blood races, and you produce the half-breed. Now, the half-breed is a calamity. For why? He is neither one thing nor another, he is

divided against himself. His blood of one race tells him one thing, his blood of another race tells him another. He is an unfortunate, a calamity to himself. And it is hopeless.

"And this is Mexico. The Mexicans of mixed blood are hopeless. Well then! There are only two things to be done. All the foreigners and the Mexicans clear out and leave the country to the Indians, the pure-blooded Indians. But already you have a difficulty. How can you distinguish the pure-blooded Indian, after so many generations? Or else the half-breed or mixed-blood Mexicans who are all the time on top shall continue to destroy the country till the Americans from the United States flood in. We are as California and New Mexico now are, swamped under the dead white sea.

"But let me tell you something further. I hope we are not Puritans. I hope I may say that it depends on the moment of coition. At the moment of coition, either the spirit of the father fuses with the spirit of the mother, to create a new being with a soul, or else nothing fuses but the germ of procreation.

"Now consider. How have these Mexicans of mixed blood been begotten, for centuries? In what spirit? What was the moment of coition like? Answer me that, and you have told me the reason for this Mexico which makes us despair and which will go on making everybody despair, till it destroys itself. In what spirit have the Spanish and other foreign fathers gotten children of the Indian women? What sort of spirit was it? What sort of coition? And then, what sort of race do you expect?"

"But what sort of a spirit is there between white men and white women!" said Kate.

"At least," replied the didactic Toussaint, "the blood is homogenous, so that consciousness automatically unrolls in continuity."

"I hate its unrolling in automatic continuity," said Kate.

"Perhaps! But it makes life possible. Without developing continuity in consciousness, you have chaos. And this comes of mixed blood."

"And then," said Kate, "surely the Indian men are fond of their women! The men seem manly, and the women seem very lovable and womanly."

"It is possible that the Indian children are pure-blooded, and there is the continuity of blood. But the Indian consciousness is

swamped under the stagnant water of the white man's Dead Sea consciousness. Take a man like Benito Juarez, a pure Indian. He floods his old consciousness with the new white ideas, and there springs up a whole forest of verbiage, new laws, new constitutions and all the rest. But it is a sudden weed. It grows like a weed on the surface, saps the strength of the Indian soil underneath, and helps the process of ruin. No, madam! There is no hope for Mexico short of a miracle."

"Ah!" cried Mirabal, flourishing his wine glass. "Isn't that wonderful, when only the miracle will save us! When we must produce the miracle? *We! We!* We must make the miracle!" He hit his own breast emphatically. "Ah, I think that is marvellous!" And he returned to his turkey in black sauce.

"Look at the Mexicans!" Toussaint flared on. "They don't care about anything. They eat food so hot with chili, it burns holes in their insides. And it has no nourishment. They live in houses that a dog would be ashamed of, and they lie and shiver with cold. But they don't *do* anything. They could make, easily, easily, a bed of maize leaves or similar leaves. But they don't do it. They don't do anything. They roll up in a thin serape and lie on a thin mat on the bare ground, whether it is wet or dry. And Mexican nights are cold. But they lie down like dogs, anyhow, as if they lay down to die. I say dogs! But you will see the dogs looking for a dry sheltered place. The Mexicans, no! Anywhere, nothing, nothing! And it is terrible. It is terrible! As if they wanted to punish themselves for being alive!"

"But then, why do they have so many children?" said Kate.

"Why do they? The same, because they don't care. They don't care. They don't care about money, they don't care about making anything, they don't care about nothing, nothing, nothing. Only they get an excitement out of women, as they do out of chili. They like to feel the red pepper buring holes in their insides, and they like to feel the other thing, the sex, burning holes in them too. But after the moment, they don't care. They don't care a bit.

"And that is bad. I tell you, excuse me, but all, everything, depends on the moment of coition. At that moment many things can come to a crisis: all a man's hope, his honour, his faith, his trust, his belief in life and creation and God, all these things can come to a crisis in the moment of coition. And these things will be handed on in continuity to the child. Believe me, I am a crank on this idea, but it is true. It is certainly absolutely true."

"I believe it is true," said Kate, rather coldly.

"Ah! you do! Well then! Look at Mexico! The only *conscious* people are half-breeds, people of mixed blood, begotten in greed and selfish brutality."

"Some people believe in the mixed blood," said Kate.

"Ah! They do, do they? Who?"

"Some of your serious-minded men. They say the half-breed is better than the Indian."

"Better! Well! The Indian has his hopelessness. The moment of coition is his moment of supreme hoplessness, when he throws himself down the pit of despair."

The Austrian, European blood, which fans into fire of conscious understanding, died down again, leaving what was Mexican in Julio Toussaint sunk in irredeemable gloom.

"It is true," said Mirabal, out of the gloom. "The Mexicans who have any feeling always prostitute themselves, one way or another, and so they can never *do* anything. And the Indians can never do anything either, because they haven't got hope in anything. But it is always darkest before the dawn. We must make the miracle come. The miracle is superior even to the moment of coition."

It seemed, however, as if he said it by an effort of will.

The dinner was ending in silence. During the whirl of talk, or of passionate declaration, the servants had carried round the food and wine. Doña Isabel, completely oblivious of the things that were being said, watched and directed the servants with nervous anxiety and excitement, her hands with their old jewellery trembling with agitation. Don Ramón had kept his eye on his guests' material comfort, at the same time listening, as it were, from the back of his head. His big brown eyes were inscrutable, his face impassive. But when he had anything to say, it was always with a light laugh and a teasing accent. And yet his eyes brooded and smouldered with an incomprehensible, unyielding fire.

Kate felt she was in the presence of men. Here were men face to face not with death and self-sacrifice, but with the life-issue. She felt for the first time in her life, a pang almost like fear, of men who were passing beyond what she knew, beyond her depth.

Cipriano, his rather short but intensely black, curved eyelashes lowering over his dark eyes, watched his plate, only sometimes looking up with a black, brilliant glance, either at whosoever

was speaking, or at Don Ramón, or at Kate. His face was changeless and intensely serious, serious almost with a touch of childishness. But the curious blackness of his eyelashes lifted so strangely, with such intense unconscious maleness from his eyes, the movement of his hand was so odd, quick, light as he ate, so easily a movement of shooting, or of flashing a knife into the body of some adversary, and his dark-coloured lips were so helplessly savage, as he ate or briefly spoke, that her heart stood still. There was something undeveloped and intense in him, the intensity and the crudity of the semi-savage. She could well understand the potency of the snake upon the Aztec and Maya imagination. Something smooth, undeveloped, yet vital in this man suggested the heavy-ebbing blood of reptiles in his veins. That was what it was, the heavy-ebbing blood of powerful reptiles, the dragon of Mexico.

So that unconsciously she shrank when his black, big, glittering eyes turned on her for a moment. They were not, like Don Ramón's, *dark* eyes. They were black, as black as jewels into which one could not look without a sensation of fear. And her fascination was tinged with fear. She felt somewhat as the bird feels when the snake is watching it.

She wondered almost that Don Ramón was not afraid. Because she had noticed that usually, when an Indian looked to a white man, both men stood back from actual contact, from actual meeting of each other's eyes. They left a wide space of neutral territory between them. But Cipriano looked at Ramón with a curious intimacy, glittering, steady, warrior-like, and at the same time betraying an almost menacing trust in the other man.

Kate realised that Ramón had a good deal to stand up to. But he kept a little, foiling laugh on his face, and lowered his beautiful head with the black hair touched with grey, as if he would put a veil before his countenance.

"Do you think one can make this miracle come?" she asked of him.

"The miracle is always there," he said, "for the man who can pass his hand through to it, to take it."

They finished dinner, and went to sit out on the verandah, looking into the garden where the light from the house fell uncannily on the blossoming trees and the dark tufts of Yucca and the strange great writhing trunks of the Laurel de India.

Cipriano had sat down next to her, smoking a cigarette.

"It is a strange darkness, the Mexican darkness!" she said.

"Do you like it?" he asked.

"I don't know yet," she said. "Do you?"

"Yes. Very much. I think I like best the time when the day is falling and the night coming on like something else. Then, one feels more free, don't you think? Like the flowers that send out their scent at night, but in the daytime they look at the sun and don't have any smell."

"Perhaps the night here scares me," she laughed.

"Yes. But why not? The smell of the flowers at night may make one feel afraid, but it is a good fear. One likes it, don't you think?"

"I am afraid of fear," she said.

He laughed shortly.

"You speak such English English," she said. "Nearly all the Mexicans who speak English speak American English. Even Don Ramón does, rather."

"Yes. Don Ramón graduated in Columbia University. But I was sent to England, to school in London, and then to Oxford."

"Who sent you?"

"My god-father. He was an Englishman: Bishop Severn, Bishop of Oaxaca. You have heard of him?"

"No," said Kate.

"He was a very well-known man. He died only about ten years ago. He was very rich, too, before the revolution. He had a big hacienda in Oaxaca, with a very fine library. But they took it away from him in the revolution, and they sold the things, or broke them. They didn't know the value of them, of course."

"And did he adopt you?"

"Yes! In a way. My father was one of the overseers on the hacienda. When I was a little boy I came running to my father, when the Bishop was there, with something in my hands—so!"—and he made a cup of his hand. "I don't remember. This is what they tell me. I was a small child—three or four years of age—somewhere there. What I had in my hands, was a yellow scorpion, one of the small ones, very poisonous, no?"

And he lifted the cup of his small, slender, dark hands, as if to show Kate the creature.

"Well, the Bishop was talking to my father, and he saw what I had got before my father did. So he told me at once, to put the scorpion in his hat—the Bishop's hat, no? Of course I did what

he told me, and I put the scorpion in his hat, and it did not bite me. If it had stung me I should have died, of course. But I didn't know, so I suppose the alacran was not interested. The Bishop was a very good man, very kind. He liked my father, so he became my god-father. Then he always took an interest in me, and he sent me to school, and then to England. He hoped I should be a priest. He always said that the one hope for Mexico was if she had really fine native priests." He ended rather wistfully.

"And didn't you want to become a priest?" said Kate.

"No!" he said sadly. "No!"

"Not at all?" she asked.

"No! When I was in England it was different from Mexico. Even God was different, and the Blessed Mary. They were changed so much, I felt I didn't know them any more. Then I came to understand better, and when I understood I didn't believe any more. I used to think it was the images of Jesus, and the Virgin, and the Saints, that were doing everything in the world. And the world seemed to me so strange, no? I couldn't see that it was bad, because it was all so very strange and mysterious, when I was a child, in Mexico. Only in England I learned about the laws of life, and some science. And then when I knew why the sun rose and set, and how the world really was, I felt quite different."

"Was your god-father disappointed?"

"A little, perhaps. But he asked me if I would rather be a soldier, so I said I would. Then when the revolution came, and I was twenty-two years old, I had to come back to Mexico."

"Did you like your god-father?"

"Yes, very much. But the revolution carried everything away. I felt I must do what my god-father wished. But I could see that Mexico was not the Mexico he believed in. It was different. He was too English, and too good to understand. In the revolutions, I tried to help the man I believed was the best man. So you see, I have always been half a priest and half a soldier."

"You never married?"

"No. I couldn't marry, because I always felt my god-father was there, and I felt I had promised him to be a priest—all those things, you know. When he died he told me to follow my own conscience, and to remember that Mexico and all the Indians were in the hands of God, and he made me promise never to take sides against God. He was an old man when he died, seventy-five."

Kate could see the spell of the old bishop's strong, rather grandiose personality upon the impressionable Indian. She could see the curious recoil into chastity, perhaps characteristic of the savage. And at the same time she felt the intense masculine yearning, coupled with a certain male ferocity, in the man's breast.

"Your husband was James Joachim Leslie, the famous Irish leader?" he asked her: and added:

"You had no children?"

"No. I wanted Joachim's children so much, but I didn't have any. But I have a boy and a girl from my first marriage. My first husband was a lawyer, and I was divorced from him for Joachim."

"Did you like him—that first one?"

"Yes. I liked him. But I never felt anything very deep for him. I married him when I was young, and he was a good deal older than I. I was fond of him, in a way. But I had never realised that one could be more than fond of a man, till I knew Joachim. I thought that was all one could ever expect to feel— that you just liked a man, and that he was in love with you. It took me years to understand that a woman *can't* love a man—at least a woman like I am can't—if he is only the sort of good, decent citizen. With Joachim I came to realise that a woman like me *can* only love a man who is fighting to *change* the world, to make it freer, more alive. Men like my first husband, who are good and trustworthy and who work to keep the world going on well in the same state they found it in, they let you down horribly, somewhere. You feel so terribly sold. Everything is just a sell: it becomes so small. A woman who isn't quite ordinary herself can only love a man who is fighting for something beyond the ordinary life."

"And your husband fought for Ireland?"

"Yes—for Ireland, and for something he never quite realised. He ruined his health. And when he was dying, he said to me: *Kate, perhaps I've let you down. Perhaps I haven't really helped Ireland. But I couldn't help myself. I feel as if I'd brought you to the doors of life, and was leaving you there. Kate, don't be disappointed in life because of me. I didn't really get anywhere. I haven't really got anywhere. I feel as if I'd made a mistake. But perhaps when I'm dead I shall be able to do more for you than I have done while I was alive. Say you'll never feel disappointed!*"

There was a pause. The memory of the dead man was coming over her again, and all her grief.

"And I don't feel disappointed," she went on, her voice beginning to shake. "But I loved him. And it was bitter, that he had to die, feeling he hadn't—hadn't——"

She put her hands before her face, and the bitter tears came through her fingers.

Cipriano sat motionless as a statue. But from his breast came that dark, surging passion of tenderness the Indians are capable of. Perhaps it would pass, leaving him indifferent and fatalistic again. But at any rate for the moment he sat in a dark, fiery cloud of passionate male tenderness. He looked at her soft, wet white hands over her face, and at the one big emerald on her finger, in a sort of wonder. The wonder, the mystery, the magic that used to flood over him as a boy and a youth, when he kneeled before the babyish figure of the Santa Maria de la Soledad, flooded him again. He was in the presence of the goddess, white-handed, mysterious, gleaming with a moon-like power and the intense potency of grief.

Then Kate hastily took her hands from her face and with head ducked looked for her handkerchief. Of course she hadn't got one. Cipriano lent her his, nicely folded. She took it without a word, and rubbed her face and blew her nose.

"I want to go and look at the flowers," she said in a strangled voice.

And she dashed into the garden with his handkerchief in her hand. He stood up and drew aside his chair, to let her pass, then stood a moment looking at the garden, before he sat down again and lighted a cigarette.

CHAPTER IV

TO STAY OR NOT TO STAY

OWEN had to return to the United States, and he asked Kate whether she wanted to stay on in Mexico.

This put her into a quandary. It was not an easy country for a woman to be alone in. And she had been beating her wings in an effort to get away. She felt like a bird round whose body a snake has coiled itself. Mexico was the snake.

The curious influence of the country, pulling one down, pulling one down. She had heard an old American, who had been forty years on the Republic, saying to Owen: "No man who hasn't a strong moral backbone should try to settle in Mexico. If he does, he'll go to pieces, morally and physically, as I've seen hundreds of young Americans do."

To pull one down. It was what the country wanted to do all the time, with a slow, reptilian insistence, to pull one down. To prevent the spirit from soaring. To take away the free, soaring sense of liberty.

"There is no such thing as liberty," she heard the quiet, deep, dangerous voice of Don Ramón repeating. "There is no such thing as liberty. The greatest liberators are usually slaves of an idea. The freest people are slaves to convention and public opinion, and more still, slaves to the industrial machine. There is no such thing as liberty. You only change one sort of domination for another. All we can do is to choose our master."

"But surely that *is* liberty—for the mass of people."

"They don't choose. They are tricked into a new form of servility, no more. They go from bad to worse."

"You yourself—aren't you free?" she asked.

"I?" he laughed. "I spent a long time trying to pretend. I thought I could have my own way. Till I realised that having my own way meant only running about smelling all the things in the street, like a dog that will pick up something. Of myself, I have no way. No man has any way in himself. Every man who goes along a way is led by one of three things: by an appetite—

68

and I class ambition among appetite; or by an idea; or by an inspiration."

"I used to think my husband was inspired about Ireland," said Kate doubtfully.

"And now?"

"Yes! Perhaps he put his wine in old, rotten bottles that wouldn't hold it. No!—Liberty is a rotten old wine-skin. It won't hold one's wine of inspiration or passion any more," she said.

"And Mexico!" he said. "Mexico is another Ireland. Ah no, no man can be his own master. If I must serve, I will not serve an idea, which cracks and leaks like an old wine-skin. I will serve the God that gives me my manhood. There is no liberty for a man, apart from the God of his manhood. Free Mexico is a bully, and the old, colonial ecclesiastical Mexico was another sort of bully. When man has nothing but his *will* to assert—even his good-will—it is always bullying. Bolshevism is one sort of bullying, capitalism another: and liberty is a change of chains."

"Then what's to be done?" said Kate. "Just nothing?"

And with her own will, she wanted nothing to be done. Let the skies fall!

"One is driven, at last, back to the far distance, to look for God," said Ramón uneasily.

"I rather hate this search-for-God business, and religiosity," said Kate.

"I know!" he said, with a laugh. "I've suffered from would-be-cocksure religion myself."

"And you can't *really* 'find God'!" she said. "It's a sort of sentimentalism, and creeping back into old, hollow shells."

"No!" he said slowly. "I can't *find* God, in the old sense. I know it's a sentimentalism if I pretend to. But I am nauseated with humanity and the human will: even with my own will. I have realised that *my will,* no matter how intelligent I am, is only another nuisance on the face of the earth, once I start exerting it. And other people's *wills* are even worse."

"Oh! isn't human life horrible!" she cried. "Every human being exerting his will all the time—over other people, and over himself, and nearly always self-righteous!"

Ramón made a grimace of repulsion.

"To me," he said, "that is just the weariness of life! For a time, it can be amusing: exerting your own will, and resisting all

the other people's wills, that they try to put over you. But at a certain point, a nausea sets in at the very middle of me: my *soul* is nauseated. My soul is nauseated, and there is nothing but death ahead, unless I find something else."

Kate listened in silence. She knew the road he had gone, but she herself had not yet come to the end of it. As yet she was still strong in the pride of her own—her very own *will*.

"Oh, people are repulsive!" she cried.

"My own will becomes even more repulsive at last," he said. "My own will, merely as my own will, is even more distasteful to me than other people's wills. From being the god in my own machine, I must either abdicate, or die of disgust—self-disgust, at that."

"How amusing!" she cried.

"It is rather funny," he said sardonically.

"And then?" she asked, looking at him with a certain malevolent challenge.

He looked back at her slowly, with an ironical light in his eyes.

"Then!" he repeated. "Then!—I ask, what else is there in the world, besides human will, human appetite? because ideas and ideals are only instruments of human will and appetite."

"Not entirely," said Kate. "They may be disinterested."

"May they? If the appetite *isn't* interested, the will is."

"Why not?" she mocked. "We can't be mere detached blocks."

"It nauseates me—I look for something else."

"And what do you find?"

"My own manhood!"

"What does that mean?" she cried, jeering.

"If you looked, and found your own womanhood, you would know."

"But I *have* my own womanhood!" she cried.

"And then—when you find your own manhood—your womanhood," he went on, smiling faintly at her—"then you know it is not your own, to do as you like with. You don't have it of your own will. It comes from—from the middle—from the God. Beyond me, at the middle, is the God. And God gives me my manhood, then leaves me to it. I have nothing but my manhood. The God gives it me, and leaves me to do further."

Kate would not hear any more. She broke off into banalities. The immediate question, for her, was whether she would stay in Mexico or not. She was not really concerned with Don

Ramón's soul—or even her own. She was concerned with her immediate future. Should she stay in Mexico? Mexico meant the dark-faced men in cotton clothes, big hats: the peasants, peons, pelados, Indians, call them what you will. The mere natives.

Those pale-faced Mexicans of the Capital, politicians, artists, professionals, and business people, they did not interest her. Neither did the hacendados and the ranch-owners, in their tight trousers and weak, soft sensuality, pale victims of their own emotional undiscipline. Mexico still meant the mass of silent peons, to her. And she thought of them again, these silent, stiff-backed men, driving their strings of asses along the country roads, in the dust of Mexico's infinite dryness, past broken walls, broken houses, broken haciendas, along the endless desolation left by the revolutions; past the vast stretches of maguey, the huge cactus, or aloe, with its gigantic rosette of upstarting, pointed leaves, that in its iron rows covers miles and miles of ground in the Valley of Mexico, cultivated for the making of that bad-smelling drink, pulque. The Mediterranean has the dark grape, old Europe has malted beer, and China has opium from the white poppy. But out of the Mexican soil a bunch of black-tarnished swords bursts up, and a great unfolded bud of the once-flowering monster begins to thrust at the sky. They cut the great phallic bud and crush out the sperm-like juice for the pulque. *Agua miel!* *Pulque!*

But better pulque than the fiery white brandy distilled from the maguey: mescal, tequila: or in the low lands, the hateful sugar-cane brandy, aguardiente.

And the Mexican burns out his stomach with those beastly fire-waters and cauterises the hurt with red-hot chili. Swallowing one hell-fire to put out another.

Tall fields of wheat and maize. Taller, more brilliant fields of bright-green sugar-cane. And threading in white cotton clothes, with dark, half-visible face, the eternal peón of Mexico, his great white calico drawers flopping round his ankles as he walks, or rolled up over his dark, handsome legs.

The wild, sombre, erect men of the north! The too-often degenerate men of Mexico Valley, their heads through the middle of their ponchos! The big men in Tlascala, selling ice-cream or huge half-sweetened buns and fancy bread! The quick little Indians, quick as spiders, down in Oaxaca! The queer-looking, half-Chinese natives towards Vera Cruz! The dark faces and the big

black eyes on the coast of Sinaloa! The handsome men of Jalisco, with a scarlet blanket folded on one shoulder!

They were of many tribes and many languages, and far more alien to one another than Frenchmen, English, and Germans are. Mexico! It is not really even the beginnings of a nation: hence the rabid assertion of nationalism in the few. And it is not a race.

Yet it is a people. There is some Indian quality which pervades the whole. Whether it is men in blue overalls and a slouch, in Mexico City, or men with handsome legs in skin-tight trousers, or the floppy, white, cotton-clad labourers in the fields, there is something mysteriously in common. The erect, prancing walk, stepping out from the base of the spine with lifted knees and short steps. The jaunty balancing of the huge hats. The thrown-back shoulders with a folded serape like a royal mantle. And most of them handsome, with dark, warm-bronze skins so smooth and living, their proudly-held heads, whose black hair gleams like wild, rich feathers. Their big, bright black eyes that look at you wonderingly, and have no centre to them. Their sudden, charming smile, when you smile first. But the eyes unchanged.

Yes, and she had to remember, too, a fair proportion of smaller, sometimes insignificant looking men, some of them scaly with dirt, who looked at you with a cold, mud-like antagonism as they stepped cattishly past. Poisonous, thin, stiff little men, cold and unliving like scorpions, and as dangerous.

And then the truly terrible faces of some creatures in the city, slightly swollen with the poison of tequila, and with black, dimmed, swivel eyes swinging in pure evil. Never had she seen such faces of pure brutish evil, cold and insect-like, as in Mexico City.

The country gave her a strange feeling of hopelessness and of dauntlessness. Unbroken, eternally resistant, it was a people that lived without hope, and without care. Gay even, and laughing with indifferent carelessness.

They were something like her own Irish, but gone to a much greater length. And also, they did what the self-conscious and pretentious Irish rarely do, they touched her bowels with a strange fire of compassion.

At the same time, she feared them. They would pull her down, pull her down, to the dark depths of nothingness.

It was the same with the women. In their full long skirts and bare feet, and with the big, dark-blue scarf or shawl called a rebozo over their womanly small heads and tight round their

shoulders, they were images of wild submissiveness, the primitive womanliness of the world, that is so touching and so alien. Many women kneeling in a dim church, all hooded in their dark-blue rebozos, the pallor of their skirts on the floor, their heads and shoulders wrapped dark and tight, as they swayed with devotion of fear and ecstasy! A churchful of dark-wrapped women sunk there in wild, humble supplication of dread and of bliss filled Kate with tenderness and revulsion. They crouched like people not quite created.

Their soft, untidy black hair, which they scratched for lice; the round-eyed baby joggling like a pumpkin in the shawl slung over the woman's shoulder, the never-washed feet and ankles, again somewhat reptilian under the long, flounced, soiled cotton skirt; and then, once more, the dark eyes of half-created women, soft, appealing, yet with a queer void insolence! Something lurking, where the womanly centre should have been; lurking snake-like. Fear! The fear of not being able to find full creation. And the inevitable mistrust and lurking insolence, insolent against a higher creation, the same thing that is in the striking of a snake.

Kate, as a woman, feared the women more than the men. The women were little and insidious, the men were bigger and more reckless. But in the eyes of each, the uncreated centre, where the evil and the insolence lurked.

And sometimes she wondered whether America really was the great death-continent, the great *No!* to the European and Asiatic and even African *Yes!* Was it really the great melting pot, where men from the creative continents were smelted back again, not to a new creation, but down into the homogeneity of death? Was it the great continent of the undoing, and all its peoples the agents of the mystic destruction! Plucking, plucking at the created soul in a man, till at last it plucked out the growing germ, and left him a creature of mechanism and automatic reaction, with only one inspiration, the desire to pluck the quick out of every living spontaneous creature.

Was that the clue to America, she sometimes wondered. Was it the great death-continent, the continent that destroyed again what the other continents had built up. The continents whose spirit of place fought purely to pick the eyes out of the face of God. Was that America?

And all the people who went there, Europeans, negroes, Japanese, Chinese, all the colours and the races, were they the spent

people, in whom the God impulse had collapsed, so they crossed to the great continent of the negation, where the human will declares itself "free," to pull down the soul of the world? Was it so? And did this account for the great drift to the New World, the drift of spent souls passing over to the side of Godless democracy, energetic negation? The negation which is the life-breath of materialism. And would the great negative pull of the Americans at last break the heart of the world?

This thought would come to her, time and again.

She herself, what had she come to America for?

Because the flow of her life had broken, and she knew she could not re-start it, in Europe.

These handsome natives! Was it because they were death-worshippers, Moloch-worshippers, that they were so uncowed and handsome? Their pure acknowledgment of death, and their undaunted admission of nothingness kept so erect and careless.

White men had had a soul, and lost it. The pivot of fire had been quenched in them, and their lives had started to spin in the reversed direction, widdershins. That reversed look which is in the eyes of so many white people, the look of nullity, and life wheeling in the reversed direction. Widdershins.

But the dark-faced natives, with their strange soft flame of life wheeling upon a dark void: were they centreless and widdershins too, as so many white men now are?

The strange, soft flame of courage in the black Mexican eyes. But still it was not knit to a centre, that centre which is the soul of a man in a man.

And all the efforts of white men to bring the soul of the dark men of Mexico into final clinched being has resulted in nothing but the collapse of the white man. Against the soft, dark flow of the Indian the white man at last collapses, with his God and his energy he collapses. In attempting to convert the dark man to the white man's way of life, the white man has fallen helplessly down the hole he wanted to fill up. Seeking to save another man's soul, the white man lost his own, and collapsed upon himself.

Mexico! The great, precipitous, dry, savage country, with a handsome church in every landscape, rising as it were out of nothing. A revolution broken landscape, with lingering, tall, handsome churches whose domes are like inflations that are going to burst, and whose pinnacles and towers are like the trembling pagodas of an unreal race. Gorgeous churches waiting, above

the huts and straw hovels of the natives, like ghosts to be dismissed.

And noble ruined haciendas, with ruined avenues approaching their broken splendour.

And the cities of Mexico, great and small, that the Spaniards conjured up out of nothing. Stones live and die with the spirit of the builders. And the spirit of Spaniards in Mexico dies, and the very stones in the building die. The natives drift into the centre of the plazas again, and in unspeakable empty weariness the Spanish buildings stand around, in a sort of dry exhaustion.

The conquered race! Cortes came with his iron heel and his iron will, a conqueror. But a conquered race, unless grafted with a new inspiration, slowly sucks the blood of the conquerors, in the silence of a strange night and the heaviness of a hopeless will. So that now, the race of the conquerors in Mexico is soft and boneless, children crying in helpless hopelessness.

Was it the dark negation of the continent?

Kate could not look at the stones of the National Museum in Mexico without depression and dread. Snakes coiled like excrement, snakes fanged and feathered beyond all dreams of dread. And that was all.

The ponderous pyramids of San Juan Teotihuacan, the House of Quetzalcoatl wreathed with the snake of all snakes, his huge fangs white and pure to-day as in the lost centuries when his makers were alive. He has not died. He is not so dead as the Spanish churches, this all-enwreathing dragon of the horror of Mexico.

Cholula, with its church where the altar was! And the same ponderousness, the same unspeakable sense of weight and downward pressure of the blunt pyramid. Down-sinking pressure and depression. And the great market-place with its lingering dread and fascination.

Mitla under its hills, in the parched valley where a wind blows the dust and the dead souls of the vanished race in terrible gusts. The carved courts of Mitla, with a hard, sharp-angled, intricate fascination, but the fascination of fear and repellence. Hard, four-square, sharp-edged, cutting, zig-zagging Mitla, like continual blows of a stone axe. Without gentleness or grace or charm. Oh America, with your unspeakable hard lack of charm, what then is your final meaning! Is it forever the knife of sacrifice, as you put out your tongue at the world?

Charmless America! With your hard, vindictive beauty, are you waiting forever to smite death? Is the world your everlasting victim?

So long as it will let itself be victimised.

But yet! But yet! The gentle voices of the natives. The voices of the boys, like birds twittering among the trees of the plaza of Tehuacan! The soft touch, the gentleness. Was it the dark-fingered quietness of death, and the music of the presence of death in their voices?

She thought again of what Don Ramón had said to her.

"They pull you down! Mexico pulls you down, the people pull you down like a great weight! But it may be they pull you down as the earth's pull of gravitation does, that you can balance on your feet. Maybe they draw you down as the earth draws down the roots of a tree, so that it may be clinched deep in soil. Men are still part of the Tree of Life, and the roots go down to the centre of the earth. Loose leaves, and aeroplanes, blow away on the wind, in what they call freedom. But the Tree of Life has fixed, deep, gripping roots.

"It may be you need to be drawn down, down, till you send roots into the deep places again. Then you can send up the sap and the leaves back to the sky, later.

"And to me, the men in Mexico are like trees, forests that the white men felled in their coming. But the roots of the trees are deep and alive and forever sending up new shoots.

"And each new shoot that comes up overthrows a Spanish church or an American factory. And soon the dark forest will rise again, and shake the Spanish buildings from the face of America.

"All that matters to me are the roots that reach down beyond all destruction. The roots and the life are there. What else it needs is the word, for the forest to begin to rise again. And some man among men must speak the word."

The strange doom-like sound of the man's words! But in spite of the sense of doom on her heart, she would not go away yet. She would stay longer in Mexico.

CHAPTER V

THE LAKE

OWEN left, Villiers stayed on a few days to escort Kate to the lake. If she liked it there, and could find a house, she could stay by herself. She knew sufficient people in Mexico and in Guadalajara to prevent her from being lonely. But she still shrank from travelling alone in this country.

She wanted to leave the city. The new President had come in quietly enough, but there was an ugly feeling of uppishness in the lower classes, the bottom dog clambering mangily to the top. Kate was no snob. Man or woman, she cared nothing about the social class. But meanness, sordidness she hated. She hated bottom dogs. They all were mangy, they all were full of envy and malice, many had the rabies. Ah no, let us defend ourselves from the bottom dog, with its mean growl and its yellow teeth.

She had tea with Cipriano before leaving.

"How do you get along with the Government?" she asked.

"I stand for the law and the constitution," he said. "They know I don't want anything to do with cuartelazos or revolutions. Don Ramón is my chief."

"In what way?"

"Later, you will see."

He had a secret, important to himself, on which he was sitting tight. But he looked at her with shining eyes, as much as to say that soon she would share the secret, and then he would be much happier.

He watched her curiously, from under his wary black lashes. She was one of the rather plump Irishwomen, with soft brown hair and hazel eyes, and a beautiful, rather distant repose. Her great charm was her soft repose, and her gentle, unconscious inaccessibility. She was taller and bigger than Cipriano: he was almost boyishly small. But he was all energy, and his eyebrows tilted back and with a barbarian conceit, above his full, almost insolent black eyes.

77

He watched her continually, with a kind of fascination: the same spell that the absurd little figures of the doll Madonna had cast over him as a boy. She was the mystery, and he the adorer, under the semi-ecstatic spell of the mystery. But once he rose from his knees, he rose in the same strutting conceit of himself as before he knelt: with all his adoration in his pocket again. But he had a good deal of magnetic power. His education had not diminished it. His education lay like a film of white oil on the black lake of his barbarian consciousness. For this reason, the things he said were hardly interesting at all. Only what he *was*. He made the air around him seem darker, but richer and fuller. Sometimes his presence was extraordinarily grateful, like a healing of the blood. And sometimes he was an intolerable weight on her. She gasped to get away from him.

"You think a great deal of Don Ramón?" she said to him.

"Yes," he said, his black eyes watching her. "He is a very fine man."

How trivial the words sounded! That was another boring thing about him: his English seemed so trivial. He wasn't really expressing himself. He was only flipping at the white oil that lay on his surface.

"You like him better than the Bishop, your god father?"

He lifted his shoulders in a twisted, embarrassed shrug.

"The same!" he said. "I like him the same."

Then he looked away into the distance, with a certain hauteur and insolence.

"Very different, no?" he said. "But in some ways, the same. He knows better what is Mexico. He knows better what I am. Bishop Severn did not know the real Mexico: how could he, he was a sincere Catholic! But Don Ramón knows the real Mexico, no?"

"And what is the real Mexico?" she asked.

"Well—you must ask Don Ramón. I can't explain."

She asked Cipriano about going to the lake.

"Yes!" he said. "You can go! You will like it. Go first to Orilla, no?—you take a ticket on the railway to Ixtlahuacan. And in Orilla in a hotel with a German manager. Then from Orilla you can go in a motor-boat, in a few hours, to Sayula. And there you will find a house to live in."

He wanted her to do this, she could tell.

"How far is Don Ramón's hacienda from Sayula?" she asked.

"Near! About an hour in a boat. He is there now. And at the beginning of the month I am going with my division to Guadalajara: now there is a new Governor. So I shall be quite near too."

"That will be nice," she said.

"You think so?" he asked quickly.

"Yes," she said, on her guard, looking at him slowly. "I should be sorry to lose touch with Don Ramón and you."

He had a little tension on his brow, haughty, unwilling, conceited, and at the same time, yearning and desirous.

"You like Don Ramón very much?" he said. "You want to know him more?"

There was a peculiar anxiety in his voice.

"Yes," she said. "One knows so few people in the world nowadays, that one can respect—and fear a little. I am a little afraid of Don Ramón: and I have the *greatest* respect for him—" she ended on a hot note of sincerity.

"It is good!" he said. "It is very good. You may respect him more than any other man in the world."

"Perhaps that is true," she said, turning her eyes slowly to his.

"Yes! Yes!" he cried impatiently. "It is true. You will find out later. And Ramón likes you. He told me to ask you to come to the lake. When you come to Sayula, when you are coming, write to him, and no doubt he can tell you about a house, and all those things."

"Shall I?" she said, hesitant.

"Yes. Yes! of course, we say what we mean."

Curious little man, with his odd, inflammable *hauteur* and conceit, something burning inside him, that gave him no peace. He had an almost childish faith in the other man. And yet she was not sure that he did not, in some corner of his soul, resent Ramón somewhat.

Kate set off by the night train for the west, with Villiers. The one Pullman coach was full: people going to Guadalajara and Colima and the coast. There were three military officers, rather shy in their new uniforms, and rather swaggering at the same time, making eyes at the empty air, as if they felt they were conspicuous, and sitting quickly in their seats, as if to obliterate themselves. There were two country farmers or ranchers, in tight trousers and cart-wheel hats stitched with silver. One was a tall man with a big moustache, the other was a smaller, grey man. But they both

had the handsome, alive legs of the Mexicans, and the rather quenched faces.   There was a widow buried in crape, accompanied by a criada, a maid.   The rest were townsmen, Mexicans on business, at once shy and fussy, unobtrusive and self-important.

The Pullman was clean and neat, with its hot green-plush seats. But, full of people, it seemed empty compared with a Pullman in the United States.   Everybody was very quiet, very soft and guarded.   The farmers folded their beautiful serapes and laid them carefully on the seats, sitting as if their section were a lonely little place.   The officers folded their cloaks and arranged dozens of little parcels, little cardboard hatboxes and heterogeneous bundles, under the seats and on the seats.   The business men had the oddest luggage, canvas hold-alls embroidered in wool, with long, touching mottoes.

And in all the crowd, a sense of guardedness and softness and self-effacement: a curious soft *sensibilité,* touched with fear.   It was already a somewhat conspicuous thing to travel in the Pullman, you had to be on your guard.

The evening for once was grey: the rainy season really approaching.   A sudden wind whirled dust and a few spots of rain. The train drew out of the formless, dry, dust-smitten areas fringing the city, and wound mildly on for a few minutes, only to stop in the main street of Tacubaya, the suburb-village.   In the grey approach of evening the train halted heavily in the street, and Kate looked out at the men who stood in groups, with their hats tilted against the wind and their blankets folded over their shoulders and up to their eyes, against the dust, motionless standing like sombre ghosts, only a glint of eyes showing between the dark serape and the big hat-brim; while donkey-drivers in a dust-cloud ran frantically, with uplifted arms like demons, uttering short, sharp cries to prevent their donkeys from poking in between the coaches of the train.   Silent dogs trotted in-and-out under the train, women, their faces wrapped in their blue rebozos, came to offer tortillas folded in a cloth to keep them warm, or pulque in an earthenware mug, or pieces of chicken smothered in red, thick, oily sauce; or oranges or bananas or pitahayas, anything.   And when few people bought, because of the dust, the women put their wares under their arm, under the blue rebozo, and covered their faces and motionless watched the train.

It was about six o'clock.   The earth was utterly dry and stale. Somebody was kindling charcoal in front of a house.   Men were

hurrying down the wind, balancing their great hats curiously. Horsemen on quick, fine little horses, guns slung behind, trotted up to the train, lingered, then trotted quickly away again into nowhere.

Still the train stood in the street. Kate and Villiers got down. They watched the sparks blowing from the charcoal which a little girl was kindling in the street, to cook tortillas.

The train had a second-class coach and a first-class. The second class was jam-full of peasants, Indians, piled in like chickens with their bundles and baskets and bottles, endless things. One woman had a fine peacock under her arm. She put it down and in vain tried to suppress it beneath her voluminous skirts. It refused to be suppressed. She took it up and balanced it on her knee, and looked round again over the medley of jars, baskets, pumpkins, melons, guns, bundles and human beings.

In the front was a steel car with a guard of little scrubby soldiers in their dirty cotton uniforms. Some soldiers were mounted on top of the train with their guns: the look-out.

And the whole train, seething with life, was curiously still, subdued. Perhaps it is the perpetual sense of danger which makes the people so hushed, without clamour or stridency. And with an odd, hushed politeness among them. A sort of demon-world.

At last the train moved on. If it had waited forever, no one would have been deeply surprised. For what might not be ahead? Rebels, bandits, bridges blown up—anything.

However, quietly, stealthily, the train moved out and along the great weary valley. The circling mountains, so relentless, were invisible save near at hand. In a few broken adobe huts, a bit of fire sparked red. The adobe was grey-black, of the lava dust, depressing. Into the distance the fields spread dry, with here and there patches of green irrigation. There was a broken hacienda with columns that supported nothing. Darkness was coming, dust still blew in the shadow; the valley seemed encompassed in a dry, stale, weary gloom.

Then there came a heavy shower. The train was passing a pulque hacienda. The rows of the giant maguey stretched bristling their iron-black barbs in the gloom.

All at once, the lights came on, the Pullman attendant came swiftly lowering the blinds, so that the brilliance of the windows should attract no bullets from the dark outside.

There was a poor little meal at exorbitant prices, and when this

was cleared away, the attendant came with a clash to make the beds, pulling down the upper berths. It was only eight o'clock, and the passengers looked up in resentment. But no good. The pug-faced Mexican in charge, and his small-pox-pitted assistant insolently came in between the seats, inserted the key over-head, and brought down the berth with a crash. And the Mexican passengers humbly crawled away to the smoking-room or the toilet, like whipped dogs.

At half-past eight everybody was silently and with intense discretion going to bed. None of the collar-stud-snapping bustle and "homely" familiarity of the United States. Like subdued animals they all crept in behind their green serge curtains.

Kate hated a Pullman, the discreet indiscretion, the horrible nearness of other people, like so many larvae in so many sections, behind the green serge curtains. Above all, the horrible intimacy of the noise of going to bed. She hated to undress, struggling in the oven of her berth, with her elbow butting into the stomach of the attendant who was buttoning up the green curtain outside.

And yet, once she was in bed and could put out her light and raise the window blind, she had to admit it was better than a *wagon-lit* in Europe: and perhaps the best that can be done for people who must travel through the night in trains.

There was a rather cold wind, after the rain, up there on that high plateau. The moon had risen, the sky was clear. Rocks, and tall organ cactus, and more miles of maguey. Then the train stopped at a dark little station on the rim of the slope, where men swathed in dark serapes held dusky, red lanterns that lit up no faces at all, only dark gaps. Why did the train stay so long? Was something wrong?

At last they were going again. Under the moon she saw beyond her a long downslope of rocks and cactus, and in the distance below, the lights of a town. She lay in her berth watching the train wind slowly down the wild, rugged slope. Then she dozed.

To wake at a station that looked like a quiet inferno, with dark faces coming near the windows, glittering eyes in the half-light, women in their rebozos running along the train balancing dishes of meat, tamales, tortillas on one hand, black-faced men with fruit and sweets, and all calling in a subdued, intense, hushed hubbub. Strange and glaring, she saw eyes at the dark screen of the Pullman, sudden hands thrusting up something to sell. In fear, Kate dropped her window. The wire screen was not enough.

The platform below the Pullman all was dark. But at the back of the train she could see the glare of the first-class windows, on the dark station. And a man selling sweetmeats—*Cajetas! Cajetas! La de Celaya!*

She was safe inside the Pullman with nothing to do but to listen to an occasional cough behind the green curtains, and to feel the faint bristling apprehension of all the Mexicans in their dark berths. The dark Pullman was full of a subdued apprehension, fear lest there might be some attack on the train.

She went to sleep and woke at a bright station: probably Queretaro. The green trees looked theatrical in the electric light. *Opales!* she heard the men calling softly. If Owen had been there he would have got up in his pyjamas to buy opals. The call would have been too strong.

She slept fitfully, in the shaken saloon, vaguely aware of stations and the deep night of the open country. Then she started from a complete sleep. The train was dead still, no sound. Then a tremendous jerking as the Pullman was shunted. It must be Irapuato, where they branched to the west.

She would arrive at Ixtlahuacan soon after six in the morning. The man woke her at daybreak, before the sun had risen. Dry country with mesquite bushes, in the dawn: then green wheat alternating with ripe wheat. And men already in the pale, ripened wheat reaping with sickles, cutting short little handfuls from the short straw. A bright sky, with a bluish shadow on earth. Parched slopes with ragged maize stubble. Then a forlorn hacienda and a man on horseback, in a blanket, driving a silent flock of cows, sheep, bulls, goats, lambs, rippling a bit ghostly in the dawn, from under a tottering archway. A long canal beside the railway, a long canal paved with bright green leaves from which poked the mauve heads of the lirio, the water hyacinth. The sun was lifting up, red. In a moment, it was the full, dazzling gold of a Mexican morning.

Kate was dressed and ready, sitting facing Villiers, when they came to Ixtlahuacan. The man carried out her bags. The train drifted in to a desert of a station. They got down. It was a new day.

In the powerful light of morning, under a turquoise blue sky, she gazed at the helpless-looking station, railway lines, some standing trucks, and a remote lifelessness. A boy seized their bags and ran across the lines to the station yard, which was paved with

cobble stones, but overgrown with weeds. At one side stood an old tram-car with two mules, like a relic. One or two men, swathed up to the eyes in scarlet blankets, were crossing on silent white legs.

"Adonde?" said the boy.

But Kate went to see her big luggage taken out. It was all there.

"Orilla Hotel," said Kate.

The boy said they must go in the tram-car, so in the tram-car they went. The driver whipped his mules, they rolled in the still, heavy morning light away down an uneven, cobbled road with holes in it, between walls with falling mortar and low, black adobe houses, in the peculiar *vacuous* depression of a helpless little Mexican town, towards the plaza. The strange emptiness, everything empty of life!

Occasional men on horseback clattered suddenly by, occasional big men in scarlet serapes went noiselessly on their own way, under big hats. A boy on a high mule was delivering milk from red globe-shaped jars slung on either side his mount. The street was stony, uneven, vacuous, sterile. The stones seemed dead, the town seemed made of dead stone. The human life came with a slow, sterile unwillingness, in spite of the low-hung power of the sun.

At length they were in the plaza, where brilliant trees flowered in a blaze of pure scarlet, and some in pure lavender, around the basins of milky-looking water. Milky-dim the water bubbled up in the basins, and women, bleary with sleep, uncombed, came from under the dilapidated arches of the portales, and across the broken pavement, to fill their water-jars.

The tram stopped and they got down. The boy got down with the bags, and told them they must go to the river to take a boat.

They followed obediently down the smashed pavements, where every moment you might twist your ankle or break your leg. Everywhere the same weary indifference and brokenness, a sense of dirt and of helplessness, squalor of far-gone indifference, under the perfect morning sky, in the pure sunshine and the pure Mexican air. The sense of life ebbing away, leaving dry ruin.

They came to the edge of the town, to a dusty, humped bridge, a broken wall, a pale-brown stream flowing full. Below the bridge a cluster of men.

Each one wanted her to hire his boat. She demanded a motor-

boat: the boat from the hotel. They said there wasn't one. She didn't believe it. Then a dark-faced fellow with his black hair down his forehead, and a certain intensity in his eyes, said: Yes, yes; The Hotel had a boat, but it was broken. She must take a row-boat. In an hour and a half he would row her there.

"How long?" said Kate.

"An hour and a half."

"And I am so hungry!" cried Kate. "How much do you charge?"

"Two pesos." He held up two fingers.

Kate said yes, and he ran down to his boat. Then she noticed he was a cripple with inturned feet. But how quick and strong!

She climbed with Villiers down the broken bank to the river, and in a moment they were in the boat. Pale green willow trees fringed from the earthen banks to the fuller-flowing, pale-brown water. The river was not very wide, between deep banks. They slipped under the bridge, and past a funny high barge with rows of seats. The boatman said it went up the river to Jocotlan: and he waved his hand to show the direction. They were slipping down-stream, between lonely banks of willow-trees.

The crippled boatman was pulling hard, with great strength and energy. When she spoke to him in her bad Spanish and he found it hard to understand, he knitted his brow a little, anxiously. And when she laughed he smiled at her with such a beautiful gentleness, sensitive, wistful, quick. She felt he was naturally honest and truthful, and generous. There was a beauty in these men, a wistful beauty and a great physical strength. Why had she felt so bitterly about the country?

Morning was still young on the pale buff river, between the silent earthen banks. There was a blue dimness in the lower air, and black water-fowl ran swiftly, unconcernedly back and forth from the river's edge, on the dry, baked banks that were treeless now, and wider. They had entered a wide river, from the narrow one. The blueness and the moistness of the dissolved night seemed to linger under the scattered pepper-trees of the far shore.

The boatman rowed short and hard upon the flimsy, soft, sperm-like water, only pausing at moments swiftly to smear the sweat from his face with an old rag he kept on the bench beside him. The sweat ran from his bronze-brown skin like water, and the black hair on his high-domed, Indian head, smoked with wetness.

"There is no hurry," said Kate, smiling to him.

"What does the Señorita say?"

"There is no hurry," she repeated.

He paused, smiling, breathing deeply, and explained that now he was rowing against stream. This wider river flowed out of the lake, full and heavy. See! even as he rested a moment, the boat began to turn and drift! He quickly took his oars.

The boat moved slowly, in the hush of departed night, upon the soft, full-flowing buff water, that carried little tufts of floating water-hyacinth. Some willow-trees stood near the edge, and some pepper-trees of most delicate green foliage. Beyond the trees and the level of the shores, big hills rose up to high, blunt points, baked incredibly dry, like biscuit. The blue sky settled against them nakedly, they were leafless and lifeless save for the iron-green shafts of the organ cactus, that glistered blackly, yet atmospherically, in the ochreous aridity. This was Mexico again, stark-dry and luminous with powerful light, cruel and unreal.

On a flat near the river a peon, perched on the rump of his ass, was slowly driving five luxurious cows towards the water to drink. The big black-and-white animals stepped in a dream-pace past the pepper-trees to the bank, like moving pieces of light-and-shade: the dun cows trailed after, in the incredible silence and brilliance of the morning.

Earth, air, water were all silent with new light, the last blue of night dissolving like a breath. No sound, even no life. The great light was stronger than life itself. Only, up in the blue, some turkey-buzzards were wheeling with dirty-edged wings, as everywhere in Mexico.

"Don't hurry!" Kate said again to the boatman, who was again mopping his face, while his black hair ran sweat. "We can go slowly."

The man smiled deprecatingly.

"If the Señorita will sit in the back," he said.

Kate did not understand his request at first. He had rowed in towards a bend in the right bank, to be out of the current. On the left bank Kate had noticed some men bathing: men whose wet skins flashed with the beautiful brown-rose colour and glitter of the naked natives, and one stout man with the curious creamy-biscuit skin of the city Mexicans. Low against the water across-stream she watched the glitter of naked men, half-immersed in the river.

She rose to step back into the stern of the boat, where Villiers

was. As she did so, she saw a dark head and the flashing ruddy shoulders of a man swimming towards the boat. She wavered—and as she was sitting down, the man stood up in the water and was wading near, the water washing at the loose little cloth he had round his loins. He was smooth and wet and of a lovely colour, with the rich smooth-muscled physique of the Indians. He was coming towards the boat, pushing back his hair from his forehead.

The boatman watched him, transfixed, without surprise, a little subtle half-smile, perhaps of mockery, round his nose. As if he had expected it!

"Where are you going?" asked the man in the water, the brown river running softly at his strong thighs.

The boatman waited a moment for his patrons to answer, then, seeing they were silent, replied in a low, unwilling tone: "Orilla."

The man in the water took hold of the stern of the boat, as the boatman softly touched the water with the oars to keep her straight, and he threw back his longish black hair with a certain effrontery.

"Do you know whom the lake belongs to?" he asked, with the same effrontery.

"What do you say?" asked Kate, haughty.

"If you know whom the lake belongs to?" the young man in the water repeated.

"To whom?' said Kate, flustered.

"To the old gods of Mexico," the stranger said. "You have to make a tribute to Quetzalcoatl, if you go on the lake."

The strange calm effrontery of it! But truly Mexican.

"How?" said Kate.

"You can give me something," he said.

"But why should I give something to you, if it is a tribute to Quetzalcoatl?" she stammered.

"I am Quetzalcoatl's man, I," he replied, with calm effrontery.

"And if I don't give you anything?" she said.

He lifted his shoulders and spread his free hand, staggering a little, losing his footing in the water as he did so.

"If you wish to make an enemy of the lake!—" he said, coolly, as he recovered his balance.

And then for the first time he looked straight at her. And as he did so, the demonish effrontery died down again, and the peculiar American tension slackened and left him.

He gave a slight wave of dismissal with his free hand, and pushed the boat gently forward.

"But it doesn't matter," he said, with a slight insolent jerk of his head sideways, and a faint, insolent smile. "We will wait till the Morning Star rises."

The boatman softly but powerfully pulled the oars. The man in the water stood with the sun on his powerful chest, looking after the boat in half-seeing abstraction. His eyes had taken again the peculiar gleaming far-awayness, suspended between the realities, which, Kate suddenly realised, was the central look in the native eyes. The boatman, rowing away, was glancing back at the man who stood in the water, and his face, too, had the abstracted, transfigured look of a man perfectly suspended between the world's two strenuous wings of energy. A look of extraordinary, arresting beauty, the silent, vulnerable centre of all life's quivering, like the nucleus gleaming in tranquil suspense, within a cell.

"What does he mean," said Kate, "by 'We will wait till the Morning Star rises?'"

The man smiled slowly.

"It is a name," he said.

And he seemed to know no more. But the symbolism had evidently the power to soothe and sustain him.

"Why did he come and speak to us?" asked Kate.

"He is one of those of the god Quetzalcoatl, Señorita."

"And you? are you one too?"

"Who knows!" said the man, putting his head on one side. Then he added: "I think so. We are many."

He watched Kate's face with that gleaming, intense semi-abstraction, a gleam that hung unwavering in his black eyes, and which suddenly reminded Kate of the morning star, or the evening star, hanging perfect between night and the sun.

"You have the morning star in your eyes," she said to the man.

He flashed her a smile of extraordinary beauty.

"The Señorita understands," he said.

His face changed again to a dark-brown mask, like semi-transparent stone, and he rowed with all his might. Ahead, the river was widening, the banks were growing lower, down to the water's level, like shoals planted with willow trees and with reeds. Above the willow trees a square white sail was standing, as if erected on the land.

"Is the lake so near?" said Kate.

The man hastily mopped his running wet face.

"Yes, Señorita! The sailing boats are waiting for the wind, to come into the river. We will pass by the canal."

He indicated with a backward movement of the head a narrow, twisting passage of water between deep reeds. It made Kate think of the little river Anapo: the same mystery unbroken. The boatman, with creases half of sadness and half of exaltation in his bronze, still face, was pulling with all his might. Water-fowl went swimming into the reeds, or rose on wing and wheeled into the blue air. Some willow trees hung a dripping, vivid green, in the stark dry country. The stream was narrow and winding. With a nonchalant motion, first of the right then of the left hand, Villiers was guiding the boatman, to keep him from running aground in the winding, narrow water-way.

And this put Villiers at his ease, to have something practical and slightly mechanical to do and to assert. He was striking the American note once more, of mechanical dominance.

All the other business had left him incomprehending, and when he asked Kate, she had pretended not to hear him. She sensed a certain delicate, tender mystery in the river, in the naked man in the water, in the boatman, and she could not bear to have it subjected to the tough American flippancy. She was weary to death of American automatism and American flippant toughness. It gave her a feeling of nausea.

"Quite a well-built fellow, that one who laid hold of the boat. What did he want, anyway?" Villiers insisted.

"Nothing!" said Kate.

They were slipping out past the clay-coloured, loose stony edges of the land, through a surge of ripples, into the wide white light of the lake. A breeze was coming from the east, out of the upright morning, and the surface of the shallow, flimsy, dun-coloured water was in motion. Shoal-water rustled near at hand. Out to the open, large, square white sails were stepping gingerly forward, and beyond the buff-coloured, pale desert of water rose far-away blue, sharp hills of the other side, many miles away, pure pale blue with distance, yet sharp-edged and clear in form.

"Now," said the boatman, smiling to Kate, "it is easier. Now we are out of the current."

He pulled rhythmically through the frail-rippling, sperm-like water, with a sense of peace. And for the first time Kate felt

she had met the mystery of the natives, the strange and mysterious gentleness between a Scylla and a Charybdis of violence; the small poised, perfect body of the bird that waves wings of thunder and wings of fire and night, in its flight. But central between the flash of day and the black of night, between the flash of lightning and the break of thunder, the still, soft body of the bird poised and soaring, forever. The mystery of the evening-star brilliant in silence and distance between the downward-surging plunge of the sun and the vast, hollow seething of inpouring night. The magnificence of the watchful morning-star, that watches between the night and the day, the gleaming clue to the two opposites.

This kind of frail, pure sympathy she felt at the moment between herself and the boatman, between herself and the man who had spoken from the water. And she was not going to have it broken by Villiers' American jokes.

There was a sound of breaking water. The boatman drew away, and pointed across to where a *canoa,* a native sailing-boat, was lying at an angle. She had run aground in a wind, and now must wait till another wind would carry her off the submerged bank again. Another boat was coming down the breeze, steering cautiously among the shoals, for the river outlet. She was piled high with petates, the native leaf mats, above her hollowed black sides. And bare-legged men with loose white drawers rolled up, and brown chests showing, were running with poles as the shallows heaved up again, pushing her off, and balancing their huge hats with small, bird-like shakes of the head.

Beyond the boats, sea-wards, were rocks outcropping and strange birds like pelicans standing in silhouette, motionless.

They had been crossing a bay of the lake-shore, and were nearing the hotel. It stood on a parched dry bank above the pale-brown water, a long, low building amid a tender green of bananas and pepper-trees. Everywhere the shores rose up pale and cruelly dry, dry to cruelty, and on the little hills the dark statues of the organ cactus poised in nothingness.

There was a broken-down landing-place, and a boat-house in the distance, and someone in white flannel trousers was standing on the broken masonry. Upon the filmy water ducks and black water-fowl bobbed like corks. The bottom was stony. The boatman suddenly backed the boat, and pulled round. He pushed up his sleeve and hung over the bows, reaching into the water. With a quick motion he grabbed something, and scrambled into the

boat again. He was holding in the pale-skinned hollow of his palm a little earthenware pot, crusted by the lake deposit.

"What is it?" she said.

"Ollita of the gods," he said. "Of the old dead gods. Take it, Señorita."

"You must let me pay for it," she said.

"No, Señorita. It is yours," said the man, with that sensitive, masculine sincerity which comes sometimes so quickly from a native.

It was a little, rough round pot with protuberances.

"Look!" said the man, reaching again for the little pot. He turned it upside-down, and she saw cut-in eyes and the sticking-out ears of an animal's head.

"A cat!" she exclaimed. "It is a cat."

"Or a coyote!"

"A coyote!"

"Let's look!" said Villiers. "Why how awfully interesting! Do you think it's old?"

"It is old?" Kate asked.

"The time of the old gods," said the boatman. Then with a sudden smile: "The dead gods don't eat much rice, they only want little casseroles while they are bone under the water." And he looked her in the eyes.

"While they are bone?" she repeated. And she realised he meant the skeletons of gods that cannot die.

They were at the landing stage; or rather, at the heap of collapsed masonry which had once been a landing stage. The boatman got out and held the boat steady while Kate and Villiers landed. Then he scrambled up with the bags.

The man in white trousers and a *mozo* appeared. It was the hotel manager. Kate paid the boatman.

"Adios, Señorita!" he said with a smile. "May you go with Quetzalcoatl."

"Yes!" she cried. "Goodbye!"

They went up the slope between the tattered bananas, whose ragged leaves were making a hushed, distant patter in the breeze. The green fruit curved out its bristly-soft bunch, the purple flower-bud depending stiffly.

The German manager came to talk to them: a young man of about forty, with his blue eyes going opaque and stony behind his spectacles, though the centres were keen. Evidently a German

who had been many years out in Mexico—out in the lonely places. The rather stiff look, the slight look of fear in the *soul*—not physical fear—and the look of defeat, characteristic of the European who has long been subjected to the unbroken spirit of place! But the defeat was in the soul, not the will.

He showed Kate to her room in the unfinished quarter, and ordered her breakfast. The hotel consisted of an old low ranch-house with a verandah—and this was the dining-room, lounge, kitchen and office. Then there was a two-storey new wing, with a smart bath-room between each two bedrooms, and almost up-to-date fittings: very incongruous.

But the new wing was unfinished—had been unfinished for a dozen years and more, the work abandoned when Porfirio Diaz fled. Now it would probably never be finished.

And this is Mexico. Whatever pretentiousness and modern improvements it may have, outside the capital, they are either smashed or raw and unfinished, with rusty bones of iron girders sticking out.

Kate washed her hands and went down to breakfast. Before the long verandah of the old ranch-house, the green pepper-trees dropped like green light, and small cardinal birds with scarlet bodies and blazing impertinent heads like poppy-buds flashed among the pinkish pepper-heads, closing their brown wings upon the audacity of their glowing redness. A train of geese passed in the glaring sun, automatic, towards the eternal tremble of pale, earth-coloured water beyond the stones.

It was a place with a strange atmosphere: stony, hard, broken, with round cruel hills and the many fluted bunches of the organ-cactus behind the old house, and an ancient road trailing past, deep in ancient dust. A touch of mystery and cruelty, the stony-ness of fear, a lingering, cruel sacredness.

Kate loitered hungrily, and was glad when the Mexican in shirt-sleeves and patched trousers, another lingering remnant of Don Porfirio's day, brought her her eggs and coffee.

He was muted as everything about the place seemed muted, even the very stones and the water. Only those poppies on wing, the cardinal birds, gave a sense of liveliness: and they were un-canny.

So swiftly one's moods changed! In the boat, she had glimpsed the superb rich stillness of the morning-star, the poignant inter-mediate flashing its quiet between the energies of the cosmos.

She had seen it in the black eyes of the natives, in the sunrise of the man's rich, still body, Indian-warm.

And now again already the silence was of vacuity, arrest, and cruelty: the uncanny empty unbearableness of many Mexican mornings. Already she was uneasy, suffering from the malaise which tortures one inwardly in that country of cactuses.

She went up to her room, pausing at the corridor window to look out at the savage little hills that stood at the back of the hotel in desiccated heaps, with the dark-green bulks of organ-cactus sticking up mechanically and sinister, sombre in all the glare. Grey ground-squirrels like rats slithered ceaselessly around. Sinister, strangely dark and sinister, in the great glare of the sun!

She went to her room to be alone. Below her window, in the bricks and fallen rubble of unfinished masonry, a huge white turkey-cock, dim-white, strutted with his brown hens. And sometimes he stretched out his pink wattles and gave vent to fierce, powerful turkey-yelps, like some strong dog yelping; or else he ruffled all his feathers like a great, soiled white peony, and he chuffed, hissing here and there, raging the metal of his plumage.

Below him, the eternal tremble of pale-earth, unreal waters, far beyond which rose the stiff resistance of mountains losing their pristine blue. Distinct, frail distances far off on the dry air, dim-seeing, yet sharp and edged with menace.

Kate took her bath in the filmy water that was hardly like water at all. Then she went and sat on the collapsed masonry, in the shade of the boat-house below. Small white ducks bobbed about on the shallow water below her, or dived, raising clouds of submarine dust. A canoe came paddling in; a lean fellow with sinewy brown legs. He answered Kate's nod with the aloof promptness of an Indian, made fast his canoe inside the boat-house, and was gone, stepping silent and barefoot over the bright green water-stones, and leaving a shadow, cold as flint, on the air behind him.

No sound on the morning save a faint touching of water, and the occasional powerful yelping of the turkey-cock. Silence, an aboriginal, empty silence, as of life *withheld*. The vacuity of a Mexican morning. Resounding sometimes to the turkey-cock.

And the great, lymphatic expanse of water, like a sea, trembling, trembling, trembling to a far distance, to the mountains of substantial nothingness.

Near at hand, a ragged shifting of banana trees, bare hills with immobile cactus, and to the left, a hacienda with peons' square mud boxes of houses. An occasional ranchero in skin-tight trousers and big hat, rode trotting through the dust on a small horse, or peons on the rump of their asses, in floppy white cotton, going like ghosts.

Always something ghostly. The morning passing all of a piece, empty, vacuous. All sound withheld, all life withheld, everything *holding back*. The land so dry as to have a quality of invisibility, the water earth-filmy, hardly water at all. The lympnatic milk of fishes, somebody said.

CHAPTER VI

THE MOVE DOWN THE LAKE

IN Porfirio Diaz' day, the Lake-side began to be the Riviera of Mexico, and Orilla to be the Nice, or at least, the Mentone of the country. But revolutions started erupting again, and in 1911 Don Porfirio fled to Paris with, it is said, thirty million gold pesos in his pocket: a peso being half a dollar, nearly half-a-crown. But we need not believe all that is said, especially by a man's enemies.

During the subsequent revolutions, Orilla, which had begun to be a winter paradise for the Americans, lapsed back into barbarism and broken brickwork. In 1921 a feeble new start had been made.

The place belonged to a German-Mexican family, who also owned the adjacent hacienda. They acquired the property from the American Hotel Company, who had undertaken to develop the lake-shore, and who had gone bankrupt during the various revolutions.

The German-Mexican owners were not popular with the natives. An angel from heaven would not have been popular, these years, if he had been known as the owner of property. However, in 1921 the hotel was very modestly opened again, with an American manager.

Towards the end of the year, José, son of the German-Mexican owner, came to stay with his wife and children in the hotel, in the new wing. José was a bit of a fool, as most foreigners are, after the first generation in Mexico. Having business to settle, he went into Guadalajara to the bank and returned with a thousand gold pesos in a bag, keeping the matter, as he thought, a dead secret.

Everyone had just gone to bed, on a brilliant moonlight night in winter, when two men appeared in the yard calling for José: they had to speak to him. José, suspecting nothing, left his wife and two children, and went down. In a moment he called for the American manager. The manager, thinking it was some bargaining to be done, also came down. As he came out of the

door, two men seized him by the arms, and said: *"Don't make a noise!"*

"What's amiss?" said Bell, who had built up Orilla, and had been twenty years on the lake.

Then he noticed that two other men had hold of José. "Come," they said.

There were five Mexicans—Indians, or half-Indians—and the two captives. They went, the captives in slippers and shirt-sleeves, to the little office away at the end of the other part of the hotel, which had been the old ranch-house.

"What do you want?" said Bell.

"Give us the money," said the bandits.

"Oh, all right," said the American. There were a few pesos only in the safe. He opened, showed them, and they took the money.

"Now give us the rest," they said.

"There is no more," said the manager, in all sincerity; for José had not confessed to the thousand pesos.

The five peons then began to search the poor little office. They found a pile of red blankets—which they appropriated—and a few bottles of red wine—which they drank.

"Now," they said, "give us the money."

"I can't give you what there isn't to give," said the manager.

"Good!" they said, and pulled out the hideous machetes, the heavy knives of the Mexicans.

José, intimidated, produced the suit-case with the thousand pesos. The money was wrapped up in the corner of a blanket.

"Now, come with us," said the bandits.

"Where to?" asked the manager, beginning at last to be scared.

"Only out on to the hill, where we will leave you, so that you cannot telephone to Ixtlahuacan before we have time to get away," said the Indians.

Outside, in the bright moon, the air was chill. The American shivered, in his trousers and shirt and a pair of bedroom slippers.

"Let me take a coat," he said.

"Take a blanket," said the tall Indian.

He took a blanket, and with two men holding his arms, he followed José, who was likewise held captive, out of the little gate, across the dust of the road, and up the steep little round hill on which the organ-cactus thrust up their sinister clumps, like bunches of cruel fingers, in the moonlight. The hill was

stony and steep, the going, slow. José, a fat young man of twenty-eight, protested in the feeble manner of the well-to-do Mexicans.

At last they came to the top of the hill. Three men took José apart, leaving Bell alone near a cactus clump. The moon shone in a perfect Mexican heaven. Below, the big lake glimmered faintly, stretching its length towards the west. The air was so clear, the mountains across, thirty miles away, stood sharp and still in the moonlight. And not a sound nor a motion anywhere! At the foot of the hill was the hacienda, with the peons asleep in their huts. But what help was there in them?

José and the three men had gone behind a cactus tree that struck up straight like a great black bundle of poles, poised on one central foot, and cast a sharp, iron shadow. The American could hear the voices, talking low and rapidly, but could not distinguish the words. His two guards drew away from him a little, to hear what the others were saying, behind the cactus.

And the American, who knew the ground he stood on and the sky that hung over him, felt again the black vibration of death in the air, the black thrill of the death-lust. Unmistakeable he felt it seething in the air, as any man may feel it, in Mexico. And the strange aboriginal fiendishness, awake now in the five bandits, communicated itself to his blood.

Loosening his blanket, he listened tensely in the moonlight. And came the *thud! thud! thud!* of a machete striking with lust in a human body, then the strange voice of José: *"Perdoneme! —Forgive me!"* the murdered man cried as he fell.

The American waited for no more. Dropping his blanket, he jumped for the cactus cover, and stooping, took the down-slope like a rabbit. The pistol-shots rang out after him, but the Mexicans don't as a rule take good aim. His bedroom slippers flew off, and barefoot, the man, thin and light, sped down over the stones and the cactus, down to the hotel.

When he got down, he found everyone in the hotel awake and shouting.

"They are killing José!" he said, and he rushed to the telephone, expecting every moment the five bandits would be on him.

The telephone was in the old ranch-building, in the dining-room. There was no answer—no answer—no answer. In her little bedroom over the kitchen, the cook-woman, the traitress, was yelling. Across in the new wing, a little distance away,

José's Mexican wife was screaming. One of the servant boys appeared.

"Try and get the police in Ixtlahuacan," said the American, and he ran to the new wing, to get his gun and to barricade the doors. His daughter, a motherless girl, was crying with José's wife.

There was no answer on the telephone. At dawn, the cook, who said the bandits would not hurt a woman, went across to the hacienda to fetch the peons. And when the sun rose, a man was sent for the police.

They found the body of José, pierced with fourteen holes. The American was carried to Ixtlahuacan, and kept in bed, having cactus spines dug out of his feet by two native women.

The bandits fled across the marshes. Months later, they were identified by the stolen blankets, away in Michoacan; and, pursued, one of them betrayed the others.

After this, the hotel was closed again, and had been reopened only three months, when Kate arrived.

But Villiers came with another story. Last year the peons had murdered the manager of one of the estates across the lake. They had stripped him and left him naked on his back, with his sexual organs cut off and put into his mouth, his nose slit and pinned back, the two halves, to his cheeks, with long cactus spines.

"Tell me no more!" said Kate.

She felt there was doom written on the very sky, doom and horror.

She went to Don Ramón in Sayula, saying she wanted to go back to Europe. True, she herself had seen no horrors, apart from the bull-fight. And she had had some exquisite moments, as coming to this hotel in the boat. The natives had a certain mystery and beauty, to her. But she could not bear the unease, and the latest sense of horror.

True, the peons were poor. They used to work for twenty cents, American, a day; and now the standard price was fifty cents, or one peso. But then in the old days they received their wage all the year round. Now, only at harvest time or sowing time. No work, no pay. And in the long dry season, it was mostly no work.

"Still," said the German manager of the hotel, a man who had run a rubber plantation in Tabasco, a sugar plantation in the state of Vera Cruz, and a hacienda growing wheat, maize, oranges,

in Jalisco: "Still, it isn't a question of money with the peons. It doesn't start with the peons. It starts in Mexico City, with a lot of malcontents who want to put their spoke in the wheel, and who lay hold of pious catchwords, to catch the poor. There's no more in it than that. Then the agitators go round and infect the peons. It is nothing but a sort of infectious disease, like syphilis, all this revolution and socialism."

"But why does no one oppose it," said Kate. "Why don't the hacendados put up a fight, instead of caving in and running away?"

"The Mexican hacendado!" The man's German eyes gave out a spark. "The Mexican *gentleman* is such a brave man, that while the soldier is violating his wife on the bed, he is hiding under the bed and holding his breath so they shan't find him. He's as brave as that."

Kate looked away uncomfortably.

"They all want the United States to intervene. They hate the Americans; but they want the United States to intervene, to save them their money and their property. That's how brave they are! They hate the Americans personally, but they love them because they can look after money and property. So they want the United States to annex Mexico, the beloved patria; leaving the marvellous green and white and red flag, and the eagle with the snake in its claws, for the sake of appearances and *honour!* They're simply bottled full of honour; of that sort."

Always the same violence of bitterness, Kate thought to herself. And she was so weary of it. How, how weary she was of politics, of the very words "Labour" and *"Socialism!"* and all that sort! It suffocated her.

"Have you heard of the men of Quetzalcoatl?" asked Kate.

"Quetzalcoatl!" exclaimed the manager, giving a little click of the final 'l,' in a peculiar native fashion. "That's another try-on of the Bolshevists. They thought socialism needed a god, so they're going to fish him out of this lake. He'll do for another pious catchword in another revolution."

The man went away, unable to stand any more.

"Oh dear!" thought Kate. "It really is hard to bear."

But she wanted to hear more of Quetzalcoatl.

"Did you know," she said to the man later, showing him the little pot, "that they find those things in the lake?"

"They're common enough!" he said. "They used to throw

them in, in the idolatrous days.   May still do so, for what I know.
Then get them out again to sell to tourists."

"They call them ollitas of Quetzalcoatl."

"That's a new invention."

"Why, do you think?"

"They're trying to start a new thing, that's all.   They've
got this society on the lake here, of the Men of Quetzalcoatl, and
they go round singing songs.   It's another dodge for national-
socialism, that's all."

"What do they do, the Men of Quetzalcoatl?"

·"I can't see they do anything, except talk and get excited over
their own importance."

"But what's the idea?"

"I couldn't say.   Don't suppose they have any.   But if they
have, they won't let on to you.   You're a gringo—or a gringita,
at the best.   And this is for pure Mexicans.   For los señores, the
workmen, and los caballeros, the peons.   Every peon is a
caballero nowadays, and every workman is a señor.   So I suppose they're going to get themselves a special god, to put the final
feather in their caps."

"Where did it start, the Quetzalcoatl thing?"

"Down in Sayula.   They say Don Ramón Carrasco is at the
back of it.   Maybe he wants to be the next President—or maybe
he's aiming higher, and wants to be the first Mexican Pharaoh."

Ah, how tired it made Kate feel; the hopelessness, the ugliness,
the cynicism, the emptiness.   She felt she could cry aloud, for the
unknown gods to put the magic back into her life, and to save her
from the dry-rot of the world's sterility.

She thought again of going back to Europe.   But what was
the good?   She knew it!   It was all politics or jazzing or slushy
mysticism or sordid spiritualism.   And the magic had gone.   The
younger generation, so smart and *interesting,* but so without
any mystery, any background.   The younger the generation, the
flatter and more jazzy, more and more devoid of wonder.

No, she could not go back to Europe.

And no!   She refused to take the hotel manager's estimate of
Quetzalcoatl.   How should a hotel manager judge?—even if he
was not really an hotel manager, but a ranch-overseer.   She had
seen Ramón Carrasco, and Cipriano.   And they were men.
They wanted something beyond.   She would believe in them.

Anything, anything rather than this sterility of nothingness which was the world, and into which her life was drifting.

She would send Villiers away, too. He was nice, she liked him. But he, too, was widdershins, unwinding the sensations of disintegration and anti-life. No, she must send him away. She must, she must free herself from these mechanical connections.

Every one of them, like Villiers, was like a cog-wheel in contact with which all one's workings were reversed. Everything he said, everything he did, reversed her real life flow, made her go against the sun.

And she did not want to go against the sun. After all, in spite of the horrors latent in Mexico, when you got these dark-faced people away from wrong contacts like agitators and socialism, they made one feel that life was vast, if fearsome, and death was fathomless.

Horrors might burst out of them. But something must burst out, sometimes, if men are not machines.

No! no! no! no! no! she cried to her own soul. *Let me still believe in some human contact. Let it not be all cut off for me!*

But she made up her mind, to be alone, and to cut herself off from all the mechanical widdershin contacts. Villiers must go back to his United States. She would be alone in her own milieu. Not to be touched by any, any of the mechanical cog-wheel people. To be left alone, not to be touched. To hide, and be hidden, and never really be spoken to.

Yet at the same time, with her blood flowing softly sunwise, to let the sunwise sympathy of unknown people steal in to her. To shut doors of iron against the mechanical world. But to let the sunwise world steal across to her, and add its motion to her, the motion of the stress of life, with the big sun and the stars like a tree holding out its leaves.

She wanted an old Spanish house, with its inner patio of flowers and water. Turned inwards, to the few flowers walled in by shadow. To turn one's back on the cog-wheel world. Not to look out any more on to that horrible machine of the world. To look at one's own quiet little fountain and one's own little orange trees, with only heaven above.

So, having soothed her heart, she wrote Don Ramón again, that she was coming to Sayula to look for a house. She sent Villiers away. And the next day she set off with a man-servant,

in the old motor-boat of the hotel, down to the village of Sayula.

It was thirty-five miles to travel, down the long lake. But the moment she set off, she felt at peace. A tall dark-faced fellow sat in the stern of the boat, steering and attending to the motor. She sat on cushions in the middle. And the young man-servant perched in the prow.

They started before sunrise, when the lake was bathed in motionless light. Odd tufts of water-hyacinth were travelling on the soft spermy water, holding up a green leaf like a little sail of a boat, and nodding a delicate, mauve blue flower.

Give me the mystery and let the world live again for me! Kate cried to her own soul. *And deliver me from man's auto-matism.*

The sun rose, and a whiteness of light played on the tops of the mountains. The boat hugged the north shore, turning the promontory on which the villas had started so jauntily, twenty years ago, but now were lapsing back to wilderness. All was still and motionless in the light. Sometimes, on the little bare patches high up on the dry hills were white specks; birds? No, men in their white cotton, peons hoeing. They were so tiny and so distinct, they looked like white birds settled.

Round the bend were the hot springs, the church, the inaccessible village of the pure Indians, who spoke no Spanish. There were some green trees, under the precipitous, dry mountain-side.

So on and on, the motor-boat chugging incessantly, the man in the bows coiled up like a serpent, watching; the fish-milk water gleaming and throwing off a dense light, so that the mountains away across were fused out. And Kate, under the awning, went into a kind of sleep.

They were passing the island, with its ruins of fortress and prison. It was all rock and dryness, with great broken walls and the shell of a church among its hurtful stones and its dry grey herbage. For a long time the Indians had defended it against the Spaniards. Then the Spaniards used the island as a fortress against the Indians. Later, as a penal settlement. And now the place was a ruin, repellent, full of scorpions, and otherwise empty of life. Only one or two fishermen lived in the tiny cove facing the mainland, and a flock of goats, specks of life creeping among the rocks. And an unhappy fellow put there by the Government to register the weather.

No, Kate did not want to land. The place looked too sinister.

She took food from the basket, and ate a little lunch, and dozed. In this country, she was afraid. But it was her soul more than her body that knew fear. She had realised, for the first time, with finality and fatality, what was the illusion she laboured under. She had thought that each individual had a complete self, a complete soul, an accomplished I. And now she realised as plainly as if she had turned into a new being, that this was not so. Men and women had incomplete selves, made up of bits assembled together loosely and somwhat haphazard. Man was not created ready-made. Men to-day were half-made, and women were half-made. Creatures that existed and functioned with certain regularity, but which ran off into a hopeless jumble of inconsequence.

Half-made, like insects that can run fast and be so busy and suddenly grow wings, but which are only winged grubs after all. A world full of half-made creatures on two legs, eating food and degrading the one mystery left to them, sex. Spinning a great lot of words, burying themselves inside the cocoons of words and ideas that they spin round themselves, and inside the cocoons, mostly perishing inert and overwhelmed.

Half-made creatures, rarely more than half-responsible and half-accountable, acting in terrible swarms, like locusts.

Awful thought! And with a collective insect-like will, to avoid the responsibility of achieving any more perfected being or identity. The queer, rabid hate of being urged on into purer self. The morbid fanaticism of the non-integrate.

In the great seething light of the lake, with the terrible blue-ribbed mountains of Mexico beyond, she seemed swallowed by some grisly skeleton, in the cage of his death-anatomy. She was afraid, mystically, of the man crouching there in the bows with his smooth thighs and supple loins like a snake, and his black eyes watching. A half-being, with a will to disintegration and death. And the tall man behind her at the tiller, he had the curious smoke-grey phosphorous eyes under black lashes, sometimes met among the Indians. Handsome he was, and quiet and seemingly self-contained. But with that peculiar devilish half-smile lurking under his face, the half jeering look of a part-thing, which knows its power to destroy the purer thing.

And yet, Kate told herself, both these men were manly fellows. They would not molest her, unless she communicated the thought to them, and by a certain cowardliness, prompted them.

Their souls were nascent, there was no fixed evil in them, they could sway both ways.

So in her soul she cried aloud to the greater mystery, the higher power that hovered in the interstices of the hot air, rich and potent. It was as if she could lift her hands and clutch the silent, stormless potency that roved everywhere, waiting. "Come then!" she said, drawing a long slow breath, and addressing the silent lifebreath which hung unrevealed in the atmosphere, waiting.

And as the boat ran on, and her fingers rustled in the warm water of the lake, she felt the fulness descend into her once more, the peace, and the power. The fulfilment filling her soul like the fulness of ripe grapes. And she thought to herself: "Ah, how wrong I have been, not to turn sooner to the other presence, not to take the life-breath sooner! How wrong to be afraid of these two men."

She did what she had been half-afraid to do before; she offered them the oranges and sandwiches still in the basket. And each of the men looked at her, the smoke-grey eyes looked her in the eyes, and the black eyes looked her in the eyes. And the man with the smoke-grey eyes, who was cunninger than the other man, but also prouder, said to her with his eyes: *We are living! I know your sex, and you know mine. The mystery we are glad not to meddle with. You leave me my natural honour, and I thank you for the grace.*

In his look; so quick and proud, and in his quiet *Muchas gracias!* she heard the touch of male recognition, a man glad to retain his honour, and to feel the communion of grace. Perhaps it was the Spanish word *Gracias!* But in her soul she was thinking of the communion of grace.

With the black-eyed man it was the same. He was humbler. But as he peeled his orange and dropped the yellow peel on the water, she could see the stillness, the humility, and the pathos of grace in him; something very beautiful and truly male, and very hard to find in a civilised white man. It was not of the spirit. It was of the dark, strong, unbroken blood, the flowering of the soul.

Then she thought to herself: After all, it is good to be here. It is very good to be in this boat on this lake with these two silent, semi-barbarous men. They can receive the gift of grace, and we can share it like a communion, they and I. I am very glad to

be here. It is so much better than love: the love I knew with
Joachim. This is the fulness of the vine.

"Sayula!" said the man in the bows, pointing ahead.

She saw, away off, a place where there were green trees, where
the shore was flat, and a biggish building stood out.

"What is the building?" she asked.

"The railway station."

She was suitably impressed, for it was a new-looking imposing
structure.

A little steamer was smoking, lying off from a wooden jetty
in the loneliness, and black, laden boats were poling out to her,
and merging back to shore. The vessel gave a hoot, and slowly
yet busily set off on the bosom of the water, heading in a slanting
line across the lake, to where the tiny high white twin-towers of
Tuliapán showed above the water-line, tiny and far-off, on the
other side.

They had passed the jetty, and rounding the shoal where the
willows grew, she could see Sayula; white fluted twin-towers of
the church, obelisk shaped above the pepper-trees; beyond, a
mound of a hill standing alone, dotted with dry bushes, distinct
and Japanese looking; beyond this, the corrugated, blue-ribbed,
flat-flanked mountains of Mexico.

It looked peaceful, delicate, almost Japanese. As she drew
nearer she saw the beach with the washing spread on the sand;
the fleecy green willow trees and pepper-trees, and the villas in
foliage and flowers, hanging magenta curtains of bougainvillea,
red dots of hibiscus, pink abundance of tall oleander trees; occasional palm-trees sticking out.

The boat was steering round a stone jetty, on which, in black
letters, was painted an advertisement for motor-car tyres. There
were a few seats, some deep fleecy trees growing out of the sand,
a booth for selling drinks, a little promenade, and white boats on
a sandy beach. A few women sitting under parasols, a few
bathers in the water, and trees in front of the few villas deep in
green or blazing scarlet blossoms.

"This is very good," thought Kate. "It is not too savage, and
not over civilised. It isn't broken, but it is rather out of repair.
It is in contact with the world, but the world has got a very weak
grip on it."

She went to the hotel, as Don Ramón had advised her.

"Do you come from Orilla? You are Mrs Leslie? Don Ramón Carrasco sent us a letter about you."

There was a house. Kate paid her boatmen and shook hands with them. She was sorry to be cut off from them again. And they looked at her with a touch of regret as they left. She said to herself:

"There is something rich and alive in these people. They want to be able to breathe the Great Breath. They are like children, helpless. And then they're like demons. But somewhere, I believe, they want the breath of life and the communion of the brave, more than anything."

She was surprised at herself, suddenly using this language. But her weariness and her sense of devastation had been so complete, that the Other Breath in the air and the bluish dark power in the earth had become, almost suddenly, more real to her than so-called reality. Concrete, jarring, exasperating reality had melted away, and a soft world of potency stood in its place, the velvety dark flux from the earth, the delicate yet supreme life-breath in the inner air. Behind the fierce sun the dark eyes of a deeper sun were watching, and between the bluish ribs of the mountains a powerful heart was secretly beating, the heart of the earth.

Her house was what she wanted; a low L-shaped, tiled building with rough red floors and deep verandah, and the other two sides of the patio completed by the thick, dark little mango-forest outside the low wall. The square of the patio, within the precincts of the house and the mango trees, was gay with oleanders and hibiscus, and there was a basin of water in the seedy grass. The flower-pots along the verandah were full of flowering geranium and foreign flowers. At the far end of the patio, the chickens were scratching under the silent motionlessness of ragged banana trees.

There she had it; her stone, cool, dark house, every room opening on to the verandah; her deep, shady verandah, or piazza, or corridor, looking out to the brilliant sun, the sparkling flowers and the seed-grass, the still water and the yellowing banana trees, the dark splendour of the shadow-dense mango trees.

With the house went a Mexican Juana with two thick-haired daughters and one son. This family lived in a den at the back of the projecting bay of the dining-room. There, half screened, was the well and the toilet, and a little kitchen and a sleeping

room where the family slept on mats on the floor. There the
paltry chickens paddled, and the banana trees made a chitter as
the wind came.

Kate had four bedrooms to choose from. She chose the one
whose low, barred window opened on the rough, grass and cobble-
stone street, closed her doors and windows, and went to sleep,
saying to herself as she lay down: Now I am alone. And now I
have only one thing to do; not to get caught up into the world's
cog-wheels any more, and not to lose my hold on the hidden
greater thing.

She was tired with a strange weariness, feeling she could
make no further effort. She woke up at tea-time, but there was
no tea. Juana hastened off to the hotel to buy a bit.

Juana was a woman of about forty, rather short, with a full
dark face, centreless dark eyes, untidy hair, and a limping way of
walking. She spoke rapidly, a rather plum-in-the-mouth Spanish, adding "n" to all her words. Something of a sloven, down to
her speech.

"*No, Niña, no hay masn*"—*masn* instead of *mas*. And calling
Kate, in the old Mexican style, *Niña*, which means *child*. It is
the honourable title for a mistress.

Juana was going to be a bit of a trial. She was a widow of
doubtful antecedents, a creature with passion, but not much control, strong with a certain indifference and looseness. The hotel
owner assured Kate that she was honest, but that if Kate would
rather find another *criada*, all well and good.

There was a bit of a battle to be fought between the two women.
Juana was obstinate and reckless; she had not been treated very
well by the world. And there was a touch of bottom-dog insolence
about her.

But also, sudden touches of passionate warmth and the peculiar
selfless generosity of the natives. She would be honest out of
rough defiance and indifference, so long as she was not in a state
of antagonism.

As yet, however, she was cautiously watching her ground,
with that black-eyed touch of malice and wariness to be expected.
And Kate felt that the cry: *Niña*—child! by which she was
addressed, held in it a slight note of malevolent mockery.

But there was nothing to do but to go ahead and trust the dark-
faced, centreless woman.

The second day, Kate had the energy to cast out one suite of

bent-wood and cane furniture from her salon, remove pictures and little stands.

If there is one social instinct more dreary than all the other social instincts in the world, it is the Mexican. In the centre of Kate's red-tiled salon were two crescents: a black bent-wood cane settee flanked on each side by two black bent-wood cane chairs, exactly facing a brown bent-wood cane settee flanked on each side by two brown bent-wood cane chairs. It was as if the two settees and the eight chairs were occupied by the ghosts of all the Mexican banalities ever uttered, sitting facing one another with their knees towards one another, and their feet on the terrible piece of green-with-red-roses carpet, in the weary centre of the salon. The very sight of it was frightening.

Kate shattered this face-to-face symmetry, and had the two girls, Maria and Concha, assisted by the ironic Juana, carrying off the brown bent-wood chairs and the bamboo stands into one of the spare bedrooms. Juana looked on cynically, and assisted officiously. But when Kate had her trunk, and fished out a couple of light rugs and a couple of fine shawls and a few things to make the place human, the criada began to exclaim:

"*Que bonita! Que bonita, Niña! Mire que bonita!*"

CHAPTER VII

THE PLAZA

SAYULA was a little lake resort; not for the idle rich, for Mexico has a few left; but for tradespeople from Guadalajara, and week-enders. Even of these, these were few.

Nevertheless, there were two hotels, left over, really, from the safe quiet days of Don Porfirio, as were most of the villas. The out-lying villas were shut up, some of them abandoned. Those in the village lived in a perpetual quake of fear. There were many terrors, but the two regnant were bandits and bolshevists.

Bandits are merely men who, in the outlying villages, having very often no money, no work, and no prospects, take to robbery and murder for a time—occasionally for a lifetime—as a profession. They live in their wild villages until troops are sent after them, when they retire into the savage mountains, or the marshes.

Bolshevists, somehow, seem to be born on the railway. Wherever the iron rails run, and passengers are hauled back and forth in railway coaches, there the spirit of rootlessness, of transitoriness, of first and second class in separate compartments, of envy and malice, and of iron and demonish panting engines, seems to bring forth the logical children of materialism, the bolshevists.

Sayula had her little branch of railway, her one train a day. The railway did not pay, and fought with extinction. But it was enough.

Sayula also had that real insanity of America, the automobile. As men used to want a horse and a sword, now they want a car. As women used to pine for a home and a box at the theatre, now it is a "machine." And the poor follow the middle class. There was a perpetual rush of "machines," motor-cars and motor-buses —called camions—along the one forlorn road coming to Sayula from Guadalajara. One hope, one faith, one destiny; to ride in a camion, to own a car.

There was a little bandit scare when Kate arrived in the

village, but she did not pay much heed.   At evening she went into
the plaza, to be with the people.   The plaza was a square with big
trees and a disused bandstand in the centre, a little promenade all
round, and then the cobbled streets where the donkeys and the
camions passed.   There was a further little section of real market-
place, on the north side.

The band played no more in Sayula, and the *elegancia* strolled
no more on the inner pavement around the plaza, under the trees.
But the pavement was still good, and the benches were still more-
or-less sound.   Oh Don Porfirio's day!   And now it was the
peons and Indians, in their blankets and white clothes, who filled
the benches and monopolised the square.   True, the law persisted
that the peons must wear trousers in the plaza, and not the loose
great floppy drawers of the fields.   But then the peons also
wanted to wear trousers, instead of the drawers that were the
garb of their humble labour.

The plaza now belonged to the peons.   They sat thick on the
benches, or slowly strolled round in their sandals and blankets.
Across the cobbled road on the north side, the little booths selling
soup and hot food were crowded with men, after six o'clock;
it was cheaper to eat out, at the end of a day's work.   The
women at home could eat tortillas, never mind the *caldo,* the
soup or the meat mess.   At the booths which sold tequila, men,
women, and boys sat on the benches with their elbows on the
board.   There was a mild gambling game, where the man in
the centre turned the cards, and the plaza rang to his voice:
Cinco de 'spadas!   Rey de Copas!   A large, stout, imperturbable
woman, with a cigarette on her lip and danger in her lowering
black eye, sat on into the night, selling tequila.   The sweet-meat
man stood by his board and sold sweets at one centavo each.
And down on the pavement, small tin torch-lamps flared upon
tiny heaps of mangoes or nauseous tropical red plums, two or
three centavos the little heap, while the vendor, a woman in the
full wave of her skirt, or a man with curious patient humility,
squatted waiting for a purchaser, with that strange fatal indifference and that gentle sort of patience so puzzling to a stranger.
To have thirty cents' worth of little red plums to sell; to pile
them on the pavement in tiny pyramids, five in a pyramid; and
to wait all day and on into the night, squatting on the pavement
and looking up from the feet to the far-off face of the passer-by
and potential purchaser, this, apparently, is an occupation and a

The Plaza

living. At night by the flare of the tin torch, blowing its flame on the wind.

Usually there would be a couple of smallish young men with guitars of different sizes, standing close up facing one another like two fighting cocks that are uttering a long, endless swansong, singing in tense subdued voices the eternal ballads, not very musical, mournful, endless, intense, audible only within close range; keeping on and on till their throats were scraped. And a few tall, dark men in red blankets standing around, listening casually, and rarely, very rarely making a contribution of one centavo.

In among the food booths would be another trio, this time two guitars and a fiddle, and two of the musicians blind; the blind ones singing at a high pitch, full speed, yet not very audible. The very singing seemed secretive, the singers pressing close in, face to face, as if to keep the wild, melancholy ballad re-echoing in their private breasts, their backs to the world.

And the whole village was in the plaza, it was like a camp, with the low, rapid sound of voices. Rarely, very rarely a voice rose above the deep murmur of the men, the musical ripple of the women, the twitter of children. Rarely any quick movement: the slow promenade of men in sandals, the sandals, called huaraches, making a slight cockroach shuffle on the pavement. Sometimes, darting among the trees, bare-legged boys went sky-larking in and out of the shadow, in and out of the quiet people. They were the irrepressible boot-blacks, who swarm like tiresome flies in a bare-footed country.

At the south end of the plaza, just across from the trees and cornerwise to the hotel, was a struggling attempt at an out-door café, with little tables and chairs on the pavement. Here, on week days, the few who dared flaunt their prestige would sit and drink a beer or a glass of tequila. They were mostly strangers. And the peons, sitting immobile on the seats in the background, looked on with basilisk eyes from under the great hats.

But on Saturdays and Sundays there was something of a show. Then the camions and motor-cars came in lurching and hissing. And, like strange birds alighting, you had slim and charming girls in organdie frocks and face powder and bobbed hair, fluttering into the plaza. There they strolled, arm in arm, brilliant in red organdie and blue chiffon and white muslin and pink and mauve and tangerine frail stuffs, their black hair bobbed

out, their dark slim arms interlaced, their dark faces curiously macabre in the heavy make-up; approximating to white, but the white of a clown or a corpse.

In a world of big, handsome peon men, these flappers flapped with butterfly brightness and an incongruous shrillness, manless. The supply of fifis, the male young elegants who are supposed to equate the flappers, was small. But still, fifis there were, in white flannel trousers and white shoes, dark jackets, correct straw hats, and canes. Fifis far more ladylike than the reckless flappers; and far more nervous, wincing. But fifis none the less, gallant, smoking a cigarette with an elegant flourish, talking elegant Castilian, as near as possible, and looking as if they were going to be sacrificed to some Mexican god within a twelvemonth; when they were properly plumped and perfumed. The sacrificial calves being fattened.

On Saturday, the fifis and the flappers and the motor-car people from town—only a forlorn few, after all—tried to be butterfly-gay, in sinister Mexico. They hired the musicians with guitars and fiddle, and the jazz music began to quaver, a little too tenderly, without enough kick.

And on the pavement under the trees of the alameda—under the trees of the plaza, just near the little tables and chairs of the café, the young couples began to gyrate *à la mode*. The red and the pink and the yellow and the blue organdie frocks were turning sharply with all the white flannel trousers available, and some of the white flannel trousers had smart shoes, white with black strappings or with tan brogue bands. And some of the organdie frocks had green legs and green feet, some had legs *à la nature,* and white feet. And the slim, dark arms went around the dark blue fifi shoulders—or dark blue with a white thread. And the immeasurably soft faces of the males would smile with a self-conscious fatherliness at the whitened, pretty, reckless little faces of the females; soft, fatherly, sensuous smiles, suggestive of a victim's luxuriousness.

But they were dancing on the pavement of the plaza, and on this pavement the peons were slowly strolling, or standing in groups watching with black, inscrutable eyes the uncanny butterfly twitching of the dancers. Who knows what they thought?— whether they felt any admiration and envy at all, or only just a silent, cold, dark-faced opposition. Opposition there was.

The young peons in their little white blouses, and the scarlet

serape folded jauntily on one shoulder, strolled slowly on under their big, heavy, poised hats, with a will to ignore the dancers. Slowly, with a heavy, calm balance, they moved irresistibly through the dance, as if the dance did not exist. And the fifis in white trousers, with organdie in their arms, steered as best they might, to avoid the heavy relentless passage of the young peons, who went on talking to one another, smiling and flashing powerful white teeth, in a black, heavy sang-froid that settled like a blight even on the music. The dancers and the passing peons never touched, never jostled. In Mexico you do not run into people accidentally. But the dance broke against the invisible opposition.

The Indians on the seats, they too watched the dancers for a while. Then they turned against them the heavy negation of indifference, like a stone on the spirit. The mysterious faculty of the Indians, as they sit there, so quiet and dense, for killing off any ebullient life, for quenching any light and colourful effervescence.

There was indeed a little native dance-hall. But it was shut apart within four walls. And the whole rhythm and meaning was different, heavy, with a touch of violence. And even there, the dancers were artizans and mechanics or railway-porters, the half-urban people. No peons at all—or practically none.

So, before very long, the organdie butterflies and the flannel-trouser fifis gave in, succumbed, crushed once more beneath the stone-heavy passivity of resistance in the demonish peons.

The curious, radical opposition of the Indians to the thing we call the spirit. It is spirit which makes the flapper flap her organdie wings like a butterfly. It is spirit, which creases the white flannel trousers of the fifi and makes him cut his rather pathetic dash. They try to talk the elegancies and flippancies of the modern spirit.

But down on it all, like a weight of obsidian, comes the passive negation of the Indian. He understands soul, which is of the blood. But spirit, which is superior, and is the quality of our civilisation, this, in the mass, he darkly and barbarically repudiates. Not until he becomes an artizan or connected with machinery does the modern spirit get him.

And perhaps it is this ponderous repudiation of the modern spirit which makes Mexico what it is.

But perhaps the automobile will make roads even through the inaccessible soul of the Indian.

Kate was rather sad, seeing the dance swamped. She had been sitting at a little table, with Juana for dueña, sipping a glass of absinthe.

The motor-cars returning to town left early, in a little group. If bandits were out, they had best keep together. Even the fifis had a pistol on their hips.

But it was Saturday, so some of the younger "elegance" was staying on, till the next day; to bathe and flutter in the sun.

It was Saturday, so the plaza was very full, and along the cobble streets stretching from the square, many torches fluttered and wavered upon the ground, illuminating a dark salesman and an array of straw hats, or a heap of straw mats called petates, or pyramids of oranges from across the lake.

It was Saturday, and Sunday morning was market. So, as it were suddenly, the life in the plaza was dense and heavy with potency. The Indians had come in from all the villages, and from far across the lake. And with them they brought the curious heavy potency of life which seems to hum deeper and deeper when they collect together.

In the afternoon, with the wind from the south, the big canoes, sailing-boats with black hulls and one huge sail, had come drifting across the waters, bringing the market-produce and the natives to their gathering ground. All the white specks of villages on the far shore, and on the far-off slopes, had sent their wild quota to the throng.

It was Saturday, and the Indian instinct for living on into the night, once they are gathered together, was now aroused. The people did not go home. Though market would begin at dawn, men had no thought of sleep.

At about nine o'clock, after the fifi dance was shattered, Kate heard a new sound, the sound of a drum, or tom-tom, and saw a drift of the peons away to the dark side of the plaza, where the side market would open to-morrow. Already places had been taken, and little stalls set up, and huge egg-shaped baskets, big enough to hold two men, were lolling against the wall.

There was a rippling and a pulse-like thudding of the drum, strangely arresting on the night air, then the long note of a flute playing a sort of wild, unemotional melody, with the drum for a syncopated rhythm. Kate, who had listened to the drums and the wild singing of the Red Indians in Arizona and New Mexico, instantly felt that timeless, primeval passion of the prehistoric

races, with their intense and complicated religious significance, spreading on the air.

She looked inquiringly at Juana, and Juana's black eyes glanced back at her furtively.

"What is it?" said Kate.

"Musicians, singers," said Juana evasively.

"But it's *different*," said Kate.

"Yes, it is new."

"New?"

"Yes, it has only been coming for a short time."

"Where does it come from?"

"Who knows!" said Juana, with an evasive shrug of her shoulders.

"I want to hear," said Kate.

"It's purely men," said Juana.

"Still, one can stand a little way off."

Kate moved towards the dense, silent throng of men in big hats. They all had their backs to her.

She stood on the step of one of the houses, and saw a little clearing at the centre of the dense throng of men, under the stone wall over which bougainvillea and plumbago flowers were hanging, lit up by the small, brilliantly flaring torches of sweet-smelling wood, which a boy held in his two hands.

The drum was in the centre of the clearing, the drummer standing facing the crowd. He was naked from the waist up, wore snow-white cotton drawers, very full, held round the waist by a red sash, and bound at the ankles with red cords. Round his uncovered head was a red cord, with three straight scarlet feathers rising from the back of his head, and on his forehead, a turquoise ornament, a circle of blue with a round blue stone in the centre. The flute player was also naked to the waist, but over his shoulder was folded a fine white serape with blue-and-dark edges, and fringe. Among the crowd, men with naked shoulders were giving little leaflets to the onlookers. And all the time, high and pure, the queer clay flute was repeating a savage, rather difficult melody, and the drum was giving the blood-rhythm.

More and more men were drifting in from the plaza. Kate stepped from her perch and went rather shyly forward. She wanted one of the papers. The man gave her one without looking at her. And she went into the light to read. It was a sort of ballad, but without rhyme, in Spanish. At the top of the leaflet

was a rough print of an eagle within the ring of a serpent that
had its tail in its mouth; a curious deviation from the Mexican
emblem, which is an eagle standing on an opal, a cactus with great
flat leaves, and holding in its beak and claws a writhing snake.

This eagle stood slim upon the serpent, within the circle of the
snake, that had black markings round its back, like short black rays
pointing inwards.   At a little distance, the emblem suggested an eye.

"In the place of the west
In peace, beyond the lashing of the sun's bright tail,
In the stillness where waters are born
Slept I, Quetzalcoatl.

In the cave which is called Dark Eye,
Behind the sun, looking through him as a window
Is the place.   There the waters rise,
There the winds are born.

On the waters of the after-life
I rose again, to see a star falling, and feel a breath on my face.
The breath said: Go!   And lo!
I am coming.

The star that was falling was fading, was dying.
I heard the star singing like a dying bird;
My name is Jesus, I am Mary's Son.
I am coming home.
My mother the Moon is dark.
Oh brother, Quetzalcoatl
Hold back the dragon of the sun,
Bind him with shadow while I pass
Homewards.   Let me come home.

I bound the bright fangs of the Sun
And held him while Jesus passed
Into the lidless shade,
Into the eye of the Father,
Into the womb of refreshment.

And the breath blew upon me again.
So I took the sandals of the Saviour
And started down the long slope
Past the mount of the sun.
Till I saw beneath me
White breast-tips of my Mexico
My bride.

Jesus the Crucified
Sleeps in the healing waters
The long sleep.
Sleep, sleep, my brother, sleep.
My bride between the seas
Is combing her dark hair,
Saying to herself: Quetzalcoatl."

There was a dense throng of men gathered now, and from the centre, the ruddy glow of ocote torches rose warm and strong, and the sweet scent of the cedar-like resin was on the air. Kate could see nothing, for the mass of men in big hats.

The flute had stopped its piping, and the drum was beating a slow, regular thud, acting straight on the blood. The incomprehensible hollow barking of the drum was like a spell on the mind, making the heart burst each stroke, and darkening the will.

The men in the crowd began to subside, sitting and squatting on the ground, with their hats between their knees. And now it was a little sea of dark, proud heads leaning a little forward above the soft, strong male shoulders.

Near the wall was a clear circle, with the drum in the centre. The drummer with the naked torso stood tilting his drum towards him, his shoulders gleaming smooth and ruddy in the flare of light. Beside him stood another man holding a banner that hung from a light rod. On the blue field of the banneret was the yellow sun with a black centre, and between the four greater yellow rays, four black rays emerging, so that the sun looked like a wheel spinning with a dazzling motion.

The crowd having all sat down, the six men with naked torsos, who had been giving out the leaflets and ordering the crowd, now came back and sat down in a ring, of which the drummer, with the drum tilted between his knees as he squatted on the ground, was the key. On his right hand sat the banner-bearer, on his left the flautist. They were nine men in the ring, the boy, who sat apart watching the two ocote torches, which he had laid upon a stone supported on a long cane tripod, being the tenth.

The night seemed to have gone still. The curious seed-rattling hum of voices that filled the plaza was hushed. Under the trees, on the pavements, people were still passing unconcerned, but they looked curiously lonely, isolated figures drifting in the twilight of the electric lamps, and going about some exceptional business. They seemed outside the nucleus of life.

Away on the north side, the booths were still flaring, people were buying and selling. But this quarter too, looked lonely, and outside the actual reality, almost like memory.

When the men sat down, the women began to drift up shyly, and seat themselves on the ground at the outer rim, their full cotton skirts flowering out around them, and their dark rebozos drawn tight over their small, round, shy heads, as they squatted on the ground. Some, too shy to come right up, lingered on the nearest benches of the plaza. And some had gone away. Indeed, a good many men and women had disappeared as soon as the drum was heard.

So that the plaza was curiously void. There was the dense clot of people round the drum, and then the outer world, seeming empty and hostile. Only in the dark little street that gave on to the darkness of the lake, people were standing like ghosts, half lit-up, the men with their serapes over their faces, watching erect and silent and concealed, from the shadow.

But Kate, standing back in the doorway, with Juana sitting on the doorstep at her feet, was fascinated by the silent, half-naked ring of men in the torchlight. Their heads were black, their bodies soft and ruddy with the peculiar Indian beauty that has at the same time something terrible in it. The soft, full, handsome torsos of silent men with heads softly bent a little forward: the soft, easy shoulders, that are yet so broad, and which balance upon so powerful a backbone; shoulders drooping a little, with the relaxation of slumbering, quiescent power; the beautiful ruddy skin, gleaming with a dark fineness; the strong breasts, so male and so deep, yet without the muscular hardening that belongs to white men; and the dark, closed faces, closed upon a darkened consciousness, the black moustaches and delicate beards framing the closed silence of the mouth; all this was strangely impressive, moving strange, frightening emotions in the soul. Those men who sat there in their dark, physical tenderness, so still and soft, they looked at the same time frightening. Something dark, heavy, and reptilian in their silence and their softness. Their very naked torsos were clothed with a subtle shadow, a certain secret obscurity. White men sitting there would have been strong-muscled and frank, with an openness in their very physique, a certain ostensible presence. But not so these men. Their very nakedness only revealed the soft, heavy depths of their natural secrecy, their eter-

nal invisibility. They did not belong to the realm of that which comes forth.

Everybody was quite still; the expectant hush deepened to a kind of dead, night silence. The naked-shouldered men sat motionless, sunk into themselves, and listening with the dark ears of the blood. The red sash went tight round their waists, the wide white trousers, starched rather stiff, were bound round the ankles with red cords, and the dark feet in the glare of the torch looked almost black, in huaraches that had red thongs. What did they want then, in life, these men who sat so softly and without any assertion, yet whose weight was so ponderous, arresting?

Kate was at once attracted and repelled. She was attracted, almost fascinated by the strange *nuclear* power of the men in the circle. It was like a darkly glowing, vivid nucleus of new life. Repellent the strange heaviness, the sinking of the spirit into the earth, like dark water. Repellent the silent, dense opposition to the pale-faced spiritual direction.

Yet here and here alone, it seemed to her, life burned with a deep new fire. The rest of life, as she knew it, seemed wan, bleached and sterile. The pallid wanness and weariness of her world! And here, the dark, ruddy figures in the glare of a torch, like the centre of the everlasting fire, surely this was a new kindling of mankind!

She knew it was so. Yet she preferred to be on the fringe, sufficiently out of contact. She could not bear to come into actual contact.

The man with the banner of the sun lifted his face as if he were going to speak. And yet he did not speak. He was old; in his sparse beard were grey hairs, grey hairs over his thick dark mouth. And his face had the peculiar thickness, with a few deep-scored lines, of the old among these people. Yet his hair rose vigorous and manly from his forehead, his body was smooth and strong. Only, perhaps, a little smoother, heavier, softer than the shoulders of the younger men.

His black eyes gazed sightless for some time. Perhaps he was really blind; perhaps it was a heavy abstraction, a sort of heavy memory working in him, which made his face seem sightless.

Then he began, in a slow, clear, far-off voice, that seemed strangely to echo the vanished barking of the drum:

"Listen to me, men! Listen to me, women of these men! A

long time ago, the lake started calling for men, in the quiet of the night. And there were no men. The little charales were swimming round the shore, looking for something, and the bágari and the other big fish would jump out of the water, to look around. But there were no men.

"So one of the gods with hidden faces walked out of the water, and climbed the hill—" he pointed with his hand in the night towards the invisible round hill at the back of the village—"and looked about. He looked up at the sun, and through the sun he saw the dark sun, the same that made the sun and the world, and will swallow it again like a draught of water.

"He said: *Is it time?* And from behind the bright sun the four dark arms of the greater sun shot out, and in the shadow men arose. They could see the four dark arms of the sun in the sky. And they started walking.

"The man on the top of the hill, who was a god, looked at the mountains and the flat places, and saw men very thirsty, their tongues hanging out. So he said to them: Come! Come here! Here is my sweet water!

"They came like dogs running with their tongues out, and kneeled on the shore of the lake. And the man on the top of the hill heard them panting with having drunk much water. He said to them: Have you drunk too much with yourselves? Are your bones not dry enough?

"The men made houses on the shore, and the man on the hill, who was a god, taught them to sow maize and beans, and build boats. But he said to them: No boat will save you, when the dark sun ceases to hold out his dark arms abroad in the sky.

"The man on the hill said: I am Quetzalcoatl, who breathed moisture on your dry mouths. I filled your breasts with breath from beyond the sun. I am the wind that whirls from the heart of the earth, the little winds that whirl like snakes round your feet and your legs and your thighs, lifting up the head of the snake of your body, in whom is your power. When the snake of your body lifts its head, beware! It is I, Quetzalcoatl, rearing up in you, rearing up and reaching beyond the bright day, to the sun of darkness beyond, where is your home at last. Save for the dark sun at the back of the day-sun, save for the four dark arms in the heavens, you were bone, and the stars were bone, and the moon an empty sea-shell on a dry beach, and the yellow sun were an empty cup, like the dry thin bone of a dead coyote's head. So beware!

"Without me you are nothing. Just as I, without the sun that is back of the sun, am nothing.

"When the yellow sun is high in the sky, then say: Quetzalcoatl will lift his hand and screen me from this, else I shall burn out, and the land will wither.

"For, say I, in the palm of my hand is the water of life, and on the back of my hand is the shadow of death. And when men forget me, I lift the back of my hand, farewell! Farewell, and the shadow of death.

"But men forgot me. Their bones were moist, their hearts weak. When the snake of their body lifted its head, they said: This is the tame snake that does as we wish. And when they could not bear the fire of the sun, they said: The sun is angry. He wants to drink us up. Let us give him blood of victims.

"And so it was, the dark branches of shade were gone from heaven, and Quetzalcoatl mourned and grew old, holding his hand before his face, to hide his face from men.

"He mourned and said: Let me go home. I am old, I am almost bone. Bone triumphs in me, my heart is a dry gourd. I am weary in Mexico.

"So he cried to the Master-Sun, the dark one, of the unuttered name: I am withering white like a perishing gourd-vine. I am turning to bone. I am denied of these Mexicans. I am waste and weary and old. Take me away.

"Then the dark sun reached an arm, and lifted Quetzalcoatl into the sky. And the dark sun beckoned with a finger, and brought white men out of the east. And they came with a dead god on the Cross, saying: Lo! This is the Son of God! He is dead, he is bone! Lo, your god is bled and dead, he is bone. Kneel and sorrow for him, and weep. For your tears he will give you comfort again, from the dead, and a place among the scentless rose-trees of the after-life, when you are dead.

"Lo! His mother weeps, and the waters of the world are in her hands. She will give you drink, and heal you, and lead you to the land of God. In the land of God you shall weep no more. Beyond the gates of death, when you have passed from the house of bone, into the garden of white roses.

"So the weeping Mother brought her Son who was dead on the Cross to Mexico, to live in the temples. And the people looked up no more, saying: The Mother weeps. The Son of her womb is bone. Let us hope for the place of the west, where the dead

have peace among the scentless rose-trees, in the Paradise of God.

"For the priests would say: It is beautiful beyond the grave.

"And then the priests grew old, and the tears of the Mother were exhausted, and the Son on the Cross cried out to the dark sun far beyond the sun: *What is this that is done to me? Am I dead for ever, and only dead? Am I always and only dead, but bone on a Cross of bone?*

"So this cry was heard in the world, and beyond the stars of the night, and beyond the sun of the day.

"Jesus said again: *Is it time? My Mother is old like a sinking moon, the old bone of her can weep no more. Are we perished beyond redeem?*

"Then the greatest of the great suns spoke aloud from the back of the sun: I will take my Son to my bosom, I will take His Mother on my lap. Like a woman I will put them in My womb, like a mother I will lay them to sleep, in mercy I will dip them in the bath of forgetting and peace and renewal.

"That is all. So hear now, you men, and you women of these men.

"Jesus is going home, to the Father, and Mary is going back, to sleep in the belly of the Father. And they both will recover from death, during the long long sleep.

"But the Father will not leave us alone. We are not abandoned.

"The Father has looked around, and has seen the Morning Star, fearless between the rushing of the oncoming yellow sun, and the backward reel of the night. So the Great One, whose name has never been spoken, says: Who art thou, bright watchman? And the down-star answering: It is I, the Morning Star, who in Mexico was Quetzalcoatl. It is I, who look at the yellow sun from behind, have my eye on the unseen side of the moon. It is I, the star, midway between the darkness and the rolling of the sun. I, called Quetzalcoatl, waiting in the strength of my days.

"The Father answered: It is well. It is well. And again: It is time.

"Thus the big word was spoken behind the back of the world. The Nameless said: It is time.

"Once more the word has been spoken: It is time.

"Listen, men, and the women of men: It is time. Know now it is time. Those that left us are coming back. Those that came are leaving again. Say welcome, and then farewell!

"Welcome! Farewell!"

The old man ended with a strong, suppressed cry, as if really calling to the gods:

"Bienvenido! Bienvenido! Adios! Adios!"

Even Juana, seated at Kate's feet, cried out without knowing what she did:

"Bienvenido! Bienvenido! Adios! Adios! Adios-n!"

On the last adios! she trailed out to a natural human "n."

The drum began to beat with an insistent, intensive rhythm, and the flute, or whistle, lifted its odd, far-off calling voice. It was playing again and again the peculiar melody Kate had heard at first.

Then one of the men in the circle lifted his voice, and began to sing the hymn. He sang in the fashion of the Old Red Indians, with intensity and restraint, singing inwardly, singing to his own soul, not outward to the world, nor yet even upward to God, as the Christians sing. But with a sort of suppressed, tranced intensity, singing to the inner mystery, singing not into space, but into the other dimension of man's existence, where he finds himself in the infinite room that lies inside the axis of our wheeling space. Space, like the world, cannot but move. And like the world, there is an axis. And the axis of our worldly space, when you enter, is a vastness where even the trees come and go, and the soul is at home in its own dream, noble and unquestioned.

The strange, inward pulse of the drum, and the singer singing inwardly, swirled the soul back into the very centre of time, which is older than age. He began on a high, remote note, and holding the voice at a distance, ran on in subtle, running rhythms, apparently unmeasured, yet pulsed underneath by the drum, and giving throbbing, three-fold lilts and lurches. For a long time, no melody at all was recognisable: it was just a lurching, running, far-off crying, something like the distant faint howling of a coyote. It was really the music of the old American Indian.

There was no recognisable rhythm, no recognisable emotion, it was hardly music. Rather a far-off, perfect crying in the night. But it went straight through to the soul, the most ancient and everlasting soul of all men, where alone can the human family assemble in immediate contact.

Kate knew it at once, like a sort of fate. It was no good resisting. There was neither urge nor effort, nor any speciality. The sound sounded in the innermost far-off place of the human core, the ever-present, where there is neither hope nor emotion, but

passion sits with folded wings on the nest, and faith is a tree of shadow.

Like fate, like doom. Faith is the Tree of Life itself, inevitable, and the apples are upon us, like the apples of the eye, the apples of the chin, the apple of the heart, the apples of the breast, the apple of the belly, with its deep core, the apples of the loins, the apples of the knees, the little, side-by-side apples of the toes. What do change and evolution matter? We are the Tree with the fruit forever upon it. And we are faith forever. Verbum Sap.

The one singer had finished, and only the drum kept on, touching the sensitive membrane of the night subtly and knowingly. Then a voice in the circle rose again on the song, and like birds flying from a tree, one after the other, the individual voices arose, till there was a strong, intense, curiously weighty soaring and sweeping of male voices, like a dark flock of birds flying and dipping in unison. And all the dark birds seemed to have launched out of the heart, in the inner forest of the masculine chest.

And one by one, voices in the crowd broke free, like birds launching and coming in from a distance, caught by the spell. The words did not matter. Any verse, any words, no words, the song remained the same: a strong, deep wind rushing from the caverns of the breast, from the everlasting soul! Kate herself was too shy and wincing to sing: too blenched with disillusion. But she heard the answer away back in her soul, like a far-off mocking-bird at night. And Juana was singing in spite of herself, in a crooning feminine voice, making up the words unconsciously.

The half-naked men began to reach for their serapes: white serapes, with borders of blue and earth-brown bars, and dark fringe. A man rose from the crowd and went towards the lake. He came back with ocote and with faggots that a boat had brought over. And he started a little fire. After a while, another man went for fuel, and started another fire in the centre of the circle, in front of the drum. Then one of the women went off soft and barefoot, in her full cotton skirt. And she made a little bonfire among the women.

The air was bronze with the glow of flame, and sweet with smoke like incense. The song rose and fell, then died away. Rose, and died. The drum ebbed on, faintly touching the dark membrane of the night. Then ebbed away. In the abso-

lute silence could be heard the soundless stillness of the dark lake.

Then the drum started again, with a new, strong pulse. One of the seated men, in his white poncho with the dark blackish-and-blue border, got up, taking off his sandals as he did so, and began softly to dance the dance step. Mindless, dancing heavily and with a curious bird-like sensitiveness of the feet, he began to tread the earth with his bare soles, as if treading himself deep into the earth. Alone, with a curious pendulum rhythm, leaning a little forward from a powerful backbone, he trod to the drum-beat, his white knees lifting and lifting alternately against the dark fringe of his blanket, with a queer dark splash. And another man put his huaraches into the centre of the ring, near the fire, and stood up to dance. The man at the drum lifted up his voice in a wild, blind song. The men were taking off their ponchos. And soon, with the firelight on their breasts and on their darkly abstracted faces, they were all afoot, with bare torsos and bare feet, dancing the savage bird-tread.

"Who sleeps shall wake! Who sleeps shall wake! Who treads down the path of the snake in the dust shall arrive at the place; in the path of the dust shall arrive at the place and be dressed in the skin of the snake: shall be dressed in the skin of the snake of the earth, that is father of stone; that is father of stone and the timber of earth; of the silver and gold, of the iron, the timber of earth from the bone of the father of earth, of the snake of the world, of the heart of the world, that beats as a snake beats the dust in its motion on earth, from the heart of the world.

"Who slee-eeps, sha-all wake! Who slee-eeps, sha-all wake! Who sleeps, sha-ll wake in the way of the snake of the dust of the earth, of the stone of the earth, of the bone of the earth."

The song seemed to take new wild flights, after it had sunk and rustled to a last ebb. It was like waves that rise out of the invisible, and rear up into form and a flying, disappearing whiteness and a rustle of extinction. And the dancers, after dancing in a circle in a slow, deep absorption, each man changeless in his own place, treading the same dust with the soft churning of bare feet, slowly, slowly began to revolve, till the circle was slowly revolving round the fire, with always the same soft, down-sinking, churning tread. And the drum kept the changeless living beat, like a heart, and the song rose and soared and fell, ebbed and ebbed to a sort of extinction, then heaved up again.

Till the young peons could stand it no more. They put off

their sandals and their hats and their blankets, and shyly, with inexpert feet that yet knew the old echo of the tread, they stood behind the wheeling dancers, and danced without changing place. Till soon the revolving circle had a fixed yet throbbing circle of men outside.

Then suddenly one of the naked-shouldered dancers from the inner circle stepped back into the outer circle and with a slow leaning, slowly started the outer circle revolving in the reverse direction from the inner. So now there were two wheels of the dance, one within the other, and revolving in different directions.

They kept on and on, with the drum and the song, revolving like wheels of shadow-shapes around the fire. Till the fires died low, and the drum suddenly stopped, and the men suddenly dispersed, returning to their seats again.

There was silence, then the low hum of voices and the sound of laughter. Kate had thought, so often, that the laughter of the peons broke from them in a sound almost like pain. But now the laughs came like little invisible flames, suddenly from the embers of the talk.

Everybody was waiting, waiting. Yet nobody moved at once, when the thud of the drum struck again like a summons. They sat still talking, listening with a second consciousness. Then a man arose and threw off his blanket, and threw wood on the central fire. Then he walked through the seated men to where the women clustered in the fullness of their skirts. There he waited, smiling with a look of abstraction. Till a girl rose and came with utmost shyness towards him, holding her rebozo tight over her lowered head with her right hand, and taking the hand of the man in her left. It was she who lifted the motionless hand of the man in her own, shyly, with a sudden shy snatching. He laughed, and led her through the now risen men, towards the inner fire. She went with dropped head, hiding her face in confusion. But side by side and loosely holding hands, they began to tread the soft, heavy dance-step, forming the first small segment of the inner, stationary circle.

And now all the men were standing facing outwards, waiting to be chosen. And the women quickly, their shawled heads hidden, were slipping in and picking up the loose right hand of the man of their choice. The inner men with the naked shoulders were soon chosen. The inner circle, of men and women in pairs, hand in hand, was closing.

"Come, Niña, come!" said Juana, looking up at Kate with black, gleaming eyes.

"I am afraid!" said Kate. And she spoke the truth.

One of the bare-breasted men had come across the street, out of the crowd, and was standing waiting, near the doorway in which Kate stood, silently, with averted face.

"Look! Niña! This master is waiting for you. Then come! Oh Niña, come!"

The voice of the criada had sunk to the low, crooning, almost magical appeal of the women of the people, and her black eyes glistened strangely, watching Kate's face. Kate, almost mesmerised, took slow, reluctant steps forward, towards the man who was standing with averted face.

"Do you mind?" she said in English, in great confusion. And she touched his fingers with her own.

His hand, warm and dark and savagely suave, loosely, almost with indifference, and yet with the soft barbaric nearness, held her fingers, and he led her to the circle. She dropped her head, and longed to be able to veil her face. In her white dress and green straw hat, she felt a virgin again, a young virgin. This was the quality these men had been able to give back to her.

Shyly, awkwardly, she tried to tread the dance-step. But in her shoes she felt inflexible, insulated, and the rhythm was not in her. She moved in confusion.

But the man beside her held her hand in the same light, soft grasp, and the slow, pulsing pendulum of his body swayed untrammelled. He took no notice of her. And yet he held her fingers in his soft, light touch.

Juana had discarded her boots and stockings, and with her dark, creased face like a mask of obsidian, her eyes gleaming with the timeless female flame, dark and unquenchable, she was treading the step of the dance.

"As the bird of the sun treads the earth at the dawn of the day like a brown hen under his feet, like a hen and the branches of her belly droop with the apples of birth, with the eggs of gold, with the eggs that hide the globe of the sun in the waters of heaven, in the purse of the shell of earth that is white from the fire of the blood, tread the earth, and the earth will conceive like the hen 'neath the feet of the bird of the sun; 'neath the feet of the heart, 'neath the heart's twin feet. Tread the earth, tread the earth that squats as a pullet with wings closed in—"

The circle began to shift, and Kate was slowly moving round between two silent and absorbed men, whose arms touched her arms. And the one held her fingers softly, loosely, but with transcendent nearness. And the wild song rose again like a bird that has alighted for a second, and the drum changed rhythm incomprehensibly.

The outer wheel was all men. She seemed to feel the strange dark glow of them upon her back. Men, dark, collective men, non-individual. And herself woman, wheeling upon the great wheel of womanhood.

Men and women alike danced with faces lowered and expressionless, abstract, gone in the deep absorption of men into the greater manhood, women into the greater womanhood. It was sex, but the greater, not the lesser sex. The waters over the earth wheeling upon the waters under the earth, like an eagle silently wheeling above its own shadow.

She felt her sex and her womanhood caught up and identified in the slowly revolving ocean of nascent life, the dark sky of the men lowering and wheeling above. She was not herself, she was gone, and her own desires were gone in the ocean of the great desire. As the man whose fingers touched hers was gone in the ocean that is male, stooping over the face of the waters.

The slow, vast, soft-touching revolution of the ocean above upon ocean below, with no vestige of rustling or foam. Only the pure sliding conjunction. Herself gone into her greater self, her womanhood consummated in the greater womanhood. And where her fingers touched the fingers of the man, the quiet spark, like the dawn-star, shining between her and the greater manhood of men.

How strange, to be merged in desire beyond desire, to be gone in the body beyond the individualism of the body, with the spark of contact lingering like a morning star between her and the man, her woman's greater self, and the greater self of man. Even of the two men next to her. What a beautiful slow wheel of dance, two great streams streaming in contact, in opposite directions.

She did not know the face of the man whose fingers she held. Her personal eyes had gone blind, his face was the face of dark heaven, only the touch of his fingers a star that was both hers and his.

Her feet were feeling the way into the dance-step. She was beginning to learn softly to loosen her weight, to loosen the uplift

of all her life, and let it pour slowly, darkly, with an ebbing gush, rhythmical in soft, rhythmic gushes from her feet into the dark body of the earth. Erect, strong like a staff of life, yet to loosen all the sap of her strength and let it flow down into the roots of the earth.

She had lost count of time. But the dance of itself seemed to be wheeling to a close, though the rhythm remained exactly the same to the end.

The voice finished singing, only the drum kept on. Suddenly the drum gave a rapid little shudder, and there was silence. And immediately the hands were loosened, the dance broke up into fragments. The man gave her a quick, far-off smile and was gone. She would never know him by sight. But by presence she might know him.

The women slipped apart, clutching their rebozos tight round their shoulders. The men hid themselves in their blankets. And Kate turned to the darkness of the lake.

"Already you are going, Niña?" came Juana's voice of mild, aloof disappointment.

"I must go now," said Kate hurriedly.

And she hastened towards the dark of the lake, Juana running behind her with shoes and stockings in her hand.

Kate wanted to hurry home with her new secret, the strange secret of her greater womanhood, that she could not get used to. She would not look at her watch. She would lay her watch face down to hide its phosphorous figures. She would not be timed.

She hastened along the uneven path of the edge of the lake shore, that lay dark in shadow, though the stars gave enough light to show the dark bulks and masts of the sailing-canoes against the downy obscurity of the water. Night, timeless, hourless night! She would not look at her watch. She would lay her watch face down, to hide its phosphorous figures. She would not be timed.

And as she sank into sleep, she could hear the drum again, like a pulse inside a stone beating.

CHAPTER VIII

NIGHT IN THE HOUSE

OVER the gateway of Kate's house was a big tree called a cuenta tree, because it dropped its fruits, that were little, round, hard balls like little dark marbles, perfect in shape. for the natives to gather up and string for beads, cuentas, or more particularly, for the Pater Noster beads of the rosary. At night, the little road outside was quite dark, and the dropping of the cuentas startled the silence.

The nights, which at first had seemed perfectly friendly, began to be full of terrors. Fear had risen again. A band of robbers had gathered in one of the outlying villages on the lake, a village where the men had bad characters, as being ready to turn bandit at any moment. And this gang, invisible in the daytime, consisting during the day of lake fishermen and labourers on the land, at night would set off on horseback to sack any lonely, or insufficiently-protected house.

Then the fact that a gang of bandits was out always set the isolated thieves and scoundrels in action. Whatever happened, it would be attributed to the bandits. And so, many an unsuspected, seemingly honest man, with the old lust in his soul, would steal out by night with his machete and perhaps a pistol, to put his fingers in the pie of the darkness.

And again Kate felt the terror clot and thicken in the black silence of the Mexican night, till the sound of a cuenta falling was terrible. She would lie and listen to the thickening darkness. A little way off would sound the long, shrill whistle of the police watch. And in a while, the police patrol, on horseback, would go clattering lightly by. But the police in most countries are never present save where there is no trouble.

The rainy season was coming, and the night-wind rose from the lake, making strange noises in the trees, and shaking the many loose doors of the house. The servants were away in their distant recess. And in Mexico. at night, each little distance isolates itself absolutely, like a man in a black cloak turning his back.

In the morning, Juana would appear from the plaza, her eyes blob-like and inky, and the old, weary, monkey look of subjection to fear, settled on her bronze face. A race old in subjection to fear, and unable to shake it off. She would immediately begin to pour forth to Kate, in a babbling, half intelligent stream, some story of a house broken into and a woman stabbed. And she would say, the owner of the hotel had sent word that it was not safe for Kate to sleep alone in the house. She must go to the hotel to sleep.

The whole village was in that state of curious, reptile apprehension which comes over dark people. A panic fear, a sense of devilment and horror thick in the night air. When blue morning came they would cheer up. But at night, like clotting blood the air would begin to thicken again.

The fear, of course, was communicated from one person to another. Kate was sure that if Juana and her family had not been huddled in reptile terror away at the far end of the house, she herself would have been unafraid. As it was, Juana was like a terror-stricken lizard.

There was no man about the place. Juana had two sons, Jesús, who was about twenty, and Ezequiel, about seventeen. But Jesús —she pronounced it *Hezoosn*—ran the little gasoline motor for the electric light, and he and Ezequiel slept together on the floor of the little engine house. So that Juana huddled with her two girls, Concha and Maria, in the den at the end of Kate's house, and seemed to sweat a rank odour of fear.

The village was submerged. Usually the plaza kept alive till ten o'clock, with the charcoal fires burning and the ice-cream man going round with his bucket on his head, endlessly crying: *Nieve! Nieve!* and the people gossiping on the streets or listening to the young men with guitars.

Now, by nine o'clock, the place was deserted, curiously stony and vacuous. And the Jefe sent out the order that anybody in the streets after ten o'clock would be arrested.

Kate hurried to her house and locked herself in. It is not easy to withstand the panic fear of a black-eyed, semi-barbaric people. The thing communicates itself like some drug on the air, wringing the heart and paralysing the soul with a sense of evil; black, horrible evil.

She would lie in her bed in the absolute dark: the electric light was cut off completely, everywhere, at ten o'clock, and primitive

darkness reigned. And she could feel the demonish breath of evil moving on the air in waves.

She thought of the grisly stories of the country, which she had heard. And she thought again of the people, outwardly so quiet, so nice, with a gentle smile. But even Humboldt had said of the Mexicans, that few people had such a gentle smile, and at the same time, such fierce eyes. It was not that their eyes were exactly fierce. But their blackness was inchoate, with a dagger of white light in it. And in the inchoate blackness the blood-lust might arise, out of the sediment of the uncreated past.

Uncreated, half-created, such a people was at the mercy of old black influences that lay in a sediment at the bottom of them. While they were quiet, they were gentle and kindly, with a sort of limp naïveté. But when anything shook them at the depths, the black clouds would arise, and they were gone again in the old grisly passions of death, blood-lust, incarnate hate. A people incomplete, and at the mercy of old, upstarting lusts.

Somewhere at the bottom of their souls, she felt, was a fathomless resentment, like a raw wound. The heavy, bloody-eyed resentment of men who have never been able to win a soul for themselves, never been able to win themselves a nucleus, an individual integrity out of the chaos of passions and potencies and death. They are caught in the toils of old lusts and old activities as in the folds of a black serpent that strangles the heart. The heavy, evil-smelling weight of an unconquered past.

And under this weight they live and die, not really sorry to die. Clogged and tangled in the elements, never able to extricate themselves. Blackened under a too-strong sun, surcharged with the heavy sundering electricity of the Mexican air, and tormented by the bubbling of volcanoes away below the feet. The tremendous potent elements of the American continent, that give men powerful bodies, but which weigh the soul down and prevent its rising into birth. Or, if a man arrives with a soul, the maleficent elements gradually break it, gradually, till he decomposes into ideas and mechanistic activities, in a body full of mechanical energy, but with his blood-soul dead and putrescent.

So these men, unable to overcome the elements, men held down by the serpent tangle of sun and electricity and volcanic emission, they are subject to an ever-recurring, fathomless lust of resentment, a demonish hatred of life itself. Then, the instriking thud of a heavy knife, stabbing into a living body, this is the best

No lust of women can equal that lust. The clutching throb of gratification as the knife strikes in and the blood spurts out!

It is the inevitable supreme gratification of a people entangled in the past, and unable to extricate itself. A people that has never been redeemed, that has not known a Saviour.

For Jesus is no Saviour to the Mexicans. He is a dead god in their tomb. As a miner who is entombed underground by the collapsing of the earth in the gangways, so do whole nations become entombed under the slow subsidence of their past. Unless there comes some Saviour, some Redeemer to drive a new way out, to the sun.

But the white men brought no salvation to Mexico. On the contrary, they find themselves at last shut in the tomb along with their dead god and the conquered race.

Which is the *status quo*.

Kate lay and thought hard, in the black night. At the same time, she was listening intensely, with a clutch of horror. She could not control her heart. It seemed wrenched out of place, and really hurt her. She was, as she had never been before, absolutely physically afraid, blood afraid. Her blood was wrenched in a paralysis of fear.

In England, in Ireland, during the war and the revolution she had known *spiritual* fear. The ghastly fear of the rabble: and during the war, nations were nearly all rabble. The terror of the rabble that, mongrel-like, wanted to break the free *spirit* in individual men and women. It was the cold, collective lust of millions of people, to break the spirit in the outstanding individuals. They wanted to break this spirit, so that they could start the great downhill rush back to old underworld levels, old gold worship and murder lust. The rabble.

In those days, Kate had known the agony of cold social fear, as if a democracy were a huge, huge cold centipede which, if you resisted it, would dig every claw into you. And the flesh would mortify around every claw.

That had been her worst agony of fear. And she had survived.

Now she knew the real heart-wrench of blood fear. Her heart seemed pulled out of place, in a stretched pain.

She dozed, and wakened suddenly, at a small noise. She sat up in bed. Her doors on to the verandah had shutters. The doors themselves were fastened, but the shutters were open for

air, leaving the upper space, like the window of the door, open. And against the dark grey of the night she saw what looked like a black cat crouching on the bottom of the panel-space.

"What is that?" she said automatically.

Instantly, the thing moved, slid away, and she knew it was the arm of a man that had been reaching inside to pull the bolt of the door. She lay for a second paralysed, prepared to scream. There was no movement. So she leaned and lit a candle.

The curious panic fear was an agony to her. It paralysed her and wrenched her heart out of place. She lay prostrate in the anguish of night-terror. The candle blazed duskily. There was a far-off mutter of thunder. And the night was horrible, horrible, Mexico was ghastly to her beyond description.

She could not relax, she could not get her heart into place. "Now," she thought to herself, "I am at the mercy of this thing, and I have lost myself." And it was a terrible feeling, to be lost, scattered, as it were, from herself in a horror of fear.

"What can I do?" she thought, summoning her spirit. "How can I help myself?" She knew she was all alone.

For a long time she could do nothing. Then a certain relief came to her as she thought: "I am believing in evil. I mustn't believe in evil. Panic and murder never start unless the leading people let slip the control. I don't really believe in evil. I don't believe the old Pan can wrench us back into the old, evil forms of consciousness, unless we wish it. I do believe there is a greater power, which will give us the greater strength, while we keep the faith in it, and the spark of contact. Even the man who wanted to break in here, I don't think he really had the power. He was just trying to be mean and wicked, but something in him would have to submit to a greater faith and a greater power."

So she re-assured herself, till she had the courage to get up and fasten her door-shutters at the top. After which she went from room to room, to see that all was made fast. And she was thankful to realise that she was afraid of scorpions on the floor, as well as of the panic horror.

Now she had seen that the five doors and the six windows of her wing of communicating rooms were fast. She was sealed inside the darkness, with her candle. To get to the other part of the house, the dining-room and kitchen, she had to go outside on the verandah.

She grew quieter, shut up with the dusky glow of her candle.

And her heart, still wrenched with the pain of fear, was thinking:
"Joachim said that evil was the lapsing back to old life-modes that
have been surpassed in us. This brings murder and lust. But
the drums of Saturday night are the old rhythm, and that dancing
round the drum is the old savage form of expression. Consciously reverting to the savage. So perhaps it is evil."

But then again her instinct to believe came up.

"No! It's not a helpless, panic reversal. It is conscious,
carefully chosen. We must go back to pick up old threads. We
must take up the old, broken impulse that will connect us with
the mystery of the cosmos again, now we are at the end of our
own tether. We must do it. Don Ramón is right. He must be
a great man, really. I thought there *were* no really great men
any more: only great financiers and great artists and so on, but no
great *men*. He must be a great man."

She was again infinitely reassured by this thought.

But again, just as she had blown out the candle, vivid flares of
white light spurted through all the window-cracks, and thunder
broke in great round balls, smashing down. The bolts of thunder
seemed to fall on her heart. She lay absolutely crushed, in a
kind of quiescent hysterics, tortured. And the hysterics held
her listening and tense and abject, until dawn. And then she was
a wreck.

In the morning came Juana, also looking like a dead insect,
with the conventional phrase: "How have you passed the night,
Niña?"

"Badly!" said Kate. Then she told the story of the black
cat, or the man's arm.

"*Mire!*" said Juana, in a hushed voice. "The poor innocent
will be murdered in her bed. No, Niña, you must go and sleep
in the hotel. No, no, Niña, you can't leave your window shutter
open. No, no, impossible. See now, will you go to the hotel
to sleep? The other señora does it."

"I don't want to," said Kate.

"You don't want to, Niña? Ah! *Entonces! Entonces*, Niña,
I will tell Ezequiel to sleep here outside your door, with his pistol.
He has a pistol, and he will sleep outside your door, and you
can leave your shutter open, for air in the hot night. Ah, Niña,
we poor women, we need a man and a pistol. We ought not to
be left alone all the night. We are afraid, the children are afraid.
And imagine it, that there was a robber trying to open the bolt

of your door! Imagine it to yourself! No, Niña, we will tell Ezequiel at mid-day."

Ezequiel came striding proudly in, at mid-day. He was a wild, shy youth, very erect and proud, and half savage. His voice was breaking, and had a queer resonance.

He stood shyly while the announcement was being made to him. Then he looked at Kate with flashing black eyes, very much the man to the rescue.

"Yes! Yes!" he said. "I will sleep here on the corridor. Don't have any fear. I shall have my pistol."

He marched off, and returned with the pistol, an old long-barrelled affair.

"It has five shots," he said, showing the weapon. "If you open the door in the night, you must say a word to me first. Because if I see anything move, I shall fire five shots. *Pst! Pst!*"

She saw by the flash of his eyes *what* satisfaction it would give him to fire five shots at something moving in the night. The thought of shots being fired at *him* gave him not the least concern.

"And, Niña," said Juana, "if you come home late, after the light is out, you must call *Ezequiel!* Because if not, *Brumm! Brumm!*—and who knows who will be killed!"

Ezequiel slept on a straw mat on the brick verandah outside Kate's door, rolled up in his blanket, and with the pistol at his side. So she could leave her shutter open for air. And the first night she was kept awake once more by his fierce snoring. Never had she heard such a tremendous resonant sound! What a chest that boy must have! It was sound from some strange, savage other world. The noise kept her awake, but there was something in it which she liked. Some sort of wild strength.

CHAPTER IX

CASA DE LA CUENTAS

KATE was soon fond of the limping, untidy Juana, and of the girls. Concha was fourteen, a thick, heavy, barbaric girl with a mass of black waving hair which she was always scratching. Maria was eleven, a shy, thin bird-like thing with big eyes that seemed almost to absorb the light round her.

It was a reckless family. Juana admitted a different father for Jesús, but to judge from the rest, one would have suspected a different father for each of them. There was a basic, sardonic carelessness in the face of life, in all the family. They lived from day to day, a stubborn, heavy obstinate life of indifference, careless about the past, careless about the present, careless about the future. They had even no interest in money. Whatever they got they spent in a minute, and forgot it again.

Without aim or purpose, they lived absolutely *à terre,* down on the dark, volcanic earth. They were not animals, because men and women and their children *cannot* be animals. It is not granted us. *Go, for once gone, thou never canst return!* says the great Urge which drives us creatively on. When man tries brutally to return to the older, previous levels of evolution, he does so in the spirit of cruelty and misery.

So in the black eyes of the family, a certain vicious fear and wonder and misery. The misery of human beings who squat helpless outside their own unbuilt selves, unable to win their souls out of the chaos, and indifferent to all other victories.

White people are becoming soulless too. But they have conquered the lower worlds of metal and energy, so they whizz around in machines, circling the void of their own emptiness.

To Kate, there was a great pathos in her family. Also a certain repulsiveness.

Juana and her children, once they accepted their Niña as their own, were honest with intensity. Point of honour, they were honest to the least little plum in the fruit bowl. And almost intensely eager to serve.

Themselves indifferent to their surroundings, they would live in squalor. The earth was the great garbage bowl. Everything discarded was flung on the earth and they did not care. Almost they liked to live in a milieu of fleas and old rags, bits of paper, banana skins and mango stones. Here's a piece torn off my dress! Earth, take it. Here's the combings of my hair! Earth, take them!

But Kate could not bear it. She cared. And immediately, the family was quite glad, thrilled that *she* cared. They swept the patio with the twig broom till they swept the very surface of the earth away. Fun! The Niña had feelings about it.

She was a source of wonder and amusement to them. But she was never a class superior. She was a half-incomprehensible, half-amusing wonder-being.

The Niña wanted the *aguador* to bring two *botes* of hot water, quick, from the hot springs, to wash herself all over every morning. Fun! Go, Maria, tell the *aguador* to *run* with the Niña's water.

Then they almost resented it that she shut herself off to have her bath. She was a sort of goddess to them, to provide them with fun and wonder, but she ought always to be accessible. And a god who is forever accessible to human beings has an unenviable time of it, Kate soon discovered.

No, it was no sinecure, being a Niña. At dawn began the scrape-scrape of the twig broom outside. Kate stayed on in bed, doors fastened but shutters open. Flutter outside! Somebody wanted to sell two eggs. Where is the Niña? She is sleeping! The visitor does not go. Continual flutter outside.

The *aguador*! Ah, the water for the Niña's bath! She is sleeping, she is sleeping. "No!" called Kate, slipping into a dressing-gown and unbolting the door. In come the children with the bath tub, in comes the *aguador* with the two square kerosene cans full of hot water. Twelve centavos! Twelve centavos for the *aguador*! *No hay*! We haven't got twelve centavos. Later! Later! Away trots the *aguador*, pole over his shoulder. Kate shuts her doors and shutters and starts her bath.

"Niña? Niña?"

"What do you want?"

"Eggs boiled or fried or rancheros? Which do you want?"

"Boiled."

"Coffee or chocolate?"

"Coffee."

"Or do you want tea?"

"No, coffee."

Bath proceeds.

"Niña?"

"Yes."

"There is no coffee. We are going to buy some."

"I'll take tea."

"No, Niña! I am going. Wait for me."

"Go then."

Kate comes out to breakfast on the verandah. The table is set, heaped with fruit and white bread and sweet buns.

"Good morning, Niña. How have you passed the night? Well! Ah, praised be God! Maria, the coffee. I'm going to put the eggs in the water. Oh, Niña, that they may not be boiled hard!—Look, what feet of the Madonna! Look! *Bonitos!*"

And Juana stooped down fascinated to touch with her black finger Kate's white soft feet, that were thrust in light sandals, just a thong across the foot.

The day had begun. Juana looked upon herself as dedicated entirely to Kate. As soon as possible she shooed her girls away, to school. Sometimes they went: mostly they didn't. The Niña said they must go to school. Listen! Listen now! Says the Niña that you must go to school! Away! Walk!

Juana would limp back and forth down the long verandah from kitchen to the breakfast table, carrying away the dishes one by one. Then, with a great splash, she was washing up.

Morning! Brilliant sun pouring into the patio, on the hibiscus flowers and the fluttering yellow and green rags of the banana trees. Birds swiftly coming and going, with tropical suddenness. In the dense shadow of the mango-grove, white clad Indians going like ghosts. The sense of fierce sun and almost more impressive, of dark, intense shadow. A twitter of life, yet a certain heavy weight of silence. A dazzling flicker and brilliance of light, yet the feeling of weight.

Kate would sit alone, rocking on her verandah, pretending to sew. Silently appears an old man with one egg held up mysteriously, like some symbol. Would the patrona buy it for five centavos. La Juana only gives four centavos. All right?

Where is Juana?

Juana appears from the plaza with more purchases. The egg!

The four centavos! The account of the spendings. *Entonces! Entonces! Luego! Luego! Ah, Niña, no tengo memoria!* Juana could not read nor write. She scuffled off to the market with her pesos, bought endless little things at one or two centavos each, every morning. And every morning there was a reckoning up. Ah! Ah! Where are we? I have no memory. Well then —ah—yes—I bought ocote for three centavos! How much? How much, Niña? How much it is now?

It was a game which thrilled Juana to the marrow, reckoning up the centavos to get it just right. If she was a centavo short in the change, she was paralysed. Time after time she would reappear. *There is a centavo short, Niña? Ah, how stupid I am? But I will give you one of mine!"*

"Don't bother," said Kate. "Don't think of it any more."

"But yes. But yes!" and away she limped in distraction.

Till an hour later, loud cry from the far end of the house. Juana waving a scrap of greenery.

"Mire! Niña! Compré perjil a un centavo—I bought parsley for one cent. Is it right?"

"It is right," said Kate.

And life could proceed once more.

There were two kitchens, the one next the dining-room, belonging to Kate, and the narrow little shed under the banana trees, belonging to the servants. From her verandah Kate looked away down to Juana's kitchen shed. It had a black window hole.

Clap! Clap! Clap! Clap! Why I thought Concha was at school! said Kate to herself.

No!—there, in the darkness of the window hole was Concha's swarthy face and mane, peering out like some animal from a cave, as she made the tortillas. Tortillas are flat pancakes of maize dough, baked dry on a flat earthen-ware plate over the fire. And the making consists of clapping a bit of new dough from the palm of one hand to the other, till the tortilla is of the requisite thinness, roundness, and so-called lightness.

Clap! Clap! Clap! Clap! Clap! Clap! Clap! It was as inevitable as the tick of some spider, the sound of Concha making tortillas in the heat of the morning, peering out of her dark window hole. And some time after mid-day, the smoke would be coming out of the window hole; Concha was throwing the raw tortillas on the big earthen plate over the slow wood fire.

Then Ezequiel might or might not stride in, very much the

man, serape poised over one shoulder and big straw hat jauntily curled, to eat the mid-day tortillas. If he had work in the fields at any distance, he would not appear till nightfall. If he appeared, he sat on the doorstep and the women served him his tortillas and fetched him his drink of water as if he was a king, boy though he might be. And his rough, breaking voice was heard in quiet command.

Command was the word. Though he was quiet and gentle, and very conscientious, there was calm, kingly command in his voice when he spoke to his mother or sisters. The old male prerogative. Somehow, it made Kate want to ridicule him.

Came her own meal: one of her trials. Hot, rather greasy soup. Inevitable hot, greasy, rather peppery rice. Inevitable meat in hot, thick, rather greasy sauce. Boiled calabacitas or egg-plant, salad, perhaps some dulce made with milk—and the big basket of fruit. Overhead, the blazing tropical sun of late May.

Afternoon, and greater heat. Juana set off with the girls and the dishes. They would do the washing up in the lake. Squatting on the stones, they would dabble the plates one by one, the spoons and the forks one by one in the filmy water of the lake, then put them in the sun to dry. After which Juana might wash a couple of towels in the lake and the girls might bathe. Sauntering the day away—sauntering the day away.

Jesús, the eldest son, a queer, heavy, greasy fellow, usually appeared in the afternoon, to water the garden. But he ate his meals at the hotel, and really lived there, had his home there. Not that he had any home, any more than a zopilote had a home. But he ran the *planta,* and did odd jobs about the hotel, and worked every day in the year till half past ten at night, earning twenty-two pesos, eleven dollars, a month. He wore a black shirt, and his thick, massive black hair dropped over his brow. Very near to an animal. And though, to order, he wore a black Fascisti shirt, he had the queer, animal jeering of the socialists, an instinct for pulling things down.

His mother and he had a funny intimacy of quiet and indifferent mutual taunting of one another. He would give her some money if she were in a strait. And there was a thin little thread of blood-bondage between them. Apart from that, complete indifference.

Ezequiel was a finer type. He was slender and so erect that he almost curved backwards. He was very shy, farouche. Proud

also, and more responsible to his family. He would not go to
work in an hotel. No. He was a worker in the fields, and he
was proud of it. A man's work. No equivocal sort of half-
service for him.

Though he was just a hired labourer, yet, working on the
land he never felt he was working for a master. It was the
land he worked for. Somewhere inside himself he felt that
the land was his, and he belonged in a measure to it. Perhaps a
lingering feeling of tribal, communal land-ownership and service.

When there was work, he was due to earn a peso a day. There
was often no work: and often only seventy-five centavos a day for
wage. When the land was dry, he would try to get work on the
road, though this he did not like. But he earned his peso a day.

Often, there was no work. Often, for days, sometimes for
weeks, he would have to hang about, nothing to do, nothing to
do. Only, when the Socialist Government had begun giving the
peasants bits of land, dividing up the big haciendas, Ezequiel had
been allotted a little piece outside the village. He would go and
gather the stones together there, and prepare to build a little
hut. And he would break the earth with a hoe, his only imple-
ment, as far as possible. But he had no blood connection with this
square allotment of unnatural earth, and he could not get himself
into relations with it. He was fitful and diffident about it.
There was no incentive, no urge.

On workdays he would come striding in about six o'clock,
shyly greeting Kate as he passed. He was a gentleman in his
barbarism. Then, away in the far recess, he would rapidly fold
tortilla after tortilla, sitting on the floor with his back to the
wall, rapidly eating the leathery things that taste of mortar, because the maize is first boiled with lime to loosen the husk, and
accepting another little pile, served on a leaf, from the cook,
Concha. Juana, cook for the Niña, would no longer condescend
to cook for her own family. And sometimes there was a mess
of meat and chile for Ezequiel to scoop up out of the earthenware
casserole, with his tortillas. And sometimes there was not. But
always, he ate with a certain blind, rapid indifference, that also
seems to be Mexican. They seem to *eat* even with a certain hostile
reluctance, and have a strange indifference to what or when
they eat.

His supper finished, as a rule he was off again like a shot,

to the plaza, to be among men. And the women would sit desultorily about, on the ground. Sometimes Kate would come in at nine o'clock to an empty place—Ezequiel in the plaza, Juana and Maria disappeared somewhere or other, and Concha lying asleep like a heap of rags on the gravel of the patio. When Kate called her, she would raise her head, stupefied and hopeless; then get up like a dog and crawl away to the gate. The strange stupor of boredom and hopelessness that was always sinking upon them would make Kate's heart stand still with dread.

The peculiar indifference to everything, even to one another. Juana washed a cotton shirt and a pair of cotton trousers for each of her sons, once a week, and there her maternal efforts ended. She saw hardly anything of them, and was often completely unaware of what Ezequiel was doing, where he was working or at what. He had just gone off to work, no more.

Yet again, sometimes she had hot, fierce pangs of maternal protectiveness, when the boy was unjustly treated, as he often was. And if she thought he were ill, a black sort of fatalistic fear came over her. But Kate had to rouse her into getting some simple medicine.

Like animals, yet not at all like animals. For animals are complete in their isolation and their insouciance. With them it is not indifference. It is completeness in themselves. But with the family there was always a kind of bleeding of incompleteness, a terrible stupor of boredom settling down.

The two girls could not be apart: they must always be running after one another. Yet Concha continually teased the big-eyed, naïve simpleton of a Maria. And Maria was always in tears. Or the two were suddenly throwing stones at one another. But with no real aim to hit. And Juana was abusing them with sudden vehemence, that flickered in a minute to complete indifference again.

Queer, the savage ferocity with which the girls would suddenly be throwing stones at one another. But queerer still, they always aimed *just to miss*. Kate noticed the same in the savage attacks the boys made on one another, on the beach; hurling large stones with intense, terrible ferocity. But almost always, aiming with a curious cast in the eyes, just to miss.

But sometimes not. Sometimes hitting with a sharp cut. And then the wounded one would drop right down, with a howl, as if dead. And the other boys would edge away, in a silent kind of

dread. And the wounded boy would be prostrate, not really much hurt, but as if he was killed.

Then, maybe, suddenly he would be up, with a convulsion of murder in his face, pursuing his adversary with a stone. And the adversary would abjectly flee.

Always the same thing among the young: a ceaseless, endless taunting and tormenting. The same as among the Red Indians. But the Pueblo Indians rarely lapsing from speech into violence. The Mexican boys almost always. And almost always, one boy in murderous rage, pursuing his taunter till he had hurt him: then an abject collapse of the one hurt. Then, usually, a revival of the one hurt, the murderous frenzy transferred to him, and the first attacker fleeing abjectly, in terror. One or the other always abject.

They were a strange puzzle to Kate. She felt something must be done. She herself was inspired to help. So she had the two girls for an hour a day, teaching them to read, to sew, to draw. Maria wanted to learn to read: that she did want. For the rest, they began well. But soon, the regularity and the slight insistence of Kate on their attention made them take again that peculiar invisible jeering tone, something peculiar to the American Continent. A quiet, invisible, malevolent mockery, a desire to wound. They would press upon her, trespassing upon her privacy, and with a queer effrontery, doing all they could to walk over her. With their ugly little wills, trying to pull her will down.

"No, don't lean on me, Concha. Stand on your own feet."

The slight grin of malevolence on Concha's face, as she stood on her own feet. Then:

"Do you have lice in your hair, Niña?"

The question asked with a peculiar, subtle, Indian insolence.

"No!" said Kate, suddenly angry. "And now go! Go! Go away from me! Don't come near me."

They slunk out, abject. So much for educating them.

Kate had visitors from Guadalajara—great excitement. But while the visitors were drinking tea with Kate on the verandah, at the other side of the patio, full in view, Juana, Concha, Maria, and Felipa, a cousin of about sixteen, squatted on the gravel with their splendid black hair down their backs, displaying themselves as they hunted in each other's hair for lice. They wanted to be full in view. And they were it. They wanted the basic fact of lice to be thrust under the noses of those white people.

Kate strode down the verandah.

"If you must pick lice," she said in a shaking voice to Juana, shaking with anger, "pick them there, in your own place, where you can't be seen."

One instant, Juana's black inchoate eyes gleamed with a malevolent ridicule, meeting Kate's. The next instant, humble and abject, the four with their black hair down their backs slunk into the recess out of sight.

But it pleased Juana that she had been able to make Kate's eyes blaze with anger. It pleased her. She felt a certain low power in herself. True, she was a little afraid of that anger. But that was what she wanted. She would have no use for a Niña of whom she was not a bit afraid. And she wanted to be able to provoke that anger, of which she felt a certain abject twinge of fear.

Ah the dark races! Kate's own Irish were near enough, for her to have glimpsed some of the mystery. The dark races belong to a bygone cycle of humanity. They are left behind in a gulf out of which they have never been able to climb. And on to the particular white man's levels they never will be able to climb. They can only follow as servants.

While the white man keeps the impetus of his own proud, onward march, the dark races will yield and serve, perforce. But let the white man once have a misgiving about his own leadership, and the dark races will at once attack him, to pull him down into the old gulfs. To engulf him again.

Which is what is happening. For the white man, let him bluster as he may, is hollow with misgiving about his own supremacy.

Full speed ahead, then, for the débâcle.

But once Kate had been roused to a passion of revulsion from these lice-picking, down-dragging people, they changed again, and served her with a certain true wistfulness that could not but touch her. Juana cared really about nothing. But just that last thread of relationship that connected her with Kate and the upper world of daylight and fresh air, she didn't want to break. No, no, she didn't want finally to drive her Niña away. No, no, the only one thing she did want, ultimately, was to serve her Niña.

But at the same time, she cherished a deep malevolent grudge against rich people, white people, superior people. Perhaps the white man has finally betrayed his own leadership. Who knows! But it is a thing of the brave, on-marching soul, and perhaps this

has been betrayed already by the white man. So that the dark are rising upon him.

Juana would come to Kate, telling her stories from the past. And the sinister mocking film would be on her black eyes, and her lined copper face would take on its reptile mask as she would continue: "Usted sabe, Niña, los gringos, los gringitos llevan todo—you know, Niña, the *gringos* and the *gringitos* take away everything. . . ."

The *gringos* are the Americans. But Kate herself was included by Juana in the *gringitos:* the white foreigners. The woman was making another sliding, insolent attack.

"It is possible," said Kate coldly. "But tell me what I take away from Mexico."

"No, Niña, No!" The subtle smile of satisfaction lurked under the bronze tarnish of Juana's face. She had been able to get at the other woman, touch the raw. "I don't speak of you, Niña!" But there was too much protest in it.

Almost, they wanted to drive her away: to insult her and drag her down and make her want to go away. They couldn't help it. Like the Irish, they could cut off their nose to spite their face. The backward races!

At the same time there was a true pathos about them. Ezequiel had worked for a man for two months, building a house, when he was a boy of fourteen, in order to get a serape. At the end of the two months, the man had put him off, and he had not got the serape: had never got it. A bitter disappointment.

But then, Kate was not responsible for that. And Juana seemed almost to make her so.

A people without the energy of *getting on,* how could they fail to be hopelessly exploited. They had been hopelessly and cruelly exploited, for centuries. And their backbones were locked in malevolent resistance.

"But," as Kate said to herself, "I don't want to exploit them. Not a bit. On the contrary, I am willing to give more than I get. But that nasty insinuating insultingness is not fair in the game. I never insult them. I am so careful not to hurt them. And then they *deliberately* make these centipede attacks on me, and are pleased when I am hurt."

But she knew her own Irish at the game. So she was able to put Juana and the girls away from her, and isolate herself from

them. Once they were put away, their malevolence subsided
and they remembered what Kate wanted. While she stayed ami-
able, they forgot. They forgot to sweep the patio, they forgot to
keep themselves clean. Only when they were shoved back, into
isolation, did they remember again.

The boy, Ezequiel, seemed to her to have more honour than the
women. He never made these insidious attacks.

And when her house was clean and quiet, and the air seemed
cleaned again, the soul renewed, her old fondness for the family
came back. Their curious flitting, coming and going, like birds:
the busy clap—clap—clapping of tortillas, the excited scrunching
of tomatoes and chile on the metate, as Juana prepared sauce. The
noise of the bucket in the well. Jesús, come to water the garden.

The game, the game of it all! Everything they did must be fun,
or they could not do it. They could not abstract themselves to
a routine. Never. Everything must be fun, must be variable,
must be a bit of an adventure. It was confusion, but after all, a
living confusion, not a dead, dreary thing. Kate remembered her
English servants in the English kitchens: so mechanical and somehow inhuman. Well, this was the other extreme.

Here there was no discipline nor method at all. Although Juana
and her brats really wanted to do the things Kate wished, they
must do them their own way. Sometimes Kate felt distracted:
after all, the mechanical lines are so much *easier* to follow. But
as far as possible, she let the family be. She had to get used,
for example, to the vagaries of her dining table: a little round
table that always stood on the verandah. At breakfast time it
would be discreetly set under the *plantas* by the salon; for dinner,
at one o'clock, it would have travelled way down the verandah; for
tea it might be under a little tree on the grass. And then Juana
would decide that the Niña must take supper, two eggs, *rancheros,*
in the dining-room itself, isolated at the corner of the long dining-
table meant for fourteen people.

The same with the dishes. Why they should, after washing
up in the big bowls in the kitchen for several days, suddenly
struggle way down to the lake with the unwashed pots in a basket
on Concha's shoulder, Kate never knew. Except for the fun of
the thing.

Children! But then, not at all children. None of the wondering insouciance of childhood. Something dark and cognisant in
their souls all the time: some heavy weight of resistance. They

worked in fits and starts, and could be very industrious; then
came days when they lay about on the ground like pigs. At
times they were merry, seated round on the ground in groups, like
Arabian nights, and laughing away. Then suddenly resisting
even merriment in themselves, relapsing into the numb gloom.
When they were busily working, suddenly for no reason, throwing
away the tool, as if resenting having given themselves. Careless
in their morals, always changing their loves, the men at least resisted all the time any real giving of themselves. They didn't
want the thing they were pursuing. It was the women who drew
them on. And a young man and a girl going down the road from
the lake in the dark, teasing and poking each other in excitement,
would startle Kate because of their unusualness—the men and
women never walked their sex abroad, as white people do. And
the sudden, sexual laugh of the man, so strange a sound of pain
and desire, obstinate reluctance and helpless passion, a noise as
if something was tearing in his breast, was a sound to remember.

Kate felt her household a burden. In a sense, they were like
parasites, they wanted to live on her life, and pull her down, pull
her down. Again, they were so generous with her, so good and
gentle, she felt they were wonderful. And then once more she
came up against that unconscious, heavy, reptilian indifference in
them, indifference and resistance.

Her servants were the clue to all the native life, for her. The
men always together, erect, handsome, balancing their great hats
on the top of their heads and sitting, standing, crouching with a
snake-like impassivity The women together separately, soft, and
as if *hidden*, wrapped tight in their dark rebozos. Men and
women seemed always to be turning their backs on one another, as
if they didn't want to see one another. No flirting, no courting.
Only an occasional quick, dark look, the signal of a weapon-like
desire, given and taken.

The women seemed, on the whole, softly callous and determined
to go their own way: to change men if they wished. And the
men seemed not to care very profoundly. But it was the women
who wanted the men.

The native women, with their long black hair streaming down
their full, ruddy backs, would bathe at one end of the beach,
usually wearing their chemise, or a little skirt. The men took
absolutely no notice. They didn't even look the other way. It
was the women bathing, that was all. As it were, like the charales

swimming, just a natural part of the lake life. The men just left that part of the lake to the women. And the women sat in the shallows of the lake, isolated in themselves like moor-fowl, pouring water over their heads and over their ruddy arms from a gourd scoop.

The quiet, unobtrusive, but by no means down-trodden women of the peon class. They went their own way, enveloped in their rebozos as in their own darkness. They hurried nimbly along, their full cotton skirts swinging, chirping and quick like birds. Or they sat in the lake with long hair streaming, pouring water over themselves: again like birds. Or they passed with a curious slow inevitability up the lake-shore, with a heavy red jar of water perched on one shoulder, one arm over the head, holding the rim of the jar. They had to carry all water from the lake to their houses. There was no town supply. Or, especially on Sunday afternoons, they sat in their doorways lousing one another. The most resplendent *belles,* with magnificent black wavy hair, were most thoroughly loused. It was as if it were a meritorious public act.

The men were the obvious figures. They assert themselves on the air. They are the dominant. Usually they are in loose groups, talking quietly, or silent: always standing or sitting apart, rarely touching one another. Often a single man would stand alone at a street corner in his serape, motionless for hours, like some powerful spectre. Or a man would lie on the beach as if he had been cast up dead from the waters. Impassive, motionless, they would sit side by side on the benches of the plaza, not exchanging a word. Each one isolated in his own fate, his eyes black and quick like a snake's, and as blank.

It seemed to Kate that the highest thing this country might produce would be some powerful relationship of man to man. Marriage itself would always be a casual thing. Though the men seemed very gentle and protective to the little children. Then they forgot them.

But sex itself was a powerful, potent thing, not to be played with or paraded. The one mystery. And a mystery greater than the individual. The individual hardly counted.

It was strange to Kate to see the Indian huts on the shore, little holes built of straw or corn-stalks, with half-naked children squatting on the naked earth floor, and a lousy woman-squalor around, a litter of rags and bones, and a sharp smell of human excrement.

The people have no noses.   And standing silent and erect not far
from the hole of the doorway, the man, handsome and impassive.
How could it be, that such a fine-looking human male should be
so absolutely indifferent, content with such paltry squalor?

But there he was, unconscious.   He seemed to have life and
passion in him.   And she knew he was strong.   No men in the
world can carry heavier loads on their backs, for longer distances,
than these Indians.   She had seen an Indian trotting down a
street with a piano on his back: holding it, also, by a band round
his forehead.   From his forehead, and on his spine he carried it,
trotting along.   The women carry with a band round the breast.

So there is strength.   And *apparently*, there is passionate life.
But no energy.   Nowhere in Mexico is there any sign of energy.
This is, as it were, switched off.

Even the new artizan class, though it imitates the artizan class
of the United States, has no real energy.   There are workmen's
clubs.   The workmen dress up and parade a best girl on their arm.
But somehow, it seems what it is, only a weak imitation.

Kate's family was increased, without her expecting it.   One day
there arrived from Ocotlan a beautiful ox-eyed girl of about
fifteen, wrapped in her black cotton rebozo, and somewhat towny
in her Madonna-meekness: Maria del Carmen.   With her, Julio,
a straight and fierce young man of twenty-two.   They had just
been married, and had come to Sayula for a visit.   Julio was
Juana's cousin.

Might they sleep in the patio with herself and the girls, was
Juana's request.   They would stay only two days.

Kate was amazed   Maria del Carmen must have had some
Spanish blood, her beauty was touched with Spain.   She seemed
even refined and superior.   Yet she was to sleep out on the ground
like a dog, with her young husband.   And he, so erect and proud-
looking, possessed nothing in the world but an old serape.

"There are three spare bedrooms," said Kate.   "They may
sleep in one of those."

The beds were single beds.   Would they need more blankets?
she asked Juana.

No!   They would manage with the one serape of Julio's.

The new family had arrived.   Julio was a bricklayer.   That is
to say, he worked building the adobe walls of the little houses.
He belonged to Sayula, and had come back for a visit.

The visit continued.   Julio would come striding in at midday

and at evening; he was looking for work. Maria del Carmen, in her one black dress, would squat on the floor and pat tortillas. She was allowed to cook them in Juana's kitchen hole. And she talked and laughed with the girls. At night, when Julio was home, he would lie on the ground with his back to the wall, impassive, while Maria del Carmen fondled his thick black hair.

They were in love. But even now, he was not yielding to his love.

She wanted to go back to Ocotlan, where she was at home, and more a señorita than here in Sayula. But he refused. There was no money: the young ménage lived on about five American cents a day.

Kate was sewing. Maria del Carmen, who didn't even know how to put a chemise together, watched with great eyes. Kate taught her, and bought a length of cotton material. Maria del Carmen was sewing herself a dress!

Julio had got work at a peso a day. The visit continued. Kate thought Julio wasn't very nice with Maria del Carmen: his quiet voice was so overbearing in command when he spoke to her. And Maria del Carmen, who was a bit towny, did not take it well. She brooded a little.

The visit stretched into weeks. And now Juana was getting a bit tired of her relative.

But Julio had got a bit of money. He had rented a little one-room adobe house, at one peso fifty per week. Maria del Carmen was going to move into her own home.

Kate saw the new outfit got together. It consisted of one straw mat, three cooking plates of earthenware, five bits of native crockery, two wooden spoons, one knife and Julio's old blanket. That was all. But Maria del Carmen was moving in.

Kate presented her with a large old eiderdown, whose silk was rather worn, a couple of bowls, and a few more bits of crockery. Maria del Carmen was set up. *Good! Good! Oh Good!* Kate heard her voice down the patio. *I have got a coverlet! I have got a coverlet!*

In the rainy season, the nights can be very cold, owing to evaporation. Then the natives lie through the small hours like lizards, numb and prostrate with cold. They are lying on the damp earth on a thin straw mat, with a corner of an old blanket to cover them. And the same terrible inertia makes them endure it, without trying to make any change. They could carry in corn

husks or dry banana leaves for a bed. They could even cover themselves with banana leaves.

But no! On a thin mat on damp cold earth they lie and tremble with cold, night after night, night after night, night after night.

But Maria del Carmen was a bit towny. *Oh good! Oh good! I've got a coverlet!*

CHAPTER X

DON RAMÓN AND DOÑA CARLOTA

KATE had been in Sayula ten days before she had any sign from Don Ramón. She had been out in a boat on the lake, and had seen his house, round the bend of the western point. It was a reddish-and-yellow two-storey house with a little stone basin for the boats, and a mango grove between it and the lake. Among the trees, away from the lake, were the black adobe huts, two rows, of the peons.

The hacienda had once been a large one. But it had been irrigated from the hills, and the revolutions had broken all the aqueducts. Only a small supply of water was available. Then Don Ramón had had enemies in the Government. So that a good deal of his land was taken away to be divided among the peons. Now, he had only some three hundred acres. The two hundred acres along the lake shore were mostly lost to him. He worked a few acres of fruit land round the house, and in a tiny valley just in the hills, he raised sugar cane. On the patches of the mountain slope, little patches of maize were to be seen.

But Doña Carlota had money. She was from Torreon, and drew still a good income from the mines.

A mozo came with a note from Don Ramón: might he bring his wife to call on Kate?

Doña Carlota was a thin, gentle, wide-eyed woman, with a slightly startled expression, and soft, brownish hair. She was pure European in extraction, of a Spanish father and French mother: very different from the usual stout, over-powdered, ox-like Mexican matron. Her face was pale, faded, and without any make-up at all. Her thin, eager figure had something English about it, but her strange, wide brown eyes were not English. She spoke only Spanish—or French. But her Spanish was so slow and distinct and slightly plaintive, that Kate understood her at once.

The two women understood one another quickly, but were a little nervous of one another. Doña Carlota was delicate and sen-

153

sitive like a Chihuahua dog, and with the same slightly prominent eyes. Kate felt she had rarely met a woman with such a doglike finesse of gentleness. And the two women talked. Ramón, large and muted, kept himself in reserve. It was as if the two women rushed together to unite against his silence and his powerful, different significance.

Kate knew at once that Doña Carlota loved him, but with a love that was now nearly all *will*. She had worshipped him, and she had had to leave off worshipping him. She had had to question him. And she would never now cease from questioning.

So he sat apart, a little constrained, his handsome head hanging a little, and his dark, sensitive hands dangling between his thighs.

"I had such a wonderful time!" Kate said suddenly to him. "I danced a dance round the drum with the Men of Quetzalcoatl."

"I heard," he said, with a rather stiff smile.

Doña Carlota understood English, though she would not speak it.

"You danced with the men of Quetzalcoatl!" she said in Spanish, in a pained voice. "But, Señora, why did you do such a thing? Oh, why?"

"I was fascinated," said Kate.

"No, you must not be fascinated. No! No! It is not good. I tell you, I am *so sorry* my husband interests himself in this thing. I am so sorry."

Juana was bringing a bottle of vermouth: all that Kate had to offer her visitors, in the morning.

"You went to see your boys in the United States?" said Kate to Doña Carlota. "How were they?"

"Oh, better, thank you. They are well; that is, the younger is very delicate."

"You didn't bring him home?"

"No! No! I think they are better in school. Here—here—there are so many things to trouble them. No! But they will come home next month, for the vacation."

"How nice!" said Kate. "Then I shall see them. They will be here, won't they?—on the lake?"

"Well!—I am not sure. Perhaps for a little while. You see I am so busy in Mexico with my Cuna."

"What is a Cuna?" said Kate; she only knew it was the Spanish for cradle.

It turned out to be a foundlings' home, run by a few obscure Carmelite sisters. And Doña Carlota was the director. Kate gathered that Don Ramón's wife was an intense, almost exalted Catholic. She exalted herself in the Church, and in her work for the Cuna.

"There are so many children born in Mexico," said Doña Carlota, "and so many die. If only we could save them, and equip them for life. We do a little, all we can."

It seemed, the waste, unwanted babies could be delivered in at the door of the Cuna, like parcels. The mother had only to knock, and hand in the little living bundle.

"It saves so many mothers from neglecting their babies, and letting them die," said Doña Carlota. "Then we do what we can. If the mother doesn't leave a name, I name the child. Very often I do. The mothers just hand over a little naked thing, sometimes without a name or a rag to cover it. And we never ask."

The children were not all kept in the Home. Only a small number. Of the others, some decent Indian woman was paid a small sum to take the child into her home. Every month she must come with the little one to the Cuna, to receive her wage. The Indians are so very rarely unkind to children. Careless, yes. But rarely, rarely unkind.

In former days, Doña Carlota said, nearly every well-born lady in Mexico would receive one or more of these foundlings into her home, and have it brought up with the family. It was the loose, patriarchal generosity innate in the bosoms of the Spanish-Mexicans. But now, few children were adopted. Instead, they were taught as far as possible to be carpenters or gardeners or house-servants, or, among the girls, dressmakers, even school-teachers.

Kate listened with uneasy interest. She felt there was so much real human feeling in this Mexican charity: she was almost rebuked. Perhaps what Doña Carlota was doing was the best that could be done, in this half-wild, helpless country. At the same time, it was such a forlorn hope, it made one's heart sink.

And Doña Carlota, confident as she was in her good works, still had just a bit the look of a victim; a gentle, sensitive, slightly startled victim. As if some secret enemy drained her blood.

Don Ramón sat there impassive, listening without heeding; solid and unmoving *against* the charitable quiver of his wife's emotion. He let her do as she would. But against her work

and against her flow he was in silent, heavy, unchanging opposition. She knew this, and trembled in her nervous eagerness, as she talked to Kate about the Cuna, and won Kate's sympathy. Till it seemed to her that there was something cruel in Don Ramón's passive, masked poise. An impassive male cruelty, changeless as a stone idol.

"Now won't you come and spend the day with me while I am here with Don Ramón?" said Doña Carlota. "The house is very poor and rough. It is no longer what it used to be. But it is your house if you will come."

Kate accepted, and said she would prefer to walk out. It was only four miles, and surely she would be safe, with Juana.

"I will send a man to come with you," said Don Ramón. "It might not be quite safe."

"Where is General Viedma?" asked Kate.

"We shall try to get him out when you come," replied Doña Carlota. "I am so very fond of Don Cipriano, I have known him for many years, and he is the godfather of my younger son. But now he is in command of the Guadalajara division, he is not very often able to come out."

"I wonder why he is a general," said Kate. "He seems to me too human."

"Oh, but he is very human too. But he is a general; yes, yes, he wants to be in command of the soldiers. And I tell you, he is very strong. He has great power with his regiments. They believe in him, oh, they believe in him. He has that power, you know, that some of the higher types of Indians have, to make many others want to follow them and fight for them. You know? Don Cipriano is like that. You can never change him. But I think a woman might be wonderful for him. He has lived so without any woman in his life. He won't care about them."

"What does he care about?" asked Kate.

"Ah!" Doña Carlota started as if stung. Then she glanced quickly, involuntarily at her husband, as she added: "I don't know. Really, I don't know."

"The Men of Quetzalcoatl," said Don Ramón heavily, with a little smile.

But Doña Carlota seemed to be able to take all the ease and the banter out of him. He seemed stiff and a bit stupid.

"Ah, there! There! There you have it! The Men of Quetzalcoatl—that is a nice thing for him to care about! A nice thing,

I say," fluttered Doña Carlota, in her gentle, fragile, scolding way. And it was evident to Kate that she adored both the men, and trembled in opposition to their wrongness, and would never give in to them.

To Ramón it was a terrible burden, his wife's quivering, absolute, blind opposition, taken in conjunction with her helpless adoration.

A man-servant appeared at nine o'clock one morning, to accompany Kate to the hacienda, which was called Jamiltepec. He had a basket, and had been shopping in the market. An elderly man, with grey in his moustache, he had bright young eyes and seemed full of energy. His bare feet in the huaraches were almost black with exposure, but his clothes were brilliantly white.

Kate was glad to be walking. The one depressing thing about life in the villages was that one could not walk out into the country. There was always the liability to be held up or attacked. And she had walked already, as far as possible, in every direction, in the neighbourhood of the village, accompanied usually by Ezequiel. Now she was beginning to feel a prisoner.

She was glad, then, to be setting off. The morning was clear and hot, the pale brown lake quite still, like a phantom. People were moving on the beach, in the distance tiny, like dots of white: white dots of men following the faint dust of donkeys. She wondered often why humanity was like specks in the Mexican landscape; just specks of life.

They passed from the lake shore to the rough, dusty road going west, between the steep slope of the hills and the bit of flat by the lake. For almost a mile there were villas, most of them shut up fast, some of them smashed, with broken walls and smashed windows. Only flowers bloomed in masses above the rubble.

In the empty places were flimsy straw huts of the natives, haphazard, as if blown there. By the road under the hill, were black-grey adobe huts, like boxes, and fowls running about, and brown pigs or grey pigs spotted with black careered and grunted, and half naked children, dark orange-brown, trotted or lay flat on their faces in the road, their little naked posteriors hutched up, fast asleep. Already asleep again.

The houses were many of them being re-thatched, or the tiled roofs were being patched by men who assumed a great air of importance at having undertaken such a task. They were pretending to hurry, too, because the real rains might begin any day.

And in the little stony levels by the lake, the land was being scratch-ploughed by a pair of oxen and a lump of pointed wood.

But this part of the road Kate knew. She knew the fine villa on the knoll, with its tufts of palms, and the laid-out avenues that were laid out, indeed, as the dead are, to crumble back again. She was glad to be past the villas, where the road came down to the lake again, under big shady trees that had twisted, wriggly beans. On the left was the water, the colour of turtle doves, lapping the pale fawn stones. At a water-hole of a stream in the beach, a cluster of women were busily washing clothes. In the shallows of the lake itself two women sat bathing, their black hair hanging dense and wet. A little further along, a man was wading slowly, stopping to throw his round net skilfully upon the water, then slowly stooping and gathering it in, picking out the tiny, glittery fish called charales. Strangely silent and remote everything, in the gleaming morning, as if it were some distant period of time.

A little breeze was coming from the lake, but the deep dust underfoot was hot. On the right the hill rose precipitous, baked and yellowish, giving back the sun and the intense dryness, and exhaling the faint, dessicated, peculiar smell of Mexico, that smells as if the earth had sweated itself dry.

All the time strings of donkeys trotted laden through the dust, their drivers stalking erect and rapid behind, watching with eyes like black holes, but always answering Kate's salute with a respectful *Adios!* And Juana echoed her laconic *Adiosn!* She was limping, and she thought it horrible of Kate to walk four miles, when they might have struggled out in an old hired motor-car, or gone in a boat, or even ridden donkey-back.

But to go on foot! Kate could hear all her criada's feelings in the drawled, sardonic *Adiosn!* But the man behind strode bravely and called cheerfully. His pistol was prominent in his belt.

A bluff of yellow rock came jutting at the road. The road wound round it, and into a piece of flat open country. There were fields of dry stone, and hedges of dusty thorn and cactus. To the left the bright green of the willows by the lake-shore. To the right the hills swerved inland, to meet the sheer, fluted sides of dry mountains. Away ahead, the hills curved back at the shore, and a queer little crack or niche showed. This crack in the hills led from Don Ramón's shore-property to the little valley

where he grew the sugar cane. And where the hills approached the lake again, there was a dark clustering of mango trees, and the red upper-storey of the hacienda house.

"There it is!" cried the man behind. "Jamiltepec, Señorita. La hacienda de Don Ramón!"

And his eyes shone as he said the name. He was a proud peon, and he really seemed happy.

"Look! How far!" cried Juana.

"Another time," said Kate, "I shall come alone, or with Ezequiel."

"No, Niña! Don't say so. Only my foot hurts this morning."

"Yes. Better not to bring you."

"No, Niña! I like to come, very much!"

The tall windmill fan for drawing up water from the lake was spinning gaily. A little valley came down from the niche in the hills, and at the bottom a little water running. Towards the lake, where this valley flattened out, was a grove of banana plants, screened a little from the lake breeze by a vivid row of willow-trees. And on the top of the slope, where the road ran into the shade of mango trees, were the two rows of adobe huts, like a village, set a little back from the road.

Women were coming up between the trees, on the patch from the lake, with jars of water on their shoulders; children were playing around the doors, squatting with little naked posteriors in deep dust; and here and there a goat was tethered. Men in soiled white clothes were lounging, with folded arms and one leg crossed in front of the other, against the corner of a house, or crouching under the walls. Not by any means *dolce far niente*. They seemed to be waiting, eternally waiting for something.

"That way, Señorita!" called the man with the basket, running to her side and indicating the smoother road sloping down between some big trees, towards the white gate of the hacienda. "We are here!"

Always he spoke with pleased delight, as if the place were a wonder-place to him.

The big doors of the zaguan, the entrance, stood open, and in the shade of the entrance-way a couple of little soldiers were seated. Across the cleared, straw-littered space in front of the gates two peons were trotting, each with a big bunch of bananas on his head. The soldiers said something, and the two peons halted in their trotting, and slowly turned under their yellow-green

load, to look back at Kate and Juana and the man Martin, approaching down the road. Then they turned again and trotted into the courtyard, barefoot.

The soldiers stood up. Martin, trotting at Kate's side again, ushered her into the arched entrance, where the ox-wagons rumbling through had worn deep ruts. Juana came behind, making a humble nose.

Kate found herself in a big, barren yard, that seemed empty. There were high walls on the three sides, with sheds and stables. The fourth side, facing, was the house, with heavily-barred windows looking on to the courtyard, but with no door. Instead, there was another zaguan, or passage with closed doors, piercing the house.

Martin trotted ahead to knock on the closed doors. Kate stood looking round at the big yard. In a shed in one corner, four half-naked men were packing bunches of bananas. A man in the shade was sawing poles, and two men in the sun were unloading tiles from a donkey. In a corner was a bullock wagon, and a pair of big black-and-white oxen standing with heads pressed down, waiting.

The big doors opened, and Kate entered the second zaguan. It was a wide entrance way, with stairs going up on one side, and Kate lingered to look through the open iron gates in front of her, down a formal garden hemmed in with huge mango trees, to the lake, with its little artificial harbour where two boats were moored. The lake seemed to give off a great light, between the dark walls of mango.

At the back of the new-comers the servant woman closed the big doors on to the yard, then waved Kate to the stairs.

"Pass this way, Señorita."

A bell tinkled above. Kate climbed the stone stairs. And there above her was Doña Carlota, in white muslin and with white shoes and stockings, her face looking curiously yellow and faded by contrast. Her soft brown hair was low over her ears, and she held out her thin brownish arms with queer effusiveness.

"So, you have come! And you have walked, walked all the way? Oh, imagine walking in so much sun and dust! Come, come in and rest."

She took Kate's hands and led her across the open terrace at the top of the stairs.

"It is beautiful here," said Kate.

She stood on the terrace, looking out past the mango trees at the lake. A distant sailing canoe was going down the breeze, on the pallid, unreal water. Away across rose the bluish, grooved mountains, with the white speck of a village: far away in the morning it seemed, in another world, in another life, in another mode of time.

"What is that village?" Kate asked.

"That one? That one there? It is Ildefonso," said Doña Carlota, in her fluttering eagerness.

"But it is beautiful here!" Kate repeated.

"Hermoso—si! Si, bonito!" quavered the other woman uneasily, always answering in Spanish.

The house, reddish and yellow in colour, had two short wings towards the lake. The terrace, with green plants on the terrace wall, went round the three sides, the roof above supported by big square pillars that rose from the ground. Down below, the pillars made a sort of cloister around the three sides, and in the little stone court was a pool of water. Beyond, the rather neglected formal garden with strong sun and deep mango-shade.

"Come, you will need to rest!" said Doña Carlota.

"I would like to change my shoes," said Kate.

She was shown into a high, simple, rather bare bedroom with red-tiled floor. There she changed into the shoes and stockings Juana had carried, and rested a little.

As she lay resting, she heard the dulled thud-thud of the tom-tom drum, but, save the crowing of a cock in the distance, no other sound on the bright, yet curiously hollow Mexican morning. And the drum, thudding with its dulled, black insistence, made her uneasy. It sounded like something coming over the horizon.

She rose, and went into the long, high salon where Doña Carlota was sitting talking to a man in black. The salon, with its three window-doors open on to the terrace, its worn, red floor tiled with old square bricks, its high walls colour-washed a faint green, and the many-beamed ceiling white-washed; and with its bareness of furniture; seemed like part of the out-of-doors, like some garden-arbour put for shade. The sense, which houses have in hot climates, of being just three walls wherein one lingers for a moment, then goes away again.

As Kate entered the room, the man in black rose and shook

hands with Doña Carlota, bowing very low and deferential. Then with a deferential sideways sort of bow to Kate, he vanished out of doors.

"Come!" said Doña Carlota to Kate. "Are you sure now you are rested?" And she pulled forward one of the cane rocking-chairs that had poised itself in the room, en route to nowhere.

"Perfectly!" said Kate. "How still it seems here! Except for the drum. Perhaps it is the drum that makes it seem so still. Though I always think the lake *makes* a sort of silence."

"Ah, the drum!" cried Doña Carlota, lifting her hand with a gesture of nervous, spent exasperation. "I cannot hear it. No, I cannot, I cannot bear to hear it."

And she rocked herself in a sudden access of agitation.

"It does hit one rather below the belt," said Kate. "What is it?"

"Ah, do not ask me! It is my husband."

She made a gesture of despair, and rocked herself almost into unconsciousness.

"Is Don Ramón drumming?"

"Drumming?" Doña Carlota seemed to start. "No! Oh no! He is not drumming, himself. He brought down two Indians from the north to do that."

"Did he!" said Kate, non-committal.

But Doña Carlota was rocking in a sort of semi-consciousness. Then she seemed to pull herself together.

"I *must talk* to somebody, I must!" she said, suddenly straightening herself in her chair, her face creamy and creased, her soft brown hair saggling over her ears, her brown eyes oddly desperate. "May I talk to you?"

"Do!" said Kate, rather uneasy.

"You know what Ramón is doing?" she said, looking at Kate almost furtively, suspiciously.

"Does he want to bring back the old gods?" said Kate vaguely.

"Ah!" cried Doña Carlota, again with that desperate, flying jerk of her hand. "As if it were *possible!* As if it were possible! The old gods! Imagine it, Señora! The old gods! Why what are they? Nothing but dead illusions. And ugly, repulsive illusions! Ah! I always thought my husband such a clever man, so superior to me! Ah, it is terrible to have to change one's idea! This is such *nonsense.* How dare he! How dare he take such nonsense seriously! How does he dare!"

"Does he believe in it himself?" asked Kate.

"Himself? But, Señora—" and Doña Carlota gave a pitiful, pitying smile of contempt. "How could he! As if it were possible. After all he is an educated man! How could he believe in such nonsense!"

"Then why does he do it?"

"Why? Why?" There was a tone of unspeakable weariness in Doña Carlota's voice. "I wish I knew. I think he has gone insane, as Mexicans do. Insane like Francisco Villa, the bandit."

Kate thought of the pug-faced notorious Pancho Villa in wonder, unable to connect him with Don Ramón.

"All the Mexicans, as soon as they rise above themselves, go that way," said Doña Carlota. "Their pride gets the better of them. And then they understand nothing, nothing but their own foolish will, their will to be very, very important. It is just the male vanity. Don't you think, Señora, that the beginning and the end of a man is his vanity? Don't you think it was just against this danger that Christ came, to teach men a proper humility? To teach them the sin of pride? But that is why they hate Christ so much, and His teaching. First and last, they want their own vanity."

Kate had often thought so herself. Her own final conclusion about men was that *they* were the vanity of vanities, nothing but vanity. They must be flattered and made to feel great: Nothing else.

"And now, my husband wants to go to the other extreme of Jesus. He wants to exalt pride and vanity higher than God. Ah, it is terrible, terrible! And foolish like a little boy! Ah, what is a man but a little boy who needs a nurse and a mother! Ah, Señora, I can't bear it."

Doña Carlota covered her face with her hand, as if swooning.

"But there is something wonderful, too, about Don Ramón," said Kate coaxingly: though at the moment she hated him.

"Wonderful! Ah yes, he has gifts. He has great gifts! But what are gifts to a man who perverts them!"

"Tell me what you think he really wants," said Kate.

"Power! Just power! Just foolish, wicked power. As if there had not been enough horrible, wicked power let loose in this country. But he—he—he wants to be beyond them all. He—he —he wants to be worshipped. To be worshipped! To be worshipped! A God! He, whom I've held, I've held in my arms!

He is a child, as all men are children. And now he wants—to be worshipped—!" She went off into a shrill, wild laughter, covering her face with her hands, and laughing shrilly, her laughter punctuated by hollow, ghastly sobs.

Kate sat in absolute dismay, waiting for the other woman to recover herself. She felt cold against these hysterics, and exerted all her heavy female will to stop them.

"After all," she said, when Doña Carlota became quiet, her face in her hands, "it isn't your fault. We can't be responsible, even for our husbands. I know *that*, since my husband died, and I couldn't prevent him dying. And then—then I learned that no matter how you love another person, you can't really do anything, you are helpless when it comes to the last things. You have to leave them to themselves, when they want to die: or when they want to do things that seem foolish, so, so foolish, to a woman."

Doña Carlota looked up at the other woman.

"You loved your husband very much—and he died?" she said softly.

"I *did* love him. And I shall never, never love another man. I couldn't. I've lost the power."

"And why did he die?"

"Ah, even that was really his own fault. He broke his own soul and spirit, in those Irish politics. I knew it was wrong. What does Ireland matter, what does nationalism and all that rubbish matter, really! And revolutions! They are so, so stupid and *vieux jeu*. Ah! It would have been *so* much better if Joachim had been content to live his life in peace, with me. It could be so jolly, so lovely. And I tried and tried and tried with him. But it was no good. He *wanted* to kill himself with that beastly Irish business, and I tried in vain to prevent him."

Doña Carlota stared slowly at Kate.

"As a woman *must* try to prevent a man, when he is going wrong," she said. "As I try to prevent Ramón. As he will get himself killed, as surely as they all do, down to Francisco Villa. And when they are dead, what good is it all?"

"When they *are* dead," said Kate, "then you *know* it's no good."

"You do! Oh, Señora, if you think you can help me with Ramón, *do* help me, *do!* For it means the death either of me or him. And *I* shall die, though he is wrong. Unless he gets killed."

"Tell me what he wants to do," said Kate. "What does he

think he wants to do, anyhow?—Like my husband thought he wanted to make a free Ireland and a great Irish people. But I knew all the time, the Irish aren't a great people any more, and you *can't* make them free. They are only good at destroying— just mere stupid destroying. How can you make a people free, if they *aren't* free. If something inside them compels them to go on destroying!"

"I know! I know! And that is Ramón. He wants to destroy even Jesus and the Blessed Virgin, for this people. Imagine it! To destroy Jesus and the Blessed Virgin! the last thing they've got!"

"But what does he say himself, that he wants to do?"

"He says he wants to make a new connection between the people and God. He says himself, God is always God. But man loses his connection with God. And then he can never recover it again, unless some new Saviour comes to give him his new connection. And every new connection is different from the last, though God is always God. And now, Ramón says, the people have lost God. And the Saviour cannot lead them to Him any more. There must be a new Saviour with a new vision. But ah, Señora, that is not true for me. God is love, and if Ramón would only submit to love, he would know that he had found God. But he is perverse. Ah, if we could be together, quietly loving, and enjoying the beautiful world, and *waiting in the love of God!* Ah, Señora, *why,* why, why can't he see it? Oh, why can't he see it! Instead of doing all these—"

The tears came to Doña Carlota's eyes, and spilled over her cheeks. Kate also was in tears, mopping her face.

"It's no good!" she said, sobbing. "I know it's no good, no matter what we do. They don't *want* to be happy and peaceful. They *want* this strife and these other false, horrible connections. It's no good whatever we do! That's what's so bitter, so bitter!"

The two women sat in their bent-wood rocking-chairs and just sobbed. And as they sobbed, they heard a step coming along the terrace, the faint swish of the sandals of the people.

It was Don Ramón, drawn unconsciously by the emotional disturbance of the two women.

Doña Carlota hastily dabbed her eyes and her sniffing nose, Kate blew her nose like a trumpet, and Don Ramón stood in the doorway.

He was dressed in white, dazzling, in the costume of the peons,

the white blouse jacket and the white, wide pantaloon trousers. But the white was linen, slightly starched, and brilliant, almost unnatural in its whiteness. From under his blouse, in front, hung the ends of a narrow woollen sash, white, with blue and black bars, and a fringe of scarlet. And on his naked feet were the plaited huaraches, of blue and black strips of leather, with thick, red-dyed soles. His loose trousers were bound round the ankles with blue, red and black woollen braids.

Kate glanced at him as he stood in the sun, so dazzlingly white, that his black hair and dark face looked like a hole in the atmosphere. He came forward, the ends of his sash swinging against his thighs, his sandals slightly swishing.

"I am pleased to see you," he said, shaking hands with Kate. "How did you come?"

He dropped into a chair, and sat quite still. The two women hung their heads, hiding their faces. The presence of the man seemed to put their emotion out of joint. He ignored all the signs of their discomfort, overlooking it with a powerful will. There was a certain strength in his presence. They all cheered up a bit.

"You didn't know my husband had become one of the people a real peon—a Señor Peon, like Count Tolstoy became a Señor Moujik?" said Doña Carlota, with an attempt at raillery.

"Anyway it suits him," said Kate.

"There!" said Don Ramón. "Give the devil his dues."

But there was something unyielding, unbending about him. He laughed and spoke to the women only from a surface self. Underneath, powerful and inscrutable, he made no connection with them.

So it was at lunch. There was a flitting conversation, with intervals of silence. It was evident that Ramón was thinking in another world, in the silence. And the ponderous silence of his will, working in another sphere, made the women feel overshadowed.

"The Señora is like me, Ramón," said Doña Carlota. "She cannot bear the sound of that drum. Must it play any more this afternoon?"

There was a moment's pause, before he answered:

"After four o'clock only."

"*Must* we have that noise to-day?" Carlota persisted.

"Why not to-day like other days!" he said. But a certain

darkness was on his brow, and it was evident he wanted to leave the presence of the two women.

"Because the Señora is here: and I am here: and we neither of us like it. And to-morrow the Señora will not be here, and I shall be gone back to Mexico. So why not spare us to-day! Surely you can show us this consideration."

Ramón looked at her, and then at Kate. There was anger in his eyes. And Kate could almost feel, in his powerful chest, the big heart swelling with a suffocation of anger. Both women kept mum. But it pleased them, anyhow, that they could make him angry.

"Why not row with Mrs Leslie on the lake!" he said, with quiet control.

But under his dark brows was a level, indignant anger.

"We may not want to," said Carlota.

Then he did what Kate had not known anyone to do before. He withdrew his consciousness away from them as they all three sat at table, leaving the two women, as it were, seated outside a closed door, with nothing more happening. Kate felt for the time startled and forlorn, then a slow anger burned in her warm ivory cheek.

"Oh, yes," she said. "I can start home before then."

"No! No!" said Doña Carlota, with a Spanish wail. "Don't leave me. Stay with me till evening, and help me to amuse Don Cipriano. He is coming to supper."

CHAPTER XI

LORDS OF THE DAY AND NIGHT

WHEN lunch was over, Ramón went to his room, to sleep for an hour. It was a hot, still afternoon. Clouds were standing erect and splendid, at the west end of the lake, like messengers. Ramón went into his room and closed the window-doors and the shutters, till it was quite dark, save for yellow pencils of light that stood like substance on the darkness, from the cracks of the shutters.

He took off his clothes, and in the darkness thrust his clenched fists upwards above his head, in a terrible tension of stretched, upright prayer. In his eyes was only darkness, and slowly the darkness revolved in his brain, too, till he was mindless. Only a powerful will stretched itself and quivered from his spine in an immense tension of prayer. Stretched the invisible bow of the body in the darkness with inhuman tension, erect, till the arrows of the soul, mindless, shot to the mark, and the prayer reached its goal.

Then suddenly, the clenched and quivering arms dropped, the body relaxed into softness. The man had reached his strength again. He had broken the cords of the world, and was free in the other strength.

Softly, delicately, taking great care not to think, not to remember, not to disturb the poisonous snakes of mental consciousness, he picked up a thin, fine blanket, wrapped it round him, and lay down on the pile of mats on the floor. In an instant he was asleep.

He slept in complete oblivion for about an hour. Then suddenly he opened his eyes wide. He saw the velvety darkness, and the pencils of light gone frail. The sun had moved. Listening, there seemed not a sound in the world: there was no world.

Then he began to hear. He heard the faint rumble of an ox-wagon: then leaves in a wind: then a faint tapping noise: then the creak of some bird calling.

He rose and quickly dressed in the dark, and threw open the doors. It was mid-afternoon, with a hot wind blowing, and

clouds reared up dark and bronze in the west, the sun hidden. But the rain would not fall yet. He took a big straw hat and balanced it on his head. It had a round crest of black and white and blue feathers, like an eye, or a sun, in front. He heard the low sound of women talking. Ah, the strange woman! He had forgotten her. And Carlota! Carlota was here! He thought of her for a moment, and of her curious opposition. Then, before he could be angry, he lifted his breast again in the black, mindless prayer, his eyes went dark, and the sense of opposition left him

He went quickly, driftingly along the terrace to the stone stairs that led down to the inner entrance-way. Going through to the courtyard, he saw two men packing bales of bananas upon donkeys, under a shed. The soldiers were sleeping in the zaguan. Through the open doors, up the avenue of trees, he could see an ox-wagon slowly retreating. Within the courtyard there was the sharp ringing of metal hammered on an anvil. It came from a corner where was a smithy, where a man and a boy were working. In another shed, a carpenter was planing wood.

Don Ramón stood a moment to look around. This was his own world. His own spirit was spread over it like a soft, nourishing shadow, and the silence of his own power gave it peace.

The men working were almost instantly aware of his presence. One after the other the dark, hot faces glanced up at him, and glanced away again. They were men, and his presence was wonderful to them; but they were afraid to approach him, even by staring at him. They worked the quicker for having seen him, as if it gave them new life.

He went across to the smithy, where the boy was blowing the old-fashioned bellows, and the man was hammering a piece of metal, with quick, light blows. The man worked on without lifting his head, as the *patrón* drew near.

"It is the bird?" said Ramón, standing watching the piece of metal, now cold upon the anvil.

"Yes, *Patrón!* It is the bird. Is it right?" And the man looked up with black, bright, waiting eyes.

The smith lifted with the tongs the black, flat, tongue-shaped piece of metal, and Ramón looked at it for a long time.

"I put the wings on after," said the smith.

Ramón traced with his dark, sensitive hand an imaginary line, outside the edge of the iron. Three times he did it. And the movement fascinated the smith.

"A little more slender—so!" said Ramón.

"Yes, *Patrón!* Yes! Yes! I understand," said the man eagerly.

"And the rest?"

"Here it is!" The man pointed to two hoops of iron, one smaller than the other, and to some flat discs of iron, triangular in shape.

"Lay them on the ground."

The man put the hoops on the ground, one within the other. Then, taking the triangular discs, he placed them with quick, sensitive hands, so that their bases were upon the outer circle, and their apices touched the inner. There were seven. And thus they made a seven-pointed sun of the space inside.

"Now the bird," said Ramón.

The man quickly took the long piece of iron: it was the rudimentary form of a bird, with two feet, but as yet without wings. He placed it in the centre of the inner circle, so that the feet touched the circle and the crest of the head touched opposite.

"So! It fits," said the man.

Ramón stood looking at the big iron symbol on the ground. He heard the doors of the inner entrance: Kate and Carlota walking across the courtyard.

"I take it away?" asked the workman quickly.

"Never mind," Ramón answered quietly.

Kate stood and stared at the great wreath of iron on the ground.

"What is it?" she asked brightly.

"The bird within the sun."

"Is that a bird?"

"When it has wings."

"Ah, yes! When it has wings. And what is it for?"

"For a symbol to the people."

"It is pretty."

"Yes."

"Ramón!" said Doña Carlota, "will you give me the key for the boat? Martin will row us out."

He produced the key from under his sash.

"Where did you get that beautiful sash?" asked Kate.

It was the white sash with blue and brown-black bars, and with a heavy red fringe.

"This?" he said. "We wove it here."

"And did you make the sandals too?"

"Yes! They were made by Manuel. Later I will show you."

"Oh, I should like to see!—They are beautiful, don't you think, Doña Carlota?"

"Yes! Yes! It is true. But whether beautiful things are wise things, I don't know. So much I don't know, Señora. Ay, so much!—And you, do you know what is wise?"

"I?" said Kate. "I don't care very much."

"Ah! You don't care!—You think Ramón is wise, to wear the peasants' clothes, and the huaraches?" For once Doña Carlota was speaking in slow English.

"Oh, yes!" cried Kate. "He looks so handsome!—Men's clothes are so hideous, and Don Ramón looks so handsome in those!" With the big hat poised on his head, he had a certain air of nobility and authority.

"Ah!" cried Doña Carlota, looking at the other woman with intelligent, half-scared eyes, and swinging the key of the boat. "Shall we go to the lake?"

The two women departed. Ramón, laughing to himself, went out of the gate and across the outer yard, to where a big, barn-like building stood near the trees. He entered the barn, and gave a low whistle. It was answered from the loft above, and a trap-door opened. Don Ramón went up the steps, and found himself in a sort of studio and carpenter's shop. A fattish young man with curly hair, wearing an artist's blouse, and with mallet and chisels in his hand, greeted him.

"How is it going?" asked Ramón.

"Yes—well—"

The artist was working on a head, in wood. It was larger than life, conventionalised. Yet under the conventional lines the likeness to Ramón revealed itself.

"Sit for me for half an hour," said the sculptor.

Ramón sat in silence, while the other man bent over his model, working in silent concentration. And all the time, Ramón sat erect, almost motionless, with a great stillness of repose and concentration, thinking about nothing, but throwing out the dark aura of power, in the spell of which the artist worked.

"That is enough," he said at last, quietly rising.

"But give me the pose before you go," said the artist.

Ramón slowly took off his blouse-skirt, and stood with naked torso, the sash with its blue and black bars tight round his naked waist. For some moments he stood gathering himself together. Then suddenly, in a concentration of intense, proud prayer, he flung his right arm up above his head, and stood transfixed, his left arm hanging softly by his side, the fingers touching his thigh. And on his face that fixed, intense look of pride which was at once a prayer.

The artist gazed with wonder, and with an appreciation touched with fear. The other man, large and intense, with big dark eyes staring with intense pride, yet prayerful, beyond the natural horizons, sent a thrill of dread and of joy through the artist. He bowed his head as he looked.

Don Ramón turned to him.

"Now you!" he said.

The artist was afraid. He seemed to quail. But he met Ramón's eyes. And instantly, that stillness of concentration came over him, like a trance. And then suddenly, out of the trance, he shot his arm aloft, and his fat, pale face took on an expression of peace, a noble, motionless transfiguration, the blue-grey eyes calm, proud, reaching into the beyond, with prayer. And though he stood in his blouse, with a rather pudgy figure and curly hair, he had the perfect stillness of nobility.

"It is good!" said Ramón, bowing his head.

The artist suddenly changed; Ramón held out his two hands, the artist took them in his two hands. Then he lifted Ramón's right hand and placed the back of it on his brow.

"Adios!" said Ramón, taking his blouse again.

"Adios, señor!" said the artist.

And with a proud, white look of joy in his face, he turned again to his work.

Ramón visited the adobe house, its yard fenced with cane and overshadowed by a great mango tree, where Manuel and his wife and children, and two assistants, were spinning and weaving. Two little girls were assiduously carding white wool and brown wool under a cluster of banana trees: the wife and a young maiden were spinning fine, fine thread. On the line hung dyed wool, red, and blue, and green. And under the shed stood Manuel and a youth, weaving at two heavy hand-looms.

"How is it going?" called Don Ramón.

"Muy bien! Muy bien!" answered Manuel, with that curious look of transfiguration glistening in his black eyes and in the smile of his face. "It is going well, very well, señor!"

Ramón paused to look at the fine white serape on the loom. It had a zig-zag border of natural black wool and blue, in little diamonds, and the ends a complication of blackish and blue diamond-pattern. The man was just beginning to do the centre—called the *boca,* the mouth: and he looked anxiously at the design that was tacked to the loom. But it was simple: the same as the iron symbol the smith was making: a snake with his tail in his mouth, the black triangles on his back being the outside of the circle: and in the middle, a blue eagle standing erect, with slim wings touching the belly of the snake with their tips, and slim feet upon the snake, within the hoop.

Ramón went back to the house, to the upper terrace, and round to the short wing where his room was. He put a folded serape over his shoulder, and went along the terrace. At the end of this wing, projecting to the lake, was a square terrace with a low, thick wall and a tiled roof, and a coral-scarlet bignonia dangling from the massive pillars. The terrace, or loggia, was strewn with the native palm-leaf mats, *petates,* and there was a drum in one corner, with the drum-stick upon it. At the far inner corner, went down an enclosed stone staircase, with an iron door at the bottom.

Ramón stood a while looking out at the lake. The clouds were dissolving again, the sheet of water gave off a whitish light. In the distance he could see the dancing speck of a boat, probably Martin with the two women.

He took off his hat and his blouse, and stood motionless, naked to the waist. Then he lifted the drum-stick, and after waiting a moment or two, to become still in soul, he sounded the rhythmic summons, rather slow, yet with a curious urge in its strong-weak, one-two rhythm. He had got the old barbaric power into the drum.

For some time he stood alone, the drum, or tom-tom, lifted by its thong against his legs, his right hand drumming, his face expressionless. A man entered, bareheaded, running from the inner terrace. He was in the white cotton clothes, snow white, but with a dark serape folded on his shoulder, and he held a key in his hand. He saluted Ramón by putting the back of his right

hand in front of his eyes for a moment, then he went down the stone stairway and opened the iron door.

Immediately men were coming up, all dressed alike, in the white cotton clothes and the huaraches, each with a folded serape over his shoulder. But their sashes were all blue, and their sandals blue and white. The sculptor came too, and Mirabal was there, also dressed in the cotton clothes.

There were seven men, besides Ramón. At the top of the stairs, one after another, they saluted. Then they took their serapes, dark brown, with blue eyes filled with white, along the edges, and threw them down along the wall, their hats beside them. Then they took off their blouses, and flung them on their hats.

Ramón left the drum, and sat down on his own serape, that was white with the blue and black bars, and the scarlet fringe. The drummer sat down and took the drum. The circle of men sat cross-legged, naked to the waist, silent. Some were of a dark, ruddy coffee-brown, two were white, Ramón was of a soft creamy brown. They sat in silence for a time, only the monotonous, hypnotic sound of the drum pulsing, touching the inner air. Then the drummer began to sing, in the curious, small, inner voice, that hardly emerges from the circle, singing in the ancient falsetto of the Indians:

"Who sleeps—shall wake! Who sleeps—shall wake! Who treads down the path of the snake shall arrive at the place; in the path of the dust shall arrive at the place and be dressed in the skin of the snake—"

One by one the voices of the men joined in, till they were all singing in the strange, blind infallible rhythm of the ancient barbaric world. And all in the small, inward voices, as if they were singing from the oldest, darkest recess of the soul, not outwards, but inwards, the soul singing back to herself.

They sang for a time, in the peculiar unison like a flock of birds that fly in one consciousness. And when the drum shuddered for an end, they all let their voices fade out, with the same broad, clapping sound in the throat.

There was silence. The men turned, speaking to one another, laughing in a quiet way. But their daytime voices, and their daytime eyes had gone.

Then Ramón's voice was heard, and the men were suddenly silent, listening with bent heads. Ramón sat with his face lifted, looking far away, in the pride of prayer.

"There is no Before and After, there is only Now," he said, speaking in a proud, but inward voice.

"The great Snake coils and uncoils the plasm of his folds, and stars appear, and worlds fade out. It is no more than the changing and easing of the plasm.

"*I always am,* says his sleep.

"As a man in a deep sleep knows not, but is, so is the Snake of the coiled cosmos, wearing its plasm.

"As a man in a deep sleep has no to-morrow, no yesterday, nor to-day, but only *is,* so is the limpid, far-reaching Snake of the eternal Cosmos, Now, and forever Now.

"Now, and only Now, and forever Now.

"But dreams arise and fade in the sleep of the Snake.

"And worlds arise as dreams, and are gone as dreams.

"And man is a dream in the sleep of the Snake.

"And only the sleep that is dreamless breathes *I Am!*

"In the dreamless Now, *I Am.*

"Dreams arise as they must arise, and man is a dream arisen.

"But the dreamless plasm of the Snake is the plasm of a man, of his body, his soul, and his spirit at one.

"And the perfect sleep of the Snake *I Am* is the plasm of a man, who is whole.

"When the plasm of the body, and the plasm of the soul, and the plasm of the spirit are at one, in the Snake *I Am.*

"I am Now.

"Was-not is a dream, and shall-be is a dream, like two separate, heavy feet.

"But Now, I Am.

"The trees put forth their leaves in their sleep, and flowering emerge out of dreams, into pure I Am.

"The birds forget the stress of their dreams, and sing aloud in the Now, I Am! I Am!

"For dreams have wings and feet, and journeys to take, and efforts to make.

"But the glimmering Snake of the Now is wingless and footless, and undivided, and perfectly coiled.

"It is thus the cat lies down, in the coil of Now, and the cow curves round her nose to her belly, lying down.

"In the feet of a dream the hare runs uphill. But when he pauses, the dream has passed, he has entered the timeless Now, and his eyes are the wide I Am.

"Only man dreams, dreams, and dreams, and changes from dream to dream, like a man who tosses on his bed.

"With his eyes and his mouth he dreams, with his hands and his feet, with phallos and heart and belly, with body and spirit and soul, in a tempest of dreams.

"And rushes from dream to dream, in the hope of the perfect dream.

"But I, I say to you, there is no dream that is perfect, for every dream has an ache and an urge, an urge and an ache.

"And nothing is perfect, save the dream pass out into the sleep, I Am.

"When the dream of the eyes is darkened, and encompassed with Now.

"And the dream of the mouth resounds in the last I Am.

"And the dream of the hands is a sleep like a bird on the sea, that sleeps and is lifted and shifted, and knows not.

"And the dreams of the feet and the toes touch the core of the world, where the Serpent sleeps.

"And the dream of the phallos reaches the great I Know Not.

"And the dream of the body is the stillness of a flower in the dark.

"And the dream of the soul is gone in the perfume of Now.

"And the dream of the spirit lapses, and lays down its head, and is still with the Morning Star.

"For each dream starts out of Now, and is accomplished in Now.

"In the core of the flower, the glimmering, wakeless Snake.

"And what falls away is a dream, and what accrues is a dream. There is always and only Now, Now and I Am."

There was silence in the circle of men. Outside, the sound of the bullock-wagon could be heard, and from the lake, the faint knocking of oars. But the seven men sat with their heads bent, in the semi-trance, listening inwardly.

Then the drum began softly to beat, as if of itself. And a man began to sing, in a small voice:

> The Lord of the Morning Star
> Stood between the day and the night:
> As a bird that lifts its wings, and stands
> With the bright wing on the right
> And the wing of the dark on the left,
> The Dawn Star stood into sight.

Lo! I am always here!
Far in the hollow of space
I brush the wing of the day
And put light on your face.
The other wing brushes the dark.
But I, I am always in place.

Yea, I am always here. I am Lord
In every way. And the lords among men
See me through the flashing of wings.
They see me and lose me again.
But lo! I am always here
Within ken.

The multitude see me not.
They see only the waving of wings,
The coming and going of things.
The cold and the hot.

But ye that perceive me between
The tremors of night and the day,
I make you the Lords of the Way
Unseen.

The path between gulfs of the dark and the steeps of the light;
The path like a snake that is gone, like the length of a fuse to ignite
The substance of shadow, that bursts and explodes into sight.

I am here undeparting. I sit tight
Between the wings of the endless flight,
At the depths of the peace and the fight.

Deep in the moistures of peace,
And far down the muzzle of the fight
You shall find me, who am neither increase
Nor destruction, different quite.

I am far beyond
The horizons of love and strife.
Like a star, like a pond
That washes the lords of life.

"Listen!" said Ramón, in the stillness. "We will be masters
among men, and lords among men. But lords of men, and masters of men we will not be. Listen! We are lords of the night.

Lords of the day and night.   Sons of the Morning Star, sons of the Evening Star.   Men of the Morning and the Evening Star.

"We are not lords of men: how can men make us lords?   Nor are we masters of men, for men are not worth it.

"But I am the Morning and the Evening Star, and lord of the day and the night.   By the power that is put in my left hand, and the power that I grasp in my right, I am lord of the two ways.

"And my flower on earth is the jasmine flower, and in heaven the flower Hesperus.

"I will not command you, nor serve you, for the snake goes crooked to his own house.

"Yet I will be with you, so you depart not from yourselves.

"There is no giving, and no taking.   When the fingers that give touch the fingers that receive, the Morning Star shines at once, from the contact, and the jasmine gleams between the hands. And thus there is neither giving nor taking, nor hand that proffers nor hand that receives, but the star between them is all, and the dark hand and the light hand are invisible on each side.   The jasmine takes the giving and the receiving in her cup, and the scent of the oneness is fragrant on the air.

"Think neither to give nor to receive, only let the jasmine flower.

"Let nothing spill from you in excess, let nothing be reived from you.

"And reive nothing away.   Not even the scent from the rose, nor the juice from the pomegranate, nor the warmth from the fire.

"But say to the rose: Lo! I take you away from your tree, and your breath is in my nostrils, and my breath is warm in your depths.   Let it be a sacrament between us.

"And beware when you break the pomegranate; it is sunset you take in your hands.   Say: I am coming, come thou.   Let the Evening Star stand between us.

"And when the fire burns up and the wind is cold and you spread your hands to the blaze, listen to the flame saying: Ah! Is it thou?   Comest thou to me?   Lo, I was going the longest journey, down the path of the greatest snake.   But since thou comest to me, I come to thee.   And where thou fallest into my hands, fall I into thine, and jasmine flowers on the burning bush between us.   Our meeting is the burning bush, whence the jasmine flowers.

"Reive nothing away, and let nothing be reived from you.   For

reiver and bereaved alike break the root of the jasmine flower, and spit upon the Evening Star.

"Take nothing, to say: *I have it!* For you can possess nothing, not even peace.

"Nought is possessible, neither gold, nor land nor love, nor life, nor peace, nor even sorrow nor death, nor yet salvation.

"Say of nothing: It is mine.

"Say only: It is with me.

"For the gold that is with thee lingers as a departing moon, looking across thy way, saying: Lo! We are beholden of each other. Lo! for this little while, to each other thou and I are beholden.

"And thy land says to thee: Ah, my child of a far-off father! Come, lift me, lift me a little while, that poppies and wheat may blow on the level wind that moves between my breast and thine! Then sink with me, and we will make one mound.

"And listen to thy love saying: Beloved! I am mown by thy sword like mown grass, and darkness is upon me, and the tremble of the Evening Star. And to me thou art darkness and nowhere. Oh thou, when thou risest up and goest thy way, speak to me, only say: The star rose between us.

"And say to thy life: Am I thine? Art thou mine? Am I the blue curve of day around thine uncurved night? Are my eyes the twilight of neither of us, where the star hangs? Is my upper lip the sunset and my lower lip the dawn, does the star tremble inside my mouth?

"And say to thy peace: Ah! risen, deathless star! Already the waters of dawn sweep over thee, and wash me away on the flood!

"And say to thy sorrow: Axe, thou art cutting me down!

"Yet did a spark fly from out of thy edge and my wound!

"Cut then, while I cover my face, father of the Star.

"And say to thy strength: Lo, the night is foaming up my feet and my loins, day is foaming down from my eyes and my mouth to the sea of my breast. Lo, they meet! My belly is a flood of power, that races in down the sluice of bone at my back, and a star hangs low on the flood, over a troubled dawn.

"And say to thy death: Be it so! I, and my soul, we come to thee, Evening Star. Flesh, go thou into the night. Spirit, farewell, 'tis thy day. Leave me now. I go in last nakedness now to the nakedest Star."

CHAPTER XII

THE FIRST WATERS

THE men had risen and covered themselves, and put on their hats, and covered their eyes for a second, in salute before Ramón, as they departed down the stone stair. And the iron door at the bottom had clanged, the doorkeeper had returned with the key, laid it on the drum, and softly, delicately departed.

Still Ramón sat on his serape, leaning his naked shoulders on the wall, and closing his eyes. He was tired, and in that state of extreme separateness which makes it very hard to come back to the world. On the outside of his ears he could hear the noises of the hacienda, even the tinkle of tea-spoons, and the low voice of women, and later, the low, labouring sound of a motor-car struggling over the uneven road, then swirling triumphantly into the courtyard.

It was hard to come back to these things. The noise of them sounded on the outside of his ears, but inside them was the slow, vast, inaudible roar of the cosmos, like in a sea-shell. It was hard to have to bear the contact of commonplace daily things, when his soul and body were naked to the cosmos.

He wished they would leave him the veils of his isolation awhile. But they would not: especially Carlota. She wanted him to be present to her: in familiar contact.

She was calling: "Ramón! Ramón! Have you finished? Cipriano is here." And even so, in her voice was fear, and an over-riding temerity.

He pushed back his hair and rose, and very quickly went out, as he was, with naked torso. He didn't want to dress himself into everyday familiarity, since his soul was unfamiliar.

They had a tea-table out on the terrace, and Cipriano, in uniform, was there. He got up quickly, and came down the terrace with outstretched arms, his black eyes gleaming with an intensity almost like pain, upon the face of the other man. And Ramón looked back at him with wide, seeing, yet unchanging eyes.

The two men embraced, breast to breast, and for a moment Cipriano laid his little blackish hands on the naked shoulders of the bigger man, and for a moment was perfectly still on his breast. Then very softly, he stood back and looked at him, saying not a word.

Ramón abstractly laid his hand on Cipriano's shoulder, looking down at him with a little smile.

"Que tal?" he said, from the edge of his lips. "How goes it?"

"Bien! Muy bien!" said Cipriano, still gazing into the other man's face with black, wondering, childlike, searching eyes, as if he, Cipriano, were searching for *himself,* in Ramón's face. Ramón looked back into Cipriano's black, Indian eyes with a faint, kind smile of recognition, and Cipriano hung his head as if to hide his face, the black hair, which he wore rather long and brushed sideways, dropping over his forehead.

The women watched in absolute silence. Then, as the two men began slowly to come along the terrace to the tea-table, Carlota began to pour tea. But her hand trembled so much, the teapot wobbled as she held it, and she had to put it down and clasp her hands in the lap of her white muslin dress.

"You rowed on the lake?" said Ramón abstractedly, coming up.

"It was lovely!" said Kate. "But hot when the sun came."

Ramón smiled a little, then pushed his hand through his hair. Then, leaning one hand on the parapet of the terrace wall, he turned to look at the lake, and a sigh lifted his shoulders unconsciously.

He stood thus, naked to the waist, his black hair ruffled and splendid, his back to the women, looking out at the lake. Cipriano stood lingering beside him.

Kate saw the sigh lift the soft, quiescent, cream-brown shoulders. The soft, cream-brown skin of his back, of a smooth, *pure* sensuality, made her shudder. The broad, square, rather high shoulders, with neck and head rising steep, proudly. The full-fleshed, deep chested, rich body of the man made her feel dizzy. In spite of herself, she could not help imagining a knife stuck between those pure, male shoulders. If only to break the arrogance of their remoteness.

That was it. His nakedness was so aloof, far-off and intangible, in another day. So that to *think* of it was almost a violation, even to look at it with prying eyes. Kate's heart suddenly shrank in her breast. This was how Salome had looked at John. And this was the beauty of John, that he had had; like a pome-

granate on a dark tree in the distance, naked, but not undressed!
Forever still and clothe-less, and with another light about it, of a
richer day than our paltry, prying, sneak-thieving day.

The moment Kate had imagined a knife between his shoulders,
her heart shrank with grief and shame, and a great stillness came
over her. Better to take the hush into one's heart, and the sharp,
prying beams out of one's eyes. Better to lapse away from one's
own prying, assertive self, into the soft, untrespassing self, to
whom nakedness is neither shame nor excitement, but clothed
like a flower in its own deep, soft consciousness, beyond cheap
awareness.

The evening breeze was blowing very faintly. Sailing boats
were advancing through the pearly atmosphere, far off, the sun
above had a golden quality. The opposite shore, twenty miles
away, was distinct, and yet there seemed an opalescent, spume-
like haze in the air, the same quality as in the filmy water. Kate
could see the white specks of the far-off church towers of
Tuliapan.

Below, in the garden below the house, was a thick grove of
mango trees. Among the dark and reddish leaves of the mangos,
scarlet little birds were bustling, like suddenly-opening poppy-
buds, and pairs of yellow birds, yellow underneath as yellow butterflies, so perfectly clear, went skimming past. When they settled for a moment and closed their wings, they disappeared, for
they were grey on top. And when the cardinal birds settled, they
too disappeared, for the outside of their wings was brown, like a
sheath.

"Birds in this country have all their colour below," said Kate.

Ramón turned to her suddenly.

"They say the word *Mexico* means *below this!*" he said, smiling, and sinking into a rocking chair.

Dona Carlota had made a great effort over herself, and with
eyes fixed on the tea-cups, she poured out the tea. She handed
him his cup without looking at him. She did not trust herself to
look at him. It made her tremble with a strange, hysterical anger: she, who had been married to him for years, and knew him,
ah, knew him: and yet, and yet, had not got him at all. None of
him.

"Give me a piece of sugar, Carlota," he said, in his quiet voice.

But at the sound of it, his wife stopped as if some hand had
suddenly grasped her.

"Sugar! Sugar!" she repeated abstractedly to herself.

Ramón sat forward in his rocking-chair, holding his cup in his hand, his breasts rising in relief. And on his thighs the thin linen seemed to reveal him almost more than his own dark nakedness revealed him. She understood why the cotton pantaloons were forbidden on the plaza. The living flesh seemed to emanate through them.

He was handsome, almost horribly handsome, with his black head poised as it were without weight, above his darkened, smooth neck. A pure sensuality, with a powerful purity of its own, hostile to her sort of purity. With the blue sash round his waist, pressing a fold in the flesh, and the thin linen seeming to gleam with the life of his hips and thighs, he emanated a fascination almost like a narcotic asserting his pure, fine sensuality against her. The strange, soft, still sureness of him, as he sat secure within his own dark aura. And as if this dark aura of his militated against her presence, and against the presence of his wife. He emitted an effluence so powerful that it seemed to hamper her consciousness, to bind down her limbs.

And he was utterly still and quiescent, without desire, soft and unroused, within his own *ambiente*. Cipriano going the same, the pair of them so quiet and dark and heavy, like a great weight bearing the women down.

Kate knew now how Salome felt. She knew now how John the Baptist had been, with his terrible, aloof beauty, inaccessible yet so potent.

"Ah!" she said to herself. "Let me close my eyes to him, and open only my soul. Let me close my prying, *seeing* eyes, and sit in dark stillness along with these two men. They have got more than I, they have a richness that I haven't got. They have got rid of that itching of the eye, and the desire that works through the eye. The itching, prurient, *knowing,* imagining eye, I am cursed with it, I am hampered up in it. It is my curse of curses, the curse of Eve. The curse of Eve is upon me, my eyes are like hooks, my knowledge is like a fish-hook through my gills, pulling me in spasmodic desire. Oh, who will free me from the grappling of my eyes, from the impurity of sharp sight! Daughter of Eve, of greedy vision, why don't these men save me from the sharpness of my own eyes!"

She rose and went to the edge of the terrace. Yellow as daffodils underneath, two birds emerged out of their own invisibility.

In the little shingle bay, with a small breakwater, where the boat was pulled up and chained, two men were standing in the water, throwing out a big, fine round net, catching the little silvery fish called *charales,* which flicked out of the brownish water sometimes like splinters of glass.

"Ramón!" Kate heard Dona Carlota's voice. "Won't you put something on?"

The wife had been able to bear it no more.

"Yes! Thank you for the tea," said Ramón, rising.

Kate watched him go down the terrace, in his own peculiar silence, his sandals making a faint swish on the tiles.

"Oh, Señora Caterina!" came the voice of Carlota. "Come and drink your tea. Come!"

Kate returned to the table, saying:

"It seems so wonderfully peaceful here."

"Peaceful!" echoed Carlota. "Ah, I do not find it peaceful. There is a horrible stillness, which makes me afraid."

"Do you come out very often?" said Kate, to Cipriano.

"Yes. Fairly often. Once a week. Or twice," he replied, looking at her with a secret consciousness which she could not understand, lurking in his black eyes.

These men wanted to take her *will* away from her, as if they wanted to deny her the light of day.

"I must be going home now," she said. "The sun will be setting."

"*Ya va?*" said Cipriano, in his soft, velvety Indian voice, with a note of distant surprise and reproach. "Will you go already?"

"Oh, no, Señora!" cried Carlota. "Stay until to-morrow. Oh, yes, stay until to-morrow, with me."

"They will expect us home," she said, wavering.

"Ah, no! I can send a boy to say you will come to-morrow. Yes? You will stay? Ah, good, good!"

And she laid her hand caressively on Kate's arm, then rose to hurry away to the servants.

Cipriano had taken out his cigarette case. He offered it to Kate.

"Shall I take one?" she said. "It is my vice."

"Do take one," he said. "It isn't good, to be perfect."

"It isn't, is it?" she laughed, puffing her cigarette.

"Now would you call it peace?" he asked with incomprehensible irony.

"Why?" she cried.

"Why do white people always want peace?" he asked.

"Surely peace is natural! Don't all people want it? Don't you?"

"Peace is only the rest after war," he said. "So it is not more natural than fighting: perhaps not so natural."

"No, but there is another peace: the peace that passes all understanding. Don't you know that?"

"I don't think I do," he said.

"What a pity!" she cried.

"Ah!" he said. "You want to teach me! But to me it is different. Each man has two spirits in him. The one is like the early morning in the time of rain, very quiet, and sweet, moist, no?—with the mocking-bird singing, and birds flying about, very fresh. And the other is like the dry season, the steady, strong hot light of the day, which seems as if it will never change."

"But you like the first better," she cried.

"I don't know!" he replied. "The other lasts longer."

"I am sure you like the fresh morning better," she said.

"I don't know! I don't know!" He smiled a crumpled sort of smile, and she could tell he really did *not* know. "In the first time, you can feel the flowers on their stem, the stem very strong and full of sap, no?—and the flower opening on top like a face that has the perfume of desire. And a woman might be like that.— But this passes, and the sun begins to shine very strong, very hot, no? Then everything inside a man changes, goes dark, no! And the flowers crumple up, and the breast of a man becomes like a steel mirror. And he is all darkness inside, coiling and uncoiling like a snake. All the flowers withered up on shrunk stems, no? And then women don't exist for a man. They disappear like the flowers."

"And then what does he want?" said Kate.

"I don't know. Perhaps he wants to be a very big man, and master all the people."

"Then why doesn't he?" said Kate.

He lifted his shoulders.

"And you," he said to her. "You seem to me like that morning I told you about."

"I am just forty years old," she laughed shakily.

Again he lifted his shoulders.

"It doesn't matter," he said. "It is the same. Your body

seems to me like the stem of the flower I told you about, and in your face it will always be morning, of the time of the rains."

"Why do you say that to me?" she said, as an involuntary strange shudder shook her.

"Why not say it!" he replied. "You are like the cool morning, very fresh. In Mexico, we are the end of the hot dry day."

He watched her, with a strange lingering desire in his black eyes, and what seemed to her a curious, lurking sort of insolence. She dropped her head to hide from him, and rocked in her chair.

"I would like to marry you," he said; "if ever you will marry. I would like to marry you."

"I don't think I shall *ever* marry again," she flashed, her bosom heaving like suffocation, and a dark flush suffusing over her face, against her will.

"Who knows!" said he.

Ramón was coming down the terrace, his fine white serape folded over his naked shoulder, with its blue-and-dark pattern at the borders, and its long scarlet fringe dangling and swaying as he walked. He leaned against one of the pillars of the terrace, and looked down at Kate and Cipriano. Cipriano glanced up with that peculiar glance of primitive intimacy.

"I told the Señora Caterina," he said, "if ever she wanted to marry a man, she should marry me."

"It is plain talk," said Ramón, glancing at Cipriano with the same intimacy, and smiling.

Then he looked at Kate, with a slow smile in his brown eyes, and a shadow of curious knowledge on his face. He folded his arms over his breast, as the natives do when it is cold and they are protecting themselves; and the cream-brown flesh, like opium, lifted the bosses of his breast, full and smooth.

"Don Cipriano says that white people always want peace," she said, looking up at Ramón with haunted eyes. "Don't you consider yourselves white people?" she asked, with a slight, deliberate impertinence.

"No whiter than we are," smiled Ramón. "Not lily-white, at least."

"And don't you want peace?" she asked.

"I? I shouldn't think of it. The meek have inherited the earth, according to prophecy. But who am I, that I should envy them their peace! No, Señora. Do I look like a gospel of

peace?—or a gospel of war either? Life doesn't split down that division, for me."

"I don't know what you want," said she, looking up at him with haunted eyes.

"We only half know ourselves," he replied, smiling with changeful eyes. "Perhaps not so much as half."

There was a certain vulnerable kindliness about him, which made her wonder, startled, if she had ever realised what real fatherliness meant. The mystery, the nobility, the inaccessibility, and the vulnerable compassion of man in his separate fatherhood.

"You don't like brown-skinned people?" he asked her gently.

"I think it is beautiful to look at," she said. "But"—with a faint shudder—"I am glad I am white."

"You feel there could be no contact?" he said, simply.

"Yes!" she said. "I mean that."

"It is as you feel," he said.

And as he said it, she knew he was more beautiful to her than any blond white man, and that, in a remote, far-off way, the contact with him was more precious than any contact she had known.

But then, though he cast over her a certain shadow, he would never encroach on her, he would never seek any close contact. It was the incompleteness in Cipriano that sought her out, and seemed to trespass on her.

Hearing Ramón's voice, Carlota appeared uneasily in a doorway. Hearing him speak English, she disappeared again, on a gust of anger. But after a little while, she came once more, with a little vase containing the creamy-coloured, thick flowers that are coloured like freesias, and that smell very sweet.

"Oh, how nice!" said Kate. "They are temple flowers! In Ceylon the natives tiptoe into the little temples and lay one flower on the table at the foot of the big Buddha statues. And the tables of offering are all covered with these flowers, all put so neatly. The natives have that delicate oriental way of putting things down."

"Ah!" said Carlota, setting the vase on the table. "I did not bring them for any gods, especially strange ones. I brought them for you, Señora. They smell so sweet."

"Don't they!" said Kate.

The two men went away, Ramón laughing.

"Ah, Señora!" said Carlota, sitting down tense at the table. "Could you follow Ramón? Could *you* give up the Blessed Virgin?—I could sooner die!"

"Ha!" said Kate, with a little weariness. "Surely we don't want any *more* gods."

"More gods, Señora!" said Doña Carlota, shocked. "But how is it possible!—Don Ramón is in mortal sin."

Kate was silent.

"And he wants to lead more and more people into the same," continued Carlota. "It is the sin of pride. Men wise in their own conceit!—The cardinal sin of men. Ah, I have told him.— And I am so glad, Señora, that you feel as I feel. I am so afraid of American women, women like that. They wish to have men's minds, so they accept all the follies and wickedness of men.—You are Catholic, Señora?"

"I was educated in a convent," said Kate.

"Ah, of course! Of course!—Ah, Señora, as if a woman who had ever known the Blessed Virgin could ever part from her again. Ah, Señora, what woman would have the heart to put Christ back on the Cross, to crucify him twice! But men, men! This Quetzalcoatl business! What buffoonery, Señora; if it were not horrible sin! And two clever, well-educated men! Wise in their own conceit!"

"Men usually are," said Kate.

It was sunset, with a big level cloud like fur overhead, only the sides of the horizon fairly clear. The sun was not visible. It had gone down in a thick, rose-red fume behind the wavy ridge of the mountains. Now the hills stood up bluish, all the air was a salmon-red flush, the fawn water had pinkish ripples. Boys and men, bathing a little way along the shore, were the colour of deep flame.

Kate and Carlota had climbed up to the azotea, the flat roof, from the stone stairway at the end of the terrace. They could see the world: the hacienda with its courtyard like a fortress, the road between deep trees, the black mud huts near the broken high road, and little naked fires already twinkling outside the doors. All the air was pinkish, melting to a lavender blue, and the willows on the shore, in the pink light, were apple-green and glowing. The hills behind rose abruptly, like mounds, dry and pinky. Away in the distance, down the lake, the two white obelisk towers of Sayula glinted among the trees, and villas peeped out. Boats were creeping into the shadow, from the outer brightness of the lake.

And in one of these boats was Juana, being rowed, disconsolate, home.

CHAPTER XIII

THE FIRST RAIN

RAMON and Cipriano were out by the lake. Cipriano also had changed into the white clothes and sandals, and he looked better than when in uniform.

"I had a talk with Montes when he came to Guadalajara," Cipriano said to Ramón. Montes was the President of the Republic.

"And what did he say?"

"He is careful. But he doesn't like his colleagues. I think he feels lonely. I think he would like to know you better."

"Why?"

"Perhaps that you could give him your moral support. Perhaps that you might be Secretary, and President when Montes' term is up."

"I like Montes," said Ramón. "He is sincere and passionate. Did you like him?"

"Yes!" said Cipriano. "More or less. He is suspicious, and jealous for fear anyone else might want to share in his power. He has the cravings of a dictator. He wanted to find out if I would stick to him."

"You let him know you would?"

"I told him that all I cared for was for you and for Mexico."

"What did he say?"

"Well, he is no fool. He said: 'Don Ramón sees the world with different eyes from mine. Who knows which of us is right. I want to save my country from poverty and unenlightenment, he wants to save its soul. I say, a hungry and ignorant man has no place for a soul. An empty belly grinds upon itself, so does an empty mind, and the soul doesn't exist. Don Ramón says, if a man has no soul, it doesn't matter whether he is hungry or ignorant. Well, he can go his way, and I mine. We shall never hinder one another, I believe. I give you my word I won't have him interfered with. He sweeps the patio and I sweep the street."

"Sensible!" said Ramón. "And honest in his convictions."

"Why should you not be Secretary in a few months' time? And follow to the Presidency?" said Cipriano.

"You know I don't want that. I must stand in another world, and act in another world.—Politics must go their own way, and society must do as it will. Leave me alone, Cipriano. I know you want me to be another Porfirio Diaz, or something like that. But for me that would be failure pure and simple."

Cipriano was watching Ramón with black, guarded eyes, in which was an element of love, and of fear, and of trust, but also incomprehension, and the suspicion that goes with incomprehension.

"I don't understand, myself, *what* you want," he muttered.

"Yes, yes, you do. Politics, and all this *social* religion that Montes has got is like washing the outside of the egg, to make it look clean. But I, myself, I want to get inside the egg, right to the middle, to start it growing into a new bird. Ay! Cipriano! Mexico is like an old, old egg that the bird of Time laid long ago; and she has been sitting on it for centuries, till it looks foul in the nest of the world. But still, Cipriano, it is a good egg. It is not addled. Only the spark of fire has never gone into the middle of it, to start it.—Montes wants to clean the nest and wash the egg. But meanwhile, the egg will go cold and die. The more you save these people from poverty and ignorance, the quicker they will die: like a dirty egg that you take from under the hen-eagle, to wash it. While you wash the egg, it chills and dies. Poor old Montes, all his ideas are American and European. And the old Dove of Europe will never hatch the egg of dark-skinned America. The United States can't die, because it isn't alive. It is a nestful of china eggs, made of pot. So they can be kept clean.—But here, Cipriano, here, let us hatch the chick before we start cleaning up the nest."

Cipriano hung his head. He was always testing Ramón, to see if he could change him. When he found he couldn't, then he submitted, and new little fires of joy sprang up in him. But meanwhile, he had to try, and try again.

"It is no good, trying to mix the two things. At this stage of affairs, at least, they won't mix. We have to shut our eyes and sink down, sink away from the surface, away, like shadows, down to the bottom. Like the pearl divers. But you keep bobbing up like a cork."

Cipriano smiled subtly. He knew well enough.

"We've got to open the oyster of the cosmos, and get our manhood out of it. Till we've got the pearl, we are only gnats on the surface of the ocean," said Ramón.

"My manhood is like a devil inside me," said Cipriano.

"It's very true," said Ramón. "That's because the old oyster has him shut up, like a black pearl. You must let him walk out."

"Ramón," said Cipriano, "wouldn't it be good to be a serpent, and be big enough to wrap one's folds round the globe of the world, and crush it like that egg?"

Ramón looked at him and laughed.

"I believe we could do that," said Cipriano, a slow smile curling round his mouth. "And wouldn't it be good?"

Ramón shook his head, laughing.

"There would be *one* good moment, at least," he said.

"Who asks for more!" said Cipriano.

A spark flashed out of Ramón's eyes too. Then he checked himself, and gathered himself together.

"What would be the good!" he said heavily. "If the egg was crushed, and we remained, what could we do but go howling down the empty passages of darkness. What's the good, Cipriano?"

Ramón got up and walked away. The sun had set, the night was falling. And in his soul the great, writhing anger was alive again. Carlota provoked it into life: the two women seemed to breathe life into the black monster of his inward rage, till it began to lash again. And Cipriano stirred it up till it howled with desire.

"My manhood is like a demon howling inside me," said Ramón to himself, in Cipriano's words.

And he admitted the justice of the howling, his manhood being pent up, humiliated, goaded with insult inside him. And rage came over him, against Carlota, against Cipriano, against his own people, against all mankind, till he was filled with rage like the devil.

His people would betray him, he knew that. Cipriano would betray him. Given one little vulnerable chink, they would pierce him. They would leap at the place out of nowhere, like a tarantula, and bite in the poison.

While ever there was one little vulnerable chink. And what man can be invulnerable?

He went upstairs by the outer stairway, through the iron door at the side of the house, under the heavy trees, up to his room,

and sat on his bed. The night was hot, heavy, and ominously still.

"The waters are coming," he heard a servant say. He shut the doors of his room till it was black dark inside. Then he threw aside his clothing, saying: I put off the world with my clothes. And standing nude and invisible in the centre of his room he thrust his clenched fist upwards, with all his might, feeling he would break the walls of his chest. And his left hand hung loose, the fingers softly curving downwards.

And tense like the gush of a soundless fountain, he thrust up and reached down in the invisible dark, convulsed with passion. Till the black waves began to wash over his consciousness, over his mind, waves of darkness broke over his memory, over his being, like an incoming tide, till at last it was full tide, and he trembled, and fell to rest. Invisible in the darkness, he stood soft and relaxed, staring with wide eyes at the dark, and feeling the dark fecundity of the inner tide washing over his heart, over his belly, his mind dissolved away in the greater, dark mind, which is undisturbed by thoughts.

He covered his face with his hands, and stood still, in pure unconsciousness, neither hearing nor feeling nor knowing, like a dark sea-weed deep in the sea. With no Time and no World, in the deeps that are timeless and worldless.

Then when his heart and his belly were restored, his mind began to flicker again softly, like a soft flame flowing without departing.

So he wiped his face with his hands, and put his serape over his head, and, silent inside an aura of pain, he went out and took the drum, carrying it downstairs.

Martin, the man who loved him, was hovering in the zaguan.

"*Ya, Patrón?*" he said.

"*Ya!*" said Ramón.

The man ran indoors, where a lamp was burning in the big, dark kitchen, and ran out again with an armful of the woven straw mats.

"Where, *Patrón?*" he said.

Ramón hesitated in the centre of the courtyard, and looked at the sky.

"*Viene el agua?*" he said.

"*Creo que sí, Patrón.*"

They went to the shed where the bananas had been packed and

carried away on donkeys. There the man threw down the petates. Ramón arranged them. Martin ran with canes. He was going to make lights, the simplest possible. Three pieces of thick cane, tied at the neck with a cord, stood up three-legged, waist high. In the three-pronged fork at the top he laid a piece of flat, slightly hollow lava stone. Then he came running from the house with a bit of burning ocote wood. Three or four bits of ocote, each bit no bigger than a long finger, flickered and rose in quick flames from the stone, and the courtyard danced with shadow.

Ramón took off his serape, folded it, and sat upon it. Martin lit another tripod-torch. Ramón sat with his back to the wall, the fire-light dancing on his dark brows, that were sunk in a sort of frown. His breast shone like gold in the flame. He took the drum and sounded the summons, slow, monotonous, rather sad. In a moment two or three men came running. The drummer came, Ramón stood up and handed him the drum. He ran with it to the great outer doorway, and out into the dark lane, and there sounded the summons, quick, sharp.

Ramón put on his serape, whose scarlet fringe touched his knees, and stood motionless, with ruffled hair. Round his shoulders went the woven snake, and his head was through the middle of the blue, woven bird.

Cipriano came from the house. He was wearing a serape all scarlet and dark brown, a great scarlet sun at the centre, deep scarlet zigzags at the borders, and dark brown fringe at his knees. He came and stood at Ramón's side, glancing up into Ramón's face. But the other man's brows were low, his eyes were fixed in the darkness of the sheds away across the courtyard. He was looking into the heart of the world; because the faces of men and the hearts of men are helpless quicksands. Only in the heart of the cosmos man can look for strength. And if he can keep his soul in touch with the heart of the world, then from the heart of the world new blood will beat in strength and stillness into him, fulfilling his manhood.

Cipriano turned his black eyes to the courtyard. His soldiers had drawn near, in a little group. Three or four men were standing in dark serapes, round the fire. Cipriano stood brilliant like a cardinal bird, next to Ramón. Even his sandals were bright, sealing-wax red, and his loose linen trousers were bound at the ankles with red and black bands. His face looked very dark and ruddy in the firelight, his little black tuft of a beard hung odd and

devilish, his eyes were glittering sardonically. But he caught Ramón's hand in his small hand, and stood holding it.

The peons were coming through the entrance-way, balancing their big hats. Women were hurrying barefoot, swishing their full skirts, carrying babies inside the dark wrap of their rebozos, children running after. They all clustered towards the flame-light, like wild animals gazing in at the circle of men in dark serapes, Ramón, magnificent in his white and blue and shadow, poising his beautiful head, Cipriano at his side like a glittering cardinal bird.

Carlota and Kate emerged from the inner doorway of the house. But there Carlota remained, wrapped in a black silk shawl, seated on a wooden bench where the soldiers usually sat, looking across at the ruddy flare of light, the circle of dark men, the tall beauty of her husband, the poppy-petal glitter of red, of Cipriano, the group of little, dust-coloured soldiers, and the solid throng of peons and women and children, standing gazing like animals. While through the gate men still came hurrying, and from outside, the drum sounded, and a high voice sang again and again:

> Someone will enter between the gates,
>   Now, at this moment, Ay!
> See the light on the man that waits.
>   Shall you? Shall I?
>
> Someone will come to the place of fire,
>   Now, at this moment, Ay!
> And hark to the words of their heart's desire.
>   Shall you? Shall I?
>
> Someone will knock when the door is shut,
>   Ay! in a moment, Ay!
> Hear a voice saying: I know you not!
>   Shall you? Shall I?

There was a queer, wild yell each time on the *Ay!* and like a bugle refrain: *Shall you? Shall I?* It made Carlota shiver.

Kate, wrapping her yellow shawl round her, walked slowly towards the group.

The drum outside gave a rapid shudder, and was finished. The drummer came in, the great doors were shut and barred, the drummer took his place in the ring of standing men. A dead silence supervened.

Ramón continued to gaze from under lowered brows, into space. Then in a quiet, inward voice, he said:

"As I take off this cover, I put away the day that is gone from upon me."

He took off his serape, and stood with it over his arm. All the men in the circle did the same, till they stood with naked breasts and shoulders, Cipriano very dark and strong-looking, in his smallness, beside Ramón.

"I put way the day that is gone," Ramón continued, in the same still, inward voice, "and stand with my heart uncovered in the night of the gods."

Then he looked down at the ground.

"Serpent of the earth," he said; "snake that lies in the fire at the heart of the world, come! come! Snake of the fire at the heart of the world, coil like gold round my ankles, and rise like life around my knee, and lay your head against my thigh. Come, put your head in my hand, cradle your head in my fingers, snake of the deeps. Kiss my feet and my ankles with your mouth of gold, kiss my knees and my inner thigh, snake branded with flame and shadow, come! and rest your head in my finger-basket! So!"

The voice was soft and hypnotic. It died upon a stillness. And it seemed as if really a mysterious presence had entered unseen from the underworld. It seemed to the peons as if really they saw a snake of brilliant gold and living blackness softly coiled around Ramón's ankle and knee, and resting its head in his fingers, licking his palm with forked tongue.

He looked out at the big, dilated, glittering eyes of his people, and his own eyes were wide and uncanny.

"I tell you," he said, "and I tell you truly. At the heart of this earth sleeps a great serpent, in the midst of fire. Those that go down in mines feel the heat and the sweat of him, they feel him move. It is the living fire of the earth, for the earth is alive. The snake of the world is huge, and the rocks are his scales, trees grow between them. I tell you the earth you dig is alive as a snake that sleeps. So vast a serpent you walk on, this lake lies between his folds as a drop of rain in the folds of a sleeping rattlesnake. Yet he none the less lives. The earth is alive.

"And if he died, we should all perish. Only his living keeps the soil sweet, that grows you maize. From the roots of his scales we dig silver and gold, and the trees have root in him, as the hair of my face has root in my lips.

"The earth is alive. But he is very big, and we are very small, smaller than dust. But he is very big in his life, and sometimes he is angry. *These people, smaller than dust,* he says, *they stamp on me and say I am dead. Even to their asses they speak, and shout Harreh! Burro! But to me they speak no word. Therefore I will turn against them, like a woman who lies angry with her man in bed, and eats away his spirit with her anger, turning her back to him.*

"That is what the earth says to us. He sends sorrow into our feet, and depression into our loins.

"Because as an angry woman in the house can make a man heavy, taking his life from him, so the earth can make us heavy, make our souls cold, and our life dreary in our feet.

"Speak then to the snake of the heart of the world, put oil on your fingers and lower your fingers for him to taste the oil of the earth, and let him send life into your feet and ankles and knees, like sap in the young maize pressing against the joints and making the milk of the maize bud among its hair.

"From the heart of the earth man feels his manhood rise up in him, like the maize that is proud, turning its green leaves outwards. Be proud like the maize, and let your roots go deep, deep, for the rains are here, and it is time for us to be growing in Mexico."

Ramón ceased speaking, the drum softly pulsed. All the men of the ring were looking down at the earth and softly letting their left hands hang.

Carlota, who had not been able to hear, drifted up to Kate's side, spell-bound by her husband. Kate unconsciously glanced down at the earth, and secretly let her fingers hang softly against her dress. But then she was afraid of what might happen to her, and she caught her hand up into her shawl.

Suddenly the drum began to give a very strong note, followed by a weak: a strange, exciting thud.

Everybody looked up. Ramón had flung his right arm tense into the air, and was looking up at the black dark sky. The men of the ring did the same, and the naked arms were thrust aloft like so many rockets.

"Up Up! Up!" said a wild voice.

"Up! Up!" cried the men of the ring, in a wild chorus.

And involuntarily the men in the crowd twitched, then shot their arms upwards, turning their faces to the dark heavens.

Even some of the women boldly thrust up their naked arms, and relief entered their hearts as they did so.

But Kate would not lift her arm.

There was dead silence, even the drum was silent. Then the voice of Ramón was heard, speaking upwards to the black sky:

"Your big wings are dark, Bird, you are flying low to-night. You are flying low over Mexico, we shall soon feel the fan of your wings on our face.

"Ay, Bird! You fly about where you will. You fly past the stars, and you perch on the sun. You fly out of sight, and are gone beyond the white river of the sky. But you come back like the ducks of the north, looking for water and winter.

"You sit in the middle of the sun, and preen your feathers. You crouch in the river of stars, and make the star-dust rise around you. You fly away into the deepest hollow place of the sky, whence there seems no return.

"You come back to us, and hover overhead, and we feel your wings fanning our faces—"

Even as he spoke the wind rose, in sudden gusts, and a door could be heard slamming in the house, with a shivering of glass, and the trees gave off a tearing sound.

"Come then, Bird of the great sky!" Ramón called wildly. "Come! Oh Bird, settle a moment on my wrist, over my head, and give me power of the sky, and wisdom. Oh Bird! Bird of all the wide heavens, even if you drum your feathers in thunder, and drop the white snake of fire from your beak back to the earth again, where he can run in, deep down the rocks again, home: even if you come as the Thunderer, come! Settle on my wrist a moment, with the clutch of the power of thunder, and arch your wings over my head, like a shadow of clouds; and bend your breast to my brow, and bless me with the sun. Bird, roaming Bird of the Beyond, with thunder in your pinions and the snake of lightning in your beak, with the blue heaven in the socket of your wings and cloud in the arch of your neck, with sun in the burnt feathers of your breast and power in your feet, with terrible wisdom in your flight, swoop to me a moment, swoop!"

Sudden gusts of wind tore at the little fires of flame, till they could be heard to rustle, and the lake began to speak in a vast hollow noise, beyond the tearing of trees. Distant lightning was beating far off, over the black hills.

Ramón dropped his arm, which had been bent over his head. The drum began to beat. Then he said:

"Sit down a moment, before the Bird shakes water out of his wings. It will come soon. Sit down."

There was a stir. Men put their serapes over their faces, women clutched their rebozos tighter, and all sat down on the ground. Only Kate and Carlota remained standing, on the outer edge. Gusts of wind tore at the flames, the men put their hats on the ground in front of them.

"The earth is alive, and the sky is alive," said Ramón in his natural voice, "and between them, we live. Earth has kissed my knees, and put strength in my belly. Sky has perched on my wrist, and sent power into my breast.

"But as in the morning the Morning-star stands between earth and sky, a star can rise in us, and stand between the heart and the loins.

"That is the manhood of man, and for woman, her womanhood.

"You are not yet men. And women, you are not yet women.

"You run about and toss about and die, and still you have not found the star of your manhood rise within you, the stars of your womanhood shine out serene between your breasts, women.

"I tell you, for him that wishes it, the star of his manhood shall rise within him, and he shall be proud, and perfect even as the Morning-star is perfect.

"And the star of a woman's womanhood can rise at last, from between the heavy rim of the earth and the lost grey void of the sky.

"But how? How shall we do it? How shall it be?

"How shall we men become Men of the Morning Star? And the women the Dawn-Star Women?

"Lower your fingers to the caress of the Snake of the earth.

"Lift your wrist for a perch to the far-lying Bird.

"Have the courage of both, the courage of lightning and the earthquake.

"And wisdom of both, the wisdom of the snake and the eagle.

"And the peace of both, the peace of the serpent and the sun.

"And the power of both, the power of the innermost earth and the outermost heaven.

"But on your brow, Men! the undimmed Morning Star, that neither day nor night, nor earth nor sky can swallow and put out.

"And between your breasts, Women! the Dawn-Star, that cannot be dimmed.

"And your home at last is the Morning Star. Neither heaven nor earth shall swallow you up at the last, but you shall pass into the place beyond both, into the bright star that is lonely yet feels itself never alone.

"The Morning Star is sending you a messenger, a god who died in Mexico. But he slept his sleep, and the invisible Ones washed his body with water of resurrection. So he has risen, and pushed the stone from the mouth of the tomb, and has stretched himself. And now he is striding across the horizons even quicker than the great stone from the tomb is tumbling back to the earth, to crush those that rolled it up.

"The Son of the Star is coming back to the Sons of Men, with big, bright strides.

"Prepare to receive him. And wash yourselves, and put oil on your hands and your feet, on your mouth and eyes and ears and nostrils, on your breast and navel and on the secret places of your body, that nothing of the dead days, no dust of skeletons and evil things may pass into you and make you unclean.

"Do not look with the eyes of yesterday, nor like yesterday listen, nor breathe, nor smell, nor taste, nor swallow food and drink. Do not kiss with the mouths of yesterday, nor touch with the hands, nor walk with yesterday's feet. And let your navel know nothing of yesterday, and go into your women with a new body, enter the new body in her.

"For yesterday's body is dead, and carrion, the Xopilote is hovering above it.

"Put yesterday's body from off you, and have a new body. Even as your God who is coming. Quetzalcoatl is coming with a new body, like a star, from the shadows of death.

"Yes, even as you sit upon the earth this moment, with the round of your body touching the round of the earth, say: Earth! Earth! you are alive as the globes of my body are alive. Breathe the kiss of the inner earth upon me, even as I sit upon you.

"And so, it is said. The earth is stirring beneath you, the sky is rushing its wings above. Go home to your homes, in front of the waters that will fall and cut you off forever from your yesterdays.

"Go home, and hope to be men of the Morning Star, Women of the Star of Dawn.

"You are not yet men and women——"

He rose up and waved to the people to be gone. And in a moment they were on their feet, scurrying and hastening with the quiet Mexican hurry, that seems to run low down upon the surface of the earth.

The black wind was all loose in the sky, tearing with the thin shriek of torn fabric, in the mango trees. Men held their big hats on their heads and ran with bent knees, their serapes blowing. Women clutched their rebozos tighter and ran barefoot to the zaguan.

The big doors were open, a soldier stood with a gun across his back, holding a hurricane lamp. And the people fled like ghosts through the doors, and away up the black lane like bits of paper veering away into nothingness, blown out of their line of flight. In a moment, they had all silently gone.

Martin barred the great doors. The soldier put down his lamp on the wooden bench, and he and his comrades sat huddled in their dark shawls, in a little bunch like toadstools in the dark cavern of the zaguan. Already one had curled himself up on the wooden bench, wrapped like a snail in his blanket, head disappeared.

"The water is coming!" cried the servants excitedly, as Kate went upstairs with Doña Carlota.

The lake was quite black, like a great pit. The wind suddenly blew with violence, with a strange ripping sound in the mango trees, as if some membrane in the air were being ripped. The white-flowered oleanders in the garden below leaned over quite flat, their white flowers ghostly, going right down to the earth, in the pale beam of the lamp—like a street lamp—that shone on the wall at the front entrance. A young palm-tree bent and spread its leaves on the ground. Some invisible juggernaut car rolling in the dark over the outside world.

Away across the lake, south-west, lightning blazed and ran down the sky like some portentous writing. And soft, velvety thunder broke inwardly, strangely.

"It frightens me!" cried Doña Carlota, putting her hand over her eyes and hastening into a far corner of the bare salon.

Cipriano and Kate stood on the terrace, watching the coloured flowers in the pots shake and fly to bits, disappearing up into the void of darkness. Kate clutched her shawl. But the wind suddenly got under Cipriano's blanket, and lifted it straight up in

the air, then dropped it in a scarlet flare over his head. Kate watched his deep, strong Indian chest lift as his arms quickly fought to free his head. How dark he was, and how primitively physical, beautiful and deep-breasted, with soft, full flesh! But all, as it were, for himself. Nothing that came forth from him to meet with one outside. All oblivious of the outside, all for himself.

"Ah! the water!" he cried, holding down his serape.

The first great drops were flying darkly at the flowers, like arrows. Kate stood back into the doorway of the salon. A pure blaze of lightning slipped three-fold above the black hills, seemed to stand a moment, then slip back into the dark.

Down came the rain with a smash, as if some great vessel had broken. With it, came a waft of icy air. And all the time, first in one part of the sky, then in another, in quick succession the blue lightning, very blue, broke out of heaven and lit up the air for a blue, breathless moment, looming trees and ghost of a garden, then was gone, while thunder dropped and exploded continually.

Kate watched the dropping masses of water in wonder. Already, in the blue moments of lightning, she saw the garden below a pond, the walks were rushing rivers. It was cold. She turned indoors.

A servant was going round the rooms with a lantern, to look if scorpions were coming out. He found one scuttling across the floor of Kate's room, and one fallen from the ceiling beams on to Carlota's bed.

They sat in the salon in rocking chairs, Carlota and Kate, and rocked, smelling the good wetness, breathing the good, chilled air. Kate had already forgotten what really chill air was like. She wrapped her shawl tighter round her.

"Ah, yes, you feel cold! You must take care in the nights, now. Sometimes in the rainy season the nights are very cold. You must be ready with an extra blanket. And the servants, poor things, they just lie and shudder, and they get up in the morning like corpses.—But the sun soon warms them again, and they seem to think they must bear what comes. So they complain sometimes, but still they don't provide."

The wind had gone, suddenly. Kate was uneasy, uneasy, with the smell of water, almost of ice, in her nostrils, and her blood still hot and dark. She got up and went again to the terrace.

Cipriano was still standing there, motionless and inscrutable, like a monument, in his red and dark serape.

The rain was abating. Down below in the garden, two bare-footed women-servants were running through the water, in the faint light of the zaguan lamp, running across the garden and putting ollas, and square gasoline cans under the arching spouts of water that seethed down from the roof, then darting away while they filled, then struggling in with the frothy vessel. It would save making trips to the lake, for water.

"What do you think of us?" Cipriano said to her.

"It is strange to me," she replied, wondering and a little awed by the night.

"Good, no?" he said, in an exultant tone.

"A little scaring," she replied, with a slight laugh.

"When you are used to it," he said, "it seems natural, no? It seems natural so—as it is. And when you go to a country like England, where all is so safe and ready-made, then you miss it. You keep saying to yourself: 'What am I missing? What is it that is not here?'"

He seemed to be gloating in his native darkness. It was curious, that though he spoke such good English, it seemed always foreign to her, more foreign than Doña Carlota's Spanish.

"I can't understand that people want to have everything, all life, no?—so safe and ready-made as in England and America. It is good to be *awake*. On the *qui vive*, no?"

"Perhaps," she said.

"So I like it," he said, "when Ramón tells the people the earth is alive, and the sky has a big bird in it, that you don't see. I think it is true. Certainly! And it is good to know it, because then one is on the *qui vive*, no?"

"But it's tiring to be always on the *qui vive*," she said.

"Why? Why tiring? No, I think, on the contrary, it is refreshing.—Ah, you should marry, and live in Mexico. At least, I am sure, you would like it. You would keep waking up more and more to it."

"Or else going more and more deadened," she said. "That is how most foreigners go, it seems to me."

"Why deadened?" he said to her. "I don't understand. Why deadened? Here you have a country where night is night, and rain comes down and you know it. And you have a people with

whom you must be on the *qui vive* all the time, all the time. And that is very good, no? You don't go sleepy. Like a pear! Don't you say a pear goes sleepy, no?—cuando se echa a perder?"

"Yes!" she said.

"And here you have also Ramón. How does Ramón seem to you?"

"I don't know. I don't want to say anything. But I do think he is almost too much: too far.—And I *don't* think he is Mexican."

"Why not? Why not Mexican? He is Mexican."

"Not as you are."

"How not as I am? He is Mexican."

"He seems to me to belong to the old, old Europe," she said.

"And he seems to me to belong to the old, old Mexico—and also to the new," he added quickly.

"But you don't believe in him."

"How?"

"You—yourself. You don't believe in him. You think it is like everything else, a sort of game. Everything is a sort of game, a put-up job, to you Mexicans. You don't *really* believe, in anything."

"How not believe? I not believe in Ramón?—Well, perhaps not, in that way of kneeling before him and spreading out my arms and shedding tears on his feet. But I—I believe in him, too. Not in your way, but in mine. I tell you why. Because he has the power to compel me. If he hadn't the power to *compel* me, how should I believe?"

"It is a queer sort of belief that is compelled," she said.

"How else should one believe, except by being compelled? I like Ramón for that, that he can compel me. When I grew up, and my godfather could not compel me to believe, I was very unhappy. It made me very unhappy.—But Ramón *compels* me, and that is very good. It makes me very happy, when I know I can't escape. It would make you happy too."

"To know I could not escape from Don Ramón?" she said ironically.

"Yes, that also. And to know you could not escape from Mexico. And even from such a man, as me."

She paused in the dark before she answered, sardonically:

"I don't think it would make me happy to feel I couldn't es-

cape from Mexico. No, I feel, unless I was sure I could get out any day, I couldn't bear to be here."

In her mind she thought: And perhaps Ramón is the only one I couldn't quite escape from, because he really touches me somewhere inside. But from you, you little Cipriano, I should have no need even to escape, because I could not be caught by you.

"Ah!" he said quickly. "You think so. But then you don't know. You can only think with American thoughts. It is natural. From your education, you have only American thoughts, U.S.A. thoughts, to think with. Nearly all women are like that: even Mexican women of the Spanish-Mexican class. They are all thinking nothing but U.S.A. thoughts, because those are the ones that go with the way they dress their hair. And so it is with you. You think like a modern woman, because you belong to the Anglo-Saxon or Teutonic world, and dress your hair in a certain way, and have money, and are altogether free.—But you only think like this because you have had these thoughts put in your head, just as in Mexico you spend centavos and pesos, because that is the Mexican money you have put in your pocket. It's what they give you at the bank.—So when you say you are free, you are *not* free. You are compelled all the time to be thinking U.S.A. thoughts—*compelled,* I must say. You have not as much choice as a slave. As the peons must eat tortillas, tortillas, tortillas, because there is nothing else, you must think these U.S.A. thoughts, about being a woman and being free. Every day you must eat those tortillas, tortillas.—Till you don't know how you would like something else."

"What else should I like?" she said, with a grimace at the darkness.

"Other thoughts, other feelings.—You are afraid of such a man as me, because you think I should not treat you à l'américaine. You are quite right. I should not treat you as an American woman must be treated. Why should I? I don't wish to. It doesn't seem good to me."

"You would treat a woman like a real old Mexican, would you? Keep her ignorant, and shut her up?" said Kate sarcastically.

"I could not keep her ignorant if she did not start ignorant. But what more I had to teach her wouldn't be in the American style of teaching."

"What then?"

"Quien sabe! Ça reste à voir."

"Et continuera a y rester," said Kate, laughing.

CHAPTER XIV

HOME TO SAYULA

THE morning came perfectly blue, with a freshness in the air and a blue luminousness over the trees and the distant mountains, and birds so bright, absolutely like new-opened buds sparking in the air.

Cipriano was returning to Guadalajara in the automobile, and Carlota was going with him. Kate would be rowed home on the lake.

To Ramón, Carlota was still, at times, a torture. She seemed to have the power still to lacerate him, inside his bowels. Not in his mind or spirit, but in his old emotional, passional self: right in the middle of his belly, to tear him and make him feel he bled inwardly.

Because he had loved her, he had cared for her: for the affectionate, passionate, whimsical, sometimes elfish creature she had been. He had made much of her, and spoiled her, for many years.

But all the while, gradually, his nature was changing inside him. Not that he ceased to care for her, or wanted other women. That she could have understood. But inside him was a slow, blind imperative, urging him to cast his emotional and spiritual and mental self into the slow furnace, and smelt them into a new, whole being.

But he had Carlota to reckon with. She loved him, and that, to her, was the outstanding factor. She loved him, emotionally. And spiritually, she loved mankind. And mentally, she was sure she was quite right.

Yet as time went on, he had to change. He had to cast that emotional self, which she loved, into the furnace, to be smelted down to another self.

And she felt she was robbed, cheated. Why couldn't he go on being gentle, good, and loving, and trying to make the whole world more gentle, good, and loving?

He couldn't, because it was borne in upon him that the world had gone as far as it could go in the good, gentle, and loving direction, and anything further in that line meant perversity. So the time had come for the slow, great change to something else—what, he didn't know.

The emotion of love, and the greater emotion of liberty for mankind seemed to go hard and congeal upon him, like the shell on a chrysalis. It was the old caterpillar stage of Christianity evolving into something else.

But Carlota felt this was all she had, this emotion of love, for her husband, her children, for her people, for the animals and birds and trees of the world. It was her all, her Christ, and her Blessed Virgin. How could she let it go?

So she continued to love him, and to love the world, steadily, pathetically, obstinately and devilishly. She prayed for him, and she engaged in works of charity.

But her love had turned from being the spontaneous flow, subject to the unforeseen comings and goings of the Holy Ghost, and had turned into will. She loved now with her *will:* as the white world now tends to do. She became filled with charity: that cruel kindness.

Her winsomeness and her elvishness departed from her, she began to wither, she grew tense. And she blamed him, and prayed for him. Even as the spontaneous mystery died in her, the will hardened, till she was nothing but a will: a lost will.

She soon succeeded in drawing the life of her young boys all to herself, with her pathos and her subtle will. Ramón was too proud and angry to fight for them. They were her children. Let her have them.

They were the children of his old body. His new body had no children: would probably never have any.

"But remember," he said to her, with southern logic, "you do not love, save with your will. I don't like the love you have for your god: it is an assertion of your own will. I don't like the love you have for me: it is the same. I don't like the love you have for your children. If ever I see in them a spark of desire to be saved from it, I shall do my best to save them. Meanwhile have your love, have your will. But you know I dislike it. I dislike your insistence. I dislike your monopoly of one feeling, I dislike your charity works. I disapprove of the whole trend of

your life. You are weakening and vitiating the boys. You do *not* love them, you are only putting your love-will over them. One day they will turn and hate you for it. Remember I have said this to you."

Doña Carlota had trembled in every fibre of her body, under the shock of this. But she went away to the chapel of the Annunciation Convent, and prayed. And, praying for his soul, she seemed to gain a victory over him, in the odour of sanctity. She came home in frail, pure triumph, like a flower that blooms on a grave: his grave.

And Ramón henceforth watched her in her beautiful, rather fluttering, rather irritating gentleness, as he watched his closest enemy.

Life had done its work on one more human being, quenched the spontaneous life and left only the will. Killed the god in the woman, or the goddess, and left only charity, with a will.

"Carlota," he had said to her, "how happy you would be if you could wear deep, deep mourning for me.—I shall not give you this happiness."

She gave him a strange look from her hazel-brown eyes.

"Even that is in the hands of God," she had replied, as she hurried away from him.

And now, on this morning after the first rains, she came to the door of his room as he was sitting writing. As yesterday, he was naked to the waist, the blue-marked sash tied round his middle confined the white linen, loose trousers—like big, wide pyjama trousers crossed in front and tied round his waist.

"May I come in?" she said nervously.

"Do!" he replied, putting down his pen and rising.

There was only one chair—he was offering it her, but she sat down on the unmade bed, as if asserting her natural right. And in the same way she glanced at his naked breast—as if asserting her natural right.

"I am going with Cipriano after breakfast," she said.

"Yes, so you said."

"The boys will be home in three weeks."

"Yes."

"Don't you want to see them?"

"If they want to see me."

"I am sure they do."

"Then bring them here."

"Do you think it is pleasant for me?" she said, clasping her hands.

"You do not make it pleasant for me, Carlota."

"How can I? You know I think you are wrong. When I listened to you last night—there is something so beautiful in it all—and yet so monstrous. So *monstrous!*—Oh! I think to myself: What is this man doing? This man of all men, who might be such a blessing to his country and mankind—"

"Well," said Ramón. "And what is he instead?"

"You know! You know! I can't bear it.—It *isn't* for you to save Mexico, Ramón. Christ has already saved it."

"It seems to me not so."

"He has! He has! And He made you the wonderful being that you are, so that you should *work out* the salvation, in the name of Christ and of love. Instead of which—"

"Instead of which, Carlota, I try something else.—But believe me, if the real Christ has not been able to save Mexico—and He hasn't—then I am sure, the white Anti-Christ of Charity, and socialism, and politics, and reform, will only succeed in finally destroying her. That, and that alone makes me take my stand.— You, Carlota, with your charity works and your *pity:* and men like Benito Juárez, with their Reform and their Liberty: and the rest of the benevolent people, politicians and socialists and so forth, surcharged with pity for living men, in their mouths, but really with hate—the hate of the materialist *have-nots* for the materialist *haves:* they are the Anti-Christ. The old world, that's just the world. But the new world, that wants to save the People, this is the Anti-Christ. This is Christ with real poison in the communion cup.—And for this reason I step out of my ordinary privacy and individuality. I don't want everybody poisoned. About the great mass I don't care. But I don't want everybody poisoned."

"How can you be so sure that you yourself are not a poisoner of the people?—I think you are."

"Think it then. I think of you, Carlota, merely that you have not been able to come to your complete, final womanhood: which is a different thing from the old womanhoods."

"Womanhood is always the same."

"Ah, no it isn't! Neither is manhood."

Home to Sayula

"But what do you think you can do? What do you think this Quetzalcoatl nonsense amounts to?"

"Quetzalcoatl is just a living word, for these people, no more. All I want them to do is to find the beginnings of the way to their own manhood, their own womanhood. Men are not yet men in full, and women are not yet women. They are all half and half, incoherent, part horrible, part pathetic, part good creatures. Half arrived.—I mean you as well, Carlota. I mean all the world.— But these people don't assert any righteousness of their own, these Mexican people of ours. That makes me think that grace is still with them. And so, having got hold of some kind of clue to my own manhood, it is part of me now to try with them."

"You will fail."

"I shan't. Whatever happens to me, there will be a new vibration, a new call in the air, and a new answer inside some men."

"They will betray you.—Do you know what even your friend Toussaint said of you?—Ramón Carrasco's future is just the past of mankind."

"A great deal of it is the past. Naturally Toussaint sees that part."

"But the boys don't believe in you. Instinctively, they disbelieve. Cyprian said to me, when I went to see him: 'Is father doing any more of that silly talk about old gods coming back, mother? I wish he wouldn't. It would be pretty nasty for us if he got himself into the newspapers with it.'"

Ramón laughed.

"Little boys," he said, "are like little gramophones. They only talk according to the record that's put into them."

"*You* don't believe out of the mouths of babes and sucklings," said Carlota bitterly.

"Why Carlota, the babes and sucklings don't get much chance. Their mothers and their teachers turn them into little gramophones from the first, so what can they do, but say and feel according to the record the mother and teacher puts into them. Perhaps in the time of Christ, babes and sucklings were not so perfectly exploited by their elders."

Suddenly, however, the smile went off his face. He rose up, and pointed to the door.

"Go away," he said in a low tone. "Go away! I have smelt the smell of your spirit long enough."

She sat on the bed, spell-bound, gazing at him with frightened, yet obstinate, insolent eyes, wincing from his outstretched arm as if he had threatened to strike her.

Then again the fire went out of his eyes, and his arm sank. The still, far-away look came on his face.

"What have I to do with it!" he murmured softly.

And taking up his blouse and his hat, he went silently out on to the terrace, departing from her in body and in soul. She heard the soft swish of his sandals. She heard the faint resonance of the iron door to the terrace, to which he alone had access. And she sat like a heap of ash on his bed, ashes to ashes, burnt out, with only the coals of her will still smouldering.

Her eyes were very bright, as she went to join Kate and Cipriano.

After breakfast, Kate was rowed home down the lake. She felt a curious depression at leaving the hacienda: as if, for her, life now was there, and not anywhere else.

Her own house seemed empty, banal, vulgar. For the first time in her life, she felt the banality and emptiness even of her own milieu. Though the Casa de las Cuentas was not purely her own milieu.

"Ah Niña, how good! How good that you have come! Ay, in the night, how much water! Much! Much! But you were safe in the hacienda, Niña. Ah, how nice, that hacienda of Jamiltepec. Such a good man, Don Ramón—isn't he, Niña? He cares a great deal for his people. And the Señora, ah, how sympathetic she is!"

Kate smiled and was pleasant. But she felt more like going into her room and saying: For God's sake, leave me alone, with your cheap rattle.

She suffered again from the servants. Again that quiet, subterranean insolence against life, which seems to belong to modern life. The unbearable note of flippant jeering, which is underneath almost all modern utterance. It was underneath Juana's constant cry.—Niña! Niña!

At meal-times Juana would seat herself on the ground at a little distance from Kate, and talk, talk in her rapid mouthfuls of conglomerate words with trailing, wistful endings: and all the time watch her mistress with those black, unseeing eyes on which the spark of light would stir with the peculiar slow, malevolent jeering of the Indian.

Kate was not rich—she had only her moderate income.

"Ah, the rich people—!" Juana would say.

"I am not rich," said Kate.

"You are not rich, Niña?" came the singing, caressive bird-like voice: "Then, you are poor?"—this was indescribable irony.

"No, I am not poor either. I am not rich, and I am not poor," said Kate.

"You are not rich, and you are not poor, Niña!" repeated Juana, in her bird-like voice, that covered the real bird's endless, vindictive jeering.

For the words meant nothing to her. To her, who had nothing, *could* never have anything, Kate was one of that weird class, the rich. And, Kate felt, in Mexico it was a crime to be rich, or to be classed with the rich. Not even a crime, really, so much as a freak. The rich class was a freak class, like dogs with two heads or calves with five legs. To be looked upon, not with envy, but with the slow, undying antagonism and curiosity which "normals" have towards "freaks." The slow, powerful, corrosive Indian mockery, issuing from the lava-rock Indian nature, against anything which strives to be above the grey, lava-rock level.

"Is it true, Niña, that your country is through there?" Juana asked, jabbing her finger downward, towards the bowels of the earth.

"Not quite!" said Kate. "My country is more there—" and she slanted her finger at the earth's surface.

"Ah—that way!" said Juana. And she looked at Kate with a subtle leer, as if to say: what could you expect from people who came out of the earth sideways, like sprouts of camote!

"And is it true, that over there, there are people with only one eye—here!" Juana punched herself in the middle of her forehead.

"No. That isn't true. That is just a story."

"Ah!" said Juana. "Isn't it true! Do you know? Have you been to the country where they are, these people?"

"Yes," said Kate. "I have been to all the countries, and there are no such people."

"Verdad! Verdad!" breathed Juana, awestruck. "You have been to all the countries, and there are no such people!—But in your country, they are all *gringos?* Nothing but *gringos?*"

She meant, no real people and salt of the earth like her own Mexican self.

"They are all people like me," said Kate coldly.

"Like you, Niña? And they all talk like you?"

"Yes! Like me."

"And there are many?"

"Many! Many!"

"Look now!" breathed Juana, almost awestruck to think that there could be whole worlds of these freak, mockable people.

And Concha, that young, belching savage, would stare through her window-grating at the strange menagerie of the Niña and the Niña's white visitors. Concha, slapping tortillas, was real.

Kate walked down towards the kitchen. Concha was slapping the *masa,* the maize dough which she bought in the plaza at eight centavos a kilo.

"Niña!" she called in her raucous voice. "Do you eat tortillas?"

"Sometimes," said Kate.

"Eh?" shouted the young savage.

"Sometimes."

"Here! Eat one now!" And Concha thrust a brown paw with a pinkish palm, and a dingy-looking tortilla, at Kate.

"Not now," said Kate.

She disliked the heavy plasters that tasted of lime.

"Don't you want it? Don't you eat it?" said Concha, with an impudent, strident laugh. And she flung the rejected tortilla on the little pile.

She was one of those who won't eat bread: say they don't like it, that it is not food.

Kate would sit and rock on her terrace, while the sun poured in the green square of the garden, the palm-tree spread its great fans translucent at the light, the hibiscus dangled great double-red flowers, rosy red, from its very dark tree, and the dark green oranges looked as if they were sweating as they grew.

Came lunch time, madly hot: and greasy hot soup, greasy rice, splintery little fried fishes, bits of boiled meat and boiled eggplant vegetables, a big basket piled with mangoes, papayas, zapotes —all the tropical fruits one did not want, in hot weather.

And the barefoot little Maria, in a limp, torn, faded red frock, to wait at table. She was the loving one. She would stand by Juana as Juana bubbled with talk, like dark bubbles in her mouth, and she would stealthily touch Kate's white arm; stealthily touch

her again. Not being rebuked, she would stealthily lay her thin little black arm on Kate's shoulder, with the softest, lightest touch imaginable, and her strange, wide black eyes would gleam with ghostly black beatitude, very curious, and her childish, pock-marked, slightly imbecile face would take on a black, arch, beatitudinous look. Then Kate would quickly remove the thin, dark, pock-marked arm, the child would withdraw half a yard, the beatitudinous look foiled, but her very black eyes still shining exposed and absorbedly, in a rapt, reptilian sort of ecstasy.

Till Concha came to hit her with her elbow, making some brutal, savage remark which Kate could not understand. So the glozing black eyes of the child would twitch, and Maria would break into meaningless tears, Concha into a loud, brutal, mocking laugh, like some violent bird. And Juana interrupted her black and gluey flow of words to glance at her daughters and throw out some ineffectual remark.

The victim, the inevitable victim, and the inevitable victimiser.

The terrible, terrible hot emptiness of the Mexican mornings, the weight of black *ennui* that hung in the air! It made Kate feel as if the bottom had fallen out of her soul. She went out to the lake, to escape that house, that family.

Since the rains, the trees in the broken gardens of the lake front had flamed into scarlet, and poured themselves out into lavender flowers. Rose red, scarlet and lavender, quick, tropical flowers. Wonderful splashes of colour. But that was all: splashes! They made a splash, like fireworks.

And Kate thought of the black-thorn puffing white, in the early year, in Ireland, and hawthorn with coral grains, in a damp still morning in the lanes, and foxgloves by the bare rock, and tufts of ling and heather, and a ravel of hare-bells. And a terrible, terrible longing for home came over her. To escape from these tropical brilliancies and meaninglessnesses.

In Mexico, the wind was a hard draught, the rain was a sluice of water, to be avoided, and the sun hit down on one with hostility, terrific and stunning. Stiff, dry, unreal land, with sunshine beating on it like metal. Or blackness and lightning and crashing violence of rain.

No lovely fusion, no communion. No beautiful mingling of sun and mist, no softness in the air, never. Either hard heat or hard chill. Hard, straight lies and zigzags, wounding the breast.

No soft, sweet smell of earth. The smell of Mexico, however subtle, suggested violence and things in chemical conflict.

And Kate felt herself filled with an anger of resentment. She would sit under a willow tree by the lake, reading a Pio Baroja novel that was angry and full of No! No! No!—ich bin der Geist der stets vernient! But she herself was so much angrier and fuller of repudiation than Pio Baroja. Spain cannot stand for No! as Mexico can.

The tree hung fleecy above her. She sat on the warm sand in the shadow, careful not to let even her ankles lie in the biting shine of the sun. There was a faint, old smell of urine. The lake was so still and filmy as to be almost invisible. In the near distance, some dark women were kneeling on the edge of the lake, dressed only in their long wet chemises in which they had bathed. Some were washing garments, some were pouring water over themselves, scooping it up in gourd scoops and pouring it over their black heads and ruddy-dark shoulders, in the intense pressure of the sunshine. On her left were two big trees, and a cane fence, and little straw huts of Indians. There the beach itself ended, and the little Indian plots of land went down to the lakefront.

Glancing around in the great light, she seemed to be sitting isolated in a dark core of shadow, while the world moved in inconsequential specks through the hollow glare. She noticed a dark urchin, nearly naked, marching with naked, manly solemnity down to the water's edge. He would be about four years old, but more manly than an adult man. With sex comes a certain vulnerability which these round-faced, black-headed, stiff-backed infant men have not got. Kate knew the urchin. She knew his tattered rag of a red shirt, and the weird rags that were his little man's white trousers. She knew his black round head, his stiff, sturdy march of a walk, his round eyes, and his swift, scuttling run, like a bolting animal.

"What's the brat got?" she said to herself, gazing at the moving little figure within the great light.

Dangling from his tiny outstretched arm, held by the webbed toe, head down and feebly flapping its out-sinking wings, was a bird, a water-fowl. It was a black mud-chick with a white bar across the under-wing, one of many dark fowl that bobbed in little flocks along the edge of the sun-stunned lake.

The urchin marched stiffly down to the water's edge, holding the upside-down bird, that seemed big as an eagle in the tiny fist. Another brat came scuttling after. The two infant men paddled a yard into the warm, lapping water, under the great light, and gravely stooping, like old men, set the fowl on the water. It floated, but could hardly paddle. The lift of the ripples moved it. The urchins dragged it in, like a rag, by a string tied to its leg.

So quiet, so still, so dark, like tiny, chubby little infant men, the two solemn figures with the rag of a bird!

Kate turned uneasily to her book, her nerves on edge. She heard the splash of a stone. The bird was on the water, but apparently the string that held it by the leg was tied to a stone. It lay wavering, a couple of yards out. And the two little he-men, with sober steadfastness and a quiet, dark lust, were picking up stones, and throwing them with the fierce Indian aim at the feebly fluttering bird: right down upon it. Like a little warrior stood the mite in the red rag, his arm upraised, to throw the stone with all his might down on the tethered bird.

In a whiff, Kate was darting down the beach.

"Ugly boys! Ugly children! Go! Go away, ugly children, ugly boys!" she said on one breath, with quiet intensity.

The round-headed dot gave her one black glance from his manly eyes, then the two of them scuttled up the beach into invisibility.

Kate went into the water, and lifted the wet, warm bird. The bit of coarse fibre-string hung from its limp, greenish, water-fowl's ankle. It feebly tried to bite her.

She rapidly stepped out of the water and stood in the sun to unfasten the string. The bird was about as big as a pigeon. It lay in her hand with the absolute motionlessness of a caught wild thing.

Kate stooped and pulled off her shoes and stockings. She looked round. No sign of life from the reed huts dark in the shadow of the trees. She lifted her skirts and staggered out barefoot in the hot shallows of the water, almost falling on the cruel stones under the water. The lake-side was very shallow. She staggered on and on, in agony, holding up her skirts in one hand, holding the warm, wet, motionless bird in the other. Till at last she was up to her knees. Then she launched the greeny-black bird, and gave it a little push to the uprearing expanse of

filmy water, that was almost dim, invisible with the glare of light.

It lay wet and draggled on the pale, moving sperm of the water, like a buoyant rag.

"Swim then! Swim!" she said, trying to urge it away into the lake.

Either it couldn't or wouldn't. Anyhow it didn't.

But it was out of reach of those urchins. Kate struggled back from those stones, to her tree, to her shade, to her book, away from the rage of the sun. Silent with slow anger, she kept glancing up at the floating bird, and sideways at the reed huts of the Indians in the black shadow.

Yes, the bird was dipping its beak in the water, and shaking its head. It was coming to itself. But it did not paddle. It let itself be lifted, lifted on the ripples, and the ripples would drift it ashore.

"Fool of a thing!" said Kate nervously, using all her consciousness to make it paddle away into the lake.

Two companions, two black dots with white specks of faces, were coming out of the pale glare of the lake. Two mud-chicks swam busily forward. The first swam up and poked its beak at the inert bird, as if to say *Hello! What's up?* Then immediately it turned away and paddled in complete oblivion to the shore, its companion following.

Kate watched the rag of feathered misery anxiously. Would it not rouse itself, wouldn't it follow?

No! There it lay, slowly, inertly drifting on the ripples, only sometimes shaking its head.

The other two alert birds waded confidently, busily among the stones.

Kate read a bit more.

When she looked again, she could not see her bird. But the other two were walking among the stones, jauntily.

She read a bit more.

The next thing was a rather loutish youth of eighteen or so, in overall trousers, running with big strides towards the water, and the stiff little man-brat scuttling after with determined bare feet. Her heart stood still.

The two busy mud-chicks rose in flight and went low over the water into the blare of light. Gone!

But the lout in the big hat and overall trousers and those stiff Indian shoulders she sometimes hated so much, was peering

among the stones. She, however, was sure her bird had gone.

No! Actually no! The stiff-shouldered lout stooped and picked up the damp thing. It had let itself drift back.

He turned, dangling it like a rag from the end of one wing, and handed it to the man-brat. Then he stalked self-satisfied up the shore.

Ugh! and that moment how Kate hated these people: their terrible lowness, *à terre, à terre.* Their stiff broad American shoulders, and high chests, and above all, their walk, their prancing, insentient walk. As if some motor-engine drove them at the bottom of their back.

Stooping rather forward and looking at the ground so that he could turn his eyes sideways to her, without showing her his face, the lout returned to the shadow of the huts. And after him, diminutive, the dot of a man marched stiffly, hurriedly, dangling the wretched bird, that stirred very feebly, downwards from the tip of one wing. And from time to time turning his round, black-eyed face in Kate's direction, vindictively, apprehensively, lest she should swoop down on him again. Black, apprehensive male defiance of the great, white, weird female.

Kate glared back from under her tree.

"If looks would kill you, brat, I'd kill you," she said. And the urchin turned his face like clockwork at her from time to time, as he strutted palpitating towards the gap in the cane hedge, into which the youth had disappeared.

Kate debated whether to rescue the foolish bird again. But what was the good!

This country would have its victim. America would have its victim. As long as time lasts, it will be the continent divided between Victims and Victimisers. What is the good of trying to interfere!

She rose up in detestation of the flabby bird, and of the sulky-faced brat turning his full moon on her in apprehension.

Lumps of women were by the water's edge. Westwards, down the glare, rose the broken-looking villas and the white twin towers of the church, holding up its two fingers in mockery above the scarlet flame-trees and the dark mangoes. She saw the rather lousy shore, and smelt the smell of Mexico, come out in the hot sun after the rains: excrement, human and animal dried in the sun on a dry, dry earth; and dry leaves; and mango leaves; and pure air with a little refuse-smoke in it.

"But the day will come when I shall go away," she said to herself.

And sitting rocking once more on her verandah, hearing the clap-clap of tortillas from the far end of the patio, the odd, metallic noises of birds, and feeling the clouds already assembling in the west, with a weight of unborn thunder upon them, she felt she could bear it no more: the vacuity, and the pressure: the horrible uncreate elementality, so uncouth, even sun and rain uncouth, uncouth.

And she wondered over the black vision in the eyes of that urchin. The curious void.

He could not see that the bird was a real living creature with a life of its own. This, his race had never seen. With black eyes they stared out on an elemental world, where the elements were monstrous and cruel, as the sun was monstrous, and the cold, crushing black water of the rain was monstrous, and the dry, dry, cruel earth.

And among the monstrosity of the elements flickered and towered other presences: terrible uncouth things called gringos, white people, and dressed up monsters of rich people, with powers like gods, but uncouth, demonish gods. And uncouth things like birds that could fly and snakes that could crawl and fish that could swim and bite. An uncouth, monstrous universe of monsters big and little, in which man held his own by sheer resistance and guardedness, never, never going forth from his own darkness.

And sometimes, it was good to have revenge on the monsters that fluttered and strode. The monsters big and the monsters little. Even the monster of that bird, which had its own monstrous bird-nature. On this the mite could wreak the long human vengeance, and for once be master.

Blind to the creature as a soft, struggling thing finding its own fluttering way through life. Seeing only another monster of the outer void.

Walking forever through a menace of monsters, blind to the sympathy in things, holding one's own, and not giving in, nor going forth. Hence the lifted chests and the prancing walk. Hence the stiff, insentient spines, the rich physique, and the heavy, dreary natures, heavy like the dark-grey mud-bricks, with a terrible obstinate ponderosity and a dry sort of gloom.

CHAPTER XV

THE WRITTEN HYMNS OF QUETZALCOATL

THE electric light in Sayula was as inconstant as everything else. It would come on at half-past six in the evening, and it *might* bravely burn till ten at night, when the village went dark with a click. But usually it did no such thing. Often it refused to sputter into being till seven, or half-past, or even eight o'clock. But its worst trick was that of popping out just in the middle of supper, or just when you were writing a letter. All of a sudden, the black Mexican night came down on you with a thud. And then everybody running blindly for matches and candles, with a calling of frightened voices. Why were they always frightened? Then the electric light, like a wounded thing, would try to revive, and a red glow would burn in the bulbs, sinister. All held their breath—was it coming or not? Sometimes it expired for good, sometimes it got its breath back and shone, rather dully, but better than nothing.

Once the rainy season had set in, it was hopeless. Night after night it collapsed. And Kate would sit with her weary, fluttering candle, while blue lightning revealed the dark shapes of things in the patio. And half-seen people went swiftly down to Juana's end of the patio, secretly.

On such a night Kate sat on her verandah facing the deepness of the black night. A candle shone in her desert salon. Now and again she saw the oleanders and the papaya in the patio garden, by the blue gleam of lightning that fell with a noiseless splash into the pitch darkness. There was a distant noise of thunders, several storms prowling round like hungry jaguars, above the lake.

And several times the gate clicked, and crunching steps came along the gravel, someone passed on the gravel walk, saluting her, going down to Juana's quarters, where the dull light of a floating oil wick shone through the grated window-hole. Then there was a low, monotonous sound of a voice, reciting or reading. And as the wind blew and the lightning alighted again like a blue bird

among the plants, there would come the sharp noise of the round *cuentas* falling from the cuenta tree.

Kate was uneasy and a bit forlorn. She felt something was happening down in the servants' corner, something secret in the dark. And she was stranded in her isolation on her terrace.

But after all, it was her house, and she had a right to know what her own people were up to. She rose from her rocking chair and walked down the verandah and round the dining-room bay. The dining-room, which had its own two doors on the patio, was already locked up.

In the far corner beyond the well, she saw a group sitting on the ground, outside the doorway of Juana's kitchen-hole. Out of this little kitchen-shed shone the light of the floating-wick lamp, and a voice was slowly intoning, all the faces were looking into the dim light, the women dark-hooded in rebozos, the men with their hats on, their serapes over their shoulders.

When they heard Kate's footsteps, the faces looked her way, and a voice murmured in warning. Juana struggled to her feet.

"It is the Niña!" she said. "Come, then, Niña, you poor innocent all alone in the evening."

The men in the group rose to their feet she recognized the young Ezequiel, taking his hat off to her. And there was Maria del Carmen, the bride. And inside the little shed, with the wick-lamp on the floor, was Julio, the bridegroom of a few weeks ago. Concha and little Maria were there, and a couple of strangers.

"I could hear the voice—" said Kate. "I didn't know it was you, Julio. How do you do?—And I wondered so much what it was."

There was a moment's dead silence. Then Juana plunged in.

"Yes, Niña! Come! It's very nice that you come. Concha, the chair for the Niña!"

Concha got up rather unwillingly, and fetched the little low chair which formed Juana's sole article of furniture, save the one bed.

"I don't disturb you?" said Kate.

"No, Niña, you are a friend of Don Ramón, *verdad*?"

"Yes," said Kate.

"And we—we are reading the Hymns."

"Yes?" said Kate.

"The Hymns of Quetzalcoatl," said Ezequiel, in his barking young voice, with sudden bravado.

"Do go on! May I listen!"

"You hear! The Niña wants to listen. Read, Julio, read! Read then."

They all sat down once more on the ground, and Julio sat down by the lamp, but he hung his head, hiding his face in the shadow of his big hat.

"*Entonces*!—Read then," said Juana.

"He is afraid," murmured Maria del Carmen, laying her hand on the young man's knee. "However, read, Julio! Because the Niña wants to hear."

And after a moment's struggle, Julio said in a muffled voice:

"Do I begin from the beginning?"

"Yes, from the beginning! Read!" said Juana.

The young man took a sheet of paper, like an advertisement leaflet, from under his blanket. At the top it had the Quetzalcoatl symbol, called the Eye, the ring with the bird-shape standing in the middle.

He began to read in a rather muffled voice:

"I am Quetzalcoatl with the dark face, who lived in Mexico in other days.

"Till there came a stranger from over the seas, and his face was white, and he spoke with strange words. He showed his hands and his feet, that in both there were holes. And he said: 'My name is Jesus, and they called me Christ. Men crucified me on a Cross till I died. But I rose up out of the place where they put me, and I went up to heaven to my Father. Now my Father has told me to come to Mexico.'

"*Quetzalcoatl said*: You alone?

"*Jesus said*: My mother is here. She shed many tears for me, seeing me crucify. So she will hold the Sons of Mexico on her lap, and soothe them when they suffer, and when the women of Mexico weep, she will take them on her bosom and comfort them. And when she cries to the Father for her people, He will make everything well.

"*Quetzalcoatl said*: That is well. And Brother with the name Jesus, what will you do in Mexico?

"*Jesus said*: I will bring peace into Mexico. And on the naked I will put clothes, and food between the lips of the hungry, and gifts in all men's hands, and peace and love in their hearts.

"*Quetzalcoatl said*: It is very good. I am old. I could not do so much. I must go now. Farewell, people of Mexico. Fare-

well, strange brother called Jesus.   Farewell, woman called Mary. It is time for me to go.

"So Quetzalcoatl looked at his people; and he embraced Jesus, the Son of Heaven; and he embraced Maria, the Blessed Virgin, the Holy Mother of Jesus, and he turned away.   Slowly he went. But in his ears was the sound of the tearing down of his temples in Mexico.   Nevertheless he went on slowly, being old, and weary with much living.   He climbed the steep of the mountain, and over the white snow of the volcano.   As he went, behind him rose a cry of people dying, and a flame of places burning.   He said to himself: Surely those are Mexicans crying!   Yet I must not hear, for Jesus has come to the land, and he will wipe the tears from all eyes, and his Mother will make them all glad.

"He also said: Surely that is Mexico burning.   But I must not look, for all men will be brothers, now Jesus has come to the land, and the women will sit by the blue skirts of Mary, smiling with peace and with love.

"So the old god reached the top of the mountain, and looked up into the blue house of heaven.   And through a door in the blue wall he saw a great darkness, and stars and a moon shining.   And beyond the darkness he saw one great star, like a bright gateway.

"Then fire rose from the volcano around the old Quetzalcoatl, in wings and glittering feathers.   And with the wings of fire and the glitter of sparks Quetzalcoatl flew up, up, like a wafting fire, like a glittering bird, up, into the space, and away to the white steps of heaven, that lead to the blue walls, where is the door to the dark.   So he entered in and was gone.

"Night fell, and Quetzalcoatl was gone, and men in the world saw only a star travelling back into heaven, departing under the low branches of darkness.

"Then men in Mexico said: Quetzalcoatl has gone.   Even his star has departed.   We must listen to this Jesus, who speaks in a foreign tongue.

"So they learned a new speech from the priests that came from upon the great waters to the east.   And they became Christians."

Julio, who had become absorbed, ended abruptly, as the tale of the leaflet was ended.

"It is beautiful," said Kate.

"And it is true!" cried the sceptical Juana.

"It seems to me true," said Kate.

"Señora!" yelled Concha.   "Is it true that heaven is up there,

and you come down steps like clouds to the edge of the sky, like the steps from the mole into the lake? Is it true that El Señor comes and stands on the steps and looks down at us like we look down into the lake to see the charales?"

Concha shoved up her fierce swarthy face, and shook her masses of hair, glaring at Kate, waiting for an answer.

"I don't know everything," laughed Kate. "But it seems to me true."

"She believes it," said Concha, turning her face to her mother.

"And is it true," asked Juana, "that El Señor, El Cristo del Mundo, is a gringo, and that He comes from your country, with His Holy Mother?"

"Not from my country, but from a country near."

"Listen!" exclaimed Juana, awestruck. "El Señor is a gringito, and His Holy Mother is a gringita. Yes, one really knows. Look! Look at the feet of the Niña! Pure feet of the Santisima! Look!" Kate was barefoot, wearing sandals with a simple strap across the foot. Juana touched one of the Niña's white feet, fascinated. "Feet of the Santisima. And She, the Holy Mary, is a gringita. She came over the sea, like you, Niña?"

"Yes, she came over the sea!"

"Ah! You know it?"

"Yes. We know that."

"Think of it! The Santisima is a gringita, and She came over the Sea like the Niña, from the countries of the Niña!" Juana spoke in a wicked wonder, horrified, delighted, mocking.

"And the Lord is a Gringito—pure Gringito?" barked Concha.

"And Niña— It was the gringos who killed El Señor? It wasn't the Mexicans? It was those other gringos who put Him on the Cross?"

"Yes!" said Kate. "It wasn't the Mexicans.

"The gringos?"

"Yes, the gringos."

"And He Himself was a Gringo?"

"Yes!" said Kate, not knowing what else to say.

"Look!" said Juana, in her hushed, awed, malevolent voice. "He was a Gringo, and the gringos put him on the Cross."

"But a long time ago," said Kate hastily.

"A long time ago, says the Niña," echoed Juana, in her awed voice.

There was a moment of silence. The dark faces of the girls

and men seated on the ground were turned up to Kate, watching her fixedly, in the half light, counting every word. In the outer air, thunder muttered in different places.

"And now, Niña," came the cool, clear voice of Maria del Carmen, "El Señor is going back again to His Father, and our Quetzalcoatl is coming back to us?"

"And the Santisima is leaving us?" put in the hurried voice of Juana. "Think of it! The Santisima is leaving us, and this Quelzalcoatl is coming! He has no mother, he!"

"Perhaps he has a wife," said Kate.

"Quien sabe!" murmured Juana.

"They say," said the bold Concha, "that in Paradise he has grown young."

"Who?" asked Juana.

"I don't know how they call him," muttered Concha, ashamed to say the word.

"Quetzalcoatl!" said Ezequiel, in his barking strong young voice. "Yes, he is young. He is a god in the flower of life, and finely built."

"They say so! They say so!" murmured Juana. "Think of it!"

"Here it says so!" cried Ezequiel. "Here it is written. In the second Hymn."

"Read it then, Julio."

And Julio, now nothing loth, took out a second paper.

"I, Quetzalcoatl, of Mexico, I travelled the longest journey.

"Beyond the blue outer wall of heaven, beyond the bright place of the Sun, across the plains of darkness where the stars spread out like trees, like trees and bushes, far away to the heart of all the worlds, low down like the Morning Star.

"And at the heart of all the worlds those were waiting whose faces I could not see. And in voices like bees they murmured among themselves: *This is Quetzalcoatl whose hair is white with fanning the fires of life. He comes alone, and slowly.*

"Then with hands I could not see, they took my hands, and in their arms that I could not see, at last I died.

"But when I was dead, and bone, they cast not my bones away, they did not give me up to the four winds, nor to the six. No, not even to the wind that blows down to the middle of earth, nor to him that blows upward like a finger pointing, did they give me.

"*He is dead,* they said, *but unrelinquished.*

"So they took the oil of the darkness, and laid it on my brow and my eyes, they put it in my ears and nostrils and my mouth, they put it on the two-fold silence of my breasts, and on my sunken navel, and on my secret places, before and behind: and in the palms of my hands, and on the mounds of my knees, and under the tread of my feet.

"Lastly, they anointed all my head with the oil that comes out of the darkness. Then they said: He is sealed up. Lay him away.

"So they laid me in the fountain that bubbles darkly at the heart of the worlds, far, far behind the sun, and there lay I, Quetzalcoatl, in warm oblivion.

"I slept the great sleep, and dreamed not.

"Till a voice was calling: Quetzalcoatl!

"I said: Who is that?

"No one answered, but the voice said: Quetzalcoatl!

"I said: Where art thou?

"So! he said. I am neither here nor there. I am thyself. Get up.

"Now all was very heavy upon me, like a tomb-stone of darkness.

"I said: "Am I not old? How shall I roll this stone away?

"How art thou old, when I am new man? I will roll away the stone. Sit up!

"I sat up, and the stone went rolling, crashing down the gulfs of space.

"I said to myself: I am new man. I am younger than the young and older than the old. Lo! I am unfolded on the stem of time like a flower, I am at the midst of the flower of my manhood. Neither do I ache with desire, to tear, to burst the bud; neither do I yearn away like a seed that floats into heaven. The cup of my flowering is unfolded, in its middle the stars float balanced with array. My stem is in the air, my roots are in all the dark, the sun is no more than a cupful within me.

"Lo! I am neither young nor old, I am the flower unfolded, I am new.

"So I rose and stretched my limbs and looked around. The sun was below me in a daze of heat, like a hot humming-bird hovering at mid-day over the worlds. And his beak was long and very sharp, he was like a dragon.

"And a faint star was hesitating wearily, waiting to pass.

I called aloud, saying: Who is that?

My name is Jesus, I am Mary's son.
I am coming home.
My mother the Moon is dark.

Brother, Quetzalcoatl,
Hold back the wild hot sun.
Bind him with shadow while I pass.
Let me come home.

"I caught the sun and held him, and in my shade the faint star slipped past, going slowly into the dark reaches beyond the burning of the sun. Then on the slope of silence he sat down and took off his sandals, and I put them on.

" 'How do they wear the wings of love, Jesus, the Mexican people?'

" 'The souls of the Mexican people are heavy for the wings of love, they have swallowed the stone of despair.'

" 'Where is your Lady Mother in the mantle of blue, she with comfort in her lap?'

" 'Her mantle faded in the dust of the world, she was weary without sleep, for the voices of people cried night and day, and the knives of the Mexican people were sharper than the pinions of love, and their stubbornness was stronger than hope. Lo! the fountain of tears dries up in the eyes of the old, and the lap of the aged is comfortless, they look for rest. Quetzalcoatl, Sir, my mother went even before me, to her still white bed in the moon.'

" 'She is gone, and thou art gone, Jesus, the Crucified. Then what of Mexico?'

" 'The images stand in their churches, Oh, Quetzalcoatl, they don't know that I and my Mother have departed. They are angry souls, Brother, my Lord! They vent their anger. They broke my Churches, they stole my strength, they withered the lips of the Virgin. They drove us away, and we crept away like a tottering old man and a woman, tearless and bent double with age. So we fled while they were not looking. And we seek but rest, to forget forever the children of men who have swallowed the stone of despairs.'

" 'Then said I: It is good, pass on. I, Quetzalcoatl, will go down. Sleep thou the sleep without dreams. Farewell at the cross-roads, Brother Jesus.

" 'He said: Oh, Quetzalcoatl! They have forgotten thee. The feathered snake! The serpent—silent bird! They are asking for none of thee.

" 'I said: Go thy way, for the dust of earth is in thy eyes and on thy lips. For me the serpent of middle-earth sleeps in my loins and my belly, the bird of the outer air perches on my brow and sweeps her bill across my breast. But I, I am lord of two ways. I am master of up and down. I am as a man who is a new man, with new limbs and life, and the light of the Morning Star in his eyes. Lo! I am I! The lord of both ways. Thou wert lord of the one way. Now it leads thee to the sleep. Farewell!

" 'So Jesus went on towards the sleep. And Mary the Mother of Sorrows lay down on the bed of the white moon, weary beyond any more tears.

" 'And, I, I am on the threshold. I am stepping across the border. I am Quetzalcoatl, lord of both ways, star between day and the dark.' "

There was silence as the young man finished reading.

CHAPTER XVI

CIPRIANO AND KATE

ON Saturday afternoons the big black canoes with their large square sails came slowly approaching out of the thin haze across the lake, from the west, from Tlapaltepec, with big straw hats and with blankets and earthenware stuff, from Ixtlahuacan and Jaramay and Las Zemas with mats and timber and charcoal and oranges, from Tuliapan and Cuxcueco and San Cristobal with boatloads of dark-green, globular watermelons, and piles of red tomatoes, mangoes, vegetables, oranges: and boat-loads of bricks and tiles, burnt red, but rather friable; then more charcoal, more wood, from the stark dry mountains over the lake.

Kate nearly always went out about five o'clock, on Saturdays, to see the boats, flat-bottomed, drift up to the shallow shores, and begin to unload in the glow of the evening. It pleased her to see the men running along the planks with the dark-green melons, and piling them in a mound on the rough sand, melons dark-green like creatures with pale bellies. To see the tomatoes all poured out into a shallow place in the lake, bobbing about while the women washed them, a bobbing scarlet upon the water.

The long, heavy bricks were piled in heaps along the scrap of demolished break-water, and little gangs of asses came trotting down the rough beach, to be laden, pressing their little feet in the gravelly sand, and flopping their ears.

The cargadores were busy at the charcoal boats, carrying out the rough sacks.

"Do you want charcoal, Niña?" shouted a grimy cargador, who had carried the trunks from the station on his back.

"At how much?"

"Twenty-five reales the two sacks."

"I pay twenty reales."

"At twenty reales then, Señorita. But you give me two reales for the transport?"

"The owner pays for the transport," said Kate. "But I will give you twenty centavos."

Away went the man, trotting barelegged, barefoot, over the stony ground, with two large sacks of charcoal on his shoulders. The men carry huge weights, without seeming ever to think they are heavy. Almost as if they liked to feel a huge weight crushing on their iron spines, and to be able to resist it.

Baskets of spring guavas, baskets of sweet lemons called limas, baskets of tiny green and yellow lemons, big as walnuts; orangered and greenish mangoes, oranges, carrots, cactus fruits in great abundance, a few knobby potatoes, flat, pearl-white onions, little calabacitas and speckled green calabacitas like frogs, camotes cooked and raw—she loved to watch the baskets trotting up the beach past the church.

Then, rather late as a rule, big red pots, bulging red ollas for water-jars, earthenware casseroles and earthenware jugs with cream and black scratched pattern in glaze, bowls, big flat earthenware discs for cooking tortillas—much earthenware.

On the west shore, men were running up the beach wearing twelve enormous hats at once, like a trotting pagoda. Men trotting with finely woven huaraches and rough strip sandals. And men with a few dark serapes, with gaudy rose-pink patterns, in a pile on their shoulders.

It was fascinating. But at the same time, there was a heavy, almost sullen feeling on the air. These people came to market to a sort of battle. They came, not for the joy of selling, but for the sullen contest with those who wanted what they had got. The strange, black resentment always present.

By the time the church bells clanged for sunset, the market had already begun. On all the pavements round the plaza squatted the Indians with their wares, pyramids of green water-melons, arrays of rough earthenware, hats in piles, pairs of sandals side by side, a great array of fruit, a spread of collar-studs and knick-knacks, called *novedades,* little trays with sweets. And people arriving all the time out of the wild country, with laden asses.

Yet never a shout, hardly a voice to be heard. None of the animation and the frank wild clamour of a Mediterranean market. Always the heavy friction of the will; always, always, grinding upon the spirit, like the grey-black grind of lava-rock.

When dark fell, the vendors lighted their tin torch-lamps, and the flames wavered and streamed as the dark-faced men squatted

on the ground in their white clothes and big hats, waiting to sell.
They never asked you to buy. They never showed their wares.
They didn't even look at you. It was as if their static resentment
and indifference would hardly let them sell at all.

Kate sometimes felt the market cheerful and easy. But more
often she felt an unutterable weight slowly, invincibly sinking on
her spirits. And she wanted to run. She wanted above all, the
comfort of Don Ramón and the Hymns of Quetzalcoatl. This
seemed to her the only escape from a world gone ghastly.

There was talk of revolution again, so the market was uneasy
and grinding the black grit into the spirit. Foreign-looking soldiers were about, with looped hats, and knives and pistols, and
savage northern faces: tall, rather thin figures. They would
loiter about in pairs, talking in a strange northern speech, and
seeming more alien even than Kate herself.

The food-stalls were brilliantly lighted. Rows of men sat at
the plank boards, drinking soup and eating hot food with their
fingers. The milkman rode in on horseback, his two big cans of
milk slung before him, and he made his way slowly through the
people to the food-stalls. There, still sitting unmoved on horseback, he delivered bowls of milk from the can in front of him,
and then, on horseback like a monument, took his supper, his bowl
of soup, and his plate of tamales, or of minced, fiery meat spread
on tortillas. The peons drifted slowly round. Guitars were
sounding, half-secretly. A motor-car worked its way in from
the city, choked with people, girls, young men, city papas, children, in a pile.

The rich press of life, above the flare of torches upon the
ground! The throng of white-clad, big-hatted men circulating
slowly, the women with dark rebozos slipping silently. Dark trees
overhead. The doorway of the hotel bright with electricity.
Girls in organdie frocks, white, cherry-red, blue, from the city.
Groups of singers singing inwardly. And all the noise subdued,
suppressed.

The sense of strange, heavy suppression, the dead black power
of negation in the souls of the peons. It was almost pitiful to see
the pretty, pretty slim girls from Guadalajara going round and
round, their naked arms linked together, so light in their gauzy,
scarlet, white, blue, orange dresses, looking for someone to look
at them, to take note of them. And the peon men only emitting
from their souls the black vapor of negation, that perhaps was

hate. They seemed, the natives, to have the power of blighting the air with their black, rock-bottom resistance.

Kate almost wept over the slim, eager girls, pretty as rather papery flowers, eager for attention, but thrust away, victimised.

Suddenly there was a shot. The market-place was on its feet in a moment, scattering, pouring away into the streets and the shops. Another shot! Kate, from where she stood, saw across the rapidly-emptying plaza a man sitting back on one of the benches, firing a pistol into the air. He was a lout from the city, and he was half drunk. The people knew what it was. Yet any moment he might lower the pistol and start firing at random. Everybody hurried silently, melting away, leaving the plaza void.

Two more shots, pap-pap! still into the air. And at the same moment a little officer in uniform darted out of the dark street where the military station was, and where now the big hats were piled on the ground; he rushed straight to the drunkard, who was spreading his legs and waving the pistol: and before you could breathe, *slap!* and again *slap!* He had slapped the pistol-firer first on one side of the face, then on the other, with slaps that resounded almost like shots. And in the same breath he seized the arm that held the pistol and wrested the weapon away.

Two of the strange soldiers instantly rushed up and seized the man by the arms. The officer spoke two words, they saluted and marched off their prisoner.

Instantly the crowd was ebbing back into the plaza, unconcerned. Kate sat on a bench with her heart beating. She saw the prisoner pass under a lamp, streaks of blood on his cheek. And Juana, who had fled, now came scuttling back and took Kate's hand, saying:

"Look! Niña! It is the General!"

She rose startled to her feet. The officer was saluting her.

"Don Cipriano!" she said.

"The same!" he replied. "Did that drunken fellow frighten you?"

"Not much! Only startled me. I didn't *feel* any evil intention behind it."

"No, only drunk."

"But I shall go home now."

"Shall I walk with you?"

"Would you care to?"

He took his place at her side, and they turned down by the

church, to the lake shore.   There was a moon above the mountain and the air was coming fresh, not too strong, from the west. From the Pacific.   Little lights were burning ruddy by the boats at the water's edge, some outside, and some inside, under the roof-tilt of the boat's little inward shed.   Women were preparing a mouthful of food.

"But the night is beautiful," said Kate, breathing deep.

"With the moon clipped away just a little," he said.

Juana was following close on her heels: and behind, two soldiers in slouched hats.

"Do the soldiers escort you?" she said.

"I suppose so," said he.

"But the moon," she said, "isn't lovely and friendly as it is in England or Italy."

"It is the same planet," he replied.

"But the moonshine in America isn't the same.   It doesn't make one feel glad as it does in Europe.   One feels it would like to hurt one."

He was silent for some moments.   Then he said:

"Perhaps there is in you something European, which hurts our Mexican moon."

"But I come in good faith."

"European good faith.   Perhaps it is not the same as Mexican."

Kate was silent, almost stunned.

"Fancy your Mexican moon objecting to me!" she laughed ironically.

"Fancy your objecting to our Mexican moon!" said he.

"I wasn't," said she.

They came to the corner of Kate's road.   At the corner was a group of trees, and under the trees, behind the hedge, several reed huts.   Kate often laughed at the donkey looking over the dry-stone low wall, and at the black sheep with curved horns, tied to a bitten tree, and at the lad, naked but for a bit of a shirt, fleeing into the corner under the thorn screen.   The corner, of course, was an improvised W. C., and there was always a smell of human excrement.

Kate and Cipriano sat on the verandah of the House of the Cuentas.   She offered him vermouth, but he refused.

They were still.   There came the faint pip!-pip! from the little electric plant just up the road, which Jesús tended.   Then a cock from beyond the bananas crowed powerfully and hoarsely.

"But how absurd!" said Kate. "Cocks don't crow at this hour."

"Only in Mexico," laughed Cipriano.

"Yes! Only here!"

"He thinks your moon is the sun, no?" he said, teasing her.

The cock crowed powerfully, again and again.

"This is very nice, your house, your patio," said Cipriano.

But Kate was silent.

"Or don't you like it?" he said.

"You see," she answered, "I have nothing to *do!* The servants won't let me do anything. If I sweep my room, they stand and say *Que Niña! Que Niña!* As if I was standing on my head for their benefit. I sew, though I've no interest in sewing.— What is it, for a life?"

"And you read!" he said, glancing at the magazines and books.

"Ah, it is all such stupid, lifeless stuff, in the books and papers," she said.

There was a silence. After which he said:

"But what would you like to do? As you say, you take no interest in sewing. You know the Navajo women, when they weave a blanket, leave a little place for their soul to come out, at the end: not to weave their soul into it.—I always think England has woven her soul into her fabrics, into all the things she has made. And she never left a place for it to come out. So now all her soul is in her goods, and nowhere else."

"But Mexico *has* no soul," said Kate. "She's swallowed the stone of despair, as the hymn says."

"Ah! You think so? I think not. The soul is also a thing you make, like a pattern in a blanket. It is very nice while all the wools are rolling their different threads and different colours, and the pattern is being made. But once it is finished—then finished it has no interest any more. Mexico hasn't started to weave the pattern of her soul. Or she is only just starting: with Ramón. Don't you believe in Ramón?"

Kate hesitated before she answered.

"Ramón, yes! I do! But whether it's any good trying here in Mexico, as he is trying—" she said slowly.

"He *is* in Mexico. *He* tries here. Why should not you?"

"I?"

"Yes! You! Ramón doesn't believe in womanless gods, he

says. Why should you not be the woman in the Quetzalcoatl pantheon? If you will, the goddess!"

"I, a goddess in the Mexican pantheon?" cried Kate, with a burst of startled laughter.

"Why not?" said he.

"But I am not Mexican," said she.

"You may easily be a goddess," said he, "in the same pantheon with Don Ramón and me."

A strange, inscrutable flame of desire seemed to be burning on Cipriano's face, as his eyes watched her, glittering. Kate could not help feeling that it was a sort of intense, blind *ambition,* of which she was partly an object: a passionate object also: which kindled the Indian to the hottest pitch of his being.

"But I don't feel like a goddess in a Mexican pantheon," she said. "Mexico is a bit horrible to me. Don Ramón is *wonderful:* but I'm so afraid they will destroy him."

"Come, and help to prevent it."

"How?"

"You marry me.—You complain you have nothing to do. Then marry me. Marry me, and help Ramón and me. We need a woman, Ramón says, to be with us. And you are the woman. There is a great deal to do."

"But can't I help without marrying anybody?" said Kate.

"How can you?" he said simply.

And she knew it was true.

"But you see," she said, "I have no *impulse* to marry you, so how can I?"

"Why?" he said.

"You see, Mexico is *really* a bit horrible to me. And the black eyes of the people really make my heart contract, and my flesh shrink. There's a bit of horror in it. And I don't want horror in my soul."

He was silent and unfathomable. She did not know in the least what he was thinking, only a black cloud seemed over him.

"Why not?" he said at last. "Horror is real. Why not a bit of horror, as you say, among all the rest?"

He gazed at her with complete, glittering earnestness, something heavy upon her.

"But——" she stammered in amazement.

"You feel a bit of horror for me too— But why not? Perhaps

I feel a bit of horror for you too, for your light-coloured eyes and your strong white hands. But that is good."

Kate looked at him in amazement. And all she wanted was to flee, to flee away beyond the bounds of this gruesome continent.

"Get used to it," he said. "Get used to it that there must be a bit of fear, and a bit of horror in your life. And marry me, and you will find many things that are not horror. The bit of horror is like the sesame seed in the nougat, it gives the sharp wild flavour. It is good to have it there."

He sat watching her with black, glittering eyes, and talking with strange, uncanny reason. His desire seemed curiously impersonal, physical, and yet not personal at all. She felt as if, for him, she had some other name, she moved within another species. As if her name were, for example, Itzpapalotl, and she had been born in unknown places, and was a woman unknown to herself.

Yet surely, surely he was only putting his will over her?

She was breathless with amazement, because he had made her see the physical possibility of marrying him: a thing she had never even glimpsed before. But surely, surely it would not be *herself* who could marry him. It would be some curious female within her, whom she did not know and did not own.

He was emanating a dark, exultant sort of passion.

"I can't believe," she said, "that I could do it."

"Do it," he said. "And then you will know."

She shuddered slightly, and went indoors for a wrap. She came out again in a silk Spanish shawl, brown, but deeply embroidered in silver-coloured silk. She tangled her fingers nervously in the long brown fringe.

Really, he seemed sinister to her, almost repellent. Yet she hated to think that she merely was afraid: that she had not the courage. She sat with her head bent, the light falling on her soft hair and on the heavy, silvery-coloured embroidery of her shawl, which she wrapped round her tight, as the Indian women do their rebozos. And his black eyes watched her, and watched the rich shawl, with a peculiar intense glitter. The shawl, too, fascinated him.

"Well!" he said suddenly. "When shall it be?"

"What?" she said, glancing up into his black eyes with real fear.

"The marriage."

She looked at him, almost hypnotised with amazement that he

should have gone so far. And even now, she had not the power to make him retreat.

"I don't know," she said.

"Will you say in August? On the first of August?"

"I won't say any time," she said.

Suddenly the black gloom and anger of the Indians came over him. Then again he shook it off, with a certain callous indifference.

"Will you come to Jamiltepec to-morrow to see Ramón?" he asked. "He wants to speak with you."

Kate also wanted to see Ramón: she always did.

"Shall I?" she said.

"Yes! Come with me in the morning in the automobile. Yes?"

"I would like to see Don Ramón again," she said.

"You are not afraid of him, eh? Not the bit of horror, eh?" he said, smiling peculiarly.

"No. But Don Ramón isn't really Mexican," she said.

"Not really Mexican?"

"No!—He feels European."

"Really! To me he is—Mexico."

She paused and gathered herself together.

"I will row in a boat to Jamiltepec to-morrow, or I will take Alonso's motor-boat. I will come about ten o'clock."

"Very good!" said Cipriano, rising to leave.

When he had gone, she heard the sound of the drum from the plaza. It would be another meeting of the men of Quetzalcoatl. But she had not the desire nor the courage to set out afresh that day.

Instead, she went to bed, and lay breathing the inner darkness. Through the window-cracks she saw the whiteness of the moon, and through the walls she heard the small pulse of the drum. And it all oppressed her and made her afraid. She lay forming plans to escape. She must escape. She would hurriedly pack her trunks and disappear: perhaps take the train to Manzanillo, on the coast, and thence sail up to California, to Los Angeles or to San Francisco. Suddenly escape, and flee away to a white man's country, where she could once more breathe freely. How good it would be!—Yes, this was what she would do.

The night grew late, the drum ceased, she heard Ezequiel come home and lie down on the mattress outside her door. The only sound was the hoarse crowing of cocks in the moonlit night. And

in her room, like someone striking a match, came the greenish light of a firefly, intermittent, now here, now there.

Thoroughly uneasy and cowed, she went to sleep. But then she slept deeply.

And curiously enough, she woke in the morning with a new feeling of strength. It was six o'clock, the sun was making yellow pencils through her shutter-cracks. She threw open her window to the street, and looked through the iron grating at the little lane with deep shadow under the garden wall, and above the wall, banana leaves fraying translucent green, and shaggy mops of palm-trees perching high, towards the twin white tower-tips of the church, crowned by the Greek cross with four equal arms.

In the lane it was already motion: big cows marching slowly to the lake, under the bluish shadow of the wall, and a small calf, big-eyed and adventurous, trotting aside to gaze through her gate at the green watered grass and the flowers. The silent peon, following, lifted his two arms with a sudden swoop upwards, noiselessly, and the calf careered on. Only the sound of the feet of calves.

Then two boys vainly trying to urge a young bull-calf to the lake. It kept on jerking up its sharp rump, and giving dry little kicks, from which the boys ran away. They pushed its shoulder, and it butted them with its blunt young head. They were in the state of semi-frenzied bewilderment which the Indians fall into when they are opposed and frustrated. And they took the usual recourse of running to a little distance, picking up heavy stones, and hurling them viciously at the animal.

"No!" cried Kate from her window. "Don't throw stones. Drive it sensibly!"

They started as if the skies had opened, dropped their stones, and crept very much diminished after the see-sawing bull-calf.

An ancient crone appeared at the window with a plate of chopped-up young cactus leaves, for three centavos. Kate didn't like cactus vegetable, but she bought it. An old man was thrusting a young cockerel through the window-bars.

"Go," said Kate, "into the patio."

And she shut her window on the street, for the invasion had begun.

But it had only changed doors.

"Niña! Niña!" came Juana's voice. "Says the old man that you buy this chicken?"

"At how much?" shouted Kate, slipping on a dressing gown.

"At ten reales."

"Oh, no!" said Kate, flinging open her patio doors, and appearing in her fresh wrap of pale pink cotton crêpe, embroidered with heavy white flowers. "Not more than a peso!"

"A peso and ten centavos!" pleaded the old man, balancing the staring-eyed red cock between his hands. "He is nice and fat, Señorita. See!"

And he held out the cock for Kate to take it and balance it between her hands, to try its weight. She motioned to him to hand it to Juana. The red cock fluttered, and suddenly crowed in the transfer. Juana balanced him, and made a grimace.

"No, only a peso!" said Kate.

The man gave a sudden gesture of assent, received the peso, and disappeared like a shadow. Concha lurched up and took the cock, and instantly she bawled in derision:

"Está muy flaco! He is very thin."

"Put him in the pen," said Kate. "We'll let him grow."

The patio was liquid with sunshine and shadows. Ezequiel had rolled up his mattress and gone. Great rose-coloured hibiscus dangled from the tips of their boughs, there was a faint scent from the half-wild, creamy roses. The great mango trees were most sumptuous in the morning, like cliffs, with their hard green fruits dropping like the organs of some animal from the new bronze leaves, so curiously heavy with life.

"Está muy flaco!" the young Concha was bawling still in derision as she bore off the young cock to the pen under the banana trees. "He's very scraggy."

Everybody watched intent while the red cock was put in among the few scraggy fowls. The grey cock, elder, retreated to the far end of the pen, and eyed the new-comer with an eye of thunder. The red cock, *muy flaco,* stood diminished in a dry corner. Then suddenly he stretched himself and crowed shrilly, his red gills lifted like an aggressive beard. And the grey cock stirred around, preparing the thunders of his vengeance. The hens took not the slightest notice.

Kate laughed, and went back to her room to dress, in the powerful newness of the morning. Outside her window the women were passing quietly, the red water-jar on one shoulder, going to the lake for water. They always put one arm over their head, and held the jar on the other shoulder. It had a contorted look,

different from the proud way the women carried water in Sicily.

"Niña! Niña!" Juana was crying outside.

"Wait a minute," said Kate.

It was another of the hymn-sheets, with a Hymn of Quetzalcoatl.

"See, Niña, the new hymn from last evening."

Kate took the leaflet and sat upon her bed to read it.

QUETZALCOATL LOOKS DOWN ON MEXICO

Jesus had gone far up the dark slope, when he looked back.
Quetzalcoatl, my brother, he called. Send me my images,
And the images of my mother, and the images of my saints.
Sends me them by the swift way, the way of the sparks,
That I may hold them like memories in my arms when I go to sleep.

And Quetzalcoatl called back: I will do it.

Then he laughed, seeing the sun dart fiercely at him.
He put up his hand, and held back the sun with his shadow.

So he passed the yellow one, who lashed like a dragon in vain.
And having passed the yellow one, he saw the earth beneath.
And he saw Mexico lying like a dark woman with white breast-tips.

Wondering he stepped nearer, and looked at her,
At her trains, at her railways and her automobiles,
At her cities of stone and her huts of straw.
And he said: Surely this looks very curious!

He sat within the hollow of a cloud, and saw the men that worked in
    the fields, with foreign overseers.
He saw the men that were blind, reeling with aguardiente.
He saw the women that were not clean.
He saw the hearts of them all, that were black, and heavy, with a
    stone of anger at the bottom.

Surely, he said, this is a curious people I have found!

So leaning forward on his cloud, he said to himself:
I will call to them.
Holá! Holá! Mexicanos! Glance away a moment towards me.
Just turn your eyes this way, Mexicanos!

They turned not at all, they glanced not one his way.

Holálá! Mexicanos! Holálá!

They have gone stone deaf! he said.

So he blew down on them, to blow his breath in their faces.
But in the weight of their stupefaction, none of them knew.

Holálá! What a pretty people!
All gone stupefied!

A falling star was running like a white dog over a plain.
He whistled to it loudly, twice, till it fell to his hand.
In his hand it lay and went dark.
It was the Stone of Change.

This is the stone of change! he said.

So he tossed it awhile in his hand, and played with it.
Then suddenly he spied the old lake, and he threw it in.
It fell in.
And two men looked up.

Holálá! he said. *Mexicanos!*
Are there two of you awake?
So he laughed, and one heard him laughing.

Why are you laughing? asked the first man of Quetzalcoatl.

I hear the voice of my First Man ask me why I am laughing?
Holálá Mexicanos! It is funny!
To see them so glum and so lumpish!

Hey! First Man of my name! Hark here!
Here is my sign.
Get a place ready for me.

Send Jesus his images back, Mary and the saints and all.
Wash yourself, and rub oil in your skin.
On the seventh day, let every man wash himself, and put oil on his
    skin; let every woman.
Let him have no animal walk on his body, nor through the shadow of
    his hair.   Say the same to the women.
Tell them they all are fools, that I'm laughing at them.
The first thing I did when I saw them, was to laugh at the sight of
    such fools.
Such lumps, such frogs with stones in their bellies.

Tell them they are like frogs with stones in their bellies, can't hop!
Tell them they must get the stones out of their bellies,
Get rid of their heavness,
Their lumpishness,
Or I'll smother them all.
I'll shake the earth, and swallow them up, with their cities.
I'll send fire and ashes upon them, and smother them all.
I'll turn their blood like sour milk rotten with thunder,
They will bleed rotten blood, in pestilence.
Even their bones shall crumble.

Tell them so, First Man of my Name.

For the sun and the moon are alive, and watching with gleaming eyes.
And the earth is alive, and ready to shake off his fleas.
And the stars are ready with stones to throw in the faces of men.
And the air that blows good breath in the nostrils of people and beasts
Is ready to blow bad breath upon them, to perish them all.

The stars and the earth and the sun and the moon and the winds
Are about to dance the war dance round you, men!
When I say the word, they will start.
For sun and stars and earth and the very rains are weary
Of tossing and rolling the substance of life to your lips.
They are saying to one another: Let us make an end
Of those ill-smelling tribes of men, these frogs that can't jump,
These cocks that can't crow
These pigs that can't grunt
This flesh that smells
These words that are all flat
These money vermin.
These white men, and red men, and yellow men, and brown men, and
    black men
That are neither white, nor red, nor yellow, nor brown, nor black
But everyone of them dirtyish.
Let us have a spring cleaning in the world.
For men upon the body of the earth are like lice,
Devouring the earth into sores.
This is what stars and sun and earth and moon and winds and rain
Are discussing with one another; they are making ready to start.
So tell the men I am coming to,
To make themselves clean, inside and out.
To roll the grave-stone off their souls, from the cave of their bellies,
To prepare to be men.
Or else prepare for the other things.

Kate read this long leaflet again, and again, and a swift darkness like a whirlwind seemed to envelop the morning. She drank her coffee on the verandah, and the heavy papayas in their grouping seemed to be oozing like great drops from the invisible spouting of the fountain of non-human life. She seemed to see the great sprouting and urging of the cosmos, moving into weird life. And men only like green-fly clustering on the tender tips, an aberration there. So monstrous the rolling and unfolding of the life of the cosmos, as if even iron could grow like lichen deep in the earth, and cease growing, and prepare to perish. Iron and stone render up their life, when the hour comes. And men are less than the green-fly sucking the stems of the bush, so long as they live by business and bread alone. Parasites on the face of the earth.

She strayed to the shore. The lake was blue in the morning light, the opposite mountains pale and dry and ribbed like mountains in the desert. Only at their feet, next the lake, the dark strip of trees and white specks of villages.

Near her against the light five cows stood with their noses to the water drinking. Women were kneeling on the stones, filling red jars. On forked sticks stuck up on the foreshore, frail fishing nets were hung out, drying, and on the nets a small bird sat facing the sun; he was red as a drop of new blood, from the arteries of the air.

From the straw huts under the trees, her urchin of the mud-chick was scuttling towards her, clutching something in his fist. He opened his hand to her, and on the palm lay three of the tiny cooking-pots, the ollitas which the natives had thrown into the water long ago, to the gods.

"Muy chiquitas!" he said, in his brisk way, a little, fighting tradesman; "do you buy them?"

"I have no money. Tomorrow!" said Kate.

"Tomorrow!" he said, like a pistol shot.

"Tomorrow."

He had forgiven her, but she had not forgiven him.

Somebody in the fresh Sunday morning was singing rather beautifully, letting the sound, as it were, produce itself.

A boy was prowling with a sling, prowling like a cat, to get the little birds. The red bird like a drop of new blood twittered upon the almost invisible fish-nets, then in a flash was gone. The boy

prowled under the delicate green of the willow trees, stumbling over the great roots in the sand.

Along the edge of the water flew four dark birds, their necks pushed out, skimming silent near the silent surface of the lake, in a jagged level rush.

Kate knew these mornings by the lake. They hypnotised her almost like death. Scarlet birds like drops of blood, in very green willow trees. The aquador trotting to her house with a pole over his shoulder, and two heavy square gasoline cans, one at each end of the pole, filled with hot water. He had been to the hot spring for her daily supply. Now barefoot, with one bare leg, the young man trotted softly beneath the load, his dark, handsome face sunk beneath the shadows of the big hat, as he trotted in a silence, mindlessness that was like death.

Dark heads out on the water in little groups, like black water-fowl bobbing. Were they birds? Were they heads? Was this human life, or something intermediate, that lifted its orange, wet, glistening shoulders a little out of the lake, beneath the dark head?

She knew so well what the day would be. Slowly the sun thickening and intensifying in the air overhead. And slowly the electricity clotting invisibly as afternoon approached. The beach in the blind heat, strewn with refuse, smelling of refuse and the urine of creatures.

Everything going vague in the immense sunshine, as the air invisibly thickened, and Kate could feel the electricity pressing like hot iron on the back of her head. It stupefied her like morphine. Meanwhile the clouds rose like white trees from behind the mountains, as the afternoon swooned in silence, rose and spread black branches, quickly, in the sky, from which the lightning stabbed like birds.

And in the midst of the siesta stupor, the sudden round bolts of thunder, and the crash and the chill of rain.

Tea-time, and evening coming. The last sailing-boats making to depart, waiting for the wind. The wind was from the west, the boats going east and south had gone, their sails were lapsing far away on the lake. But the boats towards the west were waiting, waiting, while the water rattled under their black, flat keels.

The big boat from Tlapaltepec, bringing many people from the west, waited on into the night. She was anchored a few yards out, and in the early night her passengers came down the dark

beach, weary of the day, to go on board.   They clustered in a group at the edge of the flapping water.

The big, wide, flat-bottomed canoe, with her wooden awning and her one straight mast, lay black, a few yards out, in the dark night.   A lamp was burning under the wooden roof; one looked in, from the shore.   And this was home for the passengers.

A short man with trousers rolled up came to carry the people on board.   The men stood with their backs to him, legs apart. He suddenly dived at them, ducked his head between the fork of their legs, and rose, with a man on his shoulders.   So he waded out through the water to the black boat, and heaved his living load on board.

For a woman, he crouched down before her, and she sat on one of his shoulders.   He clasped her legs with his right arm, she clasped his dark head.   So he carried her to the ship, as if she were nothing.

Soon the boat was full of people.   They sat on the mats of the floor, with their backs to the sides of the vessel, baskets hanging from the pent roof, swaying as the vessel swayed.   Men spread their serapes and curled up to sleep.   The light of the lantern lit them up, as they sat and lay, and slept, or talked in murmurs.

A little woman came up out of the darkness; then suddenly ran back again.   She had forgotten something.   But the vessel would not sail without her, for the wind would not change yet.

The tall mast stood high, the great sail lay in folds along the roof, ready.   Under the roof, the lantern swayed, the people slept and stretched.   Probably they would not sail till midnight.   Then down the lake to Tlapaltepec, with its reeds at the end of the lake, and its dead, dead plaza, its dead dry houses of black adobe, its ruined streets, its strange, buried silence, like Pompeii.

Kate knew it.   So strange and deathlike, it frightened her, and mystified her.

But to-day!   To-day she would not loiter by the shore all morning.   She must go to Jamiltepec in a motor-boat, to see Ramón. To talk to him even about marrying Cipriano.

Ah, how could she marry Cipriano, and give her body to this death?   Take the weight of this darkness on her breast, the heaviness of this strange gloom.   Die before dying, and pass away whilst beneath the sun?

Ah no!   Better to escape to the white men's lands.

But she went to arrange with Alonso for the motor-boat.

CHAPTER XVII

FOURTH HYMN AND THE BISHOP

THE President of the Republic, as a new broom, had been sweeping perhaps a little too clean for the common liking, so there was a "rebellion." It was not a very large one. But it meant, of course, banditry, robbery, and cowed villages.

Ramón was determined to keep free from the taint of politics. But already the Church, and with the Church, the Knights of Cortes and a certain "black" faction, was preparing against him. The priests began to denounce him from the pulpits—but not very loudly—as an ambitious Anti-Christ. With Cipriano beside him, however, and with Cipriano the army of the west, he had not much to fear.

But it was possible Cipriano would have to march away in defence of the government.

"Above all things," said Ramón, "I don't want to acquire a political smell. I don't want to be pushed in the direction of any party. Unless I can stand uncontaminated, I had better abandon everything. But the Church will push me over to the socialists —and the socialists will betray me on the first opportunity. It is not myself. It is the new spirit. The surest way to kill it—and it can be killed, like any other living thing—is to get it connected with any political party."

"Why don't you see the Bishop?" said Cipriano. "I will see him too. Am I to be chief of the division in the west, for nothing?"

"Yes," said Ramón slowly. "I will see Jimenez. I have thought of it. Yes, I intend to use every means in my power. —Montes will stand for us, because he hates the Church and hates any hint of dictation from outside. He sees the possibility of a 'national' church. Though myself, I don't care about national churches. Only one has to speak the language of one's own people. You know the priests are forbidding the people to read the Hymns?"

245

"What does that matter?" said Cipriano. "These people are nothing if not perverse, nowadays. They will read them all the more."

"Maybe!—I shall take no notice. I'll let my new legend, as they call it, grow while the earth is moist. But we have to keep our eye very close on all the little bunches of 'interests'."

"Ramón!" said Cipriano. "If you can turn Mexico entirely into a Quetzalcoatl country, what then?"

"I shall be First Man of Quetzalcoatl—I know no more."

"You won't trouble about the rest of the world?"

Ramón smiled. Already he saw in Cipriano's eye the gleam of a Holy War.

"I would like," he said smiling, "to be one of the Initiates of the Earth. One of the Initiators. Every country its own Saviour, Cipriano: or every people its own Saviour. And the First Men of every people, forming a Natural Aristocracy of the World. One must have aristocrats, that we know. But natural ones, not artificial. And in some way the world must be organically united: the world of man. But in the concrete, not in the abstract. Leagues and Covenants and International Programmes. Ah! Cipriano! it's like an international pestilence. The leaves of one great tree can't hang on the boughs of another great tree. The races of the earth are like trees, in the end they neither mix nor mingle. They stand out of each other's way, like trees. Or else they crowd on one another, and their roots grapple, and it is the fight to the death.—Only from the flowers there is commingling. And the flowers of every race are the natural aristocrats of that race. And the spirit of the world can fly from flower to flower, like a humming bird, and slowly fertilise the great trees in their blossoms. Only the Natural Aristocrats can rise above their nation; and even then they do not rise beyond their race. Only the Natural Aristocrats of the World can be international, or cosmopolitan, or cosmic. It has always been so. The peoples are no more capable of it, than the leaves of the mango tree are capable of attaching themselves to the pine.—So if I want Mexicans to learn the name of Quetzalcoatl, it is because I want them to speak with the tongues of their own blood. I wish the Teutonic world would once more think in terms of Thor and Wotan, and the tree Igdrasil. And I wish the Druidic world would see, honestly, that in the mistletoe is their mystery, and that they themselves are the Tuatha De Danaan, alive, but submerged. And a new Hermes

should come back to the Mediterranean, and a new Ashtaroth to Tunis; and Mithras again to Persia, and Brahma unbroken to India, and the oldest of dragons to China. Then I, Cipriano, I, First Man of Quetzalcoatl, with you, First Man of Huitzilopochtli, and perhaps your wife, First Woman of Itzpapalotl, could we not meet, with sure souls, the other great aristocrats of the world, the First Man of Wotan and the First Woman of Freya, First Lord of Hermes, and the Lady of Astarte, the Best-Born of Brahma, and the Son of the Greatest Dragon? I tell you, Cipriano, then the earth might rejoice, when the First Lords of the West met the First Lords of South and East, in the Valley of the Soul. Ah, the earth has Valleys of the Soul, that are not cities of commerce and industry. And the mystery is one mystery, but men must see it differently. The hibiscus and the thistle and the gentian all flower on the Tree of Life, but in the world they are far apart; and must be. And I am hibiscus and you are a yucca flower, and your Caterina is a wild daffodil, and my Carlota is a white pansy. Only four of us, yet we make a curious bunch. So it is. The men and women of the earth are not manufactured goods, to be interchangeable. But the Tree of Life is one tree, as we know when our souls open in the last blossoming. We can't change ourselves, and we don't want to. But when our souls open out in the final blossoming, then as blossoms we share one mystery with all blossoms, beyond the knowledge of any leaves and stems and roots: something transcendent.

"But it doesn't matter. At the present time I have to fight my way in Mexico, and you have to fight yours. So let us go and do it."

He went away to his workshops and his men who were labouring under his direction, while Cipriano sat down to his correspondence, and his military planning.

They were both interrupted by the thudding of a motor-boat entering the little bay. It was Kate, escorted by the black-scarved Juana.

Ramón, in his white clothes with the blue-and-black figured sash, and the big hat with the turquoise-inlaid Eye of Quetzalcoatl, went down to meet her. She was in white, too, with a green hat and the shawl of pale yellow silk.

"I was so glad to come again," she said, holding out her hand to him. "Jamiltepec has become a sort of Mecca to me, my inside yearns for it."

"Then why don't you come oftener? I wish you would come."

"I am afraid of intruding."

"No! You could help if you would."

"Oh!" she said. "I am so frightened, and so sceptical of big undertakings. I think it is because, at the very bottom of me, I dislike the masses of people—anywhere. I'm afraid I rather despise people; I don't want them to touch me, and I don't want to touch them.—So how could I pretend to join any—any—any sort of Salvation Army?—which is a horrid way of putting it."

Don Ramón laughed.

"I do myself," he said. "I detest and despise masses of people. But these are my own people."

"I, ever since I was a child, since I can remember— They say of me, when I was a little girl of four, and my parents were having a big dinner party, they had the nurse bring me in to say good-night to all the people they had there dressed up and eating and drinking. And I suppose they all said nice things to me, as they do. I only answered: *You are all monkeys!* It was a great success!—But I felt it even as a child, and I feel it now. People are all monkeys to me, performing in different ways."

"Even the people nearest you?"

Kate hesitated. Then she confessed, rather unwillingly:

"Yes! I'm afraid so. Both my husbands—even Joachim—they seemed, somehow, so *obstinate* in their little stupidities—rather like monkeys. I felt a terrible revulsion from Joachim when he was dead. I thought: What peaked monkey is that, that I have been losing my blood about.—Do you think it's rather awful?"

"I do! But then I think we *all* feel like that, at moments. Or we would if we dared. It's only one of our moments."

"Sometimes," said she, "I think that is my *permanent* feeling towards people. I like the world, the sky and the earth and the greater mystery beyond. But people—yes, they are all monkeys to me."

He could see that, at the bottom of her soul, it was true.

"Puras monas!" he said to himself in Spanish. "Y lo que hacen, puras monerías."

"Pure monkeys! And the things they do, sheer monkeydom!" Then he added: "Yet you have children!"

"Yes! Yes!" she said, struggling with herself. "My first husband's children."

"And they?—*monas y no mas?*"

"No!" she said, frowning and looking angry with herself. "Only partly."

"It is bad," he said, shaking his head. "But then!" he added. —"What are my own children to me, but little monkeys? And their mother—and their mother— Ah, no! Señora Caterina! It is no good. One must be able to disentangle oneself from persons, from people. If I go to a rose-bush, to be intimate with it, it is a nasty thing that hurts me. One must disentangle oneself from persons and personalities, and see people as one sees the trees in the landscape. People in some way *dominate* you. In some way, humanity dominates your consciousness. So you must hate people and humanity, and you want to escape. But there is only one way of escape: to turn beyond them, to the greater life."

"But I do!" cried Kate. "I do nothing else. When I was with Joachim absolutely alone in a cottage, doing all the work myself, and knowing nobody at all, just living, and *feeling* the greater thing all the time; then I was free, I was happy."

"But he?" said Ramón. "Was he free and happy?"

"He was *really*. But that's where the monkeyishness comes in. He wouldn't let himself be content. He insisted on having *people* and a *cause,* just to torture himself with."

"Then why didn't you live in your cottage *quite* alone, and without him?" he said. "Why do you travel, and see people?"

She was silent, very angry. She knew she could not live quite alone. The vacuity crushed her. She needed a man there, to stop the gap, and to keep her balanced. But even when she had him, in her heart of hearts she despised him, as she despised the dog and the cat. Between herself and humanity there was a bond of subtle, helpless antagonism.

She was naturally quite free-handed and she left people their liberty. Servants would get attached to her, and casual people all liked and admired her. She had a strong life-flow of her own, and a certain assertive *joie de vivre*.

But underneath it all was the unconquerable dislike, almost *disgust* of people. More than hate, it was disgust. Whoever it was, wherever it was, however it was, after a little while this disgust overcame her. Her mother, her father, her sisters, her first husband, even her children whom she loved, and Joachim, for whom she had felt such passionate love, even these, being

near her, filled her with a certain disgust and repulsion after a little while, and she longed to fling them down the great and final oubliette.

But there is no great and final oubliette: or at least, it is never final, until one has flung *oneself* down.

So it was with Kate. Till she flung herself down the last dark oubliette of death, she would never escape from her deep, her bottomless disgust with human beings. Brief contacts were all right, thrilling even. But close contacts, or long contacts, were short and long revulsions of violent disgust.

She and Ramón had sat down on a bench under the white-flowering oleander of the garden downstairs. His face was impassive and still. In the stillness, with a certain pain and nausea, he realised the state she was in, and realised that his own state, as regards *personal* people, was the same. Mere *personal* contact, mere human contact filled him, too, with disgust. Carlota disgusted him. Kate herself disgusted him. Sometimes, Cipriano disgusted him.

But this was because, or when, he met them on a merely human, personal plane. To do so was disaster; it filled him with disgust of them and loathing of himself.

He had to meet them on another plane, where the contact was different; intangible, remote, and without *intimacy*. His soul was concerned elsewhere. So that the quick of him need not be bound to anybody. The quick of a man must turn to God alone: in some way or other.

With Cipriano he was most sure. Cipriano and he, even when they embraced each other with passion, when they met after an absence, embraced in the recognition of each other's eternal and abiding loneliness; like the Morning Star.

But women would not have this. They wanted intimacy—and intimacy means disgust. Carlota wanted to be eternally and closely identified with Ramón, consequently she hated him and hated everything which she thought drew him away from this eternal close identification with herself. It was just a horror, and he knew it.

Men and women should know that they cannot, absolutely, meet on earth. In the closest kiss, the dearest touch, there is the small gulf which is none the less complete because it is so narrow, so *nearly* non-existent. They must bow and submit in reverence, to the gulf. Even though I eat the body and drink the blood of

Christ, Christ is Christ and I am I, and the gulf is impassable. Though a woman be dearer to a man than his own life, yet he is he and she is she, and the gulf can never close up. Any attempt to close it is a violation, and the crime against the Holy Ghost.

That which we get from the beyond, we get it alone. The final me I am, comes from the farthest off, from the Morning Star. The rest is assembled. All that of me which is assembled from the mighty cosmos can meet and touch all that is assembled in the beloved. But this is never the quick. Never can be.

If we would meet in the quick, we must give up the assembled self, the daily I, and putting off ourselves one after the other, meet unconscious in the Morning Star. Body, soul and spirit can be transfigured into the Morning Star. But without transfiguration we shall never get there. We shall gnash at the leash.

Ramón knew what it was to gnash at his leashes. He had gnashed himself almost to pieces, before he had found the way to pass out in himself, in the quick of himself, to the Quick of all being and existence, which he called the Morning Star, since men must give all things names. To pass in the quick of himself, with transfiguration, to the Morning Star, and there, there alone meet his fellow man.

He knew what it was to fail even now, and to keep on failing. With Carlota he failed absolutely. She claimed him and he restrained himself in resistance. Even his very naked breast, when Carlota was there, was self-conscious and assertively naked. But then that was because she claimed it as her property.

When men meet at the quick of all things, they are neither naked nor clothed; in the transfiguration they are just complete, they are not seen in part. The final perfect strength has also the power of innocence.

Sitting on the seat beside Kate, Ramón was sad with the sense of heaviness and inadequacy. His third Hymn was angry and bitter. Carlota almost embittered his soul. In Mexico, turbulent fellows had caught at his idea and burlesqued it. They had invaded one of the churches of the city, thrown out the sacred images, and hung in their place the grotesque papier-mâché Judas figures which the Mexicans explode at Easter time. This of course made a scandal. And Cipriano, whenever he was away on his own for some time, slipped back into the inevitable Mexican General, fascinated by the opportunity for furthering his own

personal ambition and imposing his own personal will. Then came Kate, with this centre of sheer repudiation deep in the middle of her, the will to explode the world.

He felt his spirits sinking again, his limbs going like lead. There is only one thing that a man really wants to do, all his life; and that is, to find his way to his God, his Morning Star, and be alone there. Then afterwards, in the Morning Star, salute his fellow man, and enjoy the woman who has come the long way with him.

But to find the way, far, far along, to the bright Quick of all things, this is difficult, and required all a man's strength and courage, for himself. If he breaks a trail alone, it is terrible. But if every hand pulls at him, to stay him in the human places; if the hands of love drag at his entrails and the hands of hate seize him by the hair, it becomes almost impossible.

This was how Ramón felt at the moment:—I am attempting the impossible. I had better either go and take my pleasure of life while it lasts, hopeless of the pleasure which is beyond all pleasures. Or else I had getter go into the desert and take my way all alone, to the Star where at last I have my wholeness, holiness. The way of the anchorites and the men who went into the wilderness to pray. For surely my soul is craving for her consummation, and I am weary of the thing men call life. Living, I want to depart to where *I am*.

Yet, he said to himself, the woman that was with me in the Morning Star, how glad I should be of her! And the man that was with me there, what a delight his presence would be! Surely the Morning Star is a meeting-ground for us, for the joy!

Sitting side by side on the bench, Ramón and Kate forgot one another, she thinking back on the past, with the long disgust of it all, he thinking on into his future, and trying to revive his heavy spirits.

In the silence, Cipriano came out on to the balcony above, looking around. He almost started as he saw the two figures seated on the bench below, under the white oleander tree, miles apart, worlds apart, in their silence.

Ramón heard the step, and glanced up.

"We are coming up!" he called, rising and looking round at Kate. "Shall we go upstairs? Will you drink something cool, tepache, or squeezed oranges? There is no ice."

"I would like orange juice and water," she said.

He called to his servant and gave the order.

Cipriano was in the white pantaloons and blouse, like Ramón. But his sash was scarlet, with black curves, something like the markings on a snake.

"I heard you come. I thought perhaps you had gone away again," he said, looking at her with a certain black reproachfulness: an odd, hesitating wistfulness of the barbarian, who feels himself at a loss. Then also a certain resentment.

"Not yet," she said.

Ramón laughed, and flung himself into a chair.

"The Señor Caterina thinks we are all monkeys, but perhaps this particular monkey-show is the most amusing after all," he said. "So she will see a little more of it."

Cipriano, a real Indian, was offended in his pride, and the little black *imperial* on his chin seemed to become portentous.

"That's *rather* an unfair way of putting it!" laughed Kate.

The black eyes of Cipriano glanced at her in hostility. He thought she was laughing at him. And so, at the depths of her female soul, she was. She was jeering at him inwardly. Which no man can stand, least of all a dark-skinned man.

"No!" she said. "There's something else besides that."

"Ah!" said Ramón. "Take care! A little mercy is a dangerous thing."

"No! Not mercy!" she said, flushing. "Why are you being horrid to me?"

"Monkeys always end by being horrid to the spectators," said Ramón.

She looked up at him, and caught the flash of anger in his eyes.

"I came," she said, "to hear about the Mexican pantheon. I was even given to understand I might be admitted."

"Ah, that is good!" laughed Ramón. "A rare specimen of the female monkey has been added to the Ramón menagerie! I am sure you would be a good draw. There have been some pretty goddesses, I assure you, in the Aztec pantheon."

"How horrid!" she said.

"Come! Come!" he cried. "Let us keep to the bedrock of things, Señora mia. We are all monkeys. Monos somos.—Ihr seid alle Affen! Out of the mouths of babes and sucklings was it spoken, as Carlota said. You see that little male monkey, Cipriano. He had the monkey's idea of marrying you. Say the word. Marriage is a monkey's game. Say the word. He will

let you go when you've had enough; and he's had enough. He is a *general* and a very great *jefe*. He can make you monkey-queen of monkey-Mexico, if it please you. And what should monkeys do, but amuse themselves! *Vamos! Embobemonos!* Shall I be priest? *Vamos! Vamos!*"

He rose with sudden volcanic violence, and rushed away.

Cipriano looked at Kate in wonder. She had gone pale.

"What have you been saying to him?" he asked.

"Nothing!" she said, rising. "I'd better go now."

Juana was collected; and Alonso and Kate set off back down the lake. She sat with a certain obstinate offendedness under the awning of the boat. The sun was terrifically hot, and the water blinded her. She put on black spectacles, in which she looked a monster.

"Mucho calor, Niña! Mucho calor!" Juana was repeating behind her. The criada had evidently imbibed tepache.

On the pale-brown water little tufts of water-hyacinth were vaguely sailing, holding up the hand of a leaf for a sail. Everywhere the lake was dotted with these sailing tufts. The heavy rains had washed in flood down the Lerma river into the lake, washing the acres of *Lirio* loose from the marshy end of the waters, thirty miles away, and slowly setting them travelling over all the expanse of the inland sea, till the shores began to be piled, and the far-off Santiago river, which flowed out of the lake, was choked.

That day Ramón wrote his Fourth Hymn.

WHAT QUETZALCOATL SAW IN MEXICO

Who are these strange faces in Mexico?
Palefaces, yellowfaces, blackfaces? These are no Mexicans!
Where do they come from, and why?

Lord of the Two Ways, these are the foreigners.
They come out of nowhere.
Sometimes they come to tell us things,
Mostly they are the greedy ones.
What then do they want?

They want gold, they want silver from the mountains,
And oil, much oil from the coast.
They take sugar from the tall tubes of the cane,
Wheat from the high lands, and maize;

Coffee from the bushes in the hot lands, even the juicy rubber.
They put up tall chimneys that smoke,
And in the biggest houses they keep their machines, that talk
And work iron elbows up and down,
And hold myriad threads from their claws!
Wonderful are the machines of the greedy ones!

And you, Mexicans and peons, what do you do?

We work with their machines, we work in their fields,
They give us pesos made of Mexican silver.
They are the clever ones.

Do you love them then?

We love them not, and never.
Their faces are ugly, yet they make wonderful things.
And their wills are like their machines of iron.
What can we do?

I see dark things rushing across the country.

Yea, Lord! Even trains, and camions and automobiles.

Trains and camions, automobiles and aeroplanes.
How nice! says the peon, to go rushing in a train!
How nice, to get in the camion, and for twenty centavos, to be gone!
How nice, in the great cities, where all things rush, and huge lights
    flare bright, to wander and do nothing!
How nice to sit in the cine, where the picture of all the world dances
    before the eyes!
How nice if we could take all these things away from the foreigners,
    and possess them!
Take back our lands and silver and oil, take the trains and the fac-
    tories and the automobiles
And play with them all the time!
How nice!

Oh, fools! Mexicans and peons!
Who are you, to be masters of machines which you cannot make?
Which you can only break!
Those that can make are masters of these machines.
Not you, poor boobs.

How have these palefaces, yellowfaces crossed the waters of the
    world?

Oh, fools! Mexicans and peons, with muddy hearts!
Did they do it by squatting on their hams?
You do nothing but squat on your hams, and stare with vacant eyes,
    and drink fire-water, and quarrel and stab.
And then run like surly dogs at the bidding of the paleface masters.

Oh, dogs and fools, Mexicans and peons!
Watery-hearted, with wishy-washy knees.
Sulky in spirit, and inert.
What are you good for, but to be slaves, and rot away?

You are not worth a god!
Lo! the universe tangles its great dragons,
The dragons in the cosmos are stirring with anger again.

The dragon of the disappointed dead, that sleeps in the snow-white
    north
Is lashing his tail in his sleep; the winds howl, the cold rocks round.
The spirits of the cold dead whistle in the ears of the world.
Prepare for doom.

For I tell you, there are no dead dead, not even your dead.
There are dead that sleep in the waves of the Morning Star, with
    freshening limbs.
There are dead that weep in bitter rains.
There are dead that cluster in the frozen north, shuddering and
    chattering among the ice
And howling with hate.
There are dead that creep through the burning bowels of the earth,
Stirring the fires to acid of bitterness.
There are dead that sit under the trees, watching with ash-grey eyes
    for their victims.
There are dead that attack the sun like swarms of black flies, to suck
    his life.
There are dead that stand upon you, when you go in to your women,
And they dart to her womb, they fight for the chance to be born, they
    struggle at the gate you have opened,
They gnash when it closes, and hate the one that got in, to be born
    again,
Child of the living dead, the dead that live and are not refreshed.
I tell you, sorrow upon you; you shall all die.
And being dead, you shall not be refreshed.
There are no dead dead.
Being dead, you shall rove like dogs with broken haunches
Seeking the offal and garbage of life, in the invisible lanes of the
    air.

The dead that have mastered fire live on, salamanders, in fire.
The dead of the water-lords rock and glimmer in the seas.
The dead of the steel machines go up in motion, *away!*
The dead of electric masters are electricity itself.

But the dead of those who have mastered nothing, nothing at all,
Crawl like masterless dogs in the back streets of the air,
Creeping for the garbage of life, and biting with venomous mouths.
Those that have mastered the forces of the world, die into the forces,
  they have homes in death.
But you! what have you mastered, among the dragon hosts of the
  cosmos?
There are dragons of sun and ice, dragons of the moon and the earth,
  dragons of salty waters, dragons of thunder;
There is the spangled dragon of the stars at large.
And far at the centre, with one unblinking eye, the dragon of the
  Morning Star.

Conquer! says the Morning Star. Pass the dragons, and pass on
  to me.
For I am sweet, I am the last and the best, the pool of new life.
But lo! you inert ones, I will set the dragons upon you.
They shall crunch your bones.
And even then they shall spit you out, as broken-haunched dogs,
You shall have nowhere to die into.

Lo! in the back streets of the air, dead ones are crawling like curs!
Lo! I release the dragons! The great white one of the north,
Him of the disappointed dead, he is lashing and turning round.
He is breathing cold corruption upon you, you shall bleed in your
  chests.

I am going to speak to the dragon of the inner fires,
He who housels the dead of the guns,
To withdraw his warmth from your feet, so your feet turn cold with
  death.

I am about to tell the dragon of the waters to turn round on you
And spue out corrosion into your streams, on your rains.

And I wait for the final day, when the dragon of thunder, waking
  under the spider-web nets
Which you've thrown upon him, shall suddenly shake with rage,
And dart his electric needles into your bones, and curdle your blood
  like milk with electric venom.

Wait! Only wait! Little by little it all shall come upon you."

Ramón put on his black city clothes, and a black hat, and went himself with this hymn to the printer in the city. The sign of Quetzalcoatl he had printed in black and red, and the sign of the dragon, at the end, in green and black and red. And the sheet was folded.

Six soldiers of Cipriano's command took the bundles of hymns by train; one to the capital, one to Puebla and Jalapa, one to Tampico and Monterrey, one to Torreon and Chihuahua, one to Sinaloa and Sonora, and one to the mines in Pachucha, Guanajuato, and the central region. Each soldier took only a hundred sheets. But in every town there was a recognised Reader of the Hymns; or two, or three, or four, or even ten Readers in one city. And readers who went round to the villages.

Because there was a strange, submerged desire in the people for things beyond the world. They were weary of events, and weary of news and the newspapers, weary even of the things that are taught in education. Weary is the spirit of man with man's importunity. Of all things human, and humanly invented, we have had enough, they seemed to say. And though they took not much active notice of the Hymns, they craved for them, as men crave for alcohol, as a relief from the weariness and ennui of mankind's man-made world.

Everywhere, in all the towns and villages, at night-time the little flames would be seen flickering, a cluster of people was seen, sometimes standing, sometimes sitting upon the ground, listening to the slow voice of some Reader.

More rarely, in some small, out-of-the-way plaza, would sound the sinister thud of the tom-tom, beating out of the hollow of the ages. And there would be two men with white serapes with the blue edges. Then the singing of the Songs of Quetzalcoatl, and perhaps the slow round dance, with the ancient rhythm of the feet on the earth, belonging to aboriginal America.

For the old dances of the Aztecs and the Zapotecs, of all the submerged Indian races, are based upon the old, sinking bird-step of the Red Indians of the north. It is in the blood of the people; they cannot quite forget it. It comes back to them, with a sense of fear, and joy, and relief.

Of themselves, they dared not revive the old motion, nor stir the blood in the old way. The spell of the past is too terrible. But in the Songs and the Hymns of Quetzalcoatl, there spoke a new voice, the voice of a master and authority. And though they

were slow to trust, the slowest and the most untrusting, they
seized upon the new-old thrill, with a certain fear, and joy, and
relief.

The Men of Quetzalcoatl avoided the great market-places and
centres of activity. They took their stand in the little side places.
On the rim of a fountain a man in a dark blanket with blue
borders, or with the sign of Quetzalcoatl in his hat, would sit
down and begin to read aloud. It was enough. The people lingered to listen. He would read to the end, then say: "I have
finished this reading of the Fourth Hymn of Quetzalcoatl. Now
I will begin again."

In this way, by a sort of far-away note in the voice, and by
the slow monotony of repetition, the thing would drift darkly into
the consciousness of the listeners.

Already in the beginning there had been the scandal of the
Judases. Holy Week, in Mexico City, is, to all appearance, the
great week of Judas. Everywhere you see men carrying home
in triumph the great, gaudily-varnished dolls of papier-mâché.
They are all men-dolls, more or less lifelike grotesque. Most
frequently it is a fat Mexican-Spanish hacendado, landowner and
big farmer, who is represented with his tight trousers, sticking-
out belly, and huge upturned moustaches. The old-fashioned
patrón. Some of the figures are like Punch, some are like harlequin. But they all have rosy faces and the white man's get-up.
You never see the dark-faced image of a native-blooded Mexican;
always a stiff, haughty grotesque of a white man.

And all these are Judases. Judas is the fun of the fair, the
victim, the big man of Holy Week, just as the Skeleton, and the
skeleton on horseback, is the idol of the first week in November,
the days of the dead and of all the saints.

On Easter Saturdays the Judases are hung from the balconies,
the string is lighted, and at length, *bang!* Shrieks of joy, Judas
has exploded into nothingness, from a big cracker in the middle
of him!—All the town is popping with Judases.

There was the scandal of the Holy Images thrown out of one
of the churches in Mexico City, and these Judases put in their
place. The Church began to move.

But then the Church in Mexico has to move gingerly; it is not
popular, and its claws are cut. The priest may not ring the church
bells for more than three minutes. Neither priests nor monks
may wear any habit in the street, beyond the hideous black vest

and white collar of the Protestant clergy. So that the priest shows himself as little as possible in the street, and practically never in the chief streets and the chief plazas.

Nevertheless, he still has influence. Processions in the streets are forbidden, but not sermons from the pulpit, nor advice from the confessional. Montes, the President, had no love for the church, and was meditating the expulsion of all foreign priests. The Archbishop himself was an Italian. But he was also a fighter.

He gave orders to all the priests, to forbid the people from listening to anything concerned with Quetzalcoatl, to destroy any hymn-sheet that might fall into their hands, and to prevent as far as possible the Hymns from being read, and the Songs from being sung, in the parishes.

But Montes had given orders to the police and the military to afford such protection to the Men of Quetzalcoatl as was accorded to any other law-abiding citizen.

Mexico is not Mexico for nothing, however, and already blood had been shed on both sides. This Ramón particularly wanted to avoid, as he felt that violent death was not so easily wiped out of the air and out of the souls of men, as spilt blood was washed off the pavements.

Therefore, when he was in the City, he asked the Bishop of the West if he would consent to an interview with himself and Don Cipriano, and would he name the place. The Bishop—who was an old friend and adviser of Carlota, and who knew Ramón well enough, replied that he should be pleased to see Don Ramón and the *Señor General* the next day, if they would be so good as to come to his house.

The Bishop no longer occupied the great episcopal palace. This was turned into the post-office building. But he had a large house not far from the Cathedral, which had been presented by the faithful.

Ramón and Cipriano found the thin old man in a dusty, uninteresting library, waiting. He wore a simple black cassock, not too clean, with purple buttons. He received Ramón, who was in a black town suit, and Cipriano, who was in uniform, with an affable manner and suspicious looks. But he played at being the lively, genial old bird.

"Ah, Don Ramón, it is long since I saw you! How goes it, eh? Well, well? That is good! That is very good!" And he

patted Ramón on the sleeve like a fussy old uncle. "Ah, my General, much honour, much honour! Welcome to this poor house of yours. It is the house of your Honour! To serve you! Gentlemen! Won't you take a seat?"

They all sat down, in the dusty, dreary room, in the old leather chairs. The Bishop nervously looked at his thin old hands, at the fine, but rather dull amethyst ring he wore.

"Good! Señores!" he said, glancing up with his little black eyes. "At your service! Entirely at the service of your Honours."

"Doña Carlota is in the city, Father. You have seen her?" said Ramón.

"Yes, son of mine," said the Bishop.

"Then you know the latest news about me. She told you everything."

"Somewhat! Somewhat! She spoke somewhat of you, the poor little thing. Thanks to God she has her sons with her. They are safely back in their native country, in good health."

"Did you see them?"

"Yes! Yes! Two of my dearest children! Very sympathetic, very intelligent, like their father; and, like him, promising to be of very handsome presence. Yes! Yes! Smoke if you will, my General. Don't hesitate."

Cipriano lit a cigarette. From old associations, he was nervous, albeit amused.

"You know all about what I want to do, Father?" said Ramón.

"I don't know all, son of mine, but I know enough. I wouldn't want to hear more. Eh!" he sighed. "It is very sad."

"Not so very sad, Father, if we don't make it sad. Why make a sad thing out of it, Father? We are in Mexico for the most part Indians. They cannot understand the high Christianity, Father, and the Church knows it. Christianity is a religion of the spirit, and must needs be understood if it is to have any effect. The Indians cannot understand it, any more than the rabbits of the hills."

"Very good! Very good! Son of mine! But we can convey it to them. The rabbits of the hills are in the hands of God."

"No, Father, it is impossible. And without a religion that will connect them with the universe, they will all perish. Only religion will serve; not socialism, nor education, nor anything."

"Thou speakest well," said the Bishop.

"The rabbits of the hills may be in the hands of God, Father. But they are at the mercy of men. The same with Mexico. The people sink heavier and heavier into inertia, and the Church cannot help them, because the Church does not possess the key-word to the Mexican soul."

"Doesn't the Mexican soul know the Voice of God?" said the Bishop.

"Your own children may know your voice, Father. But if you go out to speak to the birds on the lake, or the deer among the mountains, will they know your voice? Will they wait and listen?"

"Who knows? It is said they waited to listen to the Holy Francisco of Assisi."

"Now, Father, we must speak to the Mexicans in their own language, and give them the clue-word to their own souls. I shall say *Quetzalcoatl*. If I am wrong, let me perish. But I am not wrong."

The Bishop fidgeted rather restlessly. He didn't want to hear all this. And he did not want to answer. He was impotent anyhow.

"Your Church is the Catholic Church, Father?"

"Surely!" said the Bishop.

"And Catholic Church means the Church of All, the Universal Church?"

"Surely, son of mine."

"Then why not let it be really catholic? Why call it catholic, when it is not only just one among many churches, but is even hostile to all the rest of the churches? Father, why not let the Catholic Church become really the Universal Church?"

"It is the Universal Church of Christ, my son."

"Why not let it be the Universal Church of Mohammed as well; since ultimately, God is One God, but the peoples speak varying languages, and each needs its own prophet to speak with its own tongue. The Universal Church of Christ, and Mohammed, and Buddha, and Quetzalcoatl, and all the others—*that* would be a Catholic Church, Father."

"You speak of things beyond me," said the Bishop, turning his ring.

"Not beyond any man," said Don Ramón. "A Catholic Church is a church of all the religions, a home on earth for all the

prophets and the Christs. A big tree under which every man who acknowledges the greater life of the soul can sit and be refreshed. Isn't *that* the Catholic Church, Father?"

"Alas, my son, I know the Apostolic Church of Christ in Rome, of which I am a humble servant. I do not understand these clever things you are saying to me."

"I am asking you for peace, Father. I am not one who hates the Church of Christ, the *Roman* Catholic Church. But in Mexico I think it has no place. When my heart is not bitter, I am grateful forever to Christ, the Son of God. The affair of the Judases grieves me more than it does you, and the affairs of bloodshed are far bitterer to me."

"I am no innovator, my son, to provoke bloodshed."

"Listen! I am going to remove the holy images from the church at Sayula, with reverence, and with reverence burn them upon the lake. Then I shall put the image of Quetzalcoatl in the church at Sayula."

The Bishop looked up furtively. For some moments he said nothing. But his silence was furtive, cornered.

"Would you dare do that, Don Ramón?" he said.

"Yes! And I shall not be prevented. General Viedma is with me."

The Bishop glanced sideways at Cipriano.

"Certainly," said Cipriano.

"Nevertheless it is illegal," said the Bishop, with acid bitterness.

"What is illegal in Mexico?" said Ramón. "What is weak is illegal. I will not be weak, my Lord."

"Lucky you!" said the Bishop, lifting his shoulders.

There was a break of silence.

"No!" said Ramón. "I come to ask you for peace. Tell the Archbishop what I say. Let him tell the Cardinals and the Pope, that the time has come for a Catholic Church of the Earth, the Catholic Church of All the Sons of Men. The Saviours are more than one, and let us pray they will still be increased. But God is one God, and the Saviours are the Sons of the One God. Let the Tree of the Church spread its branches over all the earth, and shelter the prophets in its shade, as they sit and speak their knowledge of the beyond."

"Are you one of these prophets, Don Ramón?"

"I surely am, Father. And I would speak about Quetzalcoatl in Mexico, and build his Church here."

"Nay! You would invade the Churches of Christ and the Blessed Virgin, I heard you say."

"You know my intentions. But I do not want to quarrel with the Church of Rome, nor have bloodshed and enmity, Father. Can you not understand me? Should there not be peace between the men who strive down their different ways to the God-Mystery?"

"Once more desecrate the altars! Bring in strange idols. Burn the images of Our Lord and Our Lady, and ask for peace?" said the poor Bishop, who helplessly longed to be left alone.

"All that, Father," said Ramón.

"Son, what can I answer? You are a good man smitten with the madness of pride. Don Cipriano is one more Mexican general. I am the poor old Bishop of this diocese, faithful servant of the Holy Church, humble child of the Holy Father in Rome. What can I do? What can I answer? Take me out to the cemetery and shoot me at once, General!"

"I don't want to," said Cipriano.

"It will end like that," said the Bishop.

"But why?" cried Don Ramón. "Is there no sense in what I say? Cannot you understand?"

"My son, my understanding goes no further than my faith, my duty, will allow. I am not a clever man. I live by faith, and my duty to my sacred office. Understand that I do not understand."

"Good-day, Father!' said Ramón, suddenly rising.

"Go with God, my son," said the Bishop, rising and lifting his fingers.

"Adios, Señor!" said Cipriano, clicking his spurs, and putting his hand on his sword as he turned to the door.

"Adios, Señor General," said the Bishop, darting after them his eyes of old malice, which they could feel in their backs.

"He will say nothing," said Cipriano, as he and Ramón went down the steps. "The old Jesuit, he only wants to keep his job and his power, and prevent the heart's beating. I know them. All they treasure, even more than their money, is their centipede power over the frightened people; especially over the women."

"I didn't know you hated them," laughed Ramón.

"Waste no more breath on them, my dear one," said Cipriano. "Go forward, you can walk over broken snakes such as those."

As they went on foot past the post-office square, where the modern scribes at little tables under the arches sat tapping out

letters on their typewriters for the poor and illiterate, who waited with their few centavos to have their messages turned into florid Castilian, Ramón and Cipriano met with an almost startled respect.

"Why talk to the Bishop?—he doesn't exist any more. I hear his Knights of Cortes had a big dinner the other evening, and it is said—I don't believe it—that they drank oaths in blood to have my life and yours. But I think the oaths of the Catholic Dames would frighten me more. Why, if a man stops to unfasten his trousers to make water, the Knights of Cortes run for their lives, thinking the pistol is pointed at them. Don't think about them, man! Don't try to conciliate them. They will only puff up and become insolent, thinking you are afraid of them. Six soldiers will trample down all that dirt," said the General.

It was the city, and the spirit of the city.

Cipriano had a suite in the big Palace on the Plaza de Armas.

"If I marry," he said, as they passed into the stone patio, where soldiers stood at attention, "I shall take a house in the colony, to be more private."

Cipriano in town was amusing. He seemed to exude pride and arrogant authority as he walked about. But his black eyes, glancing above his fine nose and that little goat beard, were not to be laughed at. They seemed to get everything, in the stab of a glance. A demoniacal little fellow.

CHAPTER XVIII

AUTO DA FÉ

RAMON saw Carlota and his boys in the city, but it was a rather fruitless meeting. The elder boy was just uncomfortable in the presence with his father, but the younger, Cyprian, who was delicate and very intelligent, had a rather lofty air of displeasure with his parent.

"Do you know what they sing, papa?" he said.

"Not all the things they sing," said Ramón.

"They sing—" the boy hesitated. Then, in his clear young voice, he piped up, to the tune of *La Cucaracha:*

> "Don Ramón don't drink, don't smoke.
> Doña Carlota wished he would.
> He's going to wear the sky-blue cloak
> That he's stole from the Mother of God."

"No, I'm not," said Ramón, smiling. "Mine's got a snake and a bird in the middle, and black zigzags and a red fringe. You'd better come and see it."

"No, papa! I don't want to."

"Why not?"

"I don't want to be mixed up in this affair. It makes us all look ridiculous."

"But how do you think you look, anyhow, in your striped little sailor suit and your little saintly look? We'd better dress you as the Infant Jesus."

"No, papa! You are in bad taste. One doesn't say those things."

"Now you'll have to confess to a fib. You say one doesn't say those things, when I, who am your father, said them only a moment ago, and you heard me."

"I mean good people don't. Decent people."

"Now you'll have to confess again, for calling your father indecent.—Terrible child!"

The child flushed, and tears rose to his eyes. There was silence for a while.

266

"So you don't want to come to Jamiltepec?" said Ramón, to his boys.

"Yes!" said the elder boy, slowly. "I want to come and bathe in the lake, and have a boat. But—they say it is impossible."

"Why?"

"They say you make yourself a peon, in your clothes."—The boy was shy.

"They're very nice clothes, you know. Nicer than those little breeches of yours."

"They say, also, that you pretend to be the Axtec god Quetzalcoatl."

"Not at all. I only pretend that the Axtec god Quetzalcoatl is coming back to the Mexicans."

"But, papa, it is not true."

"How do you know?"

"Because it is impossible."

"Why?"

"There never was any Quetzalcoatl, except idols."

"Is there any Jesus, except images?"

"Yes, papa."

"Where?"

"In heaven."

"Then in heaven there is also Quetzalcoatl. And what is in heaven is capable of coming back to earth. Don't you believe me?"

"I can't."

"Then go unbelieving," said the father, laughing at them and rising to leave them.

"It is very bad that they sing songs about you, and put mama in; like about Pancho Villa," said the younger boy. "It hurts me very much."

"Rub it with *Vapor-rub,* my pet," said Ramón. "Rub it with *Vapor-rub,* where it hurts you."

"What a real bad man you are, papa!"

"What a real good child are you, my son! Isn't that so?"

"I don't know, papa. I only know you are bad."

"Oh! Oh! Is that all they teach thee at thy American school?"

"Next term," said Ciprianito, "I want to change my name. I don't want to be called Carrasco any more. When thou art in the newspapers, they will laugh at us."

"Oh! Oh! I am laughing at thee *now,* little frog! What

name wilt thou choose then? Espina, perhaps. Thou knowest
Carrasco is a wild bush, on the moors in Spain, where we come
from. Wilt thou be the little thorn on the bush? Call thyself
Espina, thou art a sprig of the old tree. Entonces, Adios!
Señor Espina Espinita!"

"Adios!" said the boy abruptly, flushing with rage.

Ramón took a motor-car to Sayula, for there was a made road.
But already the rains were washing it away. The car lurched
and bumped in the great gaps. In one place, a camion lay on its
back, where it had overturned.

On the flat desert, there were already small smears of water,
and the pink cosmos flowers, and the yellow, were just sprouting
their tufts of buds. The hills in the distance were going opaque,
as leaves came out on the invisible trees and bushes. The earth
was coming to life.

Ramón called in Sayula at Kate's house. She was out, but the
wild Concha came scouring across the beach, to fetch her.—"There
is Don Ramón! There is Don Ramón!"

Kate hurried home, with sand in her shoes.

She thought Ramón looked tired, and, in his black suit, sinister.

"I didn't expect you," she said.

"I am on my way back from town."

He sat very still, with that angry look on his creamy dark face,
and he kept pushing back his black moustache from his closed,
angry lips.

"Did you see anybody in town?" she asked.

"I saw Don Cipriano—and Doña Carlota, and my boys!"

"Oh, how nice for you! Are they quite well?"

"In excellent health, I believe."

She laughed suddenly.

"You are still cross," she said. "Is it about the monkeys still?"

"Señora," he said, leaning forward, so that his black hair
dropped a little on his brow, "in monkeydom, I don't know who
is prince. But in the kingdom of fools, I believe it is I."

"Why?" she said.

And as he did not answer, she added:

"It must be a comfort to be a prince, even of fools."

He looked daggers at her, then burst into a laugh.

"Oh, Señora mia! What ails us men, when we are always
wanting to be *good?*"

"Are you repenting of it?" she laughed.

"Yes!" he said. "I am a prince of fools! Why have I started this Quetzalcoatl business? Why? Pray tell me why?"

"I suppose you wanted to."

He pondered for a time, pushing up his moustache.

"Perhaps it is better to be a monkey than a fool. I object to being called a monkey, nevertheless. Carlota is a monkey, no more; and my two boys are prize young monkeys in sailor suits. And I am a fool. Yet what is the difference between a fool and a monkey?"

"Quien sabe?" said Kate.

"One wants to be good, and the other is sure he *is* good. So I make a fool of myself. They are sure they are always good, so that makes monkeys of them. Oh, if only the world would blow up like a bomb!"

"It won't!" said Kate.

"True enough.—Ah, well!"

He drew himself erect, pulling himself together.

"Do you think, Señora Caterina, you might marry our mutual General?" Ramón had put himself aside again.

"I—I don't know!" stammered Kate. "I hardly think so "

"He is not sympathetic to you at all?"

"Yes. He is. He is alive, and there is even a certain fascination about him.—But one shouldn't try marrying a man of another race, do you think, even if he were more sympathetic?"

"Ah!" sighed Ramón. "It's no good generalising. It's no good marrying anybody, unless there will be a real fusion somewhere."

"And I feel there wouldn't," said Kate. "I feel he just wants something of me; and perhaps I just want something of him. But he would never meet me. He would never come forward himself, to meet me. He would come to take something from me and I should have to let him. And I don't want merely that. I want a man who will come half-way, just half-way, to meet me."

Don Ramón pondered, and shook his head.

"You are right," he said. "Yet, in these matters, one never knows what is half-way, nor where it is. A woman who just wants to be taken, and then to cling on, is a parasite. And a man who wants just to take, without giving, is a creature of prey."

"And I'm afraid Don Cipriano might be that," said Kate.

"Possibly," said Ramón. "He is not so with me. But perhaps he would be, if we did not meet—perhaps it is our half-way

—in some physical belief that is at the very middle of us, and
which we recognise in one another. Don't you think there might
be that between you and him?"

"I doubt if he'd feel it necessary, with a woman. A woman
wouldn't be important enough."

Ramón was silent.

"Perhaps!" he said. "With a woman, a man always wants to
let himself go. And it is precisely with a woman that he should
never let himself go. It is precisely with a woman that he should
never let himself go, but stick to his innermost belief, and meet
her just there. Because when the innermost belief coincides in
them both, if it's physical, there, and then, and nowhere else,
they can meet. And it's no good unless there is a meeting. It's
no good a man ravishing a woman, and it's absolutely no good a
woman ravishing a man. It's a sin, that is. There is such a
thing as sin, and that's the centre of it. Men and women keep
on ravishing one another. Absurd as it may sound, it is not I
who would ravish Carlota. It is she who would ravish me.
Strange and absurd and a little shameful, it is true.—Letting oneself go, is either ravishing or being ravished. Oh, if we could
only abide by our own souls, and meet in the abiding place.—
Señora, I have not a very great respect for myself. Woman and
I have failed with one another, and it is a bad failure to have in
the middle of oneself."

Kate looked at him in wonder, with a little fear. Why was he
confessing to her? Was he going to love her? She almost suspended her breathing. He looked at her with a sort of sorrow
on his brow, and in his dark eyes, anger, vexation, wisdom, and
a dull pain.

"I am sorry," he went on, "that Carlota and I are as we are
with one another. Who am I, even to talk about Quetzalcoatl,
when my heart is hollow with anger against the woman I have
married and the children she bore me.—We never met in our
souls, she and I. At first I loved her, and she wanted me to ravish her. Then after a while a man becomes uneasy. He can't
keep on wanting to ravish a woman, the same woman. He has
revulsions. Then she loved me, and she wanted to ravish me.
And I liked it for a time. But she had revulsions too. The eldest boy is really my boy, when I ravished her. And the youngest
is her boy, when she ravished me. See how miserable it is! And
now we can never meet; she turns to her crucified Jesus, and I

to my uncrucified and uncrucifiable Quetzalcoatl, who at least
cannot be ravished."

"And I'm sure you won't make him a ravisher," she said.

"Who knows? If I err, it will be on that side. But you know,
Señora, Quetzalcoatl is to me only the symbol of the best a man
may be, in the next days. The universe is a nest of dragons,
with a perfectly unfathomable life-mystery at the centre of it.
If I call the mystery the Morning Star, surely it doesn't matter!
A man's blood can't beat in the abstract. And man is a creature
who wins his own creation inch by inch from the nest of the cosmic dragons. Or else he loses it little by little, and goes to pieces.
Now we are all losing it, in the ravishing and ravished disintegration. We must pull ourselves together, hard, both men and
women, or we are all lost.—We must pull ourselves together,
hard."

"But are you a man who needs a woman in his life?" she said.

"I am a man who yearns for the sensual fulfilment of my soul,
Señora," he said. "I am a man who has no belief in abnegation
of the blood desires. I am a man who is always on the verge of
taking wives and concubines to live with me, so deep is my desire
for that fulfilment. Except that now I know that is useless—not
momentarily useless, but in the long run—my ravishing a woman
with hot desire. No matter how much she is in love with me and
desires me to ravish her. It is no good, and the very inside of
me knows it is no good. Wine, woman, and song—all that—all
that game is up. Our insides won't really have it any more. Yet
it is hard to pull ourselves together."

"So that you really want a woman to be with you?" said Kate.

"Ah, Señora! If I could trust myself; and trust her! I am
no longer a young man, who can afford to make mistakes. I am
forty-two years old, and I am making my last—and perhaps in
truth, my first great effort as a man. I hope I may perish before
I make a big mistake."

"Why should you make a mistake? You needn't?"

"I? It is very easy for me to make a mistake. Very easy, on
the one hand, for me to become arrogant and a ravisher. And
very easy, on the other hand, for me to deny myself, and make a
sort of sacrifice of my life. Which is being ravished. Easy to
let myself, in a certain sense, be ravished. I did it to a small degree even yesterday, with the Bishop of Guadalajara. And it is
bad. If I had to end my life in a mistake, Señora, I had rather

end it in being a ravisher, than in being ravished. As a hot ravisher, I can still slash and cut at the disease of the other thing,
the horrible pandering and the desire men have to be ravished,
the hateful, ignoble desire they have."

"But why don't you do as you say, stick by the innermost soul
that is in you, and meet a woman there, meet her, as you say,
where your two souls coincide in their deepest desire? Not always that horrible unbalance that you call ravishing."

"Why don't I? But which woman can I meet in the body,
without that slow degradation of ravishing, or being ravished,
setting in? If I marry a Spanish woman or a dark Mexican,
she will give herself up to me to be ravished. If I marry a woman
of the Anglo-Saxon or any blond northern stock, she will want
to ravish me, with the will of all the ancient white demons. Those
that want to be ravished are parasites on the soul, and one has revulsions. Those that want to ravish a man are vampires. And
between the two, there is nothing."

"Surely there are *some* really good women?"

"Well, show me them. They are all potential Carlotas or—or
—yes, Caterinas. I am sure you ravished your Joachim till he
died. No doubt he wanted it; even more than you wanted it.
It is not just sex. It lies in the will. Victims and victimisers.
The upper classes, craving to be victims to the lower classes; or
else craving to make victims of the lower classes. The politicians,
craving to make one people victims to another. The Church, with
its evil will for turning the people into humble, writhing things
that shall crave to be victimised, to be ravished.—I tell you, the
earth is a place of shame."

"But if *you* want to be different," said Kate, "surely a few
other people do—really."

"It may be," he said, becoming calm. "It may be. I wish I
kept myself together better. I must keep myself together, keep
myself within the middle place, where I am still. My Morning
Star. Now I am ashamed of having talked like this to you,
Señora Caterina."

"Why?" she cried. And for the first time, the flush of hurt
and humiliation came into her face.

He saw it at once, and put his hand on hers for a moment.

"No," he said. "I am not ashamed. I am relieved."

She flushed deeply at his touch, and was silent. He rose hastily,
to leave, craving to be alone again with his own soul.

"On Sunday," he said, "will you come into the plaza, in the morning, when the drum sounds? Will you come?"

"What for?" she said.

"Well! Come, and you will see."

He was gone in a flash.

There were many soldiers in the village. When she went to the post-office, she saw the men in their cotton uniforms lying about in the entrance to the military station. There must have been fifty or more, little men, not the tall soldiers in slouched hats. These were little, quick, compact men, like Cipriano, and they talked in a strange Indian language, very subdued. They were very rarely seen in the streets. They kept out of sight.

But at night, everyone was requested to be indoors by ten o'clock, and through the darkness Kate heard the patrols of horse-soldiers riding round.

There was an air of excitement and mystery in the place. The parish priest, a rather overbearing, fat man of fifty or so, had preached a famous Saturday evening sermon against Ramón and Quetzalcoatl, forbidding the heathen name to be mentioned, threatening with all the penalties any parishioner who read the Hymns, or even listened.

So, of course, he was attacked when he left the church, and had to be rescued by soldiers who were in the doorway. They marched him safely home. But his criada, the old woman who served him, was told by more women than one that the next time the padre opened his mouth against Quetzalcoatl, he would have a few inches of machete in his fat guts.

So his reverence stayed at home, and a curate officiated.

Practically all the people who came over the lake in boats on Saturdays, went to mass in Sayula church. The great doors stood open all the day. Men as they passed to and fro to the lake, took off their big hats, with a curious cringing gesture, as they went by the gateway of the church. All day long, scattered people were kneeling in the aisles or among the benches, the men kneeling erect, their big hats down by their knees, their curious tall-shaped Indian heads with the thick black hair also erect; only the kneeling legs, close together, humble. The women hooded themselves in their dark rebozos and spread their elbows as they kneeled at a bench, in a slack sort of voluptuousness.

On Saturday night, a great ruddy flickering of many candle-points, away down the dark cavern of the church; and a cluster-

ing of dark men's heads, a shuffling of women, a come and go of men arriving from the lake, of men departing to the market. A hush, not exactly of worship, but of a certain voluptuous admiration of the loftiness and glitter, a sensual, almost victimised self-abandon to the god of death, the Crucified streaked with blood, or to the pretty white woman in a blue mantle, with her little doll's face under her crown, Mary, the doll of dolls, Niña of Niñas.

It was not worship. It was a sort of numbness and letting the soul sink uncontrolled. And it was a luxury, after all the week of unwashed dullness in their squalid villages of straw huts. But it irritated Kate.

The men got up and tiptoed away in their sandals, crossing themselves front and back, on the navel and on the back of the head, with holy water. And their black eyes shone with a loose, sensuous look. Instead of having gathered themselves together and become graver, stronger, more collected and deep in their own integrity, they emerged only the more loose and sloppy and uncontrolled.

Oh, if there is one thing men need to learn, but the Mexican Indians especially, it is to collect each man his own soul together deep inside him, and to abide by it. The Church, instead of helping men to this, pushes them more and more into a soft, emotional helplessness, with the unpleasant sensuous gratification of feeling themselves victims, victimised, victimised, but at the same time with the lurking sardonic consciousness that in the end a victim is stronger than the victimiser. In the end, the victims pull down their victimiser, like a pack of hyænas on an unwary lion. They know it. Cursed are the falsely meek, for they are inheriting the earth.

On Sunday morning there was early mass at sunrise, another mass at seven o'clock, another at nine, another at eleven. Then there was a little band of violins and 'cellos, playing old-fashioned dance music; there was, especially early in the morning, a solid mass of peons and women, kneeling on the floor; and a flapping of dusky candles, a smell of the exhaust air of candles, a heavy, rolling fume of incense, and the heavy choir of men's voices, solid, powerful, impressive, from the gallery.

And the people went away in sensuous looseness, which soon turned, in the market, to hate, the old, unfathomable hate which lies at the bottom of the Indian heart, and which always rises

black and turbid when they have swayed awhile in sensuous gratification.

The church inside was a dead interior, like all Mexican churches, even the gorgeous Puebla cathedral. The interior of almost any Mexican church gives the impression of cynical barrenness, cynical meaninglessness, an empty, cynical, mocking shell. The Italian churches are built much in the same style, and yet in them lingers a shadow and stillness of old, mysterious holiness. The hush.

But not in Mexico. The churches outside are impressive. Inside, and it is curious to define it, they are blatant; void of sound and yet with no hush, simple, and yet completely vulgar, barren, sterile. More barren than a bank or a schoolroom or an empty concert-hall, less mysterious than any of these. You get a sense of plaster, of mortar, of whitewash, of smeared blue-wash or grey-wash; and of gilt laid on and ready to peel off. Even in the most gorgeous churches, the gilt is hatefully gilt, never golden. Nothing is soft nor mellow.

So the interior of Sayula church; and Kate had often been in. The white exterior was charming, and so valuable in the landscape, with the twin white pagoda-towers peering out of the green willow trees. But inside, it seemed nothing but whitewash, stencilled over with grey scroll-work decorations. The windows were high, and many, letting in the light as into a schoolroom. Jesus, streaked with blood, was in one of the transepts, and the Virgin, a doll in faded satin, stood startled inside a glass case. There were rag flowers and paper flowers, coarse lace and silver that looked like tin.

Nevertheless, it was quite clean, and very much frequented.

The Month of Mary had gone by, the blue and white paper ribbons were all taken down, the palm trees in pots were all removed from the aisle, the little girls in white dresses and little crowns of flowers no longer came with posies in their hand, at evening. Curious, the old gentle ceremonials of Europe, how trashy they seem in Mexico, just a cheap sort of charade.

The day of Corpus Christi came, with high mass and the church full to the doors with kneeling peons, from dawn till noon. Then a feeble little procession of children within the church, because the law forbids religious processions outside. But all, somehow, for nothing. Just so that the people could call it a fiesta, and so

have an excuse to be more slack, more sloshy and uncontrolled than ever. The one Mexican desire; to let themselves go in sloppy inertia.

And this was the all-in-all of the religon. Instead of doing as it should, collecting the soul into its own strength and integrity, the religious day left it all the more decomposed and degenerate.

However, the weeks passed, the crowd in the church seemed the same as ever. But the crowd in the church one hour was the crowd of Quetzalcoatl the next hour. Just a sensation.

Till the more socialistic Readers mingled a little anti-clerical bitterness in their reading. And all the peons began to say: El Señor a gringo, and the Santisima, was she nothing but a gringita?

This provoked retaliation on the part of the priests, first mere admonitions, then at last the loud denunciations and threat of that sermon. Which meant war.

Everybody waited for Saturday. Saturday came, and the church remained shut. Saturday night, the church was dark and closed. Sunday, the church was silent and the doors blank fastened.

Something like consternation spread through the market host. They had nowhere to go!—But among the consternation was a piqued curiosity. Perhaps something exciting was going to happen.

Things had happened before. In the revolutions, many of the churches in Mexico have been used for stables and for barracks. And churches are turned into schools, and concert halls, and cinematograph theatres. The convents and the monasteries are most of them barracks for the rag-tag-and-bobtail soldiers. The world changes, is bound to change.

The second Saturday of the closed church was, as it happened, a big market. Much fruit and stuff had come up the lake, from the south from far distances, even from Colima. There were men with lacquer wooden bowls, and women with glazed pottery. And as usual, men crouching in guard over twenty centavos' worth of nauseous tropical plums, or chilies, or mangoes, in tiny pyramids along the roadway.

A crowded market, with the much and the little of the Indians. And the church doors shut and locked, the church bells silent, even the clock stopped. True, the clock was always stopping. But not with such a final arrest.

No mass, no confession, no little orgy of incense and slack emotion! The low rumble of murmuring tones, the quick, apprehensive glances around. Vendors by the causeway squatting tight, as if to make themselves dense and small, squatted down on their haunches with their knees up to their shoulders, like the Aztec idols. And soldiers in twos and threes sprinkled everywhere. And Señoras and Señoritas, in their black gauze scarves or mantillas, tripping to the church for mass and shrilling round the gateway of the church, all a bubble and a froth of chatter; though they had known quite well the church was shut.

But it was Sunday morning, and something was due to happen.

At about half-past ten, a boat appeared, and men in snow-white clothes got out, one carrying a drum. They marched quickly through the people, under the old trees on the sand, across to the church. They passed through the broken iron gates into the stone courtyard in front of the church.

At the church doors, which were still shut, they took off their blouses, and stood in a ring, with dark naked shoulders and the blue-and-black sashes of Quetzalcoatl round their waists.

The drum began to beat, with a powerful, pounding note, as the men stood bare-headed and bare-breasted in a circle outside the church doors; a strange ring of lustrous, bluey-black heads and dark shoulders, above the snowy white pantaloons. Monotonously the drum beat, on and on. Then the little clay flute with the husky sound wheezed a clear melody.

The whole market pressed densely towards the gateways of the church. But there, soldiers stood guard. And on the inside of the stone yard in front of the church, soldiers quietly guarded the low walls, letting nobody mount. So that outside, under the old willow and pepper trees, in the hot morning sun, the dense crowd stood gazing at the church doors. They were mostly men in big hats; but some townsmen were there, and some women, and Kate with a parasol lined with dark blue. A close, silent, tense throng under the spangled shade, pressing round the trunks of the palm trees, climbing on the roots of the pepper-trees. And behind were the camions and the motor-cars drawn up.

The drum shuddered and went still, and the earthen flute was silent. The lake could be heard lapping, and a clink of glasses and a sound of chauffeurs' voices at the little cantina-booth. For the rest, the silent breathing of the crowd.—Soldiers were quickly dis-

tributing a few leaflets among the crowd. A strong, far-carrying male voice began to sing to the softened thud of the drum.

JESUS' FAREWELL

Farewell, Farewell, *Despedida!*
The last of my days is gone.
To-morrow Jesus and Holy Mary
Will be bone.

It is a long, long way
From Mexico to the Pool of Heaven.
Look back the last time, Mary Mother.
Let us call the eleven.

James, and John, and Mark,
Felipe and San Cristobal,
All my saints, and Anna, Teresa,
Guadalupe whose face is oval,

Come then, now, it is finished for all of us,
Let us all be gone.
Follow me now up the ladders of sparks,
Every one.

Joaquin, Francis, and Anthony
And many-named Maria,
Purisima, Refugio, and Soledad
Follow here.

Ho! all my saints and my Virgins
Troop out of your shrines,
After your master, the Crucified;
Bring all your signs.

Run up the flames, and with feet on the sparks
Troop into the sky.
Once more following the Master,
Back again now, on high.

Farewell, let all be forgotten
In Mexico.
To the pool of peace and forgetting in heaven
We go.

While this was singing, another boat had arrived, and soldiers made way through the crowd for Ramón, in his white serape with the blue edges and scarlet fringe, and a young priest of the church in a black cassock, and six men in dark serapes with the blue bor-

ders of Quetzalcoatl. This strange procession marched through the crowd and through the gateways of the yard.

As they approached, the ring of men round the drum opened, and spread into a crescent. Ramón stood tall behind the drum, the six men in dark serapes divided and went to the wings of the crescent, the young, slim priest in a black cassock stood alone, in front of the crescent, facing the crowd.

He lifted his hand; Ramón took off his hat; all the men in the crowd took off their hats.

The priest turned, met Ramón at the centre of the crescent, and, across the drum, handed him the key of the church. Then the priest waited.

Ramón unlocked the church doors and flung them open. The men in front of the crowd kneeled down suddenly, seeing the church dark like a cavern, but a trembling blaze of many candles, away, seemingly far down the mysterious darkness, shuddering with dark, ripping flame, like the Presence of the burning bush.

The crowd swayed and rustled, and subsided, kneeling. Only here and there a labourer, a chauffeur or a railway man stood erect.

The priest raised his hand a little higher, re-turning towards the people.

"My children," he said; and as he spoke the lake seemed to rustle; "God the Almighty has called home His Son, and the Holy Mother of the Son. Their days are over in Mexico. They go back to the Father.

"Jesus, the Son of God, bids you farewell.
Mary, the Mother of God, bids you farewell.
For the last time they bless you, as they leave you.
Answer *Adios!*
Say *Adios!* my children."

The men in the circle said a deep *Adios!* And from the soldiers, and from the kneeling crowd, a ragged, muttered, strange repeating of *Adios!* again and again, like a sort of storm.

Suddenly, in a blast, down the darkness of the church into which the kneeling people were staring, the burning bush of candles was gone, there was only darkness. Across the sunshine, lit here and there by a frail light of a taper, was a cave of darkness.

Men in the crowd exclaimed and groaned.

Then the drum softly touched, and two men in the crescent

began to sing, in magnificent, terrible voices, the Farewell Hymn again. They were men whom Ramón, or his followers, had found in low drinking dens in Mexico City, men with trained and amazing voices, the powerful Mexican tenor that seemed to tear the earth open. Men whom the "times" have reduced to singing in low city dives. And now they sang with all the terrible desperation that was in them, the hopeless, demonish recklessness.

When they had finished, the priest again lifted his hand, and gave the benediction; adding in a quiet voice:

"And now, with all the saints, let Me go, saith Jesus. For I go back to my Father which is in heaven, and I lead my Mother in my right hand, home to peace."

He turned and went into the church. Ramón followed. Then slowly, all the men of the crescent. Overhead the church bell rang a little while, on the deathly silence. It ceased.

And in a moment, from the depths of the church sounded a drum, with a remote, fearsome thud, and a slow monotony.

The priest, in his white vestments with rich lace, appeared in the doorway of the church, bearing a tall crucifix. He hesitated, then came into the sun. The kneeling people clasped their hands.

Candles in the dark church were clustering towards the door, lonely flames. Don Ramón came out of the dark, naked to the waist, his serape over one shoulder, bearing the front pole of the great bier whereon lies, within a glass case, the lifelike, terrible dead Christ of Holy Week. A tall, dark man, naked to the waist, held the other end of the pole on his shoulder. The crowd moaned and crossed themselves. The lifelike Dead Christ seemed really dead, as he passed the gates. As He entered the crowd, kneeling men and women lifted sightless faces and flung their arms wide apart, and so remained, arms rigid and outflung, in an unspeakable ecstasy of fear, supplication, acknowledgment of death.

After the bier of the Dead Christ, a slow procession of men naked to the waist, carrying litter after litter. First the terrible scourged Christ, with naked body striped like a tiger with blood. Then the image of the Saviour of the Sacred Heart, the well-known figure from the side altar, with long hair and outstretched hands. Then the image of Jesus of Nazareth, with a crown of Thorns.

Then the Virgin with the blue mantle and lace, and the golden

crown. The women began to moan as she emerged rather
trashily into the blazing sunlight. Behind her, in the church,
the candles were one by one going out.

Then came brown Saint Anthony of Padua, with a child in
his arms. Then Saint Francis, looking strangely at a cross in
his hand. Then Saint Anna. And at last, Saint Joaquin. And
as he emerged, the last candles in the dark church went out,
there were only open doors upon a darkness.

The images on the shoulders of the brown-skinned men rode
rather childishly out through the blazing sun, into the shadow
of trees. The drum followed last, slowly thudding. On the
glass case of the big Dead Christ the sun flashed with startling
flashes, as the powerful men carrying it turned towards the water.
The crowd murmured and swayed on its knees. Women cried:
Purisima! Purisima! Don't leave us! and some men ejacu-
lated in strangled anguish, over and over again: *Señor! Señor!
Señor!*

But the strange procession made its way slowly under the
trees, to the coarse sands, and descended again into the great
light towards the lake. There was a little breeze under a blaze
of sun. Folded serapes on naked, soft shoulders swung un-
evenly, the images rocked and tottered a little. But onwards
to the edge of the water went the tall crucifix, then the flashing
glass box. And after, came Jesus in a red silk robe, fluttering,
then a wooden Jesus all paint and streaks, then Jesus in white
with a purple mantle that blew like a kerchief, Mary in lace
that fluttered upon stiff white and blue satin. But the saints
were only painted; painted wood.

The slim, lace-smocked priest staggered down the sand under
the heavy crucifix, which had a white Christ Crucified stretched
aloft, facing the lake. By the little wall was a large black *canoa,*
sailing boat, with a broad plank gangway up to her stern. Two
bare-legged, white-clad men walked by the slim priest, whose
white sleeves blew like flags as he slowly climbed the gangway
to the ship. Men helped him on board, and he walked away
to the prow, where at length he stood the big Crucifix, with the
Christ still facing outwards.

The ship was open, without decks or hatches, but with fixed
tables for the images. Slowly Ramón ascended and descended
into the boat, the great glass case was laid down on its rest,
the two men could wipe their wet brows and their hot, black

hair. Ramón put on his blanket and his hat, against the sun. The boat heaved very slightly. The wind was from the west. The lake was pale and unreal, sun-blinded.

One after another the images rose over the stern of the boat, against the sky, then descended into the vessel, to be set down on their rests, where they rose above the black sides of the *canoa,* in view of the throng on the shore.

It was a strange and tawdry collection of images. And yet, each image had a certain pathos of its own, and a certain touch of horror, as they were grouped together for their last ride, upon the trestle-supports within the vessel. By each image stood the bearers, in hats and serapes, keeping a steady hand on the poles.

There was a little line of soldiers on the shore, and three motor-boats with soldiers waited by the big *canoa.* The shore was covered with a mass of people. Many row-boats came rowing inquisitively round, like fishes. But none came too near.

Bare-legged sailors began to pole the ship from the shore. They leaned heavily on the poles, and walked along the rim of the vessel. Slowly she began to move upon the waters, in the shallows. Slowly, she was leaving the shore, and the throng.

Two other sailors swiftly began to hoist the huge, square white sail. Quickly, yet heavily it rose in the air, and took the wind. It had the great sign of Quetzalcoatl, the circling blue snake and the blue eagle upon a yellow field, at the centre, like a great eye.

The wind came from the west, but the boat was steering south-east, for the little Island of the Scorpions, which rose like a small dim hummock from the haze of the lake. So the sail reached out, and the great eye seemed to be glancing back, at the village with the green willows and the empty white church, the throng on the shore.

Motor-boats circled the huge, slow canoe, small boats like insects followed and ranged round at a distance, never coming too close. The running water clucked and spoke, the men by the images steadied the poles with one hand, their hats with the other, the great eye on the sail ever looked back at the land, the sweep of the white canvas sweeping low above the glass case of death, the Christ caked with gore, the images in their fluttering mantles.

On the shore, the people wandered away, or sat on the sands waiting and watching in a sort of dumb patience that was half indifference. The canoe grew smaller, more inconspicuous, lapsing into the light, the little boats circled around it like mere dots. The lake tired the eyes with its light.

Away under the trees, in a half silence, a half vacancy, a woman brought a dark water-melon, smashed it open on a stone, and gave the big pinky fragments to her children. In silence, men sprinkled salt on the thick slice of cucumber sold by the woman under the tree. In silence they wandered into the church, past the soldiers on guard at the door.

The church was absolutely dark, save for the light that entered the doorway, and absolutely bare; walls, floor, altar, transepts, all stark bare and empty. The people wandered away again, in silence.

It was noon, and a hot day. The *canoa* slowly ranged to the small hummock of the island amid the waters, where lived one family of Indians—fishers, with a few goats and one dry little place where they grew a few beans and heads of maize. For the rest, the island was all dry rock and thorny bushes, and scorpions.

The vessel was poled round to the one rocky bay. Slowly she drew near the island. The motor-boats and the little boats hurried ahead. Already brown, naked men were bathing among the rocks.

The great sail sank, the *canoa* edged up to the rocky shore, men sprang from her into the water, the images were lowered and slowly carried on to the rocks. There they waited for the bearers.

Slowly the procession went up the bank of the dishevelled island, past the couple of huts, where a red cock was crowing among the litter, and over to rocks, beyond the bushes, on the far side.

The side facing Sayula was all rock, naked and painful to tread on. In a rocky hollow at the waters' edge, tall stones had been put up on end, with iron bars across the top, like a grill. Underneath, a pile of faggots ready; and at the side, a pile of faggots.

The images, the glass box of the great Dead Christ, were laid on the iron bars of the grill, in a pathetic cluster all to-

gether. The crucifix was laid against them. It was noon, the heat and the light were fierce and erect. But already down the lake clouds were pushing up fantastically.

Beyond the water, beyond the glare, the village looked like a mirage, with its trees and villages and white church towers.

Men who had come in boats crowded on the rocks of the little amphitheatre. In silence, Ramón kindled shreds of cane and ocote, with a burning glass. Little hasty flames like young snakes arose in the solid sunlight, with vapor of smoke. He set fire to the carefully-arranged pyramid of faggots beneath the grill-table of the images.

There was a crackling, and a puffing of whitish smoke, the sweet scent of ocote, and orange-red tongues of half-substantial flame were leaping up in the hot white air. Hot breaths blew suddenly, sudden flames gushed up, and the ocote, full of sweet resin, began to roar. The glass of the great box emitted strange, painful yelps as it splintered and fell tinkling. Between the iron bars, brownish flames pushed up among the images, which at once went black. The little vestments of silk and satin withered in a moment to blackness, the caked wounds of paint bubbled black.

The young priest took off his linen vestment, his stole and his chasuble, and with flushed face flung them in the flame. Then he stripped off his black cassock, and emerged in the white cotton of the men of Quetzalcoatl, his white drawers rolled up to the knee. He threw his cassock in the fire. Someone handed him a big hat, and a white serape with blue ends.

There was a smell of burning paint, and wool, and ocote. The fire rushed in a dusky mass upon the blackened, flickering images, till nothing was to be seen but a confused bush of smoke and brown-red flames, puthering, reeking, roaring. The flaming crucifix slipped aside, and fell. A man seized it and pushed it into the fire, under the images. Men in a sort of ecstasy threw on more of the heavy, resinous wood, that almost exploded into flame. Rocks cracked and exploded like guns. Everybody drew back from that roaring tree of flame, which rose ever higher and higher, its dark smoke and its sparks unfolding into heaven.

One of the supporting stones burst with a bang, bars of iron and blazing stumps of images tumbled in a confused roar. The glass case had disappeared, but ribbons of iron waved, then curled over red, into the torrent of the sudden fire. Strange

rods of iron appeared out of nowhere, protruding from solid red coals.

And soon, all that was left was a fierce glow of red coals of wood, with a medley of half-fused iron.

Ramón stood aside and watched in silence, his dark brow quite expressionless.

Then, when only the last bluish flames flickered out of a tumble of red fire, from the eminence above, rockets began to shoot into the air with a swish, exploding high in the sightless hot blue, with a glimmer of bluish showers, and of gold.

The people from the shore had seen the tree of smoke with its trunk of flame. Now they heard the heavy firing of the rockets, they looked again, exclaiming, half in dismay, half in the joyful lust of destruction:

"Señor! Señor! La Purisima! La Santisima!"

The flame and the smoke and the rockets melted as if by miracle, into nothingness, leaving the hot air unblemished. The coals of fire were shovelled and dropped down a steep hole.

As the *canoa* sailed back, the side of the lake, through filmy air, looked brownish and changeless. A cloud was rising in the south-west, from behind the dry, silent mountains, like a vast white tail, like the vast white fleecy tail of some squirrel, that had just dived out of sight behind the mountains. This wild white tail fleeced up and up, to the zenith, straight at the sun. And as the *canoa* spread her sail to tack back, already a delicate film of shadow was over the chalk-white lake.

Only on the low end of the isle of Scorpions, hot air still quivered.

Ramón returned in one of the motor-boats. Slowly the sky was clouding for the thunder and the rain. The *canoa,* unable to make her way across, was sailing for Tuliapan. The little boats hurried in silence.

They landed before the wind rose. Ramón went and locked the doors of the church.

The crowd scattered in the wind, rebozos waving wildly, leaves torn, dust racing. Sayula was empty of God, and, at heart, they were glad.

CHAPTER XIX

THE ATTACK ON JAMILTEPEC

SUDDENLY, nearly all the soldiers disappeared from the village, there was a "rebellion" in Colima. A train had been held up, people killed. And somebody, Generals Fulano and Tulano, had "pronounced" against the government.

Stir in the air, everybody enjoying those periodical shivers of fear! But for these shivers, everything much the same as usual. The church remained shut up, and dumb. The clock didn't go. Time suddenly fell off, the days walked naked and timeless, in the old, uncounted manner of the past. The strange, old, uncounted, unregistered, unreckoning days of the ancient heathen world.

Kate felt a bit like a mermaid trying to swim in a wrong element. She was swept away in some silent tide, to the old, antediluvian silence, where things moved without contact. She moved and existed without contact. Even the striking of the hours had ceased. As a drowning person sees nothing but the waters, so Kate saw nothing but the face of the timeless waters.

So, of course, she clutched at her straw. She couldn't bear it. She ordered an old, rickety Ford car, to take her bumping out to Jamiltepec, over the ruinous roads in the afternoon.

The country had gone strange and void, as it does when these "rebellions" start. As if the life-spirit were sucked away, and only some empty, anti-life void, remained in the wicked hollow countryside. Though it was not far to Jamiltepec, once outside the village, the chauffeur and his little attendant lad began to get frightened, and to go frog-like with fear.

There is something truly mysterious about the Mexican quality of fear. As if man and woman collapsed and lay wriggling on the ground like broken reptiles, unable to rise. Kate used all her will, against this cringing nonsense.

They arrived without ado at Jamiltepec. The place seemed quiet, but normal. An oxen wagon stood empty in the courtyard. There were no soldiers on guard. They had all been withdrawn, against the rebellion. But several peons were moving round, in a

desultory fashion. The day was a fiesta, when not much work
was doing. In the houses of the peons, the women were patting
tortillas, and preparing hot chile sauce, grinding away on the
metates. A fiesta! Only the windmill that pumped up water from
the lake was spinning quickly, with a little noise.

Kate drove into the yard in silence, and two mozos with guns
and belts of cartridges came to talk in low tones to the chauffeur.

"Is Doña Carlota here?" asked Kate.

"No Señora. The patrona is not here."

"Don Ramón?"

"Si Señora! Está."

Even as she hesitated, rather nervous, Ramón came out of the
inner doorway of the courtyard, in his dazzling white clothes.

"I came to see you," said Kate. "I don't know if you'd rather
I hadn't. But I can go back in the motor-car."

"No," he said. "I am glad. I was feeling deserted, I don't
know why. Let us go upstairs."

"*Patrón*!" said the chauffeur, in a low voice. "Must I stay?"

Ramón said a few words to him. The chauffeur was uneasy,
and didn't want to stay. He said he had to be back in Sayula at
such and such a time. Excuses, anyhow. But it was evident he
wanted to get away.

"Then best let him go," said Ramón to Kate. "You do not
mind going home in the boat?"

"I don't want to give you trouble."

"It is least trouble to let this fellow go, and you can leave by
boat just whenever you wish to. So we shall all be more free."

Kate paid the chauffeur, and the Ford started rattling. After
rattling a while, it moved in a curve round the courtyard, and
lurched through the zaguan, disappearing as fast as possible.

Ramón spoke to his two mozos with the guns. They went to
the outer doorway, obediently.

"Why do you have to have armed men?" she asked.

"Oh, they're afraid of bandits," he said. "Whenever there's
a rebellion anywhere, everybody is afraid of bandits. So of course
that calls bandits into life."

"But where do they come from?" said Kate, as they passed
into the inner doorways.

"From the villages," he said, closing the heavy door of that
entrance behind him, and putting the heavy iron bars across, from
wall to wall.

The inner archway was now a little prison, for the strong iron gates at the lake end of the passage were shut fast. She looked through, at the little round pond. It had some blue water-lilies on it. Beyond, the pallid lake seemed almost like a ghost, in the glare of the sun.

A servant was sent to the kitchen quarters, Ramón and Kate climbed the stone stairs to the upper terrace. How lonely, stonily lonesome and forlorn the hacienda could feel! The very stone walls could give off emptiness, loneliness, negation.

"But which villages do the bandits come from?" she insisted.

"Any of them. Mostly, they say, from San Pablo or from Ahuajijic."

"Quite near!" she cried.

"Or from Sayula," he added. "Any of the ordinary men in big hats you see around the plaza, may possibly be bandits, when banditry pays, as a profession, and isn't punished with any particular severity."

"It is hard to believe!" she said.

"It is so obvious!" he said, dropping into one of the rocking-chairs opposite her, and smiling across the onyx table.

"I suppose it is!" she said.

He clapped his hands, and his mozo Martin came up. Ramón ordered something, in a low, subdued tone. The man replied in an even lower, more subdued tone. Then the master and man nodded at each other, and the man departed, his huaraches swishing a little on the terrace.

Ramón had fallen into the low, crushed sort of voice so common in the country, as if everyone was afraid to speak aloud, so they murmured guardedly. This was unusual, and Kate noticed it in him with displeasure. She sat looking past the thick mango-trees, whose fruit was changing colour like something gradually growing hot, to the ruffled, pale-brown lake. The mountains of the opposite shore were very dark. Above them lay a heavy, but distant black cloud, out of which lightning flapped suddenly and uneasily.

"Where is Don Cipriano?" she asked.

"Don Cipriano is very much General Viedma at the moment," he replied. "Chasing rebels in the State of Colima."

"Will they be very hard to chase?"

"Probably not. Anyhow Cipriano will enjoy chasing them. He is Zapotec, and most of his men are Zapotecans, from the hills. They love chasing men who aren't."

"I wondered why he wasn't there on Sunday when you carried away the images," she said. "I think it was an awfully brave thing to do."

"Do you?" he laughed. "It wasn't. It's never half so brave, to carry something off, and destroy it, as to set a new pulse beating."

"But you have to destroy those old things, first."

"Those frowsty images—why, yes. But it's no good until you've got something else moving, from the inside."

"And have you?"

"I think I have. Don't you?"

"Yes," she said, a little doubtful.

"I think I have," he said. "I feel there's a new thing moving inside me." He was laughing at her, for her hesitation. "Why don't you come and join us?" he added.

"How?" she said. "By being married off to Don Cipriano?"

"Not necessarily. Not necessarily. Not necessarily being married to anybody."

"What are you going to do next?" she asked.

"I? I am going to re-open the church, for Quetzalcoatl to come in. But I don't like lonely gods. There should be several of them, I think, for them to be happy together."

"Does one need gods?" she said.

"Why yes. One needs manifestations, it seems to me." Kate sat in unwilling silence.

"One needs goddesses too. That is also a dilemma," he added, with a laugh.

"How I would *hate*," said Kate, "to have to be a goddess for people."

"For the monkeys?" he said, smiling.

"Yes! Of course."

At that moment, he sat erect, listening. There had been a shot, which Kate had heard, but which she had hardly noticed; to her ears, it might have been a motor-car back-firing, or even a motor-boat.

Suddenly, a sharp little volley of shots.

Ramón rose swiftly, swift as a great cat, and slammed to the iron door at the top of the stair-way, shooting the bars.

"Won't you go into that room?" he said to her, pointing to a dark doorway. "You will be all right there. Just stay a few minutes till I come back."

As he spoke, there came a shriek from the courtyard at the back, and a man's death-voice yelled *Patrón!*

Ramón's eyes dilated with terrible anger, the anger of death. His face went pale and strange, as he looked at her without seeing her, the black flame filling his eyes. He had drawn a long-barreled steel revolver from his hip.

Still without seeing her, he strode rapidly, soft and catlike along the terrace and leaped up the end staircase on to the roof. The soft, eternal passion of anger in his limbs.

Kate stood in the doorway of the room, transfixed. The light of day seemed to have darkened before her face.

"Holà! You there!" she heard his voice from the roof, in such anger it was almost a laugh, from far away.

For answer, a confused noise from the courtyard, and several shots. The slow, steady answer of shots!

She started as a rushing hiss broke on the air. In terror she waited. Then she saw it was a rocket bursting with a sound like a gun, high over the lake, and emitting a shower of red balls of light. A signal from Ramón!

Unable to go into the dark room, Kate waited as if smitten to death. Then something stirred deep in her, she flew along the terrace and up the steps to the roof. She realised that she didn't mind dying so long as she died with that man. Not alone.

The roof was glaring with sunshine. It was flat, but its different levels were uneven. She ran straight out into the light, towards the parapet wall, and had nearly come in sight of the gateway of the courtyard below, when something gave a slight smack, and bits of plaster flew in her face and her hair. She turned and fled back like a bee to the stairway.

The stairs came up in a corner, where there was a little sort of stone turret, square, with stone seats. She sank on one of these seats, looking down in terror at the turn of the stairs. It was a narrow little stone stairway, between the solid stone walls.

She was almost paralysed with shock and with fear. Yet something within her was calm. Leaning and looking out across calm sunshine of the level roof, she could not believe in death.

She saw the white figure and the dark head of Ramón within one of the small square turrets across the roof. The little tower was open, and hardly higher than his head. He was standing in a corner, looking sideways down a loop-hole, perfectly motionless.

Snap! went his revolver, deliberately. There was a muffled cry below, and a sudden volley of shots.

Ramón stood away from the loop-hole and took off his white blouse, so that it should not betray him. Above his sash was a belt of cartridges. In the shadow of the turret, his body looked curiously dark, rising from the white of his trousers. Again he took his stand quietly at the side of the long, narrow, slanting aperture. He lifted his revolver carefully, and the shots, one, two, three, slow and deliberate, startled her nerves. And again there was a volley of shots from below, and bits of stone and plaster smoking against the sky. Then again, silence, long silence. Kate pressed her hands against her body, as she sat.

The clouds had shifted, the sun shone yellowish. In the heavier light, the mountains beyond the parapet showed a fleece of young green, smoky and beautiful.

All was silent. Ramón in the shadow did not move, pressing himself against the wall, and looking down. He commanded, she knew, the big inner doors.

Suddenly, however, he shifted. With his revolver in his hand he stooped and ran, like some terrible cat, the sun gleaming on his naked back as he crouched under the shelter of the thick parapet wall, running along the roof to the corresponding front turret.

This turret was roofless, and it was nearer to Kate, as she sat spell-bound, in a sort of eternity, on the stone seat at the head of the stairs, watching Ramón. He pressed himself against the wall, and lifted his revolver to the slit. And again, one, two, three, four, five, the shots exploded deliberately. Some voice below yelled *Ay-ee! Ay-ee! Ay-ee!* in yelps of animal pain. A voice was heard shouting command. Ramón kneeled on one knee, re-loading his revolver. Then he struck a match, and again Kate almost started out of her skin, as a rocket rushed ferociously up into the sky, exploded like a gun, and let fall the balls of red flame that lingered as if loth to die away, in the high, remote air.

She sighed, wondering what it all was. It was death, she knew. But so strange, so vacant. Just these noises of shots! And she could see nothing outside. She wanted to see what was in the courtyard.

Ramón was at his post, pressing himself close to the wall, looking down, with bent head, motionless. There were shots, and a spatter of lead from below. But he did not move. She could

not see his face, only part of his back; the proud, heavy, creamy-brown shoulders, the black head bent a little forward, in concentration, the cartridge-belt dropping above his loins, over the white, floppy linen of the trousers. Still and soft in watchful concentration, almost like silence itself. Then with soft, diabolic swiftness in his movements, he changed his position, and took aim.

He was utterly unaware of her; even of her existence. Which was as it should be, no doubt. She sat motionless, waiting. Waiting, waiting, waiting, in that yellowish sunlight of eternity, with a certain changeless suspense of stillness inside her. Someone would come from the village. There would be an end. There would be an end.

At the same time, she started every time he fired, and looked at him. And she heard his voice saying: "One needs manifestations, it seems to me." Ah, how she hated the noise of shots.

Suddenly she gave a piercing shriek, and in one leap was out of her retreat. She had seen a black head turning the stairs.

Before she knew it, Ramón jumped past her like a great cat, and two men clashed in mid-air, as the unseen fellow leaped up from the stairs. Two men in a crash went down on the floor, a revolver went off, terrible limbs were writhing.

Ramón's revolver was on the floor. But again there was a shot from the tangled men, and a redness of blood suddenly appearing out of nowhere, on the white cotton clothing, as the two men twisted and fought on the floor.

They were both big men. Struggling on the ground, they looked huge. Ramón had the bandit's revolver-hand by the wrist. The bandit, with a ghastly black face with rolling eyes and sparse moustache, had got Ramón's naked arm in his white teeth, and was hanging on, showing his red gums, while with his free hand he was feeling for his knife.

Kate could not believe that the black, ghastly face with the sightless eyes and biting mouth was conscious. Ramón had him clasped round the body. The bandit's revolver fell, and the fellow's loose black hand scrabbled on the concrete, feeling for it. Blood was flowing over his teeth. Yet some blind super-consciousness seemed to possess him, as if he were a devil, not a man.

His hand nearly touched Ramón's revolver. In horror Kate ran and snatched the weapon from the warm concrete, running

away as the bandit gave a heave, a great sudden heave to his body, under the body of Ramón. Kate raised the revolver. She hated that terrible devil under Ramón as she had never hated in her life. Yet she dared not fire.

Ramón shouted something, glancing at her. She could not understand. But she ran round, to be able to shoot the man under Ramón. Even as she ran, the bandit twisted with a great lunge of his body, heaved Ramón up, and with his short free hand got Ramón's own knife from the belt at the groin, and stabbed.

Kate gave a cry! Oh, how she wanted to shoot! She saw the knife strike sideways, slanting in a short jab into Ramón's back. At the same moment there was a stumble on the stairs, and another black-headed man was leaping on to the roof from the turret.

She stiffened her wrist and fired without looking, in a sudden second of pure control. The black head came crashing to her. She recoiled in horror, lifted the revolver and fired again, and missed. But even as it passed her, she saw red blood among the black hairs of that head. It crashed down, the buttocks of the body heaving up, the whole thing twitching and jerking along, the face seeming to grin in a mortal grin.

Glancing from horror to horror, she saw Ramón, his face still as death, blood running down his arm and his back, holding down the head of the bandit by the hair and stabbing him with short stabs in the throat, one, two, while blood shot out like a red projectile; there was a strange sound like a soda-syphon, a ghastly bubbling, one final terrible convulsion from the loins of the stricken man, throwing Ramón off, and Ramón lay twisted, still clutching the man's hair in one hand, the bloody knife in the other, and gazing into the livid, disordered face, in which ferocity seemed to have gone frozen, with a steady, intent, inhuman gaze.

Then, without letting go his victim's hair, he looked up, cautiously. To see Kate's man, with black hair wet with blood, and blood running down into his glazed, awful eyes, slowly rising to his knees. It was the strangest face in the world; the high, domed head with blood-soddened hair, blood running in several streams down the narrow, corrugated brow and along the black eyebrows above the glazed, black, numb eyes, in which the last glazing was of ferocity, stranger even than wonder, the glazed and absolute ferocity which the man's last consciousness showed.

It was a long, thin, handsome face, save for those eyes of glazed ferocity, and for the longish white teeth under the sparse moustache.

The man was reduced to his last, blank term of being; a glazed and ghastly ferocity.

Ramón dropped the hair of his victim, whose head dropped sideways with a gaping red throat, and rose to a crouching position. The second bandit was on his knees, but his hand already clasped his knife. Ramón crouched. They were both perfectly still. But Ramón had got his balance, crouching between his feet.

The bandit's black, glazed eyes of blank ferocity took a glint of cunning. He was stretching. He was going to leap to his feet for his stroke.

And even as he leaped, Ramón shot the knife, that was all bright red as a cardinal bird. It flew red like a bird, and the drops of Ramón's handful of blood flew with it, splashing even Kate, who kept her revolver ready, watching near the stairway.

The bandit dropped on his knees again, and remained for a moment kneeling as if in prayer, the red pommel of the knife sticking out of his abdomen, from his white trousers. Then he slowly bowed over, doubled up, and went on his face again, once more with his buttocks in the air.

Ramón still crouched at attention, almost supernatural, his dark eyes glittering with watchfulness, in pure, savage attentiveness. Then he rose, very smooth and quiet, crossed the blood-stained concrete to the fallen man, picked up the clean, fallen knife that belonged to the fellow, lifted the red-dripping chin, and with one stroke drove the knife into the man's throat. The man susbided with the blow, not even twitching.

Then again, Ramón turned to look at the first man. He gazed a moment attentively. But that horrible black face was dead.

And then Ramón glanced at Kate, as she stood near the stairs with the revolver. His brow was like a boy's, very pure and primitive, and the eyes underneath had a certain primitive gleaming look of virginity. As men must have been, in the first awful days, with that strange beauty that goes with pristine rudimentariness.

For the most part, he did not recognise her. But there was one remote glint of recognition.

"Are they both dead?" she asked, awestruck.

"*Creo que sí!*" he replied in Spanish.

He turned to look once more, and to pick up the pistol that lay on the concrete. As he did so, he noticed that his right hand was bright red, with the blood that flowed still down his arm. He wiped it on the jacket of the dead man. But his trousers on his loins were also sodden with blood, they stuck red to his hips. He did not notice.

He was like a pristine being, remote in consciousness, and with far, remote sex.

Curious rattling, bubbling noises still came from the second man, just physical sounds. The first man lay sprawling in a ghastly fashion, his evil face fixed above a pool of blackening blood.

"Watch the stairs!" said Ramón in Spanish to her, glancing at her with farouche eyes, from some far remote jungle. Yet still the glint of recognition sparked furtively out of the darkness.

He crept to the turret, and stealthily looked out. Then he crept back, with the same stealth, and dragged the nearest dead man to the parapet, raising the body till the head looked over. There was no sound. Then he raised himself, and peeped over. No sign, no sound.

He looked at the dead body as he let it drop. Then he went to Kate, to look down the stairs.

"You grazed that man with your first shot, you only stunned him I believe," he said.

"Are there any more?" she asked, shuddering.

"I think they are all gone."

He was pale, almost white, with that same pristine clear brow, like a boy's, a sort of twilight changelessness.

"Are you much hurt?" she asked.

"I? No!" and he put his fingers round his back, to feel of the slowly welling wound, with his bloody fingers.

The afternoon was passing towards yellow, heavy evening.

He went again to look at the terrible face of the first dead man.

"Did you know him?" she said.

He shook his head.

"Not that I am aware," he said. Then: "Good that he is dead. Good that he is dead.—Good that we killed them both."

He looked at her with that glint of savage recognition from afar.

"Ugh! No! It's terrible!" she said shuddering.

"Good for me that you were there! Good that we killed them between us! Good they are dead."

The heavy, luxurious yellow light from below the clouds gilded the mountains of evening. There was the sound of a motor-car honking its horn.

Ramón went in silence to the parapet, the blood wetting his pantaloons lower and lower, since they stuck to him when he bent down. Rich yellow light flooded the blood-stained roof. There was a terrible smell of blood.

"There is a car coming," he said.

She followed, frightened, across the roof.

She saw the hills and lower slopes inland swimming in gold light like lacquer. The black huts of the peons, the lurid leaves of bananas showed up uncannily, the trees green-gold stood up, with boughs of shadow. And away up the road was a puther of dust, then the flash of glass as the automobile turned.

"Stay here," said Ramón, "while I go down."

"Why didn't your peons come and help you?" she said.

"They never do!" he replied. "Unless they are armed on purpose."

He went, picking up his blouse and putting it on. And immediately the blood came through.

He went down. She listened to his steps. Below, the courtyard was all shadow, and empty, save for two dead white-clothed bodies of men, one near the zaguan, one against a pillar of the shed.

The motor-car came sounding its horn wildly all the way between the trees. It lurched into the zaguan. It was full of soldiers, soldiers standing on the running-boards, hanging on.

"Don Ramón! Don Ramón!" shouted the officer, leaping out of the car. "Don Ramón!" He was thundering at the doors of the inner zaguan.

Why did not Ramón open? Where was he?

She leaned over the parapet and screamed like a wild bird:

"Viene! Viene Don Ramón! El viene!"

The soldiers all looked up at her. She drew back in terror. Then, in a panic, she turned downstairs, to the terrace. There was blood on the stone stairs, at the bottom, a great pool. And on the terrace near the rocking-chairs, two dead men in a great pool of blood.

One was Ramón! For a moment she went unconscious. Then slowly she crept forward. Ramón had fallen, reeking with blood from his wound, his arms round the body of the other man, who

was bleeding too. The second man opened his eyes, wildly, and in a rattling voice, blind and dying, said:

"*Patrón!*"

It was Martin, Ramón's own mozo. He was stiffening and dying in Ramón's arms. And Ramón, lifting him, had made his own wound gush with blood, and had fainted. He lay like dead. But Kate could see the faintest pulse in his neck.

She ran blindly down the stairs, and fought to get the great iron bars from across the door, screaming all the time:

"Come! Somebody! Come to Don Ramón! He will die."

A terrified boy and woman appeared from the kitchen quarters. The door was opened, just as six horse-soldiers galloped into the courtyard. The officer leaped from his horse and ran like a hare, his revolver drawn, his spurs flashing, straight through the doors and up the stairs, like a madman. When Kate got up the stairs again, the officer was standing with drawn revolver, gazing down at Ramón.

"He is dead?" he said, stupefied, looking at Kate.

"No!" she said. "It is only loss of blood."

The officers lifted Ramón and laid him on the terrace. Then quickly they got off his blouse. The wound was bleeding thickly in the back.

"We've got to stop this wound," said the lieutenant. "Where is Pablo?"

Instantly there was a cry for Pablo.

Kate ran into a bedroom for water, and she switched an old linen sheet from the bed. Pablo was a young doctor among the soldiers. Kate gave him the bowl of water, and the towel, and was tearing the sheet into bands. Ramón lay naked on the floor, all streaked with blood. And the light was going.

"Bring light!" said the young doctor.

With swift hands he washed the wound, peering with his nose almost touching it.

"It is not much!" he said.

Kate had prepared bandages and a pad. She crouched to hand them to the young man. The woman-servant set a lamp with a white shade on the floor by the doctor. He lifted it, peering again at the wound.

"No!" he said. "It is not much."

Then glancing up at the soldiers who stood motionless, peering down, the light on their dark faces:

"*Té!*" he said, making a gesture.

Quickly the lieutenant took the lamp, holding it over the inert body, and the doctor, with Kate to help, proceeded to staunch and bind the wound. And Kate, as she touched the soft, inert flesh of Ramón, was thinking to herself: This too is he, this silent body! And that face that stabbed the throat of the bandit was he! And that twilit brow, and those remote eyes, like a death-virgin, was he. Even a savage out of the twilight! And the man that knows me, where is he? One among these many men, no more! Oh God! give the man his soul back, into this bloody body. Let the soul come back, or the universe will be cold for me and for many men.

The doctor finished his temporary bandage, looked at the wound in the arm, swiftly wiped the blood off the loins and buttocks and legs, and said:

"We must put him in bed. Lift his head."

Quickly Kate lifted the heavy, inert head. The eyes were half open. The doctor pressed the closed lips, under the sparse black moustache. But the teeth were firmly shut.

The doctor shook his head.

"Bring a mattress," he said.

The wind was suddenly roaring, the lamp was leaping with a long, smoky needle of flame, inside its chimney. Leaves and dust flew rattling on the terrace, there was a splash of lightning, Ramón's body lay there uncovered and motionless, the bandage was already soaked with blood, under the darkening, leaping light of the lamp.

And again Kate saw, vividly, how the body is the flame of the soul, leaping and sinking upon the invisible wick of the soul. And now the soul, like a wick, seemed spent, the body was a sinking, fading flame.

"Kindle his soul again, oh God!" she cried to herself.

All she could see of the naked body was the terrible absence of the living soul of it. All she wanted was for the soul to come back, the eyes to open.

They got him upon the bed and covered him, closing the doors against the wind and the rain. The doctor chafed his brow and hands with cognac. And at length the eyes opened; the soul was there, but standing far back.

For some moments Ramón lay with open eyes, without seeing or moving. Then he stirred a little.

"What's the matter?" he said.

"Keep still, Don Ramón," said the doctor, who with his slim dark hands was even more delicate than a woman. "You have lost much blood. Keep still."

"Where is Martin?"

"He is outside."

"How is he?"

"He is dead."

The dark eyes under the black lashes were perfectly steady and changeless. Then came the voice:

"Pity we did not kill them all. Pity we did not kill them all. We have got to kill them all.—Where is the Señora Inglesa?"

"Here she is."

His dark eyes looked up at Kate. Then more of his consciousness came back.

"Thank you for my life," he said, closing his eyes. Then: "Put the lamp aside."

Soldiers were tapping at the glass pane, for the lieutenant. A black little fellow entered, wiping the rain from his black face and pushing his thick black hair back.

"There are two more dead on the azotea," he announced to his officer.

The lieutenant rose, and followed him out. Kate too went on the terrace. In the early darkness the rain was threshing down. A lantern was coming down from the roof: it came along the terrace to the stairs, and after it two soldiers in the pouring rain, carrying a dead body, then behind, two more, with the other body. The huraches of the soldiers clicked and shuffled on the wet terrace. The dismal cortège went downstairs.

Kate stood on the terrace facing the darkness, while the rain threshed down. She felt uneasy here, in this house of men and soldiers. She found her way down to the kitchen, where the boy was fanning a charcoal fire, and the woman was crushing tomatoes on the metate, for a sauce.

"Ay, Señora!" cried the woman. "Five men dead, and the Patrón wounded to death! Ay! Ay!"

"Seven men dead!" said the boy. "Two on the azotea!"

"Seven men! Seven men!"

Kate sat on her chair, stunned, unable to hear anything but the threshing rain, unable to feel anything more. Two or three peons came in, and two more women, the men wrapped to their noses

in their blankets. The women brought masa, and began a great clapping of tortillas. The people conversed in low, rapid tones, in the dialect, and Kate could not listen.

At length the rain began to abate. She knew it would leave off suddenly. There was a great sound of water running, gushing, splashing, pouring into the cistern. And she thought to herself: The rain will wash the blood off the roof and down the spouts into the cistern. There will be blood in the water.

She looked at her own blood-smeared white frock. She felt chilly. She rose to go upstairs again, into the dark, empty, master-less house.

"Ah, Señora! You are going upstairs? Go, Daniel, carry the lantern for the Señora!"

The boy lit a candle in a lantern, and Kate returned to the up-per terrace. The light shone out of the room where Ramón was. She went into the salon and got her hat and her brown shawl. The lieutenant heard her, and came to her quickly, very kindly and respectful.

"Won't you come in, Señora?" he said, holding the door to the room where Ramón lay; the guest-room.

Kate went in. Ramón lay on his side, his black, rather thin moustache pushed against the pillow. He was himself.

"It is very unpleasant for you here, Señora Caterina," he said. "Would you like to go to your house? The lieutenant will send you in the motor-car."

"Is there nothing I can do here?" she said.

"Ah no! Don't stay here! It is too unpleasant for you.—I shall soon get up, and I shall come to thank you for my life."

He looked at her, into her eyes. And she saw that his soul had come back to him, and with his soul he saw her and acknowledged her; though always from the peculiar remoteness that was inevi-table in him.

She went downstairs with the young lieutenant.

"Ah what a horrible affair! They were not bandits, Señora!" said the young man, with passion. "They didn't come to rob. They came to murder Don Ramón, you know, Señora! simply to murder Don Ramón. And but for your being here, they would have done it!—Ah, think of it, Señora! Don Ramón is the most precious man in Mexico. It is possible that in the world there is not a man like him. And personally, he hasn't got enemies. As a man among men, he hasn't got enemies. No Señora. Not one!

But do you know who it will be? the priests, and the Knights of Cortes."

"Are you sure?" said Kate.

"Sure, Señora!" cried the lieutenant indignantly. "Look! There are seven men dead. Two were the mozos with guns, watching in the zaguan. One was Don Ramón's own mozo Martin!—ah, what a faithful man, what a brave one! Never will Don Ramón pardon his death. Then moreover, two men killed on the azotea, and two men in the courtyard, shot by Don Ramón. Besides these, a man whom Martin wounded, who fell and broke his leg, so we have got him. Come and see them, Señora."

They were down in the wet courtyard. Little fires had been lighted under the sheds, and the little, black, devil-may-care soldiers were crouching round them, with a bunch of peons in blankets standing round. Across the courtyard, horses stamped and jingled their harness. A boy came running with tortillas in a cloth. The dark-faced little soldiers crouched like animals, sprinkled salt on the tortillas, and devoured them with small, white, strong teeth.

Kate saw the great oxen tied in their sheds, lying down, the wagons standing inert. And a little crowd of asses was munching alfalfa in a corner.

The officer marched beside Kate, his spurs sparking in the firelight. He went to the muddy car, that stood in the middle of the yard; then to his horse. From a saddle-pocket he took an electric torch, and led Kate across to the end shed.

There he suddenly flashed his light upon seven dead bodies, laid side by side. The two from the roof were wet. Ramón's dead man lay with his dark, strong breast bare, and his blackish, thick, devilish face sideways; a big fellow. Kate's man lay rigid. Martin had been stabbed in the collar bone; he looked as if he were staring at the roof of the shed. The others were two more peons, and two fellows in black boots and grey trousers and blue overall jackets. They were all inert and straight and dead, and somehow, a little ridiculous. Perhaps it is clothing that makes dead people gruesome and absurd. But also, the grotesque fact that the bodies are vacant, is always present.

"Look!" said the lieutenant, touching a body with his toe. "This is a chauffeur from Sayula; this is a boatman from Sayula. These two are peons from San Pablo. This man—" the lieutenant kicked the dead body—"we don't know." It was Ramón's dead

man. "But this man—" he kicked her dead man, with the tall domed head—"is from Ahuajijic, and he was married to the woman that now lives with a peon here.—You see, Señora! A chauffeur and a boatman from Sayula—they are Knights-of-Cortes men; and those two peons from San Pablo are priests' men.—These are not bandits. It was an attempt at assassination. But of course they would have robbed everything, everything, if they had killed Don Ramón."

Kate was staring at the dead men. Three of them were handsome; one, the boatman, with a thin line of black beard framing his shapely face, was beautiful. But dead, with the mockery of death in his face. All of them men who had been in the flush of life. Yet dead, they did not even matter. They were gruesome, but it did not matter that they were dead men. They were vacant. Perhaps even in life there had been a certain vacancy, nothingness, in their handsome physique.

For a pure moment, she wished for men who were not handsome as these dark natives were. Even their beauty was suddenly repulsive to her; the dark beauty of half-created, half-evolved things, left in the old, reptile-like smoothness. It made her shudder.

The soul! If only the soul in man, in woman, would speak to her, not always this strange, perverse materialism, or a distorted animalism. If only people were souls, and their bodies were gestures from the soul! If one could but forget both bodies and facts, and be present with strong, living souls!

She went across the courtyard, that was littered with horse-droppings, to the car. The lieutenant was choosing the soldiers who should stay behind. The horse-soldiers would stay. A peon on a delicate speckled horse, a flea-bitten roan, came trotting past the soldiers in the zaguan. He had been to Sayula for doctor's stuff, and to give messages to the Jefe.

At last the car, with little soldiers clinging on to it all round, moved slowly out of the courtyard. The lieutenant sat beside Kate. He stopped the car again at the big white barn under the trees, to talk to two soldiers picketed there.

Then they moved slowly on, under the wet trees, in the mud that crackled beneath the wheels, up the avenue to the highroad, where were the little black huts of the peons. Little fires were flapping in front of one or two huts, women were baking tortillas on the flat earthenware plates, upon the small wood fires. A

woman was going to her hut with a blazing brand, like a torch, to kindle her fire. A few peons in dirty-white clothes squatted silent against the walls of their houses, utterly silent. As the motor-car turned its great glaring head-lights upon the highroad, little sandy pigs with short, curly hair started up squealing, and faces and figures stood out blindly, as in a searchlight.

There was a hut with a wide opening in the black wall, and a grey old man was standing inside. The car stopped for the lieutenant to call to the peons under the wall. They came to the car with their black eyes glaring and glittering apprehensively. They seemed very much abashed, and humble, answering the lieutenant.

Meanwhile Kate watched a boy buy a drink for one centavo and a piece of rope for three centavos, from the grey old man at the dark hole, which was a shop.

The car went on, the great lights glaring unnaturally upon the hedges of cactus and mesquite and palo blanco trees, and upon the great pools of water in the road. It was a slow progress.

CHAPTER XX

MARRIAGE BY QUETZALCOATL

KATE hid in her own house, numbed. She could not bear to talk to people. She could not bear even Juana's bubbling discourse. The common threads that bound her to humanity seemed to have snapped. The little human things didn't interest her any more. Her eyes seemed to have gone dark, and blind to individuals. They were all just individuals, like leaves in the dark, making a noise. And she was alone under the trees.

The egg-woman wanted six centavos for an egg.

"And I said to her—I said to her—we buy them at five centavos!" Juana went on.

"Yes!" said Kate. She didn't care whether they were bought at five or fifty, or not bought at all.

She didn't care, she didn't care, she didn't care. She didn't even care about life any more. There was no escaping her own complete indifference. She felt indifferent to everything in the whole world, almost she felt indifferent to death.

"Niña! Niña! Here is the man with the sandals! Look! Look how nicely he has made them for you, Niña! Look what Mexican huaraches the Niña is going to wear!"

She tried them on. The man charged her too much. She looked at him with her remote, indifferent eyes. But she knew, in the world one must live, so she paid him less than he asked, though more than he really would have accepted.

She sat down again in her rocking-chair in the shade of the room. Only to be alone! Only that no one should speak to her. Only that no one should come near her! Because in reality her soul and spirit were gone, departed into the middle of some desert, and the effort of reaching across to people to effect an apparent meeting, or contact, was almost more than she could bear.

Never had she been so alone, and so inert, and so utterly without desire; plunged in a wan indifference, like death. Never had

304

she passed her days so blindly, so unknowingly, in stretches of nothingness.

Sometimes, to get away from her household, she sat under a tree by the lake. And there, without knowing it, she let the sun scorch her foot and burn her face inflamed. Juana made a great outcry over her. The foot blistered and swelled, her face was red and painful. But it all seemed to happen merely to her shell. And she was wearily, wanly indifferent.

Only at the very centre of her sometimes a little flame rose, and she knew that what she wanted was for her soul to live. The life of days and facts and happenings was dead on her, and she was like a corpse. But away inside her a little light was burning, the light of her innermost soul. Sometimes it sank and seemed extinct. Then it was there again.

Ramón had lighted it. And once it was lighted the world went hollow and dead, all the world-activities were empty weariness to her. Her soul! Her frail, innermost soul! She wanted to live *its* life, not her own life.

The time would come again when she would see Ramón and Cipriano, and the soul that was guttering would kindle again in her, and feel strong. Meanwhile she only felt weak, weak, weak, weak as the dying. She felt that afternoon of bloodshed had blown all their souls into the twilight of death, for the time. But they would come back. They would come back. Nothing to do but to submit, and wait. Wait, with a soul almost dead, and hands and heart of uttermost inert heaviness, indifference.

Ramón had lost much blood. And she, too, in other ways, had been drained of the blood of the body. She felt bloodless and powerless.

But wait, wait, wait, the new blood would come.

One day Cipriano came. She was rocking in her salon, in a cotton housedress, and her face red and rather swollen. She saw him, in uniform, pass by the window. He stood in the doorway on the terrace, a dark, grave, small, handsome man.

"Do come in," she said with effort.

Her eyelids felt burnt. He looked at her with his full black eyes, that always had in them so many things she did not understand. She felt she could not look back at him.

"Have you chased all your rebels?" she said.

"For the present," he replied.

He seemed to be watching, watching for something.

"And you didn't get hurt?"

"No, I didn't get hurt."

She looked away out of the door, having nothing to say in the world.

"I went to Jamiltepec yesterday evening," he said.

"How is Don Ramón?"

"Yes, he is better."

"Quite better?"

"No. Not quite better. But he walks a little."

"Wonderful how people heal."

"Yes. We die very easily. But we also come quickly back to life."

"And you? Did you fight the rebels, or didn't they want to fight?"

"Yes, they wanted to. We fought once or twice; not very much."

"Men killed?"

"Yes! Some! Not many, no? Perhaps a hundred. We can never tell, no? Maybe two hundred."

He waved his hand vaguely.

"But you had the worst rebellion at Jamiltepec, no?" he said suddenly, with heavy Indian gravity, gloom, suddenly settling down.

"It didn't last long, but it was rather awful while it did."

"Rather awful, no?—If I had known! I said to Ramón, won't you keep the soldiers?—the guard, no? He said they were not necessary. But here—you never know, no?"

"Niña!" cried Juana, from the terrace. "Niña! Don Antonio says he is coming to see you."

"Tell him to come to-morrow."

"Already he is on the way!" cried Juana, in helplessness. Don Antonio was Kate's fat landlord; and, of course, Juana's permanent master, more important in her eyes, then, even than Kate.

"Here he is!" she cried, and fled.

Kate leaned forward in her chair, to see the stout figure of her landlord on the walk outside the window, taking off his cloth cap and bowing low to her. A cloth cap!—She knew he was a great Fascista, the reactionary Knights of Cortes held him in great esteem.

Kate bowed coldly.

He bowed low again, with the cloth cap.

Kate said not a word.

He stood on one foot, then on the other, and then marched forward up the gravel walk, towards the kitchen quarters, as if he had not seen either Kate or General Viedma. In a few moments he marched back, as if he could not see either Kate or the General, through the open door.

Cipriano looked at the passing stout figure of Don Antonio in a cloth cap as if it were the wind blowing.

"It is my landlord!" said Kate. "I expect he wants to know if I am taking on the house for another three months."

"Ramón wanted me to come and see you—to see how you are, no?—and to ask you to come to Jamiltepec. Will you come with me now? The car is here."

"Must I?" said Kate, uneasily.

"No. Not unless you wish. Ramón said, not unless you wished. He said, perhaps it would be painful to you, no?— to go to Jamiltepec again—so soon after—"

How curious Cipriano was! He stated things as if they were mere bare facts with no emotional content at all. As for its being painful to Kate to go to Jamiltepec, that meant nothing to him.

"Lucky thing you were there that day, no?" he said. "They might have killed him. Very likely they would! Very likely! Awful, no?"

"They might have killed me too," she said.

"Yes! Yes! They might!" he acquiesced.

Curious he was! With a sort of glaze of the ordinary world on top, and underneath a black volcano with hell knows what depths of lava. And talking half-abstractedly from his glazed, top self, the words came out small and quick, and he was always hesitating, was saying: *No?* It wasn't himself at all talking.

"What would you have done if they had killed Ramón?" she said, tentatively.

"I?"—He looked up at her in a black flare of apprehension. The volcano was rousing. "If they had killed him?—" His eyes took on that fixed glare of ferocity, staring her down.

"Would you have cared very much?" she said.

"I? Would I?" he repeated, and the black suspicious look came into his Indian eyes.

"Would it have meant *very* much to you?"

He still watched her with a glare of ferocity and suspicion.

"To me!" he said, and he pressed his hand against the buttons

of his tunic. "To me Ramón is *more* than life. *More* than life." His eyes seemed to glare and go sightless, as he said it, the ferocity melting in a strange blind, confiding glare, that seemed sightless, either looking inward or out at the whole vast void of the cosmos, where no vision is left.

"More than anything?" she said.

"Yes!" he replied abstractedly, with a blind nod of the head. Then abruptly he looked at her and said:

"You saved his life."

By this he meant that *therefore*— But she could not understand the therefore.

She went to change, and they set off to Jamiltepec. Cipriano made her a little uneasy, sitting beside him. He made her physically aware of him, of his small but strong and assertive body, with its black currents and storms of desire. The range of him was very limited, really. The great part of his nature was just inert and heavy, unresponsive, limited as a snake or a lizard is limited. But within his own heavy, dark range he had a curious power. Almost she could *see* the black fume of power which he emitted, the dark, heavy vibration of his blood, which cast a spell over her.

As they sat side by side in the motor-car, silent, swaying to the broken road, she could feel the curious tingling heat of his blood, and the heavy power of the *will* that lay unemerged in his blood. She could see again the skies go dark, and the phallic mystery rearing itself like a whirling dark cloud, to the zenith, till it pierced the sombre, twilit zenith; the old, supreme phallic mystery. And herself in the everlasting twilight, a sky above where the sun ran smokily, an earth below where the trees and creatures rose up in blackness, and man strode along naked, dark, half-visible, and suddenly whirled in supreme power, towering like a dark whirlwind column, whirling to pierce the very zenith.

The mystery of the primeval world! She could feel it now in all its shadowy, furious magnificence. She knew now what was the black, glinting look in Cipriano's eyes. She could understand marrying him, now. In the shadowy world where men were visionless, and winds of fury rose up from the earth, Cipriano was still a power. Once you entered his mystery the scale of all things changed, and he became a living male power, undefined, and unconfined. The smallness, the limitations ceased to exist. In his black, glinting eyes the power was limitless, and it was as

if, from him, from his body of blood could rise up that pillar of cloud which swayed and swung, like a rearing serpent or a rising tree, till it swept the zenith, and all the earth below was dark and prone, and consummated. Those small hands, that little natural tuft of black goats' beard hanging light from his chin, the tilt of his brows and the slight slant of his eyes, the domed Indian head with its thick black hair, they were like symbols to her, of another mystery, the bygone mystery of the twilit, primitive world, where shapes that are small suddenly loom up huge, gigantic on the shadow, and a face like Cipriano's is the face at once of a god and a devil, the undying Pan face. The bygone mystery, that has indeed gone by, but has not passed away. Never shall pass away.

As he sat in silence, casting the old, twilit Pan-power over her, she felt herself submitting, succumbing. He was once more the old dominant male, shadowy, intangible, looming suddenly tall, and covering the sky, making a darkness that was himself and nothing but himself, the Pan male. And she was swooned prone beneath, perfect in her proneness.

It was the ancient phallic mystery, the ancient god-devil of the male Pan. Cipriano unyielding forever, in the ancient twilight, keeping the ancient twilight around him. She understood now his power with his soldiers. He had the old gift of demon-power.

He would never woo; she saw this. When the power of his blood rose in him, the dark aura streamed from him like a cloud pregnant with power, like thunder, and rose like a whirlwind that rises suddenly in the twilight and raises a great pliant column, swaying and leaning with power, clear between heaven and earth.

Ah! and what a mystery of prone submission, on her part, this huge erection would imply! Submission absolute, like the earth under the sky. Beneath an over-arching absolute.

Ah! what a marriage! How terrible! and how complete! With the finality of death, and yet more than death. The arms of the twilit Pan. And the awful, half-intelligible voice from the cloud.

She could conceive now her marriage with Cipriano; the supreme passivity, like the earth below the twilight, consummate in living lifelessness, the sheer solid mystery of passivity. Ah, what an abandon, what an abandon, what an abandon!—of so many things she wanted to abandon.

Cipriano put his hand, with its strange soft warmth and weight, upon her knee, and her soul melted like fused metal.

"En poco tiempo, verdad?" he said to her, looking into her eyes with the old, black, glinting look, of power about to consummate itself.

"In a little while, no?"

She looked back at him, wordless. Language had abandoned her, and she leaned silent and helpless in the vast, unspoken twilight of the Pan world. Her self had abandoned her, and all her day was gone. Only she said to herself:

"My demon lover!"

Her world could end in many ways, and this was one of them. Back to the twilight of the ancient Pan world, where the soul of woman was dumb, to be forever unspoken.

The car had stopped, they had come to Jamiltepec. He looked at her again, as reluctantly he opened the door. And as he stepped out, she realised again his uniform, his small figure in uniform. She had lost it entirely. She had only known his face, the face of the supreme god-demon; with the arching brows and slightly slanting eyes, and the loose, light tuft of a goat-beard. The Master. The everlasting Pan.

He was looking back at her again, using all his power to prevent her seeing in him the little general in uniform, in the worldly vision. And she avoided his eyes, and saw nothing.

They found Ramón sitting in his white clothes in a long chair on the terrace. He was creamy-brown in his pallor.

He saw at once the change in Kate. She had the face of one waking from the dead, curiously dipped in death, with a tenderness far more new and vulnerable than a child's. He glanced at Cipriano. Cipriano's face seemed darker than usual, with that secret *hauteur* and aloofness of the savage. He knew it well.

"Are you better?" Kate asked.

"Very nearly!" he said, looking up at her gently. "And you?"

"Yes, I am all right."

"You are?"

"Yes, I think so.—I have felt myself all lost, since that day. Spiritually, I mean. Otherwise I am all right. Are you healing well?"

"Oh, yes! I always heal quickly."

"Knives and bullets are horrible things."

"Yes—in the wrong place."

Kate felt rather as if she were coming to, from a swoon, as Ramón spoke to her and looked at her. His eyes, his voice seemed

kind. Kind? The word suddenly was strange to her, she had to try to get its meaning.

There was no kindness in Cipriano. The god-demon Pan preceded kindness. She wondered if she wanted kindness. She did not know. Everything felt numb.

"I was wondering whether to go to England," she said.

"Again?" said Ramón, with a slight smile. "Away from the bullets and the knives, is that it?"

"Yes!—to get away." And she sighed deeply.

"No!" said Ramón. "Don't go away. You will find nothing in England."

"But *can* I go on here?"

"Can you help it?"

"I wish I knew what to do."

"How can one know? Something happens inside you, and all your decisions are smoke.—Let happen what will happen."

"I can't *quite* drift as if I had no soul of my own, can I?"

"Sometimes it is best."

There was a pause. Cipriano stayed outside the conversation altogether, in a dusky world of his own, apart and secretly hostile.

"I have been thinking so much about you," she said to Ramón, "and wondering whether it is worth while."

"What?"

"What you are doing; trying to change the religion of these people. If they have any religion to change. I don't think they are a religious people. They are only superstitious. I have no use for men and women who go crawling down a church aisle on their knees, or holding up their arms for hours. There's something stupid and wrong about it. They never worship a God. Only some little evil power. I have been wondering so much if it is worth while giving yourself to them, and exposing yourself to them. It would be horrible if you were really killed. I have seen you *look* dead."

"Now you see me look alive again," he smiled.

But a heavy silence followed.

"I believe Don Cipriano knows them better than you do. I believe he knows best, if it is any good," she said.

"And what does he say?" asked Ramón.

"I say I am Ramón's man," replied Cipriano stubbornly.

Kate looked at him, and mistrusted him. In the long run he was nobody's man. He was that old, masterless Pan male, that

could not even conceive of service; particularly the service of mankind. He saw only glory; the black mystery of glory consummated. And himself like a wind of glory.

"I feel they'll let you down," said Kate to Ramón.

"Maybe! But I shan't let myself down. I do what I believe in. Possibly I am only the first step round the corner of change. But: ce n'est que le premier pas qui coute— Why will you not go round the corner with us? At least it is better than sitting still."

Kate did not answer his question. She sat looking at the mango trees and the lake, and the thought of that afternoon came over her again.

"How did those two men get in; those two bandits on the roof?" she asked wonderingly.

"It was a woman this time; a girl whom Carlota brought here from the Cuna in Mexico, to be a sewing girl and to teach the peon's wives to sew and do little things. She had a little room at the end of the terrace there—" Ramón pointed to the terrace projecting towards the lake, opposite the one where his own room was, and the covered balcony. "She got entangled with one of the peons; a sort of second overseer, called Guillermo. Guillermo had got a wife and four children, but he came to me to say could he change and take Maruca the sewing girl. I said no, he could stay with his family. And I sent Maruca back to Mexico. But she had had a smattering of education, and thought she was equal to anything. She got messages through to Guillermo, and he ran away and joined her in Mexico, leaving wife and four children here. The wife then went to live with another peon—the blacksmith—whose wife had died and who was supposed to be a good match; a decent fellow.

"One day appeared Guillermo, and said: could he come back? I said not with Maruca. He said he didn't want Maruca, he wanted to come back. His wife was willing to go back to him again with the children. The blacksmith was willing to let her go. I said very well; but he had forfeited his job as sub-overseer, and must be a peon again.

"And he seemed all right—satisfied. But then Maruca came and stayed in Sayula, pretending to make her living as a dressmaker. She was in with the priest; and she got Guillermo again.

"It seems the Knights of Cortes had promised a big reward for the man who would bring in my scalp; secretly, of course. The

girl got Guillermo: Guillermo got those two peons, one from San Pablo and one from Ahuajijic; somebody else arranged for the rest.

"The bedroom the girl used to have is that one, on the terrace not far from where the stairs go up to the roof. The bedroom has a lattice window, high up, looking out on the trees. There's a big *laurel de India* grows outside. It appears the girl climbed on a table and knocked the iron lattice of the window loose, while she was living here, and that Guillermo, by taking a jump from the bough—a very risky thing, but then he was one of that sort— could land on the window-sill and pull himself into the room.

"Apparently he and the other two men were going to get the scalp and pillage the house before the others could enter. So the first one, the man I killed, climbed the tree, and with a long pole shoved in the lattice of the window, and so got into the room, and up the terrace stairs.

"Martin, my man, who was waiting on the other stairs, ready if they tried to blow out the iron door, heard the smash of the window and rushed round just as the second bandit—the one you shot—was crouching on the window-sill to jump down into the room. The window is quite small, and high up.

"Before Martin could do anything the man had jumped down on top of him and stabbed him twice with his machete. Then he took Martin's knife and came up the stairs, when you shot him in the head.

"Martin was on the floor when he saw the hands of a third man gripping through the window. Then the face of Guillermo. Martin got up and gave the hands a slash with the heavy machete, and Guillermo fell smash back down on to the rocks under the wall.

"When I came down, I found Martin lying outside the door of that room. He told me— *They came through there, Patrón. Guillermo was one of them.*

"Guillermo broke his thigh on the rocks, and the soldiers found him. He confessed everything, and said he was sorry, and begged my pardon. He's in the prison hospital now."

"And Maruca?" said Kate.

"They've got her too."

"There will always be a traitor," said Kate gloomily.

"Let us hope there will also be a Caterina," said Ramón.

"But will you go on with it—your Quetzalcoatl?"

"How can I leave off? It's my *métier* now. Why don't you join us? Why don't you help me?"

"How?"

"You will see. Soon you will hear the drums again. Soon the first day of Quetzalcoatl will come. You will see. Then Cipriano will appear—in the red serape—and Huitzilopochtli will share the Mexican Olympus with Quetzalcoatl. Then I want a goddess."

"But will Don Cipriano be the god Huitzilopochtli?" she asked, taken aback.

"First Man of Huitzilopochtli, as I am First Man of Quetzalcoatl."

"Will you?" said Kate to Cipriano. "That horrible Huitzilopochtli?"

"Yes, Señor!" said Cipriano, with a subtle smile of hauteur, the secret savage coming into his own.

"Not the old Huitzilopochtli—but the new," said Ramón. "And then there must come a goddess; wife or virgin, there must come a goddess. Why not you, as the First Woman of—say Itzpapalotl, just for the sound of the name?"

"I?" said Kate. "Never! I should die of shame."

"Shame?" laughed Ramón. "Ah, Señora Caterina, why shame? This is a thing that *must* be done. There must be manifestations. We *must* change back to the vision of the living cosmos; we *must*. The oldest Pan is in us, and he will not be denied. In cold blood and in hot blood both, we must make the change. That is how man is made. I accept the *must* from the oldest Pan in my soul, and from the newest me. Once a man gathers his whole soul together and arrives at a conclusion, the time of alternatives has gone. I *must*. No more than that. I *am* the First Man of Quetzalcoatl. I am Quetzalcoatl himself, if you like. A manifestation, as well as a man. I accept myself entire, and proceed to make destiny. Why, what else can I do?"

Kate was silent. His loss of blood seemed to have washed him curiously fresh again, and he was carried again out of the range of human emotion. A strange sort of categorical imperative! She saw now his power over Cipriano. It lay in this imperative which he acknowledged in his own soul, and which really was like a messenger from the beyond.

She looked on like a child looking through a railing; rather wistful, and rather frightened.

Ah, the soul! The soul was always flashing and darkening into new shapes, each one strange to the other. She had thought Ramón and she had looked into each other's souls. And now, he was this pale, distant man, with a curious gleam, like a messenger from the beyond, in his soul. And he was remote, remote from any woman.

Whereas Cipriano had suddenly opened a new world to her, a world of twilight, with the dark, half-visible face of the god-demon Pan, who can never perish, but ever returns upon mankind from the shadows. The world of shadows and dark prostration, with the phallic wind rushing through the dark.

Cipriano had to go to the town at the end of the lake, near the State of Colima; to Jaramay. He was going in a motor-boat with a couple of soldiers. Would Kate go with him?

He waited, in heavy silence, for her answer.

She said she would. She was desperate. She did not want to be sent back to her own empty, dead house.

It was one of those little periods when the rain seems strangled, the air thick with thunder, silent, ponderous thunder latent in the air from day to day, among the thick, heavy sunshine. Kate, in these days in Mexico, felt that between the volcanic violence under the earth, and the electric violence of the air above, men walked dark and incalculable, like demons from another planet.

The wind on the lake seemed fresh, from the west, but it was a running mass of electricity, that burned her face and her eyes and the roots of her hair. When she had wakened in the night and pushed the sheets, heavy sparks fell from her finger-tips. She felt she could not live.

The lake was like some frail milk of thunder; the dark soldiers curled under the awning of the boat, motionless. They seemed dark as lava and sulphur, and full of a dormant, diabolic electricity. Like salamanders. The boatman in the stern, steering, was handsome almost like the man she had killed. But this one had pale greyish eyes, phosphorescent with flecks of silver.

Cipriano sat in silence in front of her. He had removed his tunic, and his neck rose almost black from his white shirt. She could see how different his blood was from hers, dark, blackish, like the blood of lizards among hot black rocks. She could feel

its changeless surge, holding up his light, bluey-black head as on a fountain. And she would feel her own pride dissolving, going.

She felt he wanted his blood-stream to envelop hers. As if it could possibly be. He was so still, so unnoticing, and the darkness of the nape of his neck was so like invisibility. Yet he was always waiting, waiting, waiting, invisibly and ponderously waiting.

She lay under the awning in the heat and light without looking out. The wind made the canvas crackle.

Whether the time was long or short, she knew not. But they were coming to the silent lake-end, where the beach curved round in front of them. It seemed sheer lonely sunlight.

But beyond the shingle there were willow trees, and a low ranch-house. Three anchored *canoas* rode with their black, stiff lines. There were flat lands, with maize half grown and blowing its green flags sideways. But all was as if invisible, in the intense hot light.

The warm, thin water ran shallower and shallower, to the reach of shingle beyond. Black water-fowl bobbed like corks. The motor stopped. The boat ebbed on. Under the thin water were round stones, with thin green hair of weed. They would not reach the shore—not by twenty yards.

The soldiers took off their huaraches, rolled their cotton trousers up their black legs, and got into the water. The tall boatman did the same, pulling forward the boat. She would go no farther. He anchored her with a big stone. Then with his uncanny pale eyes, under the black lashes, he asked Kate in a low tone if he could carry her ashore, offering her his shoulder.

"No, no!" she said. "I'll paddle."

And hastily she took off her shoes and stockings and stepped into the shallow water, holding up her thin skirt of striped silk. The man laughed; so did the soldiers.

The water was almost hot. She went blindly forward, her head dropped. Cipriano watched her with the silent heavy, changeless patience of his race, then when she reached the shingle he came ashore on the boatman's shoulders.

They crossed the hot shingle to the willow-trees by the maize-fields, and sat upon boulders. The lake stretched pale and unreal, far, far away into the invisible, with dimmed mountains rising on either side, bare and abstract. The *canoas* were black and stiff, their masts motionless. The white motor-boat rode near.

Black birds were bobbing like corks, at this place of the water's end and the world's end.

A lonely woman went up the shingle with a water-jar on her shoulder. Hearing a sound, Kate looked, and saw a group of fishermen holding a conclave in a dug-out hollow by a tree. They saluted, looking at her with black, black eyes. They saluted humbly, and yet in their black eyes was that ancient remote hardness and *hauteur*.

Cipriano had sent the soldiers for horses. It was too hot to walk.

They sat silent in the invisibility of this end of the lake, the great light taking sight away.

"Why am I not the living Huitzilopochtli?" said Cipriano quietly, looking full at her with his black eyes.

"Do you feel you are?" she said, startled.

"Yes," he replied, in the same low, secret voice. "It is what I feel."

The black eyes looked at her with a rather awful challenge. And the small, dark voice seemed to take all her will away. They sat in silence, and she felt she was fainting, losing her consciousness for ever.

The soldiers came, with a black Arab horse for him; a delicate thing; and for her a donkey, on which she could sit sideways. He lifted her into the saddle, where she sat only half-conscious. A soldier led the donkey, and they set off, past the long, frail, hanging fishing nets, that made long filmy festoons, into the lane.

Then out into the sun and the grey-black dust, towards the grey-black, low huts of Jaramay, that lined the wide, desert road.

Jaramay was hot as a lava oven. Black low hut-houses with tiled roofs lined the broken, long, dilapidated street. Broken houses. Blazing sun. A brick pavement all smashed and sun-worn. A dog leading a blind man along the little black walls, on the broken pavement. A few goats. And unspeakable lifelessness, emptiness.

They came to the broken plaza, with sun-decayed church and ragged palm trees. Emptiness, sun, sun-decay, sun-dilapidation. One man on a dainty Arab horse trotting lightly over the stones, gun behind, big hat making a dark face. For the rest, the waste space of the centre of life. Curious how dainty the horse looked, and the horseman sitting erect, amid the sun-roasted ruin.

They came to a big building. A few soldiers were drawn up

at the entrance. They saluted Cipriano as if they were transfixed, rolling their dark eyes.

Cipriano was down from his horse in a moment. Emitting the
dark rays of dangerous power, he found the Jefe all obsequious;
a fat man in dirty white clothes. They put their wills entirely
in his power.

He asked for a room where his *esposa* could rest. Kate was
pale and all her will had left her. He was carrying her on his
will.

He accepted a large room with a brick-tiled floor and a large,
new brass bed with a coloured cotton cover thrown over it, and
with two chairs. The strange, dry, stark emptiness, that looked
almost cold in the heat.

"The sun makes you pale. Lie down and rest. I will close
the windows," he said.

He closed the shutters till only a darkness remained.

Then in the darkness, suddenly, softly he touched her, stroking
her hip.

"I said you were my wife," he said, in his small, soft Indian
voice. "It is true, isn't it?"

She trembled, and her limbs seemed to fuse like metal melting
down. She fused into a molten unconsciousness, her will, her
very self gone, leaving her lying in molten life, like a lake of still
fire, unconscious of everything save the eternality of the fire in
which she was gone. Gone in the fadeless fire, which has no
death. Only the fire can leave *us,* and we can die.

And Cipriano the master of fire. The Living Huitzilopochtli,
he had called himself. The living firemaster. The god in the
flame; the salamander.

One cannot have one's own way, and the way of the gods. It
has to be one or the other.

When she went out into the next room, he was sitting alone,
waiting for her. He rose quickly, looking at her with black, flashing eyes from which dark flashes of light seemed to play upon her.
And he took her hand, to touch her again.

"Will you come to eat at the little restaurant?" he said.

In the uncanny flashing of his eyes she saw a gladness that
frightened her a little. His touch on her hand was uncannily soft
and inward. His words said nothing; would never say anything.
But she turned aside her face, a little afraid of that flashing,
primitive gladness, which was so impersonal and beyond her.

Wrapping a big yellow-silk shawl around her, Spanish fashion, against the heat, and taking her white sunshade lined with green, she stepped out with him past the bowing Jefe and the lieutenant, and the saluting soldiers. She shook hands with the Jefe and the lieutenant. They were men of flesh and blood, they understood her presence, and bowed low, looking up at her with flashing eyes. And she knew what it was to be a goddess in the old style, saluted by the real fire in men's eyes, not by their lips.

In her big, soft velour hat of jade green, her breast wrapped round with the yellow brocade shawl, she stepped across the sun-eaten plaza, a sort of desert made by man, softly, softly beside her Cipriano, soft as a cat, hiding her face under her green hat and her sunshade, keeping her body secret and elusive. And the soldiers and the officers and clerks of the Jefatura, watching her with fixed black eyes, saw, not the physical woman herself, but the inaccessible, voluptuous mystery of man's physical consummation.

They ate in the dusky little cavern of a *fonda* kept by a queer old woman with Spanish blood in her veins. Cipriano was very sharp and imperious in his orders, the old woman scuffled and ran in a sort of terror. But she was thrilled to her soul.

Kate was bewildered by the new mystery of her own elusiveness. She was elusive even to herself. Cipriano hardly talked to her at all; which was quite right. She did not want to be talked to, and words addressed straight at her, without the curious soft veiling which these people knew how to put into their voices, speaking only to the unconcerned, third person in her, came at her like blows. Ah, the ugly blows of direct, brutal speech! She had suffered so much from them. Now she wanted this veiled elusiveness in herself, she wanted to be addressed in the third person.

After the lunch they went to look at the serapes which were being spun for Ramón. Their two soldiers escorted them a few yards up a broken, sun-wasted wide street of little, low black houses, then knocked at big doors.

Kate entered the grateful shade of the zaguan. In the dark shade of the inner court, or patio, where sun blazed on bananas beyond, was a whole weaver's establishment. A fat, one-eyed man sent a little boy to fetch chairs. But Kate wandered, fascinated.

In the zaguan was a great heap of silky white wool, very fine,

and in the dark corridor of the patio all the people at work. Two boys with flat square boards bristling with many little wire bristles were carding the white wool into thin films, which they took off the boards in fine rolls like mist, and laid beside the two girls at the end of the shed.

These girls stood by their wheels, spinning, standing beside the running wheel, which they set going with one hand, while with the other hand they kept a long, miraculous thread of white wool-yarn dancing at the very tip of the rapidly-spinning spool-needle, the filmy rolls of the carded wool just touching the point of the spool, and at once running out into a long, pure thread of white, which wound itself on to the spool, and another piece of carded wool was attached. One of the girls, a beautiful oval-faced one, who smiled shyly at Kate, was very clever. It was almost miraculous the way she touched the spool and drew out the thread of wool almost as fine as sewing cotton.

At the other end of the corridor, under the black shed, were two looms, and two men weaving. They treddled at the wooden tread-looms, first with one foot and then the other, absorbed and silent, in the shadow of the black mud walls. One man was weaving a brilliant scarlet serape, very fine, and of the beautiful cochineal red. It was difficult work. From the pure scarlet centre zigzags of black and white were running in a sort of whorl, away to the edge, that was pure black. Wonderful to see the man, with small bobbins of fine red and white yarn, and black, weaving a bit of the ground, weaving the zigzag of black up to it, and, up to that, the zigzag of white, with deft, dark fingers, quickly adjusting his setting needle, quick as lightning threading his pattern, then bringing down the beam heavily to press it tight. The scrape was woven on a black warp, long fine threads of black, like a harp. But beautiful beyond words the perfect, delicate scarlet weaving in.

"For whom is that?" said Kate to Cipriano. "For you?"

"Yes," he said. "For me!"

The other weaver was weaving a plain white serape with blue and natural-black ends, throwing the spool of yarn from side to side, between the white harp-strings, pressing down each thread of his woof heavily, with the wooden bar, then treddling to change the long, fine threads of the warp.

In the shadow of the mud shed, the pure colours of the lustrous wool looked mystical, the cardinal scarlet, the pure, silky white,

the lovely blue, and the black, gleaming in the shadow of the blackish walls.

The fat man with the one eye brought serapes, and two boys opened them one by one. There was a new one, white, with close flowers of blue on black stalks, and with green leaves, forming the borders, and at the *boca,* the mouth, where the head went through, a whole lot of little, rainbow-coloured flowers, in a coiling blue circle.

"I love that!" said Kate. "What is that for?"

"It is one of Ramón's; they are Quetzalcoatl's colours, the blue and white and natural black. But this one is for the day of the opening of the flowers, when he brings in the goddess who will come," said Cipriano.

Kate was silent with fear.

There were two scarlet serapes with a diamond at the centre, all black, and a border-pattern of black diamonds.

"Are these yours?"

"Well, they are for the messengers of Huitzilopochtli. Those are my colours: scarlet and black. But I myself have white as well, just as Ramón has a fringe of my scarlet."

"Doesn't it make you afraid?" she said to him, looking at him rather blenched.

"How make me afraid?"

"To do this. To be the living Huitzilopochtli," she said.

"I *am* the living Huitzilopochtli," he said. "When Ramón dares to be the living Quetzalcoatl, I dare to be the living Huitzilopochtli. I *am* he.—Am I not?"

Kate looked at him, at his dark face with the little hanging tuft of beard, the arched brows, the slightly slanting black eyes. In the round, fierce gaze of his eyes there was a certain silence, like tenderness, for her. But beyond that, an inhuman assurance, which looked far, far beyond her, in the darkness.

And she hid her face from him, murmuring:

"I know you are."

"And on the day of flowers," he said, "you, too, shall come, in a green dress they shall weave you, with blue flowers at the seam, and on your head the new moon of flowers."

She hid her face, afraid.

"Come and look at the wools," he said, leading her across the patio to the shade where, on a line, the yarn hung in dripping tresses of colour, scarlet and blue and yellow and green and brown.

"See!" he said. "You shall have a dress of green, that leaves the arms bare, and a white under-dress with blue flowers."

The green was a strong apple-green colour.

Two women under the shed were crouching over big earthenware vessels, which sat over a fire which burned slowly in a hole dug in the ground. They were watching the steaming water. One took dried, yellow-brown flowers, and flung them in her water as if she were a witch brewing decoctions. She watched as the flowers rose, watched as they turned softly in the boiling water. Then she threw in a little white powder.

"And on the day of flowers you, too, will come. Ah! If Ramón is the centre of a new world, a world of new flowers shall spring up round him, and push the old world back. I call you the First Flower."

They left the courtyard. The soldiers had brought the black Arab stallion for Cipriano, and for her the donkey, on which she could perch sideways, like a peasant woman. So they went through the hot, deserted silence of the mud-brick town, down the lane of deep, dark-grey dust, under vivid green trees that were bursting into flower, again to the silent shore of the lakeend, where the delicate fishing nets were hung in long lines and blowing in the wind, loop after loop striding above the shingle and blowing delicately in the wind, as away on the low places the green maize was blowing, and the fleecy willows shook like soft green feathers hanging down.

The lake stretched pale and unreal into nowhere; the motorboat rode near in, the black *canoas* stood motionless a little further out. Two women, tiny as birds, were kneeling on the water's edge, washing

Kate jumped from her donkey on to the shingle.

"Why not ride through the water to the boat?" said Cipriano.

She looked at the boat, and thought of the donkey stumbling and splashing.

"No," she said. "I will wade again."

He rode his black Arab to the water. It sniffed, and entered with delicate feet into the warm shallows. Then, a little way in, it stood and suddenly started pawing the water, as a horse paws the ground, in the oddest manner possible, very rapidly striking the water with its fore-foot, so that little waves splashed up over its black legs and belly.

But this splashed Cipriano too. He lifted the reins and

touched the creature with his spurs. It jumped, and went half-stumbling, half-dancing through the water, prettily, with a splashing noise. Cipriano quieted it, and it waded gingerly on through the shallows of the vast lake, bending its black head down to look, to look in a sort of fascination at the stony bottom, swaying its black tail as it moved its glossy, raven haunches gingerly.

Then again it stood still, and suddenly, with a rapid beating of its fore-paw, sent the water hollowly splashing up, till its black belly glistened wet like a black serpent, and its legs were shiny wet pillars. And again Cipriano lifted its head and touched it with the spurs, so the delicate creature danced in a churn of water.

"Oh, it looks so pretty! It looks so pretty when it paws the water!" cried Kate from the shore. "Why does it do it?"

Cipriano turned in the saddle and looked back at her with the sudden, gay Indian laugh.

"It likes to be wet—who knows?" he said.

A soldier hurried wading through the water and took the horse's bridle. Cipriano dismounted neatly from the stirrup, with a little backward leap into the boat, a real savage horseman. The barefoot soldier leaped into the saddle, and turned the horse to shore. But the black horse, male and wilful, insisted on stopping to paw the waters and splash himself, with a naïve, wilful sort of delight.

"Look! Look!" cried Kate. "It's so pretty."

But the soldier was perching in the saddle, drawing up his legs like a monkey, and shouting at the horse. It would wet its fine harness.

He rode the Arab slanting through the water, to where an old woman, sitting in her own silence and almost invisible before, was squatted in the water with brown bare shoulders emerging, ladling water from a half gourd-shell over her matted grey head. The horse splashed and danced, the old woman rose with her rag of chemise clinging to her, scolding in a quiet voice and bending forward with her calabash cup; the soldier laughed, the black horse joyfully and excitedly pawed the water and made it splash high up, the soldier shouted again.—But the soldier knew he could make Cipriano responsible for the splashings.

Kate waded slowly to the boat, and stepped in. The water was warm, but the wind was blowing with strong, electric heaviness. Kate quickly dried her feet and legs on her handkerchief, and

pulled on her biscuit-colored silk stockings and brown shoes.

She sat looking back, at the lake-end, the desert of shingle, the blowing, gauzy nets, and, beyond them, the black land with green maize standing, a further fleecy green of trees, and the broken lane leading deep into the rows of old trees, where the soldiers from Jaramay were now riding away on the black horse and the donkey. On the right there was a ranch, too; a long, low black building and a cluster of black huts with tiled roofs, empty gardens with reed fences, clumps of banana and willow trees. All in the changeless, heavy light of the afternoon, the long lake reaching into invisibility, between its unreal mountains.

"It is beautiful here!" said Kate. "One could almost live here."

"Ramón says he will make the lake the centre of a new world," said Cipriano. "We will be the gods of the lake."

"I'm afraid I am just a woman," said Kate.

His black eyes came round at her swiftly.

"What does it mean, just a woman?" he said, quickly, sternly.

She hung her head. What did it mean? What indeed did it mean? Just a woman! She let her soul sink again into the lovely elusiveness where everything is possible, even that oneself is elusive among the gods.

The motor-boat, with waves slapping behind, was running quickly along the brownish pale water. The soldiers, who were in the front, for balance, crouched on the floor with the glazed, stupefied mask-faces of the people when they are sleepy. And soon they were a heap in the bottom of the boat, two little heaps lying in contact.

Cipriano sat behind her, his tunic removed, spreading his white-sleeved arms on the back of his seat. The cartridge-belt was heavy on his hips. His face was completely expressionless, staring ahead. The wind blew his black hair on his forehead, and blew his little beard. He met her eyes with a far-off, remote smile, far, far down his black eyes. But it was a wonderful recognition of her.

The boatman in the stern sat tall and straight, watching with pale eyes of shallow, superficial consciousness. The great hat made his face dark, the chin-ribbon fell black against his cheek. Feeling her look at him, he glanced at her as if she were not there.

Turning, she pushed her cushion on to the floor and slid down. Cipriano got up, in the running, heaving boat, and pulled her an-

other seat-cushion. She lay, covering her face with her shawl, while the motor chugged rapidly, the awning rattled with sudden wind, the hurrying waves rose behind, giving the boat a slap and throwing her forward, sending spray sometimes, in the heat and silence of the lake.

Kate lost her consciousness, under her yellow shawl, in the silence of men.

She woke to the sudden stopping of the engine, and sat up. They were near shore; the white towers of San Pablo among near trees. The boatman, wide-eyed, was bending over the engine, abandoning the tiller. The waves pushed the boat slowly round.

"What is it?" said Cipriano.

"More gasoline, Excellency!" said the boatman.

The soldiers woke and sat up.

The breeze had died.

"The water is coming," said Cipriano.

"The rain?" said Kate.

"Yes—" and he pointed with his fine black finger, which was pale on the inside, to where black clouds were rushing up behind the mountains, and in another place further off, great heavy banks were rising with strange suddenness. The air seemed to be knitting together overhead. Lightning flashed in various places, muffled thunder spoke far away.

Still the boat drifted. There was a smell of gasoline. The man pottered with the engine. The motor started again, only to stop again in a moment.

The man rolled up his trousers, and, to Kate's amazement, stepped into the lake, though they were a mile from the shore. The water was not up to his knees. They were on a bank. He slowly pushed the boat before him, wading in the silence.

"How deep is the lake further in?" asked Kate.

"There, Señorita, where the birds with the white breasts are swimming, it is eight and a half metres," he said, pointing as he waded.

"We must make haste," said Cipriano.

"Yes, Excellency!"

The man stepped in again, with his long, handsome brown legs. The motor spluttered. They were under way, running fast. A new chill wind was springing up.

But they rounded a bend, and saw ahead the flat promontory with the dark mango-trees, and the pale yellow upper story of the

hacienda house of Jamiltepec rising above the trees. Palm-trees stood motionless, the bougainvillea hung in heavy sheets of magenta colour. Kate could see huts of peons among the trees, and women washing, kneeling on stones at the lake-side where the stream ran in, and a big plantation of bananas just above.

A cool wind was spinning round in the heavens. Black clouds were filling up. Ramón came walking slowly down to the little harbour as they landed.

"The water is coming," he said in Spanish.

"We are in time," said Cipriano.

Ramón looked them both in the face, and knew. Kate, in her new elusiveness, laughed softly.

"There is another flower opened in the garden of Quetzalcoatl," said Cipriano in Spanish.

"Under the red cannas of Huitzilopochtli," said Ramón.

"Yes, there, Señor," said Cipriano. "Pero una florecita tan zarca! Y abrió en mi sombra, amigo."

"Sois hombre de la alta fortuna."

"Verdad!"

It was about five in the afternoon. The wind hissed in the leaves, and suddenly the rain was streaming down in a white smoke of power. The ground was a solid white smoke of water, the lake was gone.

"You will have to stay here to-night," said Cipriano to Kate, in Spanish, in the soft, lapping Indian voice.

"But the rain will leave off," she said.

"You will have to stay here," he repeated, in the same Spanish phrase, in a curious voice like a breath of wind.

Kate looked at Ramón, blushing. He looked back at her, she thought, very remote, as if looking at her from far, far away.

"The bride of Huitzilopochtli," he said, with a faint smile.

"Thou, Quetzalcoatl, thou wilt have to marry us," said Cipriano.

"Do you wish it?" said Ramón.

"Yes!" she said. "I want you to marry us, only you."

"When the sun goes down," said Ramón.

And he went away to his room. Cipriano showed Kate to her room, then left her and went to Ramón.

The cool water continued to come down, rushing with a smoke of speed down from heaven.

As the twilight came through the unceasing rain, a woman-servant brought Kate a sleeveless dress or chemise of white linen,

scalloped at the bottom and embroidered with stiff blue flowers upside-down on the black stalks, with two stiff green leaves. In the centre of the flowers was the tiny Bird of Quetzalcoatl.

"The Patron asks that you put this on!" said the woman, bringing also a lamp and a little note.

The note was from Ramón, saying in Spanish: "Take the dress of the bride of Huitzilopochtli, and put it on, and take off everything but this. Leave no thread nor thing that can touch you from the past. The past is finished. It is the new twilight."

Kate did not quite know how to put on the slip, for it had no sleeves nor arm-holes, but was just a straight slip of running string. Then she remembered the old Indian way, and tied the string over her left shoulder; rather, slipped the tied string over her left shoulder, leaving her arms and part of her right breast bare, the slip gathered full over her breasts. And she sighed. For it was but a shirt with flowers upturned at the bottom.

Ramón, barefoot, in his white clothes, came for her and took her in silence downstairs into the garden. The zaguan was dark, the rain fell steadily in the twilight, but was abating. All was dark twilight.

Ramón took off his blouse and threw it on the stairs. Then with naked breast he led her into the garden, into the massive rain. Cipriano came forward, barefoot, with naked breast, bare-headed, in the floppy white pantaloons.

They stood barefoot on the earth, that still threw back a white smoke of waters. The rain drenched them in a moment.

"Barefoot on the living earth, with faces to the living rain," said Ramón in Spanish, quietly; "at twilight, between the night and the day; man, and woman, in presence of the unfading star, meet to be perfect in one another. Lift your face, Caterina, and say: *This man is my rain from heaven.*"

Kate lifted her face and shut her eyes in the downpour.

"This man is my rain from heaven," she said.

"This woman is the earth to me—say that, Cipriano," said Ramón, kneeling on one knee and laying his hand flat on the earth.

Cipriano kneeled and laid his hand on the earth.

"This woman is the earth to me," he said.

"I, woman, kiss the feet and the heels of this man, for I will be strength to him, throughout the long twilight of the Morning Star."

Kate kneeled and kissed the feet and heels of Cipriano, and said her say.

"I, man, kiss the brow and the breast of this woman, for I will be her peace and her increase, through the long twilight of the Morning Star."

Cipriano kissed her, and said his say.

Then Ramón put Cipriano's hand over the rain-wet eyes of Kate, and Kate's hand over the rain-wet eyes of Cipriano.

"I, a woman, beneath the darkness of this covering hand, pray to this man to meet me in the heart of the night, and never deny me," said Kate. "But let it be an abiding place between us, for ever."

"I, a man, beneath the darkness of this covering hand, pray to this woman to receive me in the heart of the night, in the abiding place that is between us for ever."

"Man shall betray a woman, and woman shall betray a man," said Ramón, "and it shall be forgiven them, each of them. But if they have met as earth and rain, between day and night, in the hour of the Star; if the man has met the woman with his body and the star of his hope, and the woman has met the man with her body and the star of her yearning, so that a meeting has come to pass, and an abiding place for the two where they are as one star, then shall neither of them betray the abiding place where the meeting lives like an unsetting star. For if either betray the abiding place of the two, it shall not be forgiven, neither by day nor by night nor in the twilight of the star."

The rain was leaving off, the night was dark.

"Go and bathe in the warm water, which is peace between us all. And put oil on your bodies, which is the stillness of the Morning Star. Anoint even the soles of your feet, and the roots of your hair."

Kate went up to her room and found a big earthenware bath with steaming water, and big towels. Also, in a beautiful little bowl, oil, and a soft bit of white wool.

She bathed her rain-wet body in the warm water, dried and anointed herself with the clear oil, that was clear as water. It was soft, and had a faint perfume, and was grateful to the skin. She rubbed all her body, even among her hair and under her feet, till she glowed softly.

Then she put on another of the slips with the inverted blue flowers, that had been laid on the bed for her, and over that a

dress of green, hand-woven wool, made of two pieces joined openly together down the sides, showing a bit of the white, full under-dress, and fastened on the left shoulder. There was a stiff flower, blue, on a black stem, with two black leaves, embroidered at the bottom, at each side. And her white slip showed a bit at the breast, and hung below the green skirt, showing the blue flowers.

It was strange and primitive, but beautiful. She pushed her feet into the plaited green huaraches. But she wanted a belt. She tied a piece of ribbon round her waist.

A mozo tapped to say supper was ready.

Laughing rather shyly, she went along to the salon.

Ramón and Cipriano were both waiting, in silence, in their white clothes. Cipriano had his red serape loosely thrown over his shoulders.

"So!" said Cipriano, coming forward. "The bride of Huitzil-opochtli, like a green morning. But Huitzilopochtli will put on your sash, and you will put on his shoes, so that he shall never leave you, and you shall be always in his spell."

Cipriano tied round her waist a narrow woollen sash of white wool, with white, terraced towers upon a red and black ground. And she stooped and put on his small, dark feet the huaraches of woven red strips of leather, with a black cross on the toes.

"One more little gift," said Ramón.

He made Kate put over Cipriano's head a blue cord bearing a little symbol of Quetzalcoatl, the snake in silver and the bird in blue turquoise. Cipriano put over her head the same symbol, but in gold, with a bird in black dull jet, and hanging on a red cord.

"There!" said Ramón. "That is the symbol of Quetzalcoatl, the Morning Star. Remember the marriage is the meeting-ground, and the meeting-ground is the star. If there be no star, no meeting-ground, no true coming together of man with the woman, into a wholeness, there is no marriage. And if there is no marriage, there is nothing but an agitation. If there is no honourable meeting of man with woman and woman with man, there is no good thing come to pass. But if the meeting come to pass, then whosoever betrays the abiding place, which is the meeting-ground, which is that which lives like a star between day and night, between the dark of woman and the dawn of man, be-tween man's night and woman's morning, shall never be forgiven, neither here nor in the hereafter. For man is frail and woman is frail, and none can draw the line down which another shall

walk.   But the star that is between two people and is their meeting-ground shall not be betrayed.

"And the star that is between three people, and is their meeting-ground, shall not be betrayed.

"And the star that is between all men and all women, and be-tween all the children of men, shall not be betrayed.

"Whosoever betrays another man, betrays a man like himself, a fragment.   For if there is no star between a man and a man, or even a man and a wife, there is nothing.   But whosoever betrays the star that is between him and another man, betrays all, and all is lost to the traitor.

"Where there is no star and no abiding place, nothing is, so nothing can be lost."

CHAPTER XXI

THE OPENING OF THE CHURCH

KATE went back to her house in Sayula, and Cipriano went back to his command in the city.

"Will you not come with me?" he said. "Shall we not make a civil marriage, and live in the same house together?"

"No," she said. "I am married to you by Quetzalcoatl, no other. I will be your wife in the world of Quetzalcoatl, no other. And if the star has risen between us, we will watch it."

Conflicting feelings played in his dark eyes. He could not bear even to be the least bit thwarted. Then the strong, rather distant look came back.

"It is very good," he said. "It is the best."

And he went away without looking back.

Kate returned to her house, to her servants and her rocking-chair. Inside herself she kept very still and almost thoughtless, taking no count of time. What was going to unfold must unfold of itself.

She no longer feared the nights, when she was shut alone in her darkness. But she feared the days a little. She shrank so mortally from contact.

She opened her bedroom window one morning, and looked down to the lake. The sun had come, and queer blotty shadows were on the hills beyond the water. Way down at the water's edge a woman was pouring water from a calabash bowl over a statuesque pig, dipping rapidly and assiduously. The little group was seen in silhouette against the pale, dun lake.

But impossible to stand at her open window looking on the little lane. An old man suddenly appeared from nowhere, offering her a leaf full of tiny fish, charales, like splinters of glass, for ten centavos, and a girl was unfolding three eggs from the ragged corner of her rebozo, thrusting them imploringly forward to Kate. An old woman was shambling up with a sad story, Kate knew. She fled from her window and the importunity.

At the same instant, the sound that always made her heart

stand still woke on the invisible air. It was the sound of drums, of tom-toms rapidly beaten. The same sound she had heard in the distance, in the tropical dusk of Ceylon, from the temple at sunset. The sound she had heard from the edge of the forests in the north, when the Red Indians were dancing by the fire. The sound that wakes dark, ancient echoes in the heart of every man, the thud of the primeval world.

Two drums were violently throbbing against one another. Then gradually they were slowing down, in a peculiar uneven rhythm, till at last there was only left one slow, continual, monotonous note, like a great drop of darkness falling heavily, continually, dripping in the bright morning.

The re-evoked past is frightening, and if it be re-evoked to overwhelm the present, it is fiendish. Kate felt a real terror of the sound of a tom-tom. It seemed to beat straight on her solar plexus, to make her sick.

She went to her window. Across the lane rose a tall garden-wall of adobe brick, and above that, the sun on the tops of the orange-trees, deep gold. Beyond the orange garden rose three tall, handsome, shaggy palm trees, side by side on slim stems. And from the very top of the two outer palms, rose the twin tips of the church towers. She had noticed it so often; the two iron-work Greek crosses seeming to stand on the mops of the palms.

Now in an instant she saw the glitter of the symbol of Quetzalcoatl in the places where the cross had been; two circular suns, with the dark bird at the centre. The gold of the suns—or the serpents—flashed new in the light of the sun, the bird lifted its wings dark in outline within the circle.

Then again the two drums were speeding up, beating against one another with the peculiar uneven savage rhythm, which at first seems no rhythm, and then seems to contain a summons almost sinister in its power, acting on the helpless blood direct. Kate felt her hands flutter on her wrists, in fear. Almost, too, she could hear the heart of Cipriano beating; her husband in Quetzalcoatl.

"Listen, Nina! Listen, Niña!" came Juana's frightened voice from the verandah.

Kate went to the verandah. Ezequiel had rolled up his mattress and was hitching up his pants. It was Sunday morning, when he sometimes lay on after sunrise. His thick black hair stood up, his dark face was blank with sleep, but in his quiet

aloofness and his slightly bowed head Kate could see the secret satisfaction he took in the barbarous sound of the drums.

"It comes from the Church!" said Juana.

Kate caught the other woman's black, reptilian eyes unexpectedly. Usually, she forgot that Juana was dark, and different. For days she would not realise it. Till suddenly she met that black, void look with the glint in it, and she started inwardly, involuntarily asking herself: "Does she hate me?"

Or was it only the unspeakable difference in blood?

Now, in the dark glitter which Juana showed her for one moment, Kate read fear, and triumph, and a slow, savage, nonchalant defiance. Something very inhuman.

"What does it mean?" Kate said to her.

"It means, Niña, that they won't ring the bells any more. They have taken the bells away, and they beat the drums in the church. Listen! Listen!"

The drums were shuddering rapidly again.

Kate and Juana went across to the open window.

"Look! Niña! The Eye of the Other One! No more crosses on the church. It is the Eye of the Other One. Look! How it shines! How nice!"

"It means," said Ezequiel's breaking young voice, which was just turning deep, "that it is the church of Quetzalcoatl. Now it is the temple of Quetzalcoatl; our own God."

He was evidently a staunch Man of Quetzalcoatl.

"Think of it!" murmured Juana, in an awed voice. She seemed like a heap of darkness low at Kate's side.

Then again she glanced up, and the eyes of the two women met for a moment.

"See the Niña's eyes of the sun!" cried Juana, laying her hand on Kate's arm. Kate's eyes were a sort of hazel, changing, greygold, flickering at the moment with wonder, and a touch of fear and dismay. Juana sounded triumphant.

A man in a white serape, with the blue and black borders, suddenly appeared at the window, lifting his hat, on which was the sign of Quetzalcoatl, and pushing a little card through the window.

The card said: Come to the church when you hear the one big drum; about seven o'clock.—It was signed with the sign of Quetzalcoatl.

"Very well!" said Kate. "I will come."

It was a quarter to seven already. Outside the room was the

noise of Juana sweeping the verandah. Kate put on a white dress and a yellow hat, and a long string of pale-coloured topaz that glimmered with yellow and mauve.

The earth was all damp with rain, the leaves were all fresh and tropical thick, yet many old leaves were on the ground, beaten down.

"Niña! You are going out already! Wait! Wait! The coffee. Concha! quick!"

There was a running of bare feet, the children bringing cup and plate and sweet buns and sugar, the mother hastily limping with the coffee. Ezequiel came striding along the walk, lifting his hat. He went down to the servants' quarters.

"Ezequiel says—!" Juana came crying. When suddenly a soft, slack thud seemed to make a hole in the air, leaving a gap behind it. Thud!—Thud!—Thud!—rather slowly. It was the big drum, irresistible.

Kate rose at once from her coffee.

"I am going to the church," she said.

"Yes Niña—Ezequiel says—I am coming, Niña—"

And Juana scuttled away, to get her black rebozo.

The man in the white serape with the blue and black ends was waiting by the gate. He lifted his hat, and walked behind Kate and Juana.

"He is following us!" whispered Juana.

Kate drew her yellow shawl around her shoulders.

It was Sunday morning, sailing-boats lined the water's edge, with their black hulls. But the beach was empty. As the great drum let fall its slow, bellowing note, the last people were running towards the church.

In front of the church was a great throng of natives, the men with their dark serapes, or their red blankets over their shoulders; the nights of rain were cold; and their hats in their hands. The high, dark Indian heads!—Women in blue rebozos were pressing among. The big drum slowly, slackly exploded its note from the church-tower. Kate had her heart in her mouth.

In the middle of the crowd, a double row of men in the scarlet serapes of Huitzilopochtli with the black diamond on the shoulders, stood with rifles, holding open a lane through the crowd.

"Pass!" said her guard to her. And Kate entered the lane of scarlet and black serapes, going slow and dazed between watchful

black eyes of the men. Her guard followed her. But Juana had been turned back.

Kate looked at her feet, and stumbled. Then she looked up.

In the gateway of the yard before the church stood a brilliant figure in a serape whose zig-zag whorls of scarlet, white, and black ran curving, dazzling, to the black shoulders; above which was the face of Cipriano, calm, superb, with the little black beard and the arching brows. He lifted his hand to her in salute.

Behind him, stretching from the gateway to the closed door of the church, was a double row of the guard of Quetzalcoatl, in their blankets with the blue and black borders.

"What shall I do?" said Kate.

"Stand here with me a moment," said Cipriano, in the gateway.

It was no easy thing to do, to face all those dark faces and black, glittering eyes. After all, she was a gringita, and she felt it. A sacrifice? Was she a sacrifice? She hung her head, under her yellow hat, and watched the string of topaz twinkling and shaking its delicate, bog-watery colours against her white dress. Joachim had given it her. He had had it made up for her, the string, in Cornwall. So far away! In another world, in another life, in another era! Now she was condemned to go through these strange ordeals, like a victim.

The big drum overhead ceased, and suddenly the little drums broke like a shower of hail on the air, and as suddenly ceased.

In low, deep, inward voices, the guard of Quetzalcoatl began to speak, in heavy unison:

"Oye! Oye! Oye! Oye!"

The small, inset door within the heavy doors of the church opened and Don Ramón stepped through. In his white clothes, wearing the Quetzalcoatl serape, he stood at the head of his two rows of guards, until there was a silence. Then he raised his naked right arm.

"What is God, you shall never know!" he said, in a strong voice, to all the people.

The Guard of Quetzalcoatl turned to the people, thrusting up their right arm.

"What is God, we shall never know!" they repeated.

Then again, in the crowd, the words were re-echoed by the Guard of Huitzilopochtli.

After which there fell a dead silence, in which Kate was aware of a forest of black eyes glistening with white fire.

"But the Sons of God come and go.
They come from beyond the Morning Star;
And thither they return, from the land of men."

It was again the solemn, powerful voice of Ramón. Kate looked at his face; it was creamy-brown in its pallor, but changeless in expression, and seemed to be sending a change over the crowd, removing them from their vulgar complacency.

The Guard of Quetzalcoatl turned again to the crowd, and repeated Ramón's words to the crowd.

"Mary and Jesus have left you, and gone to the place of renewal.
And Quetzalcoatl has come. He is here.
He is your lord."

With his words, Ramón was able to put the power of his heavy, strong will over the people. The crowd began to fuse under his influence. As he gazed back at all the black eyes, his eyes seemed to have no expression, save that they seemed to be seeing the heart of all darkness in front of him, where his unknowable God-mystery lived and moved.

"Those that follow me, must cross the mountains of the sky,
And pass the houses of the stars by night.
They shall find me only in the Morning Star.

But those that will not follow, must not peep.
Peeping, they will lose their sight, and lingering, they will fall very
    lame."

He stood a moment in silence, gazing with dark brows at the crowd. Then he dropped his arm, and turned. The big doors of the church opened, revealing a dim interior. Ramón entered the church alone. Inside the church, the drum began to beat. The guard of Quetzalcoatl slowly filed into the dim interior, the scarlet guard of Huitzilopochtli filed into the yard of the church, taking the place of the guard of Quetzalcoatl. Cipriano remained in the gateway of the churchyard. His voice rang out clear and military.

"Hear me, people. You may enter the house of Quetzalcoatl. Men must go to the right and left, and remove their shoes, and stand erect. To the new God no man shall kneel.

"Women must go down the centre, and cover their faces. And they may sit upon the floor.

"But men must stand erect.

"Pass now, those who dare."

Kate went with Cipriano into the church.

It was all different, the floor was black and polished, the walls were in stripes of colour, the place seemed dark. Two files of the white-clad men of Quetzalcoatl stood in a long avenue down the centre of the church.

"This way," said one of the men of Quetzalcoatl, in a low voice, drawing her into the centre between the motionless files of men.

She went alone and afraid over the polished black floor, covering her face with her yellow shawl. The pillars of the nave were dark green, like trees rising to a deep, blue roof. The walls were vertically striped in bars of black and white, vermilion and yellow and green, with the windows between rich with deep blue and crimson and black glass, having specks of light. A strange maze, the windows.

The daylight came only from small windows, high up under the deep blue roof, where the stripes of the walls had run into a maze of green, like banana leaves. Below, the church was all dark, and rich with hard colour.

Kate went forward to the front, near the altar steps. High at the back of the chancel, above where the altar had been, burned a small but intense bluey-white light, and just below and in front of the light stood a huge dark figure, a strange looming block, apparently carved in wood. It was a naked man, carved archaic and rather flat, holding his right arm over his head, and on the right arm balanced a carved wooden eagle with outspread wings whose upper surface gleamed with gold, near the light, whose under surface was black shadow. Round the heavy left leg of the man-image was carved a serpent, also glimmering gold, and its golden head rested in the hand of the figure, near the thigh. The face of the figure was dark.

This great dark statue loomed stiff like a pillar, rather frightening in the white-lit blue chancel.

At the foot of the statue was a stone altar with a small fire of ocote-wood burning. And on a low throne by the altar sat Ramón.

People were beginning to file into the church. Kate heard the strange sound of the naked feet of the men on the black, polished floor, the white figures stole forward towards the altar steps, the dark faces gazing round in wonder, men crossing themselves in-

voluntarily. Throngs of men slowly flooded in, and women came half running, to crouch on the floor and cover their faces. Kate crouched down too.

A file of the men of Quetzalcoatl came and stood along the foot of the altar steps, like a fence with a gap in the middle, facing the people. Beyond the gap was the flickering altar, and Ramón.

Ramón rose to his feet. The men of Quetzalcoatl turned to face him, and shot up their naked right arms, in the gesture of the statue, Ramón lifted his arm, so his blanket fell in towards his shoulder, revealing the naked side and the blue sash.

"All men salute Quetzalcoatl!" said a clear voice in command.

The scarlet men of Huitzilopochtli were threading among the men of the congregation, pulling the kneeling ones to their feet, causing all to thrust up their right arm, palm flat to heaven, face uplifted, body erect and tense. It was the statue receiving the eagle.

So that around the low dark shrubs of the crouching women stood a forest of erect, upthrusting men, powerful and tense with inexplicable passion. It was a forest of dark wrists and hands up-pressing, with the striped wall vibrating above, and higher, the maze of green going to the little, iron-barred windows that stood open, letting in the light and air of the roof.

"I am the living Quetzalcoatl," came the solemn, impassive voice of Ramón.

I am the Son of the Morning Star, and child of the deeps.
No man knows my Father, and I know Him not.
My Father is deep within the deeps, whence He sent me forth.
He sends the eagle of silence down on wide wings
To lean over my head and my neck and my breast
And fill them strong with strength of wings.
He sends the serpent of power up my feet and my loins
So that strength wells up in me like water in hot springs.
But midmost shines as the Morning Star midmost shines
Between night and day, my Soul-star in one,
Which is my Father whom I know not.
I tell you, the day should not turn into glory,
And the night should not turn deep,
Save for the morning and evening stars, upon which they turn.
Night turns upon me, and Day, who am the star between.
Between your breast and belly is a star.
If it be not there
You are empty gourd-shells filled with dust and wind.

When you walk, the star walks with you, between your breast and
    your belly.
When you sleep, it softly shines.
When you speak true and true, it is bright on your lips and your
    teeth.
When you lift your hands in courage and bravery, its glow is clear
    in your palms.
When you turn to your wives as brave men turn to their women
The Morning Star and the Evening Star shine together.
For man is the Morning Star.
And woman is the Star of Evening.
I tell you, you are not men alone.
The star of the beyond is within you.
But have you seen a dead man, how his star has gone out of him?
So the star will go out of you, even as a woman will leave a man if
    his warmth never warms her.
Should you say: *I have no star; I am no star,*
So it will leave you, and you will hang like a gourd on the vine of life
With nothing but rind:
Waiting for the rats of the dark to come and gnaw your inside.
Do you hear the rats of the darkness gnawing at your inside?
Till you are as empty as rat-gnawed pomegranates hanging hollow
    on the Tree of Life?
If the star shone, they dare not, they could not.
If you were men with the Morning Star.
If the star shone within you
No rat of the dark dared gnaw you.
But I am Quetzalcoatl, of the Morning Star.
I am the living Quetzalcoatl.
And you are men who should be men of the **Morning Star.**
See you be not rat-gnawed gourds.
I am Quetzalcoatl of the eagle and the snake.
The earth and air.
Of the Morning Star.
I am Lord of the Two Ways——

    The drum began to beat, the men of Quetzalcoatl suddenly took
off their serapes, and Ramón did the same. They were now men
naked to the waist. The eight men from the altar-steps filed up
to the altar where the fire burned, and one by one kindled tall
green candles, which burned with a clear light. They ranged
themselves on either side the chancel, holding the lights high, so
that the wooden face of the image glowed as if alive, and the eyes
of silver and jet flashed most curiously.

"A man shall take the wine of his spirit and the blood of his heart, the oil of his belly and the seed of his loins, and offer them first to the Morning Star," said Ramón, in a loud voice, turning to the people.

Four men came to him. One put a blue crown with the bird on his brow, one put a red belt round his breast, another put a yellow belt round his middle, and the last fastened a white belt round his loins. Then the first one pressed a small glass bowl to Ramón's brow, and in the bowl was white liquid like bright water. The next touched a bowl to the breast, and the red shook in the bowl. At the navel the man touched a bowl with yellow fluid, and at the loins a bowl with something dark. They held them all to the light.

Then one by one they poured them into a silver mixing-bowl that Ramón held between his hands.

"For save the Unknown God pours His Spirit over my head and fire into my heart, and sends his power like a fountain of oil into my belly, and His lightning like a hot spring into my loins, I am not. I am nothing. I am a dead gourd.

"And save I take the wine of my spirit and the red of my heart, the strength of my belly and the power of my loins, and mingle them all together, and kindle them to the Morning Star, I betray my body, I betray my soul, I betray my spirit and my God who is Unknown.

"Fourfold is man. But the star is one star. And one man is but one star."

He took the silver mixing-bowl and slowly circled it between his hands, in the act of mixing.

Then he turned his back to the people, and lifted the bowl high up, between his hands, as if offering it to the image.

Then suddenly he threw the contents of the bowl into the altar fire.

There was a soft puff of explosion, a blue flame leaped high into the air, followed by a yellow flame, and then a rose-red smoke. In three successive instants the faces of the men inside the chancel were lit bluish, then gold, then dusky red. And in the same moment Ramón had turned to the people and shot up his hand.

"Salute Quetzalcoatl!" cried a voice, and men began to thrust up their arms, when another voice came moaning strangely:

"No! Ah no! Ah no!"—the voice rose in a hysterical cry.

It came from among the crouching women, who glanced round

in fear, to see a woman in black, kneeling on the floor, her black scarf falling back from her lifted face, thrusting up her white hands to the Madonna, in the old gesture.

"No! No! It is not permitted!" shrieked the voice. "Lord! Lord! Lord Jesus! Holy Virgin! Prevent him! Prevent him!"

The voice sank again to a moan, the white hands clutched the breast, and the woman in black began to work her way forward on her knees, through the throng of women who pressed aside to make her way, towards the altar steps. She came with her head lowered, working her way on her knees, and moaning low prayers of supplication.

Kate felt her blood run cold. Crouching near the altar steps, she looked round. And she knew, by the shape of the head bent in the black scarf, it was Carlota, creeping along on her knees to the altar steps.

The whole church was frozen in horror. "Saviour! Saviour! Jesus! O Holy Virgin!" Carlota was moaning to herself as she crawled along.

It seemed hours before she reached the altar steps. Ramón still stood below the great Quetzalcoatl image with arm upflung.

Carlota crouched black at the altar steps and flung up the white hands and her white face in the frenzy of the old way.

"Lord! Lord!" she cried, in a strange ecstatic voice that froze Kate's bowels with horror: "Jesus! Jesus! Jesus! Jesus! Jesus! Jesus!"

Carlota strangled in her ecstasy. And all the while, Ramón, the living Quetzalcoatl, stood before the flickering altar with naked arm upraised, looking with dark, inalterable eyes down upon the woman.

Throes and convulsions tortured the body of Carlota. She gazed sightlessly upwards. Then came her voice, in the mysterious rhapsody of prayer:

"Lord! Lord! Forgive!

"God of love, forgive! He knows not what he does.

"Lord! Lord Jesus! Make an end. Make an end, Lord of the world, Christ of the cross, make an end. Have mercy on him, Father. Have pity on him!

"Oh, take his life from him now, now, that his soul may not die."

Her voice had gathered strength till it rang out metallic and terrible.

"Almighty God, take his life from him, and save his soul."
And in the silence after that cry her hands seemed to flicker in
the air like flames of death.

"The Omnipotent," came the voice of Ramón, speaking quietly,
as if to her, "is with me, and I serve Omnipotence!"

She remained with her white clasped hands upraised, her white
arms and her white face showing mystical, like onyx, from her
thin black dress. She was absolutely rigid. And Ramón, with
his arm too upraised, looked down on her abstractedly, his black
brows a little contracted.

A strong convulsion seized her body. She became tense again,
making inarticulate noises. Then another convulsion seized her.
Once more she recovered herself, and thrust up her clenched
hands in frenzy. A third convulsion seized her as if from below, and she fell with a strangling moan in a heap on the altar
steps.

Kate had risen suddenly and ran to her, to lift her up. She
found her stiff, with a little froth on her discoloured lips, and
fixed, glazed eyes.

Kate looked up in consternation at Ramón. He had dropped
his arm, and stood with his hands against his thighs, like a statue.
But he remained with his wide, absorbed dark eyes watching with
out any change. He met Kate's glance of dismay, and his eyes
quickly glanced, like lightning, for Cipriano. Then he looked
back at Carlota, across a changeless distance. Not a muscle of
his face moved. And Kate could see that his heart had died in
its connection with Carlota, his heart was quite, quite dead in
him, out of the deathly vacancy he watched his wife. Only his
brows frowned a little, from his smooth, male forehead His
old connections were broken. She could hear him say: *There
is no star between me and Carlota.*—And how terribly true it
was!

Cipriano came quickly, switched off his brilliant serape, wrapped
it round the poor, stiff figure, and picking up the burden lightly,
walked with it through the lane of women to the door, and out
into the brilliant sun; Kate following. And as she followed, she
heard the slow, deep voice of Ramón:

> I am the Living Quetzalcoatl.
> Naked I come from out of the deep
> From the place which I call my Father.

Naked have I travelled the long way round
From heaven, past the sleeping sons of God.

Out of the depths of the sky, I came like an eagle.
Out of the bowels of the earth like a snake.

All things that lift in the lift of living between earth and sky, know
    me.

But I am the inward star invisible.
And the star is the lamp in the hand of the Unknown Mover.
Beyond me is a Lord who is terrible, and wonderful, and dark to me
    forever.
Yet I have lain in his loins, ere he begot me in Mother space.

Now I am alone on earth, and this is mine.
The roots are mine, down to the dark, moist path of the snake.
And the branches are mine, in the paths of the sky and the bird,
But the spark of me that is me is more than mine own.

And the feet of men, and the hands of women know me.
And knees and thighs and loins, and the bowels of strength and seed
    are lit with me.
The snake of my left-hand out of the darkness is hissing your feet
    with his mouth of caressive fire,
And putting his strength in your heels and ankles, his flame in your
    knees and your legs and your loins, his circle of rest in your
    belly.
For I am Quetzalcoatl, the feathered snake,
And I am not with you till my serpent has coiled his circle of rest in
    your belly.

And I, Quetzalcoatl, the eagle of the air, am brushing your faces
    with vision.
I am fanning your breasts with my breath.
And building my nest of peace in your bones.
I am Quetzalcoatl, of the Two Ways.

Kate lingered to hear the end of this hymn. Cipriano also had
lingered in the porch, with the strange figure in the brilliant
serape in his arms. His eyes met Kate's. In his black glance
was a sort of homage, to the mystery of the Two Ways; a sort
of secret. And Kate was uneasy.

They crossed quickly under the trees to the hotel, which was
very near, and Carlota was laid in bed. A soldier had gone already to find a doctor; they sent also for a priest.

Kate sat by the bed. Carlota lay on the bed, making small,

horrible moaning noises. The drums outside on the church-roof started to roll, in a savage, complicated rhythm. Kate went to the window and looked out. People were streaming dazzled from the church.

And then, from the church-roof, came the powerful singing of men's voices, fanning like a dark eagle in the bright air; a deep relentless chanting, with an undertone of passionate assurance. She went to the window to look. She could see the men on the church-roof, the people swarming down below. And the roll of that relentless chanting, with its undertone of exultance in power and life, rolled through the air like an invisible dark presence.

Cipriano came in again, glancing at Carlota and at Kate.

"They are singing the song of Welcome to Quetzalcoatl," said he.

"Is that it?" said Kate. "What are the words?"

"I will find you a song-sheet," he said.

He stood beside her, putting the spell of his presence over her. And she still struggled a little, as if she were drowning. When she wasn't drowning, she wanted to drown. But when it actually came, she fought for her old footing.

There was a crying noise from Carlota. Kate hurried to the bed.

"Where am I?" said the white-faced, awful, deathly-looking woman.

"You are resting in bed," said Kate. "Don't trouble."

"Where was I?" came Carlota's voice.

"Perhaps the sun gave you a touch of sunstroke," said Kate. Carlota closed her eyes.

Then suddenly outside the noise of drums rolled again, a powerful sound. And outside in the sunshine life seemed to be rolling in powerful waves.

Carlota started, and opened her eyes.

"What is that noise?"

"It is a fiesta," said Kate.

"Ramón, he's murdered me, and lost his own soul," said Carlota. "He has murdered me, and lost his own soul. He is a murderer, and one of the damned. The man I married! The man I married! A murderer among the damned!"

It was evident she no longer heard the sounds outside.

Cipriano could not bear the sound of her voice. He came quickly to the side of the bed.

"Doña Carlota!" he said, looking down at her dulled hazel eyes, that were fixed and unseeing: "Do not die with wrong words on your lips. If you are murdered, you have murdered yourself. You were never married to Ramón. You were married to your own way."

He spoke fiercely, avengingly.

"Ah!" said the dying woman. "Ah! I never married Ramón. No! I never married him! How could I? He was not what I would have him be. How could I marry him? Ah! I thought I married him. Ah! I am so glad I didn't—so glad."

"You are glad! You are glad!" said Cipriano in anger, angry with the very ghost of the woman, talking to the ghost. "You are glad because you never poured the wine of your body into the mixing-bowl! Yet in your day you have drunk the wine of his body and been soothed with his oil. You are glad you kept yours back? You are glad you kept back the wine of your body and the secret oil of your soul? That you gave only the water of your charity? I tell you the water of charity, the hissing water of the spirit, is bitter at last in the mouth and in the breast and in the belly, it puts out the fire. You would have put out the fire, Doña Carlota.—But you cannot. You shall not. You have been charitable and compassionless to the man you called your own. So you have put out your own fire."

"Who is talking?" said the ghost of Carlota.

"I, Cipriano Viedma, am talking."

"The oil and the wine! The oil and the wine and the bread! They are the sacrament! They are the body and the blessing of God! Where is the priest? I want the sacrament. Where is the priest? I want to confess, and take the sacrament, and have the peace of God," said the ghost of Carlota.

"The priest is coming.—But you can take no sacrament, unless you give it. The oil and the wine and the bread! They are not for the priest to give. They are to be poured into the mixing-bowl, which Ramón calls the cup of the star. If you pour neither oil nor wine into the mixing-bowl, from the mixing-bowl you cannot drink. So you have no sacrament."

"The sacrament! The bread!" said the ghost of Carlota.

"There is no bread. There is no body without blood and oil, as Shylock found out."

"A murderer, lost among the damned!" murmured Carlota. "The father of my children! The husband of my body! Ah

no! It is better for me to call to the Holy Virgin, and die."

"Call then, and die!" said Cipriano.

"My children!" murmured Carlota.

"It is well you must leave them. With your beggar's bowl of charity you have stolen their oil and their wine as well. It is good for you to steal from them no more, you stale virgin, you spinster, you born widow, you weeping mother, you impeccable wife, you just woman. You stole the very sunshine out of the sky and the sap out of the earth. Because back again, what did you pour? Only the water of dead dilution into the mixing-bowl of life, you thief. Oh die!—die!—die! Die and be a thousand times dead! Do nothing but utterly die!"

Doña Carlota had relapsed into unconsciousness; even her ghost refused to hear. Cipriano flung his sinisterly-flaming serape over his shoulders and his face, over his nose, till only his black, glittering eyes were visible as he blew out of the room.

Kate sat by the window, and laughed a little. The primeval woman inside her laughed to herself, for she had known all the time about the two thieves on the Cross with Jesus; the bullying, marauding thief of the male in his own rights, and the much more subtle, cold, sly, charitable thief of the woman in *her* own rights, forever chanting her beggar's whine about the love of God and the God of pity.

But Kate, too, was a modern woman and a woman in her own rights. So she sat on with Carlota. And when the doctor came, she accepted the obsequiousness of the man as part of her rights. And when the priest came, she accepted the obsequiousness from him, just the same, as part of her woman's rights. These two ministers of love, what were they for, but to be obsequious to her? As for herself, she could hardly be called a thief, and a sneak-thief of the world's virility, when these men came forcing their obsequiousness upon her, whining to her to take it and relieve them of the responsibility of their own manhood. No, if women are thieves, it is only because men want to be thieved from. If women thieve the world's virility, it is only because men want to have it thieved, since for men to be responsible for their own manhood seems to be the last thing men want.

So Kate sat on in the room of the dying Carlota, smiling a little cynically. Outside she heard the roll of the tom-toms and the deep chanting of the men of Quetzalcoatl. Beyond, under the

trees, in the smoothed, cleared space before the church, she saw the half-naked men dancing in a circle, to the drum; the round dance. Then later, dancing a religious dance of the return of Quetzalcoatl. It was the old, barefooted, absorbed dancing of the Indians, the dance of downward-sinking absorption. It was the dance of these people too, just the same: the dance of the Aztecs and Zapotecs and the Huicholes, just the same in essence, indigenous to America; the curious, silent, absorbed dance of the softly-beating feet and ankles, the body coming down softly, but with deep weight, upon powerful knees and ankles, to the tread of the earth, as when a male bird treads the hen. And women softly stepping in unison.

And Kate, listening to the drums, and the full-throated singing, and watching the rich, soft bodies in the dance, thought to herself a little sceptically: Yes! For these it is easier. But all the white men, of the dominant race, what are they doing at this moment?

In the afternoon there was a great dance of the *Welcome of Quetzalcoatl.* Kate could only see a little of it, in front of the church.

The drums beat vigorously all the time, the dance wound strangely to the water's edge. Kate heard afterwards that the procession of women with baskets on their heads, filled with bread and fruits all wrapped in leaves, went down to the shore and loaded the boats. Then dancers and all got into the boats and *canoas,* and rowed to the island.

They made a feast on the island, and learned the dance of the *Welcome of Quetzalcoatl,* which they would dance every year on that day. And they learned the Song of the Welcome of Quetzalcoatl; which later on Cipriano brought to Kate, as she sat in that dim room with the unconscious woman, who made small, terrible, mechanical noises.

The doctor came hastening, and the priest came after a while. Neither could do anything. They came in the afternoon again, and Kate walked out and wandered on the half-deserted beach, looking at the flock of boats drawing near the island, and feeling that life was a more terrible issue even than death. One could die and have done. But living was never done, it could never be finished, and the responsibility could never be shifted.

She went back again to the sick-room, and with the aid of a

woman she undressed poor Carlota and put a nightdress on her. Another doctor came from the city. But the sick woman was dying. And Kate was alone with her again.

The men, where were they?

The business of living? Were they really gone about the great business of living, abandoning her here to this business of dying?

It was nightfall before she heard the drums returning. And again that deep, full, almost martial singing of men, savage and remote, to the sound of the drum. Perhaps after all life would conquer again, and men would be men, so that women could be women. Till men are men indeed, women have no hope to be women. She knew that fatally enough.

Cipriano came to her, smelling of sun and sweat, his face darkly glowing, his eyes flashing. He glanced at the bed, at the unconscious woman, at the medicine bottles.

"What do they say?" he asked.

"The doctors think she may come round."

"She will die," he said.

Then he went with her to the window.

"See!" he said. "This is what they are singing."

It was the Song-sheet of the *Welcome to Quetzalcoatl.*

WELCOME TO QUETZALCOATL

We are not wasted. We are not left out.
Quetzalcoatl has come!
There is nothing more to ask for.
Quetzalcoatl has come!

He drew the Fish in the boat.
The cock rose, and crew over the waters.
The naked one climbed in.
Quetzalcoatl has come!

Quetzalcoatl loves the shades of trees.
Give him trees! Call back the trees!
We are like trees, tall and rustling.
Quetzalcoatl is among the trees.

Do not tell me my face is shining.
Quetzalcoatl has come!
Over my head his noiseless eagle
Fans a flame.

Tie my spotted shoes for dancing,
The snake has kissed my heel.
Like a volcano my hips are moving.
With fire, and my throat is full.

Blue daylight sinks in my hair.
The star comes out between the two
Wonders, shines out of everywhere,
Saying without speech: Look you!

Ah, Quetzalcoatl!
Put sleep as black as beauty in the secret of my belly.
Put star-oil over me.
Call me a man.

Even as she read, she could hear the people outside singing it, as the reed-flutes unthreaded the melody time after time. This strange dumb people of Mexico was opening its voice at last. It was as if a stone had been rolled off them all, and she heard their voice for the first time, deep, wild, with a certain exultance and menace.

The naked one climbed in.
Quetzalcoatl has come!

She could hear the curious defiance and exultance in the men's voices. Then a woman's voice, clear almost as a star itself, went up the road at the verse:

Blue daylight sinks in my hair.
The star comes out between the two
Wonders. . . .

Strange! The people had opened hearts at last. They had rolled the stone of their heaviness away, a new world had begun. Kate was frightened. It was dusk. She laid her hand on Cipriano's knee, lost. And he leaned and put his dark hand against her cheek, breathing silently.

"To-day," he said softly, "we have done well."

She felt for his hand. All was so dark. But oh, so deep, so deep and beyond her, the vast, soft, living heat! So beyond her!

Put sleep so black as beauty in the secret of my belly.
Put star-oil over me.

She could almost feel her soul appealing to Cipriano for this sacrament.

They sat side by side in darkness, as the night fell, and he held his hand loosely on hers. Outside, the people were still singing. Some were dancing round the drum. On the church-towers, where the bells had been, there were fires flickering, and white forms of men, the noise of a heavy drum, then again, the chant. In the yard before the church doors a fire was blazing, and men of Huitzilopochtli stood watching two of their men, naked save for a breech-cloth and the scarlet feathers on their head, dancing the old spear-dance, whooping challenge in the firelight.

Ramón came in, in his white clothes. He pulled off his big hat, and stood looking down at Carlota. She no longer made noises, and her eyes were turned up horribly, showing the whites. Ramón closed his eyes a moment, and turned away, saying nothing. He came to the window, where Cipriano still sat in his impenetrable but living silence, that satisfied where all speech had failed, holding Kate's hand loosely. Nor did he let go her hand.

Ramón looked out, at the fires in the church towers, the fire before the church doors, the little fires on the beach by the lake; and the figures of men in white, the figures of women in dark rebozos, with full white skirts, the two naked dancers, the standing crowd, the occasional scarlet serapes of Huitzilopochtli, the white and blue of Quetzalcoatl, the creeping away of a motor-car, the running of boys, the men clustering round the drum, to sing.

"It is life," he said, "which is the mystery. Death is hardly mysterious in comparison."

There was a knocking. The doctor had come again, and a sister to nurse the dying woman. Softly the sister paced round the room and bent over her charge.

Cipriano and Kate went away in a boat over the dark lake, away from all the fires and the noise, into the deep darkness of the lake beyond, to Jamiltepec. Kate felt she wanted to be covered with deep and living darkness, the deeps where Cipriano could lay her.

> Put sleep as black as beauty in the secret of my belly.
> Put star-oil over me.

And Cipriano, as he sat in the boat with her, felt the inward sun rise darkly in him, diffusing through him; and felt the mys-

terious flower of her woman's femaleness slowly opening to him,
as a sea-anemone opens deep under the sea, with infinite soft
fleshliness. The hardness of self-will was gone, and the soft
anemone of her deeps blossomed for him of itself, far down
under the tides.

Ramón remained behind in the hotel, in the impenetrable sanctuary of his own stillness. Carlota remained unconscious.
There was a consultation of doctors; to no effect. She died at
dawn, before her boys could arrive from Mexico; as a *canoa* was
putting off from the shore with a little breeze, and the passengers
were singing the Song of Welcome to Quetzalcoatl, unexpectedly,
upon the pale water.

CHAPTER XXII

THE LIVING HUITZILOPOCHTLI

THEY buried Doña Carlota in Sayula, and Kate, though a woman, went also to the funeral. Don Ramón followed the coffin, in his white clothes and big hat with the Quetzalcoatl sign. His boys went with him; and there were many strangers, men, in black.

The boys looked odd young shoots, in their black suits with short breeches and bare knees. They were both round-faced and creamy-brown in complexion, both had a touch of fairness. The elder, Pedro, was more like Don Ramón; but his hair was softer, more fluffy than his father's, with a hint of brown. He was sulky and awkward, and kept his head ducked. The younger boy, Cyprian, had the fluffy, upstanding brown hair and the startled hazel eyes of his mother.

They had come in a motor-car with their aunt, from Guadalajara, and were returning straight to town. In her will, the mother had named guardians in place of the father, stating that the father would consent. And her considerable fortune she had left in trust for the boys. But the father was one of the trustees.

Ramón sat in his room in the hotel, overlooking the lake, and his two boys sat on the cane settee opposite him.

"What do you want to do, my sons?" said Ramón. "To go back with your Aunt Margarita, and return to school in the United States?"

The boys remained a while in sulky silence.

"Yes!" said Cyprian at last, his brown hair seeming to fluff up with indignation. "That is what our mother wished us to do. So, of course, we shall do it."

"Very well!" said Ramón quietly. "But remember I am your father, and my door, and my arms, and my heart will always be open to you, when you come."

The elder boy shuffled with his feet, and muttered, without looking up:

"We cannot come, papa!"

"Why not, child?"

The boy looked up at him with brown eyes as challenging as his own.

"You, papa, you call yourself the Living Quetzalcoatl?"

"Yes."

"But, papa, our father is called Ramón Carrasco."

"It is also true," said Ramón, smiling.

"We," said Pedro, rather heavily, "are not the children of the Living Quetzalcoatl, papa. We are Carrasco y de Lara."

"Good names both," said Ramón.

"Never," said the young Cyprian, his eyes flashing, "never can we love you, papa. You are our enemy. You killed our mother."

"No, no!" said Ramón. "That you must not say. Your mother sought her own death."

"Mama loved you much, much, much!" cried Cyprian, the tears rising to his eyes. "Always she loved you and prayed for you—" He began to cry.

"And I, my son?" said Ramón.

"You hated her and killed her! Oh, mama! Mama! Oh, mama! I want my mother!" he wept.

"Come to me, little one!" said Ramón softly, holding out his hands.

"No!" cried Cyprian, stamping his foot and flashing his eyes through his tears. "No! No!"

The elder boy hung his head and was crying too. Ramón had the little, perplexed frown of pain on his brow. He looked from side to side, as if for some issue. Then he gathered himself together.

"Listen, my sons," he said. "You also will be men; it will not be long. While you are little boys, you are neither men nor women. But soon, the change will come, and you will have to be men. And then you will know that a man must be a man. When his soul tells him to do a thing, he must do it. When you are men, you must listen carefully to your own souls, and be sure to be true. Be true to your own souls; there is nothing else for a man to do."

"Je m'en fiche de ton âme, mon père!" said Cyprian, with one of his flashes into French. It was a language he often spoke with his mother.

"That you may, my boy," said Ramón. "But I may not."

"Papa!" put in the elder boy. "Is your soul different from mama's soul?"

"Who knows?" said Ramón. "I understand it differently."

"Because mama always prayed for your soul."

"And I, in my way, pray for hers, child. If her soul comes back to me, I will take it into my heart."

"Mama's soul," said Cyprian, "will go straight into Paradise."

"Who knows, child! Perhaps the Paradise for the souls of the dead is the hearts of the living."

"I don't understand what you say."

"It is possible," said Ramón, "that even now the only Paradise for the soul of your mother is in my heart."

The two boys stared at him with open eyes.

"Never will I believe that," said Cyprian.

"Or it may be in *thy* heart," said Ramón. "Hast thou a place in *thy* heart for the soul of thy mother?"

The young Cyprian stared with bewildered hazel eyes.

"The soul of my mother goes direct to Paradise, because she is a saint," he asserted flatly.

"Which Paradise, my son?"

"The only one. Where God is."

"And where is that?"

There was a pause.

"In the sky," said Cyprian, stubbornly.

"It is very far and very empty. But I believe, my son, that the hearts of living men are the very middle of the sky. And there God is; and Paradise; inside the hearts of living men and women. And there the souls of the dead come to rest, there, at the very centre, where the blood turns and returns; that is where the dead sleep best."

There was a very blank pause.

"And wilt thou go on saying thou art the Living Quetzalcoatl?" said Cyprian.

"Surely! And when you are a little older, perhaps you will come to me and say it too."

"Never! Thou hast killed our mother, and we shall hate thee. When we are men we ought to kill thee."

"Nay, that is bombast, child! Why wilt thou listen only to servants and priests and people of that sort? Are they not thy inferiors, since thou art my son, and thy mother's son? Why dost thou take the talk of servants and inferiors into thy mouth?

Hast thou no room for the speech of brave men? Thou wilt not kill me, neither will thy brother. For I would not allow you, even if you wished it. And you do not wish it. Talk no more of this empty lackey-talk to me, Cyprian, for I will not hear it. Art thou already a little lackey, or a priest? Come, thou art vulgar. Thou art a little vulgarian. We had better speak English; or thy French. Castilian is too good a language to turn into this currish talk."

Ramón rose and went to the window to look out at the lake. The drums on the church were sounding for midday, when every man should glance at the sun, and stand silent with a little prayer.

The sun has climbed the hill, the day is on the downward slope.
Between the morning and the afternoon, stand I here with my soul, and lift it up.
My soul is heavy with sunshine, and steeped with strength.
The sunbeams have filled me like a honeycomb,
It is the moment of fulness,
And the top of the morning.

Ramón turned and repeated the midday verse to his boys. They listened in confused silence.

"Come!" he said. "Why are you confused? If I talked to you about your new boots, or ten pesos, you would not be confused. But if I speak of the sun and your own souls filled from the sun like honeycombs, you sulk. You had better go back to your school in America, to learn to be business men. You had better say to everybody: Oh, no! we have no father! Our mother died, but we never had a father. We are children of an immaculate conception, so we should make excellent business men."

"I shall be a priest," said Cyprian.

"And I a doctor," said Pedro.

"Very good! Very good! *Shall-be* is far from *am*, and to-morrow is another day. Come to me when your heart tells you to come. You are my little boys, whatever you say, and I shall stroke your hair and laugh at you. Come! Come here!"

He looked at them, and they dared not refuse to obey, his power was so much greater than theirs.

He took his eldest son in his arms and stroked his head.

"There!" he said. "Thou are my eldest son, and I am thy father, who calls himself The Living Quetzalcoatl. When they say: 'Is it thy father who calls himself The Living Quetzalcoatl?'

—say to them : 'Yes, he is my father.' And when they ask you what you think of such a father, say : 'I am young, and I do not understand him yet. But I do not judge my father without understanding him.' Wilt thou say that, my boy, Pedro, my son?" And Ramón stroked the boy's hair with the gentleness and tenderness which filled the child with a sort of awe.

"Yes, papa! I will say that," said the boy, relieved.

"It is well," said Ramón, laying his hand on the child's head for a moment, like a blessing.

Then he turned to the younger son.

"Come then," he said, "and let me stroke thy upstanding hair."

"If I love thee, I cannot love mama!" said Cyprian.

"Nay, is thy heart so narrow? Love not at all, if it makes thee petty."

"But I do not want to come to thee, papa."

"Then stay away, my son, and come when thou dost want it."

"I do not think thou lovest me, papa."

"Nay, when thou art an obstinate monkey, I love thee not. But when thy real manhood comes upon thee, and thou art brave and daring, rather than rash and impudent, then thou wilt be lovable. How can I love thee if thou are not lovable?"

"Mama always loved me."

"She called thee her own. I do not call thee mine own. Thou art thyself. When thou art lovable, I can love thee. When thou art rash and impudent, nay, I cannot. The mill will not spin when the wind does not blow."

The boys went away. Ramón watched them as they stood in their black clothes and bare knees upon the jetty, and his heart yearned over them.

"Ah, the poor little devils!" he said to himself. And then:

"But I can do no more than keep my soul like a castle for them, to be a stronghold to them when they need it—if ever they do."

These days Kate often sat by the lake shore, in the early light of the morning. Between the rains, the day came very clear, she could see every wrinkle in the great hills opposite, and the fold, or pass, through which a river came, away at Tuliapan, was so vivid to her she felt she had walked it. The red birds looked as if rains had freshened even their poppy-buds, and in the morning frogs were whirring.

But the world was somehow different; all different. No jingle

of bells from the church, no striking of the clock. The clock
was taken away.

And instead, the drums. At dawn, the heavy drum rolling its
sound on the air. Then the sound of the Dawn-Verse chanted
from the tower, in a strong man's voice:

> The dark is dividing, the sun is coming past the wall.
> Day is at hand.
> Lift your hand, say Farewell! say Welcome!
> Then be silent.
> Let the darkness leave you, let the light come into you,
> Man in the twilight.

The voice, and the great drum ceased. And in the dawn the
men who had risen stood silent, with arm uplifted, in the moment
of change, the women covered their faces and bent their heads.
All was changeless still for the moment of change.

Then the light drum rattled swiftly, as the first sparkle of the
bright sun flashed in sheer light from the crest of the great hills.
The day had begun. People of the world moved on their way.

At about nine o'clock the light drum rattled quickly, and the
voice in the tower cried:

"Half way! Half way up the slope of the morning!"

There was the heavy drum at noon, the light drum again at
about three o'clock, with the cry:

"Half way! Half way down the slope of afternoon."

And at sunset again, the great drum rolling, and the voice
crying:

> Leave off! Leave off! Leave off!
> Lift your hand, say Farewell! say Welcome!
> Man in the twilight.
> The sun is in the outer porch, cry to him: Thanks! Oh, thanks!
> Then be silent.
> You belong to the night.

And again in the sunset everywhere men stood with lifted faces
and hand, and women covered their faces and stood with bowed
heads, all was changeless still for the moment of change.

Then the lighter drums suddenly beat, and people moved on
into the night.

The world was different, different. The drums seemed to leave
the air soft and vulnerable, as if it were alive. Above all, no
clang of metal, during the moments of change.

> Metal for resistance.
> Drums for the beating heart.
> The heart ceases not.

This was one of Ramón's little verses.

Strange, the change that was taking place in the world. Always the air had a softer, more velvety silence, it seemed alive. And there were no hours. Dawn and noon and sunset, mid-morning, or the up-slope middle, and mid-afternoon, or the down-slope middle, this was the day, with the watches of the night. They began to call the four watches of the day the watch of the rabbit, the watch of the hawk, the watch of the turkey-buzzard and the watch of the deer. And the four quarters of the night were the watch of the frog, the watch of the fire-fly, the watch of the fish, the watch of the squirrel.

"I shall come for you," wrote Cipriano to her, "when the deer is thrusting his last foot towards the forest."

That meant, she knew, in the last quarter of the hours of the deer; something after five o'clock.

It was as if, from Ramón and Cipriano, from Jamiltepec and the lake region, a new world was unfolding, unrolling, as softly and subtly as twilight falling and removing the clutter of day. It was a soft, twilit newness slowly spreading and penetrating the world, even into the cities. Now, even in the cities the blue serapes of Quetzalcoatl were seen, and the drums were heard at the Hours, casting a strange mesh of twilight over the clash of bells and the clash of traffic. Even in the capital the big drum rolled again, and men, even men in city clothes, would stand still with uplifted faces and arm upstretched, listening for the noon-verse, which they knew in their hearts, and trying not to hear the clash of metal.

> Metal for resistance.
> Drums for the beating heart.

But it was a world of metal, and a world of resistance. Cipriano, strangely powerful with the soldiers, in spite of the hatred he roused in other officials, was for meeting metal with metal. For getting Montes to declare: The Religion of Quetzalcoatl is the religion of Mexico, official and declared.—Then backing up the declaration with the army.

But no! no! said Ramón. Let it spread of itself. And wait awhile, till you can be declared the living Huitzilopochtli, and

your men can have the red and black blanket, with the snake-curve. Then perhaps we can have the open wedding with Caterina, and she will be a mother among the gods.

All the time, Ramón tried as far as possible to avoid arousing resistance and hate. He wrote open letters to the clergy, saying:

"Who am I, that I should be enemy of the One Church? I am catholics of catholics. I would have One Church of all the world, with Rome for the Central City, if Rome wish.

"But different peoples must have different Saviours, as they have different speech and different colour. The final mystery is one mystery. But the manifestations are many.

"God must come to Mexico in a blanket and in huaraches, else He is no God of the Mexicans, they cannot know Him. Naked, all men are but men. But the touch, the look, the word that goes from one naked man to another is the mystery of living. We live by manifestations.

"And men are fragile, and fragments, and strangely grouped in their fragmentariness. The invisible God has done it to us, darkened some faces and whitened others, and grouped us in groups, even as the zopilote is a bird, and the parrot of the hot lands is a bird, and the little oriole is a bird. But the angel of the zopilotes must be a zopilote, and the angel of the parrots a parrot. And to one, the dead carcase will ever smell good; to the other, the fruit.

"Priests who will come to me do not forsake either faith or God. They change their manner of speech and vestments, as the peon calls with one cry to the oxen, and with another cry to the mules. Each responds to its own call in its own way——"

To the socialists and agitators he wrote:

"What do you want? Would you make all men as you are? And when every peon in Mexico wears an American suit of clothes and shiny black shoes, and looks for life in the newspaper and for his manhood to the government, will you be satisfied? Did the government, then, give you your manhood, that you expect it to give it to these others?

"It is time to forget. It is time to put away the grudge and the pity. No man was ever the better for being pitied, every man is the worse for a grudge.

"We can do nothing with life, except live it.

"Let us seek life where it is to be found. And, having found it, life will solve the problems. But every time we deny the

living life, in order to solve a problem, we cause ten problems to spring up where was one before. Solving the problems of the people, we lose the people in a poisonous forest of problems.

"Life makes, and moulds, and changes the problem. The problem will always be there, and will always be different. So nothing can be solved, even by life and living, for life dissolves and resolves, solving it leaves alone.

"Therefore we turn to life; and from the clock to the sun and the stars, and from metal to membrane.

"This way we hope the problem will dissolve, since it can never be solved. When men seek life first, they will not seek land nor gold. The lands will lie on the lap of the gods, where men lie. And if the old communal system comes back, and the village and the land are one, it will be very good. For truly, no man can possess lands.

"But when we are deep in a bog, it is no use attempting to gallop. We can only wade out with toil. And in our haste to have a child, it is no good tearing the babe from the womb.

"Seek life, and life will bring the change.

"Seek life itself, even pause at dawn and at sunset, and life will come back into us and prompt us through the transitions.

"Lay forcible hands on nothing, only be ready to resist, if forcible hands should be laid on you. For the new shoots of life are tender, and better ten deaths than that they should be torn or trampled down by the bullies of the world. When it comes to fighting for the tender shoots of life, fight as the jaguar fights for her young, as the she-bear for her cubs.

"That which is life is vulnerable, only metal is invulnerable. Fight for the vulnerable unfolding of life. But for that, fight never to yield."

Cipriano, too, was always speaking to his soldiers, always with the same cry:

"We are men! We are fighters!

"But what can we do?

"Shall we march to simple death?

"No! No! We must march to life.

"The gringos are here. We have let them come. We must let them stay, for we cannot drive them out. With guns and swords and bayonets we can never drive them out, for they have a thousand where we have one. And if they come in peace, let them stay in peace.

"But we have not lost Mexico yet. We have not lost each other.

"We are the blood of America. We are the blood of Montezuma.

"What is my hand for? Is it to turn the handle of a machine alone?

"My hand is to salute the God of Mexicans, beyond the sky.

"My hand is to touch the hand of a brave man.

"My hand is to hold a gun.

"My hand is to make the corn grow out of the ground.

"What are my knees for?

"My knees are to hold me proud and erect.

"My knees are for marching on my way.

"My knees are the knees of a man.

"Our god is Quetzalcoatl of the blue sky, and Huitzilopochtli red at the gates, watching.

"Our gods hate a kneeling man. They shout *Ho! Erect!*

"Then what can we do?

"Wait!

"I am a man, naked inside my clothes as you are.

"Am I a big man? Am I a tall and powerful man, from Tlascala, for example?

"I am not. I am little. I am from the south. I am small—

"Yet am I not your general?

"Why?

"Why am I a general, and you only soldiers?

"I will tell you.

"I found the other strength.

"There are two strengths; the strength which is the strength of oxen and mules and iron, of machines and guns, and of men who cannot get the second strength.

"Then there is the second strength. It is the strength you want. And you can get it, whether you are small or big. It is the strength that comes from behind the sun. And you can get it; you can get it here!"—he struck his breast—"and here!"—he struck his belly—"and here!"—he struck his loins. "The strength that comes from back of the sun."

When Cipriano was roused, his eyes flashed, and it was as if dark feathers, like pinions, were starting out of him, out of his shoulders and back, as if these dark pinions clashed and flashed like a roused eagle. His men seemed to see him, as by second sight, with the demonish clashing, and dashing of wings,

like an old god. And they murmured, their eyes flashing:

"It is Cipriano! It is he! We are Ciprianistos, we are his children."

"We are men! We are men!" cried Cipriano.

"But listen. There are two kinds of men. There are men with the second strength, and men without it.

"When the first gringos came, we lost our second strength. And the padres taught us: Submit! Submit!

"The gringos had got the second strength!

"How?

"Like cunning ones, they stole it on the sly. They kept very still, like a tarantula in his hole. Then when neither sun nor moon nor stars knew he was there, Biff!—the tarantula sprang across, and bit, and left the poison and sucked the secret.

"So they got the secrets of the air and the water, and they got the secrets out of the earth. So the metals were theirs, and they made guns and machines and ships, and they made trains and telegrams and radio.

"Why? Why did they make all these things? How could they do it?

"Because, by cunning, they had got the secret of the second strength, which comes from behind the sun.

"And we had to be slaves, because we had only got the first strength, we had lost the second strength.

"Now we are getting it back. We have found our way again to the secret sun behind the sun. There sat Quetzalcoatl, and at last Don Ramón found him. There sits the red Huitzilopochtli, and I have found him. For I have found the second strength.

"When he comes, all you who strive shall find the second strength.

"And when you have it, where will you feel it?

"Not here!"—and he struck his forehead. "Not where the cunning gringos have it, in the head, and in their books. Not we. We are men, we are not spiders.

"We shall have it here!"—he struck his breast—"and here!" —he struck his belly—"and here!"—he struck his loins.

"Are we men? Can we not get the second strength? Can we not? Have we lost it forever?

"I say no! Quetzalcoatl is among us. I have found the red Huitzilopochtli. The second strength!

"When you walk or sit, when you work or lie down, when you eat or sleep, think of the second strength, that you must have it.

"Be very quiet. It is shy as a bird in a dark tree.

"Be very clean, clean in your bodies and your clothes. It is like a star, that will not shine in dirt.

"Be very brave, and do not drink till you are drunk, nor soil yourself with bad women, nor steal. Because a drunken man has lost his second strength, and a man loses his strength in bad women, and a thief is a coward, and the red Huitzilopochtli hates a coward.

"Try! Try for the second strength. When we have it, the others will lose it."

Cipriano struggled hard with his army. The curse of any army is the having nothing to do. Cirpriano made all his men cook and wash for themselves, clean and paint the barracks, make a great garden to grow vegetables, and plant trees wherever there was water. And he himself took a passionate interest in what they did. A dirty tunic, a sore foot, a badly-made huarache did not escape him. But even when they cooked their meals he went among them.

"Give me something to eat," he would say. "Give me an enchilada!"

Then he praised the cooking, or said it was bad.

Like all savages, they liked doing small things. And, like most Mexicans, once they were a little sure of what they were doing, they loved doing it well.

Cipriano was determined to get some discipline into them. Discipline is what Mexico needs, and what the whole world needs. But it is the discipline from the inside that matters. The machine discipline, from the outside, breaks down.

He had the wild Indians from the north beat their drums in the barracks-yard, and start the old dances again. The dance, the dance which has meaning, is a deep discipline in itself. The old Indians of the north still have the secret of animistic dancing. They dance to gain power; power over the *living* forces or potencies of the earth. And these dances need intense dark concentration, and immense endurance.

Cipriano encouraged the dances more than anything. He learned them himself, with curious passion. The shield and spear dance, the knife dance, the dance of ambush and the surprise

dance, he learned them in the savage villages of the north, and he danced them in the barracks-yard, by the bonfire, at night, when the great doors were shut.

Then, naked save for a black breech-cloth, his body smeared with oil and red earth-powder, he would face some heavy naked Indian and with shield and spear dance the dance of the two warriors, champions in the midst of the dense ring of soldiers. And the silent, rhythmic concentration of this duel in subtlety and rapidity kept the feet softly beating with the drum, the naked body suave and subtle, circling with sauve, primitive stealth, then crouching and leaping like a panther, with the spear poised, to a clash of shields, parting again with the crowning yell of defiance and exultance.

In this dance, no one was more suave and sudden than Cipriano. He could swerve along the ground with bent, naked back, as invisible as a lynx, circling round his opponent, his feet beating and his suave body subtly lilting to the drum. Then in a flash he was in the air, his spear pointing down at the collar-bone of his enemy and gliding over his shoulder, as the opponent swerved under, and the war-yell resounded. The soldiers in the deep circle watched, fascinated, uttering the old low cries.

And as the dance went on, Cipriano felt his strength increase and surge inside him. When all his limbs were glistening with sweat, and his spirit was at last satisfied, he was at once tired and sur-charged with extraordinary power. Then he would throw his scarlet and dark serape around him, and motion other men to fight, giving his spear and shield to another officer or soldier, going himself to sit down on the ground and watch, by the firelight. And then he felt his limbs and his whole body immense with power, he felt the black mystery of power go out of him over all his soldiers. And he sat there imperturbable, in silence, holding all those black-eyed men in splendour of his own, silent self. His own dark consciousness seemed to radiate through their flesh and their bones, they were conscious, not through themselves but through him. And as a man's instinct is to shield his own head, so that instinct was to shield Cipriano, for he was the most precious part of themselves to them. It was in him they were supreme. They got their splendour from his power and their greatest consciousness was his consciousness diffusing them.

"I am not of myself," he would say to them. "I am of the red Huitzilopochtli and the power from behind the sun. And you

are not of yourselves. Of yourselves you are nothing. You are of me, my men."

He encouraged them to dance naked, with the breech-cloth, to rub themselves with the red earth-powder, over the oil.

"This is the oil of the stars. Rub it well into your limbs and you will be strong as the starry sky. This is the red blood of volcanoes. Rub yourself with it, you will have the power of the fire of the volcanoes, from the centre of the earth."

He encouraged them to dance the silent, concentrated dances to the drum, to dance for hours, gathering power and strength.

"If you know how to tread the dance, you can tread deeper and deeper till you touch the middle of the earth with your foot. And when you touch the middle of the earth, you will have such power in your belly and your breast, no man will be able to overcome you. Get the second strength. Get it, get it out of the earth, get it from behind the sun. Get the second strength."

He made long, rapid marches across the wild Mexican country, and through the mountains, moving light and swift. He liked to have his men camping in the open, with no tents; but the watch set, and the stars overhead. He pursued the bandits with swift movements. He stripped his captives and tied them up. But if it seemed a brave man, he would swear him in. If it seemed to him a knave, a treacherous cur, he stabbed him to the heart, saying:

"I am the red Huitzilopochtli, of the knife."

Already he had got his own small, picked body of men out of the ignominious drab uniform, dressed in white with the scarlet sash and the scarlet ankle cords, and carrying the good red and black serape. And his men must be clean. On the march they would stop by some river, with the order for every man to strip and wash, and wash his clothing. Then the men, dark and ruddy, moved about naked, while the white clothing of strong white cotton dried on the earth. They moved on again, glittering with the peculiar whiteness of cotton clothes in Mexico, gun at their backs, serape and small pack on their backs, wearing the heavy straw hats with the scarlet crowns on their heads.

"They must move!" he said to his officers. "They must learn again to move swiftly and untiringly, with the old power. They must not lie about. In the sleep hours, let them sleep. In the waking, let them work, or march, or drill, or dance."

He divided his regiment up into little companies of a hundred

each, with a centurion and a sergeant in command. Each company of a hundred must learn to act in perfect unison, freely and flexibly. "Perfect your hundred," Cipriano insisted, "and I will perfect your thousands and your tens of thousands."

"Listen!" he said. "For us, no trench and cannon warfare. My men are no cannon-fodder, nor trench-dung. Where cannon are, we move away. Our hundreds break up, and we attack where the cannon are not. That we are swift, that we are silent, that we have no burdens, and that the second strength is in us: that is all. We intend to put up no battle-front, but to attack at our own moment, and at a thousand points."

And always he reiterated:

"If you can get the power from the heart of the earth, and the power from behind the sun; if you can summon the power of the red Huitzilopochtli into you, nobody can conquer you. Get the second strength."

Ramón was pressing Cipriano now openly to assume the living Huitzilopochtli.

"Come!" he said. "It is time you let General Viedma be swallowed up in the red Huitzilopochtli. Don't you think?"

"If I know what it means," said Cipriano.

They were sitting on the mast in Ramón's room, in the heat before the rain came, towards the end of the rainy season.

"Stand up!" said Ramón.

Cipriano stood up at once, with that soft, startling alertness in his movement.

Ramón came quickly to him, placed one of his hands over Cipriano's eyes, closing them. Ramón stood behind Cipriano, who remained motionless in the warm dark, his consciousness reeling in strange concentric waves, towards a centre where it suddenly plunges into the bottomless deeps, like sleep.

"Cipriano?"—the voice sounded so far off.

"Yes."

"Is it dark?"

"It is dark."

"Is it alive? Is the darkness alive?"

"Surely it is alive."

"Who lives?"

"I."

"Where?"

"I know not. In the living darkness."

Ramón then bound Cipriano's eyes and head with a strip of black fur. Then again, with a warm, soft pressure, he pressed one naked hand over Cipriano's naked breast, and one between his shoulders. Cipriano stood in profound darkness, erect and silent.

"Cipriano?"

"Yes."

"Is it dark in your heart?"

"It is coming dark."

Ramón felt the thud of the man's heart slowly slackening. In Cipriano, another circle of darkness had started slowly to revolve, from his heart. It swung in widening rounds, like a greater sleep.

"Is it dark?"

"It is dark."

"Who lives?"

"I."

Ramón bound Cipriano's arms at his sides, with a belt of fur round the breast. Then he put his one hand over the navel, his other hand in the small of the other man's back, pressing with slow, warm, powerful pressure.

"Cipriano?"

"Yes."

The voice and the answer going farther and farther away.

"Is it dark?"

"No, my Lord."

Ramón knelt and pressed his arms close round Cipriano's waist, pressing his black head against his side. And Cipriano began to feel as if his mind, his head were melting away in the darkness, like a pearl in black wine, the other circle of sleep began to swing, vast. And he was a man without a head, moving like a dark wind over the face of the dark waters.

"Is it perfect?"

"It is perfect."

"Who lives?"

"Who—!"

Cipriano no longer knew.

Ramón bound him fast round the middle, then, pressing his head against the hip, folded the arms round Cipriano's loins, closing with his hands the secret places.

"Cipriano?"

"Yes."

"Is it all dark?"

But Cipriano could not answer. The last circle was sweeping round, and the breath upon the waters was sinking into the waters, there was no more utterance. Ramón kneeled with pressed head and arms and hands, for some moments still. Then he bound the loins, binding the wrists to the hips.

Cipriano stood rigid and motionless. Ramón clasped the two knees with his hands, till they were warm, and he felt them dark and asleep like two living stones, or two eggs. Then swiftly he bound them together, and grasped the ankles, as one might grasp the base of a young tree as it emerges from the earth. Crouching on the earth, he gripped them in an intense grip, resting his head on the feet. The moments passed, and both men were unconscious.

Then Ramón bound the ankles, lifted Cipriano suddenly, with a sleep-moving softness, laid him on the skin of a big mountain-lion, which was spread upon the blankets, threw over him the red and black serape of Huitzilopochtli, and lay down at his feet, holding Cipriano's feet to his own abdomen.

And both men passed into perfect unconsciousness, Cipriano within the womb of undisturbed creation, Ramón in the death sleep.

How long they were both dark, they never knew. It was twilight. Ramón was suddenly aroused by the jerking of Cipriano's feet. He sat up, and took the blanket off Cipriano's face.

"Is it night?" said Cipriano.

"Almost night," said Ramón.

Silence followed, while Ramón unfastened the bonds, beginning at the feet. Before he unbound the eyes, he closed the window, so the room was almost dark. Then he unfastened the last binding, and Cipriano sat up, looking, then suddenly covering his eyes.

"Make it quite dark!" he said.

Ramón closed the shutters, and the room was complete night. Then he returned and sat on the mats by Cipriano. Cipriano was asleep again. After a while, Ramón left him.

He did not see him again till dawn. Then Ramón found him going down to the lake, to swim. The two men swam together,

while the sun rose. With the rain, the lake was colder. They went to the house to rub oil in their limbs.

Cipriano looked at Ramón with black eyes which seemed to be looking at all space.

"I went far," he said.

"To where there is no beyond?" said Ramón.

"Yes, there."

And in a moment or two, Cipriano was wrapped in his blanket again, and asleep.

He did not wake till the afternoon. Then he ate, and took a boat, and rowed down the lake to Kate. He found her at home. She was surprised to see him, in his white clothes and with his serape of Huitzilopochtli.

"I am going to be the living Huitzilopochtli," he said.

"Are you? When? Does it feel queer?"—Kate was afraid of his eyes, they seemed inhuman.

"On Thursday. The day of Huitzilopochtli is to be Thursday. Won't you sit beside me, and be wife of me when I am as god?"

"But do you feel you *are* a god?" she asked, querulous.

He turned his eyes on her strangely.

"I have been," he said. "And I have come back. But I belong there, where I went.

"Where?"

"Where there is no beyond, and the darkness sinks into the water, and waking and sleeping are one thing."

"No," said Kate, afraid. "I never understood mystical things. They make me uneasy."

"Is it mystical when I come in to you?"

"No," said Kate. "Surely that is physical."

"So is the other, only further. Won't you be the bride of Huitzilopochtli?" he asked again.

"Not so soon," said Kate.

"Not so soon!" he re-echoed.

There was a pause.

"Will you come back with me to Jamiltepec now?" he asked.

"Not now," she said.

"Why not now?"

"Oh, I don't know.—You treat me as if I had no life of my own," she said. "But I have."

"A life of your own? Who gave it you? Where did you get it?"

"I don't know. But I have got it. And I must live it. I can't be just swallowed up."

"Why, Malintzi?" he said, giving her a name. "Why can't you?"

"Be just swallowed up?" she said. "Well, I just can't."

"I am the living Huitzilopochtli," he said. "And I am swallowed up. I thought, so you could be, Malintzi."

"No! Not quite?" she said.

"Not quite! Not quite! Not just now! How often you say *Not*, to-day!—I must go back to Ramón."

"Yes. Go back to him. You only care about him, and your living Quetzalcoatl and your living Huitzilopochtli.—I am only a woman."

"No, Malintzi, you are more. You are more than Kate, you are Malintzi."

"I am not! I am only Kate, and I am only a woman. I mistrust all that other stuff."

"I am more than just a man, Malintzi.—Don't you see that?"

"No!" said Kate. "I don't see it. Why *should* you be more than just a man?"

"Because I am the living Hutizilopochtli. Didn't I tell you? You've got dust in your mouth to-day, Malintzi."

He went away, leaving her rocking in anger on her terrace, in love again with her old self, and hostile to the new thing. She was thinking of London and Paris and New York, and all the people there.

"Oh!" she cried to herself, stifling. "For heaven's sake let me get out of this, and back to simple human people. I loathe the very sound of Quetzalcoatl and Huitzilopochtli. I would die rather than be mixed up in it any more. Horrible, really, both Ramón and Cipriano. And they want to put it over me, with their high-flown bunk, and their Malintzi. Malintzi! I am Kate Forrester, really. I am neither Kate Leslie nor Kate Tylor. I am sick of these men putting names over me. I was born Kate Forrester, and I shall die Kate Forrester. I want to go home. Loathsome, really, to be called Malintzi.—I've had it put over me."

CHAPTER XXIII

HUITZILOPOCHTLI'S NIGHT

THEY had the Huitzilopochtli ceremony at night, in the wide yard in front of the church. The guard of Huitzilopochtli, in serapes of black, red and yellow stripes, striped like tigers or wasps, stood holding torches of blazing ocote. A tall bonfire was built, but unkindled, in the centre of the yard.

In the towers where the bells had been, fires were blazing and the heavy drum of Huitzilopochtli went rolling its deep, sinister notes. It had been sounding all the while since the sun went down.

The crowd gathered under the trees, outside the gates in front of the church. The church doors were closed.

There was a bang of four firework cannons exploding simultaneously, then four rockets shot up into the sky, leaning in the four directions, and exploding in showers of red, green, white and yellow.

The church doors opened, and Cipriano appeared, in his brilliant serape of Huitzilopochtli, and with three green parrot feathers erect on his brow. He was carrying a torch. He stooped and lit the big bonfire, then plucked out four blazing brands, and tossed them to four of his men, who stood waiting, naked save for their black breech-cloths. The men caught the brands as they flew, and ran in the four directions, to kindle the four bonfires that waited, one in each corner of the yard.

The guard had taken off their blankets and blouses, and were naked to the red sash. The lighter drum began to beat for the dance, and the dance began, the half-naked men throwing their blazing torches whirling in the air, catching them as they came down, dancing all the while. Cipriano, in the centre, threw up brand after brand from the fire.

Now that he was stripped of his blanket, his body was seen painted in horizontal bars of red and black, while from his mouth went a thin green line, and from his eyes a band of yellow.

The five fires, built hollow of little towers of ocote faggots, sent pure flame in a rush up to the dark sky, illuminating the dancing men, who sang in deep voices as they danced.

371

The fires rushed rapidly upwards in flame. The drum beat without ceasing. And the men of Huitzilopochtli danced on, like demons. Meanwhile the crowd sat in the old Indian silence, their black eyes glittering in the firelight. And gradually the fires began to die down, the white façade of the church, that had danced also to the yellow flames, began to go bluish above, merging into the night, rose-coloured below, behind the dark shapes that danced to the sinking fires.

Suddenly the dance ceased, the men threw their serapes around them, and sat down. Little ocote fires upon the cane tripods flickered here and there, in a silence that lasted for some minutes. Then the drum sounded, and a man began to sing, in a clear, defiant voice, the *First Song of Huitzilopochtli:*

> I am Huitzilopochtli,
> The Red Huitzilopochtli,
> The blood-red.
>
> I am Huitzilopochtli,
> Yellow of the sun,
> Sun in the blood.
>
> I am Huitzilopochtli,
> White of the bone,
> Bone in the blood.
>
> I am Huitzilopochtli,
> With a blade of grass between my teeth.
>
> I am Huitzilopochtli, sitting in the dark.
> With my redness staining the body of the dark.
>
> I watch by the fire.
> I wait behind men.
>
> In the stillness of my night
> The cactus sharpens his thorn.
> The grass feels with his roots for the other sun.
>
> Deeper than the roots of the mango tree
> Down in the centre of the earth
> Is the yellow, serpent-yellow shining of my sun.
>
> Oh, beware of him!
> Oh, beware of me!
> Who runs athwart my serpent-flame
> Gets bitten and must die.

I am the sleeping and waking
Of the anger of the manhood of men.
I am the leaping and quaking
Of fire bent back again.

The song came to an end. There was a pause. Then all the
men of Huitzilopochtli took it up again, changing the "I" into
"He."

He is Huitzilopochtli,
The Red Huitzilopochtli,
The blood-red.

He is Huitzilopochtli,
Yellow of the sun,
Sun in the blood.

He is Huitzilopochtli,
White of the bone,
Bone in the blood.

He is Huitzilopochtli,
With a blade of green grass between his teeth.

He is Huitzilopochtli, sitting in the dark,
With his redness staining the body of the night.

He is watching by the fire.
Waiting behind men.

In the stillness of his night
Cactuses sharpen their thorns.
Grass feels downwards with his roots.

Deeper than the roots of the mango tree
Down in the centre of the earth
Shines the yellow, serpent-yellow shining of the sun.

Oh, men, take care, take care!
Take care of him and it.
Nor run aslant his rays.
Who is bitten, dies.

He is Huitzilopochtli, sleeping or waking
Serpent in the bellies of men.

Huitzilopochtli, leaping and quaking
Fire of the passion of men.

The big fires had all died down. Only the little flames on the
tripods lit up the scene with a ruddy glow. The guard withdrew
to the outer wall of the yard, holding bayonets erect. The big
drum was going alone, slowly.

The yard was now a clear space, with the glowing red heaps of
the bonfires, and the ocote flames flapping. And now was seen
a platform erected against the white wall of the church.

In the silence the big doors of the church opened, and Cipriano
came out, in his bright serape, holding in his hand a bunch of
black leaves, or feathers, and with a tuft of scarlet feathers,
black-tipped, rising from the back of his head. He mounted the
platform and stood facing the crowd, the light of a torch on his
face and on the brilliant feathers that rose like flames from the
back of his head.

After him came a strange procession: a peon in floppy white
clothes, led prisoner between two of the guards of Huitzilopochtli:
who wore their serapes with red and black and yellow and white
and green stripes; then another peon prisoner: then another: in
all, five, the fifth one tall, limping, and with a red cross painted on
the breast of his white jacket. Last of all came a woman-prisoner,
likewise between two guards, her hair flowing loose, over a red
tunic.

They mounted the platform. The peons, prisoners, were placed
in a row, their guards behind them. The limping peon was apart,
with his two guards behind him: the woman again was apart, her
two guards behind her.

The big drum ceased, and a bugle rang out, a long, loud triumphant note, repeated three times. Then the kettle-drums, or
the small tom-toms like kettle-drums, rattled fierce as hail.

Cipriano lifted his hand, and there was silence.

Out of the silence he began to speak, in his short, martial
sentences:

> Man that is man is more than a man.
> No more is man till he is more than a man.
> Till the power is in him
> Which is not his own.
>
> The power is in me from behind the sun,
> And from middle earth.

I am Huitzilopochtli.
I am dark as the sunless under-earth,
And yellow as the fire that consumes,
And white as bone,
And red as blood.

But I touched the hand of Quetzalcoatl.
And between our fingers rose a blade of green grass.
I touched the hand of Quetzalcoatl.
Lo! I am lord of the watches of the night
And the dream of the night rises from me like a red feather.

I am the watcher, and master of the dream.
In the dream of the night I see the grey dogs prowling.
Prowling to devour the dream.

In the night the soul of a coward creeps out of him
Like a grey dog whose mouth is foul with rabies,
Creeping among the sleeping and the dreaming, who are lapped in my
    dark,
And in whom the dream sits up like a rabbit, lifting long ears tipped
    with night,
On the dream-slopes browsing like a deer in the dusk.

In the night I see the grey dogs creeping, out of the sleeping men
Who are cowards, who are liars, who are traitors, who have no
    dreams
That prick their ears like a rabbit, or browse in the dark like deer,
But whose dreams are dogs, grey dogs with yellow mouths.

From the liars, from the thieves, from the false and treacherous and
    mean
I see the grey dogs creeping out, where my deer are browsing in the
    dark.
Then I take my knife, and throw it upon the grey dog.
And lo! it sticks between the ribs of a man!
The house of the grey dog!

Beware! Beware!
Of the men and the women who walk among you.
You know not how many are houses of grey dogs.
Men that seem harmless, women with fair words,
Maybe they kennel the grey dog.

The drums began to beat and the singer began to sing, clear
and pure:

THE SONG OF THE GREY DOG

When you sleep and know it not
The grey dog creeps among you.
In your sleep, you twist, your soul hurts you.
The grey dog is chewing your entrails.

Then call on Huitzilopochtli:
The grey dog caught me at the cross-roads
As I went down the road to sleep
And crossed the road of the uneasy.

The grey dog leapt at my entrails.
Huitzilopochtli, call him off.
Lo! the Great One answers. *Track him down!*
Kill him in his unclean house.

Down the road of the uneasy
You track the grey dog home
To his house in the heart of a traitor,
A thief, a murderer of dreams.

And you kill him there with one stroke,
Crying: *Huitzilopochtli, is this well done?*
That your sleep be not as a cemetery
Where dogs creep unclean.

The song ceased, and there was silence. Then Cipriano beckoned to the men to bring forward the peon with the black cross painted on his front and back. He limped forward.

Cipriano: What man is that, limping?

Guards: It is Guillermo, overseer of Don Ramón, who betrayed Don Ramón, his master.

Cipriano: Why does he limp?

Guards: He fell from the window on to the rocks.

Cipriano: What made him wish to betray his master?

Guards: His heart is a grey dog, and a woman, a grey bitch, enticed him forth.

Cipriano: What woman enticed the grey dog forth?

The guards came forward with the woman.

Guards: This woman, Maruca, my Lord, with the grey bitch heart.

Cipriano: Is it she, indeed?

Guards: It is she.

Cipriano: The grey dog, and the grey bitch, we kill, for their
 mouths are yellow with poison? Is it well, men of Hutizilopochtli?

Guards: It is very well, my Lord.

The guards stripped the peon Guillermo of his white clothes,
leaving him naked, in a grey loin-cloth, with a grey-white cross
painted on his naked breast. The woman, too, had a grey-white
cross painted on her body. She stood in a short petticoat of
grey wool.

Cipriano: The grey dog, and the grey bitch shall run no more
 about the world. We will bury their bodies in quick-lime,
 till their souls are eaten, and their bodies, and nothing is
 left. For lime is the thirsty bone that swallows even a soul
 and is not slaked.—Bind them with the grey cords, put ash
 on their heads.

The guards quickly obeyed. The prisoners, ash-grey, gazed
with black, glittering eyes, making not a sound. A guard stood
behind each of them. Cipriano gave a sign, and quick as lightning
the guards had got the throats of the two victims in a grey cloth,
and with a sharp jerk had broken their necks, lifting them backwards in one movement. The grey cloths they tied hard and
tight round the throats, laying the twitching bodies on the floor.

Cipriano turned to the crowd:

> The Lords of Life are the Masters of Death.
> Blue is the breath of Quetzalcoatl.
> Red is Huitzilopochtli's blood.
> But the grey dog belongs to the ash of the world.
> The Lords of Life are the Masters of Death.
> Dead are the grey dogs.
> Living are the Lords of Life.
> Blue is the deep sky and the deep water.
> Red is the blood and the fire.
> Yellow is the flame.
> The bone is white and alive.
> The hair of night is dark over our faces.
> But the grey dogs are among the ashes.
> The Lords of Life are the Masters of Death.

Then, he turned once more, to the other, imprisoned peons.

Cipriano: Who are these four?

Guards: Four who came to kill Don Ramón.

Cipriano: Four men, against one man?

Guards: They were more than four, my Lord.

Cipriano: When many men come against one, what is the name of the many?

Guards: Cowards, my Lord.

Cipriano: Cowards it is. They are less than men. Men that are less than men are not good enough for the light of the sun. If men that are men will live, men that are less than men must be put away, lest they multiply too much. Men that are more than men have the judgment of men that are less than men. Shall they die?

Guards: They shall surely die, my Lord.

Cipriano: Yet my hand has touched the hand of Quetzalcoatl, and among the black leaves one sprung green, with the colour of Malintzi.

An attendant came and lifted Cipriano's serape over his head, leaving his body bare to the waist. The guards likewise took off their serapes.

Cipriano lifted up his fist, in which he held a little tuft of black feathers, or leaves.

Then he said slowly:

Huitzilopochtli gives the black blade of death.
Take it bravely.
Take death bravely.
Go bravely across the border, admitting your mistake.

Determine to go on and on, till you enter the Morning Star.
Quetzalcoatl will show you the way.
Malintzi of the green dress will open the door.
In the fountain you will lie down.
If you reach the fountain, and lie down
And the fountain covers your face, forever,
You will have departed forever from your mistake.

And the man that is more than a man in you
Will wake at last from the clean forgetting
And stand up, and look about him,
Ready again for the business of being a man.

But Huitzilopochtli touched the hand of Quetzalcoatl
And one green leaf sprang among the black.
The green leaf of Malintzi
Who pardons once, and no more.

Cipriano turned to the four peons. He held out his fist with the four black twigs, to the first. This first one, a little man, peered at the leaves curiously.

"There is no green one," he said sceptically.

"Good!" said Cipriano. "Then receive a black."

And he handed him a black leaf.

"I knew it," said the man, and threw the leaf away with contempt and defiance.

The second man drew a black leaf. He stood gazing at it, as if fascinated, turning it round.

The third man drew a leaf whose lower half was green.

"See!" said Cipriano. "The green leaf of Malintzi!"

And he handed the last black leaf to the last man.

"Have I got to die?" said the last man.

"Yes."

"I don't want to die, *Patrón*."

"You played with death, and it has sprung upon you."

The eyes of the three men were blindfolded with black cloths, their blouses and pantaloons were taken away. Cipriano took a bright, thin dagger.

"The Lords of Life are Masters of Death," he said in a loud, clear voice.

And swift as lightning he stabbed the blindfolded men to the heart, with three swift, heavy stabs. Then he lifted the red dagger and threw it down.

"The Lords of Life are Masters of Death," he repeated.

The guards lifted the bleeding bodies one by one, and carried them into the church. There remained only the one prisoner, with the green leaf.

"Put the green leaf of Malintzi between his brows; for Malintzi pardons once, and no more," said Cipriano.

"Yes, my Lord!" replied the guard.

And they led the man away into the church.

Cipriano followed, the last of his guard after him.

In a few minutes the drums began to beat and men came slowly streaming into the church. Women were not admitted. All the interior was hung with red and black banners. At the side of the chancel was a new idol: a heavy, seated figure of Huitzilopochtli, done in black lava stone. And round him burned twelve red candles. The idol held the bunch of black strips, or leaves in his hand. And at his feet lay the five dead bodies.

The fire on the altar was flickering high, to the dark statue of Quetzalcoatl. On his little throne Ramón sat, wearing his blue and white colours of Quetzalcoatl. There was another corresponding throne next him, but it was empty. Six of the guard of Quetzalcoatl stood by Ramón: but Huitzilopochtli's side of the chancel was empty save for the dead.

The hard drums of Huitzilopochtli were beating incessantly outside, with a noise like madness. Inside was the soft roll of the drum of Quetzalcoatl. And the men from the crowd outside thronged slowly in, between the guard of Quetzalcoatl.

A flute sounded the summons to close the doors. The drums of Quetzalcoatl ceased, and from the towers was heard again the wild bugle of Huitzilopochtli.

Then down the centre of the church, in silence, barefoot, came the procession of Huitzilopochtli, naked save for the black loin-cloths and the paint, and the scarlet feathers of the head-dresses. Cipriano had his face painted with a white jaw, a thin band of green stretched from his mouth, a band of black across his nose, yellow from his eyes, and scarlet on his brow. One green feather rose from his forehead, and behind his head a beautiful head-dress of scarlet feathers. A band of red was painted round his breast, yellow round his middle. The rest was ash-grey.

After him came his guard, their faces red, black and white, their bodies painted as Cipriano's, and a scarlet feather rising from the back of their head. The hard, dry drum of Huitzilopochtli beat monotonously.

As the Living Huitzilopochtli came near the altar steps, the Living Quetzalcoatl rose and came to meet him. The two saluted, each covering his eyes with his left hand for a moment, then touching fingers with the right hand.

Cipriano stood before the statue of Huitzilopochtli, dipped his hand in a stone bowl, and giving the loud cry or whoop of Huitzilopochtli, lifted up his red hand. His guard uttered the loud cry, and quickly filed past, each man dipping his hand and raising his wet, red fist. The hard drums of Huitzilopochtli rattled like madness in the church, then fell suddenly silent.

Ramón: Why is your hand red, Huitzilopochtli, my brother?

Cipriano: It is the blood of the treacherous, Oh Quetzalcoatl.

Ramón: What have they betrayed?

Cipriano: The yellow sun and the heart of darkness; the hearts of men, and the buds of women. While they lived, the Morning Star could not be seen.

Ramón: And are they verily dead?

Cipriano: Verily dead, my Lord.

Ramón: Their blood is shed?

Cipriano: Yes, my Lord, save that the grey dogs shed no blood. Two died the bloodless death of the grey dogs, three died in blood.

Ramón: Give me the blood of the three, my brother Huitzilopochtli, to sprinkle the fire.

Cipriano brought the stone bowl, and the little bunch of black leaves from Huitzilopochtli's idol. Ramón slowly, gently, sprinkled a little blood on the fire, with the black leaves.

Ramón: Darkness, drink the blood of expiation.
Sun, swallow up the blood of expiation.
Rise, Morning Star, between the divided sea.

He gave back the bowl and the leaves to Huitzilopochtli, who placed them by the black idol.

Ramón: Thou who didst take the lives of the three, Huitzilopochtli, my brother, what wilt thou do with the souls?

Cipriano: Even give them to thee, my Lord, Quetzalcoatl, my Lord of the Morning Star.

Ramón: Yea, give them to me and I will wrap them in my breath and send them the longest journey, to the sleep and the far awakening.

Cipriano: My Lord is lord of two ways.

The naked, painted guard of Huitzilopochtli came and carried the dead bodies of the three stabbed men, carried them on red biers, and laid them at the foot of the Quetzalcoatl statue.

Ramón: "So, there is a long way to go, past the sun to the gate of the Morning Star. And if the sun is angry he strikes swifter than a jaguar, and the whirr of the winds is like an angry eagle, and the upper waters strike in wrath like silver-coloured snakes. Ah, three souls, make peace now with the sun and winds and waters, and go in courage, with the breath of Quetzalcoatl around you like a cloak. Fear not and shrink not and fail not; but come to the end of the longest journey, and let the fountain cover your face. So shall all at length be made new."

When he had spoken to the dead, Ramón took incense and threw it on the fire, so clouds of blue smoke arose. Then with a censer he swung the blue smoke over the dead. Then he unfolded three blue cloths and covered the dead. Then the guards of Quetzalcoatl lifted the biers, and the flute of Quetzalcoatl sounded.

"Salute the Morning Star!" cried Ramón, turning to the light beyond the statue of Quetzalcoatl, and throwing up his right arm in the Quetzalcoatl prayer. Every man turned to the light and threw up his arm in the passion. And the silence of the Morning Star filled the church.

The drum of Quetzalcoatl sounded: the guards slowly moved away with the three blue-wrapped dead.

Then came the voice of the Living Huitzilopochtli:

"Upon the dead grey dogs the face of Quetzalcoatl cannot look. Upon the corpses of grey dogs rises no Morning Star. But the fire of corpses shall consume them."

There was a sharp rattle of the dry drums of Huitzilopochtli. Ramón remained with his back to the church, his arm upraised to the Morning Star. And the guard of Huitzilopochtli lifted the strangled bodies, laid them on biers, covered them with grey cloths, and bore them away.

The bugle of Huitzilopochtli sounded.

Cipriano: The dead are on their way. Quetzalcoatl helps them on the longest journey.—But the grey dogs sleep within the quick-lime, in the slow corpse-fire.—It is finished.

Ramón dropped his arm and turned to the church. All men dropped their hands. The soft drums of Quetzalcoatl sounded, mingling with the hard drums of Huitzilopochtli. Then both guards began to sing together:

HUITZILOPOCHTLI'S WATCH

Red Huitzilopochtli
Keeps day and night apart.

Huitzilopochtli the golden
Guards life from death, and death from life.

No grey-dogs, cowards, pass him.
No spotted traitors crawl by,
False fair ones cannot slip through
Past him, from the one to the other.

Brave men have peace at nightfall,
True men look up at the dawn,
Men in their manhood walk out
Into blue day, past Huitzilopochtli.

Red Huitzilopochtli
Is the purifier.

Black Huitzilopochtli
Is doom.

Huitzilopochtli golden
Is the liberating fire.

White Huitzilopochtli
Is washed bone.

Green Huitzilopochtli
Is Malintzi's blade of grass.

At the beginning of each stanza, the Guard of Huitzilopochtli struck their left palm with their scarlet right fist, and the drums gave a great crash, a terrific splash of noise. When the song ended, the drums gradually died down, like subsiding thunder, leaving the hearts of men re-echoing.

Ramón: Why is your hand so red, Huitzilopochtli?
Cipriano: With blood of slain men, Brother!
Ramón: Must it always be red?
Cipriano: Till green-robed Malintzi brings her water-bowl.

The bugle and the flute both sounded. The guard of Huitzilopochtli put out the red candles, one by one, the guard of Quetzalcoatl extinguished the blue candles. The church was dark, save for the small, but fierce blue-white light beyond the Quetzalcoatl statue, and the red smouldering on the altar.

Ramón began slowly to speak:

The dead are on their journey, the way is dark.
There is only the Morning Star.
Beyond the white of whiteness,
Beyond the blackness of black,
Beyond spoken day,
Beyond the unspoken passion of night,
The light which is fed from two vessels

From the black oil and the white
Shines at the gate.

A gate to the innermost place
Where the Breath and the Fountains commingle,
Where the dead are living, and the living are dead.
The deeps that life cannot fathom,
The source and the End, of which we know
Only that it is, and its life is our life and our death.

All men cover their eyes
Before the unseen.
All men be lost in silence,
Within the noiseless.

The church was utterly still, all men standing with a hand pressed over their eyes.

Till there was one note of a silver gong, and the green candles of Malintzi were being lighted in the altar place.—Ramón's voice was heard again:

Like the green candles of Malintzi
Like a new tree in new leaf.
The rain of blood is fallen, is gone into the earth.

The dead have gone the long journey
Beyond the star.
Huitzilopochtli has thrown his black mantle
To those who would sleep.
When the blue wind of Quetzalcoatl
Waves softly,
When the water of Malintzi falls
Making a greenness:
Count the red drains of the Huitzilopochtli
Fire in your hearts, Oh men.
And blow the ash away.

For the living live,
And the dead die.
But the fingers of all touch the fingers of all
In the Morning Star.

CHAPTER XXIV

MALINTZI

WHEN the women were shut out of the church, Kate went home gloomy and uneasy. The executions shocked and depressed her. She knew that Ramón and Cipriano did deliberately what they did: they believed in their deeds, they acted with all their conscience. And as men, probably they were right.

But they seemed nothing but men. When Cipriano said: *Man that is man is more than a man,* he seemed to be driving the male significance to its utmost, and beyond, with a sort of demonism. It seemed to her all terrible *will,* the exertion of pure, awful will.

And deep in her soul came a revulsion against this manifestation of pure will. It was fascinating also. There was something dark and lustrous and fascinating to her in Cipriano, and in Ramón. The black, relentless power, even passion of the will in men! The strange, sombre, lustrous beauty of it! She knew herself under the spell.

At the same time, as is so often the case with any spell, it did not bind her completely. She was spell-bound, but not utterly acquiescent. In one corner of her soul was revulsion and a touch of nausea.

Ramón and Cipriano no doubt were right for themselves, for their people and country. But for herself, ultimately, ultimately she belonged elsewhere. Not to this terrible, natural *will* which seemed to beat its wings in the very air of the American continent. Always will, will, will, without remorse or relenting. This was America to her: all the Americas. Sheer will!

The Will of God! She began to understand that once fearsome phrase. At the centre of all things, a dark, momentous Will sending out its terrific rays and vibrations, like some vast octopus. And at the other end of the vibration, men, created men, erect in the dark potency, answering Will with will, like gods or demons.

385

It was wonderful too. But where was woman, in this terrible interchange of will? Truly only a subservient, instrumental thing: the soft stone on which the man sharpened the knife of his relentless volition: the soft lodestone to magnetise his blade of steel and keep all its molecules alive in the electric flow.

Ah yes, it was wonderful. It was, as Ramón said, a manifestation, a manifestation of the Godhead. But to the Godhead as a sheer and awful Will she could not respond.

Joachim, letting himself be bled to death for people who would profit nothing by his sacrifice, he was the other extreme. The black and magnificent pride of will which comes out of the volcanic earth of Mexico had been unknown to him. He was one of the white, self-sacrificing gods. Hence her bitterness. And hence, naturally, the spell of beauty and lustrous satisfaction which Cipriano could cast over her. She was in love with him, when he was with her; in his arms, she was quite gone in his spell. She was the deep, slumbrous lodestone which set all his bones glittering with the energy of relentless pride. And she herself derived a great gratification in the embrace, a sense of passive, downward-sinking power, profound.

Yet she could not be purely this, this thing of sheer reciprocity. Surely, though her woman's nature was reciprocal to his male, surely it was more than that! Surely he and she were not two potent and reciprocal currents between which the Morning Star flashed like a spark out of nowhere. Surely this was not it? Surely she had one tiny Morning Star inside her, which was herself, her own very soul and star-self!

But he would never admit this. The tiny star of her very self he would never see. To him she was but the answer to his call, the sheath for his blade, the cloud to his lightning, the earth to his rain, the fuel to his fire.

Alone, she was nothing. Only as the pure female corresponding to his pure male, did she signify.

As an isolated individual, she had little or no significance. As a woman on her own, she was repulsive and even evil, to him. She was not real till she was reciprocal.

To a great extent this was true, and she knew it. To a great extent, the same was true of him, and without her to give him the power, he too would not achieve his own manhood and meaning. With her or without her, he would be beyond ordinary men, because the power was in him. But failing her, he would never

make his ultimate achievement, he would never be whole. He
would be chiefly an instrument.

He knew this too: though perhaps not well enough. He would
strive to keep her, to have her, for his own fulfilment. He would
not let her go.

But that little star of her own single self, would he ever recognize that? Nay, did he even recognize any single star of his own
being? Did he not conceive of himself as a power and a potency
on the face of the earth, an embodied will, like a rushing dark
wind? And hence, inevitably, she was but the stone of rest to
his potency, his bed of sleep, the cave and lair of his male will.

What else? To him there was nothing else. The star! Don
Ramón's Morning Star was something that sprung between him
and her and hung shining, the strange third thing that was both
of them and neither of them, between his night and her day.

Was it true? Was she nothing, nothing, by herself. And he,
alone, failing his last manhood, without her was he nothing, or
next to nothing? As a fig tree which grows up, but never
comes to flower.

Was this thing true, the same of both of them?—that alone, they
were next to nothing? Each of them, separate, next to nothing.
Apart in a sort of grey, mechanical twilight, without a star?

And together, in strange reciprocity, flashing darkly till the
Morning Star rose between them?

He would say to her, as Ramón had said of Carlota: "Soul!
No, you have no soul of your own. You have at best only half a
soul. It takes a man and a woman together to make a soul. The
soul is the Morning Star, emerging from the two. One alone
cannot have a soul."

This Ramón said. And she knew it conveyed what Cipriano
really felt. Cipriano could not see Kate as a being by herself.
And if he lived a thousand more years, he would never see her
as such. He would see her only as reciprocal to himself. As the
balance of him, and the correspondence on the other side of heaven.

"Let the Morning Star rise between us," he would say. "Alone
you are nothing, and I am *manqué*. But together we are the
wings of the Morning."

Was it true? Was this the final answer to man's assertion of
individuality?

Was it true? And was it her sacred duty to sit beside him in
the green dress of Malintzi, in the church, the goddess admitting

her halfness? Her halfness! Was there no star of the single soul? Was that all an illusion?

Was the individual an illusion? Man, any man, every man, by himself just a fragment, knowing no Morning Star? And every woman the same; by herself, starless and fragmentary. Even in the relation to the utmost God, still fragmentary and unblest.

Was it true, that the gate was the Morning Star, the only entrance to the Innermost? And the Morning Star rises between the two, and between the many, but never from one alone.

And was a man but a dark and arrowy will, and woman the bow from which the arrow is shot? The bow without the arrow was as nothing, and the arrow without the bow only a short-range dart, ineffectual?

Poor Kate, it was hard to have to reflect this. It meant a submission she had never made. It meant the death of her individual self. It meant abandoning so much, even her own very foundations. For she had believed truly that every man and every woman alike was founded on the individual.

Now, must she admit that the individual was an illusion and a falsification? There was no such animal. Except in the mechanical world. In the world of machines, the individual machine is effectual. The individual, like the perfect being, does not and cannot exist, in the vivid world. We are all fragments. And at the best, halves. The only whole thing is the Morning Star. Which can only rise between two: or between many.

And men can only meet in the light of the Morning Star.

She thought again of Cipriano and the executions, and she covered her hands over her face. Was this the knife to which she must be sheath? Was it such a star of power and relentlessness that must rise between her and him? Him naked and painted, with his soldiers, dancing and sweating and shouting among them. Herself unseen and nowhere!

As she sat rocking in her terrible loneliness and misgiving, she heard the drums on the towers, and the sound of rockets. She went to the gate. Over the church, in the night sky, hung a spangling cloud of red and blue fire, the colours of Huitzilopochtli and Quetzalcoatl. The night of Huitzilopochtli would be over. The sky was dark again, and there were all the stars, beyond, far, far beyond where the spangling had been.

She went indoors again, to retire. The servants had all run

out to see the rockets. Ezequiel would be in with the men in church.

She heard footsteps on the gravel walk, and suddenly Cipriano stood in the doorway, in his white clothes. He took off his hat, quickly. His black eyes were sparkling, almost blazing to her, with a flashing of light such as she had never seen. There were still smears of paint on his face. In the blazing of his eyes he seemed to be smiling to her, but in a dazzling, childish way.

"Malintzi," he said to her in Spanish. "Oh, come! Come and put on the green dress. I cannot be the Living Huitzilopochtli, without a bride. I cannot be it, Malintzi!"

He stood before her, flickering and flashing and strangely young, vulnerable, as young and boyish as flame. She saw that when the fire came free in him, he would be like this always, flickering, flashing with a flame of virgin youth. Now, not will at all. Sensitive as a boy. And calling her only with his boyish flame. The living, flickering, fiery *Wish*. This was first. The *Will* she had seen was subsidary and instrumental, the *Wish* in armour.

She had been so used to fighting for her own soul with individualistic men, that for a moment she felt old, and uncertain. The strange, flashing vulnerability in him, the nakedness of the living Wish, disconcerted her. She was used to men who had themselves well in hand, and were seeking their own ends as individuals.

"Where do you want me to come?" she said.

"To the church," he said. "It is mine to-night. I am the Huitzilopochtli: but I cannot be it alone," he added with quick, wistful, watchful smile, as if all his flesh were flickering with delicate fire.

Kate wrapped herself in a dark tartan shawl and went with him. He stepped quickly, in the short, Indian way. The night was very dark. Down on the beach some fireworks were flaming, and the people were all watching.

They entered the yard of the church from the back, by the priest's little gate. Soldiers were already rolled up in their blankets, sleeping under the wall. Cipriano opened the little vestry door. Kate passed into the darkness. He followed, lighting a candle.

"My soldiers know I am watching to-night in the church," he said. "They will keep guard."

The body of the church was quite dark, but the bluish white light burned above the statue of Quetzalcoatl, giving not much light.

Cipriano lifted his candle to the black statue of Huitzilopochtli. Then he turned to Kate, his black eyes flashing.

"I am the Huitzilopochtli, Malintzi," he said in his low, Indian Spanish. "But I cannot be it without you. Stay with me, Malintzi. Say you are the bride of the Living Huitzilopochtli."

"Yes!" she replied, "I will say it."

Convulsive flames of joy and triumph seemed to go over his face. He lit two candles in front of Huitzilopochtli.

"Come!" he said. "Put on the green dress."

He took her to the vestry, where were many folded serapes, and the silver bowl and other implements of the church, and left her while she put on the dress of Malintzi she had worn when Ramón married them.

When she stepped out she found Cipriano naked and in his paint, before the statue of Huitzilopochtli, on a rug of jaguar skins.

"I am the living Huitzilopochtli," he murmured to her in a sort of ecstasy.

"You are Malintzi," he said. "The bride of Huitzilopochtli."

The convulsion of exultance went over his face. He took her hand in his left hand, and they stood facing the bluish light.

"Cover your face!" he said to her.

They covered their faces in the salute.

"Now salute Quetzalcoatl." And he flung up his arm. She held out her left hand, in the woman's salute.

Then they turned to the statue of Huitzilopochtli.

"Salute Huitzilopochtli!" he said, bringing his right fist down with a smash in the palm of his left hand. But this was the male salute. He taught her to press her hands together in front of her breast, then shoot them out towards the idol.

Then he put a little lamp of earthenware between the feet of Huitzilopochtli. From the right knee of the idol he took a little black vessel of oil, making her take a little white vessel from the god's left knee.

"Now," he said, "together we fill the lamp."

And together they poured the oil from their little pitchers, into the saucer-shaped lamp.

"Now together we light it," he said.

He took one of the two candles burning before the black idol, she took the other, and with the flames dripping and leaping together, they kindled the floating wick of the lamp. It burned in a round blue bud, then rose higher.

"Blow out your candle," he said. "It is our Morning Star."

They blew out the two candles. It was almost dark now, with the slow light, like a snow-drop, of their united lives floating between the feet of Huitzilopochtli, and the everlasting light burning small and bluish beyond the statue of Quetzalcoatl.

At the foot of the altar, beside the chair of Huitzilopochtli, a third chair was placed.

"Sit in your throne of Malintzi," he said to her.

They sat side by side, his hand holding her hand, in complete silence, looking down the dark church. He had placed tufts of greenish flowers, like thin, greenish lilac, above her chair, and their perfume was like a dream, strong, overpoweringly sweet on the darkness.

Strange how naïve he was! He was not like Ramón, rather ponderous and deliberate in his ceremonials. Cipriano in his own little deeds to-night with her, was naïve like a child. She could hardly look at that bud of light which he said meant their united lives, without a catch at her heart. It burned so soft and round, and he had such an implicit, childish satisfaction in its symbol. It all gave him a certain wild, childish joy. The strange convulsons like flames of joy and gratification went over his face!

"Ah, God!" she thought. "There are more ways than one of becoming like a little child."

The flaminess and the magnificence of the beginning: this was what Cipriano wanted to bring to his marriage. The reeling, powerful perfume of those invisible green flowers, that the peons call *buena de noche*: good by night.

Strange—that which he brought to marriage was something flamy and unabashed, forever virginal. Not, as she had always known in men, yearning and seeking her own ends. Naïvely bringing his flame to her flame.

As she sat in that darkened church in the intense perfume of flowers, in the seat of Malintzi, watching the bud of her life united with his, between the feet of the idol, and feeling his dark hand softly holding her own, with the soft, deep Indian heat, she felt her own childhood coming back on her. The years seemed to be reeling away in great circles, falling away from her.

Leaving her sitting there like a girl in her first adolescence. The Living Huitzilopochtli! Ah, easily he was the living Huit-zilopochtli. More than anything. More than Cipriano, more than a male man, he was the living Huitzilopochtli. And she was the goddess bride, Malintzi of the green dress.

Ah, yes, it was childish. But it was actually so. She was per-haps fourteen years old, and he was fifteen. And he was the young Huitzilopochtli, and she was the bride Malintzi, the bride-girl. She had seen it. When the flame came up in him and licked him all over, he was young and vulnerable as a boy of fifteen, and he would always be so, even when he was seventy.

And this was her bridegroom. Here at last he was not a *will*. When he came clothed in his own free flame, it was not *will* that clothed him. Let him be a general, an executioner, what he liked, in the world. The flame of their united lives was a naked bud of flame. Their marriage was a young, vulnerable flame.

So he sat in silence on his throne, holding her hand in silence, till the years reeled away from her in fleeing circles, and she sat, as every real woman can sit, no matter at what age, a girl again, and for him, a virgin. He held her hand in silence, till she was Malintzi, and virgin for him, and when they looked at one an-other, and their eyes met, the two flames rippled in oneness. She closed her eyes, and was dark.

Then later, when she opened her eyes and saw the bud of flame just above her, and the black idol invisibly crouching, she heard his strange voice, the voice of a boy hissing in naïve ecstasy, in Spanish:

"Miel! Miel de Malintzi!—Honey of Malintzi!"

And she pressed him to her breast, convulsively. His inner-most flame was always virginal, it was always the first time. And it made her again always a virgin girl. She could feel their two flames flowing together.

How else, she said to herself, is one to begin again, save by re-finding one's virginity? And when one finds one's virginity, one realises one is among the gods. He is of the gods, and so am I. Why should I judge him!

So, when she thought of him and his soldiers, tales of swift cruelty she had heard of him: when she remembered his stabbing the three helpless peons, she thought: Why should I judge him? He is of the gods. And when he comes to me he lays his pure, quick flame to mine, and every time I am a young girl again, and

every time he takes the flower of my virginity, and I his. It leaves me insouciant like a young girl. What do I care if he kills people? His flame is young and clean. He is Huitzilopochtli, and I am Malintzi. What do I care, what Cipriano Viedma does or doesn't do? Or even what Kate Leslie does or doesn't do!

CHAPTER XXV

TERESA

RAMÓN somewhat surprised Kate by marrying again, a couple of months or so after the death of Doña Carlota. The new bride was a young woman of about twenty-eight, called Teresa. There was a very quiet civil wedding, and Ramón brought his new wife to Jamiltepec.

He had known her since she was a child, for she was the daughter of the famous hacienda of Las Yemas, some twelve miles inland from Jamiltepec. Don Tomas, her father, had been a staunch friend of the Carrascos.

But Don Tomas had died a year ago, leaving the large, flourishing tequila hacienda to his three children, to be administrated by Teresa. Teresa was the youngest. Her two brothers had reverted to the usual wasteful, spendthrift, brutal Mexican way. Therefore Don Tomas, in order to save the hacienda from their destructive hands, had especially appointed Teresa *administrador,* and had got the brothers' consent to this. After all, they were shiftless ne'er-do-wells, and had never shown the slightest desire to help in the rather burdensome business of managing a large tequila hacienda, during their father's life-time. Teresa had been the one. And during her father's illness the whole charge had devolved on her, while her brothers wasted themselves and their substance in the squashy prostitution-living of Mexicans of their class, away in the cities.

No sooner was the father dead, however, and Teresa in charge, than home came the two brothers, big with their intention to be hacendados. By simple brute force they ousted their sister, gave orders over her head, jeered at her, and in crushing her united for once with each other. They were putting her back into her place as a woman—that is to say, back into a secluded sort of prostitution, to which, in their eyes, women belonged.

But they were bullies, and, as bullies, cowards. And like so many Mexicans of that class, soft and suicidal towards themselves. They made friends with judges and generals. They rode about

394

in resplendent charro dress, and had motor-loads of rather doubtful visitors.

Against their soft, sensuous brutality Teresa could do nothing, and she knew it. They were all soft and sensual, or sensuous, handsome in their way, open-handed, careless, but bullies, with fear at the middle of them.

"Make yourself desirable, and get a husband for yourself," they said to her.

In their eyes, her greatest crime was that she did not make herself desirable to men of their sort. That she had never had a man, that she was not married, made her almost repulsive to them. What was woman for, but for loose, soft, prostitutional sex?

"Do you want to wear the trousers?" they jeered at her. "No, Señorita! Not while there are two men on the place, you are not going to wear the trousers. No, Señorita! The trousers, the men wear them. The women keep under their petticoats that which they are women for."

Teresa was used to these insults. But they made her soul burn.

"You, do you want to be an American woman?" they said to her. "Go off to America, then, and bob your hair and wear breeches. Buy a ranch there, and get a husband to take your orders. Go!"

She went to her lawyers, but they held up their hands. And she went to Ramón, whom she had known since she was a child.

It would have meant a hopeless and ruinous law-suit, to get the brothers ejected from the hacienda. It would have meant the rapid ruin of the estate. Ramón instead asked Teresa to marry him, and he carefully arranged her dowry, so that she should always have her own provision.

"It is a country where men despise sex, and live for it." said Ramón. "Which is just suicide."

Ramón came with his wife, to see Kate. Teresa was rather small, pale, with a lot of loose black hair and big, wide black eyes. Yet in her quiet bearing and her well-closed mouth there was an air of independence and authority. She had suffered great humiliation at the hands of her brothers, there was still a certain wanness around her eyes, the remains of tears of anger and helpless indignation, and the bitterness of insulted sex. But now she loved Ramón with a wild, virgin loyalty. That, too, was evident. He had saved her sex from the insult, restored it to her in its pride

and its beauty. And in return, she felt an almost fierce reverence for him.

But with Kate she was shy and rather distant: a little afraid of the travelled, experienced, rather assertive white-skinned woman, the woman of the other race. She sat in Kate's salon in her simple white dress with a black gauze rebozo, her brown hands motionless in her lap, her dark neck erect, her dark, slender, well-shaped cheek averted. She seemed, Kate thought, rather like a little sempstress.

But Kate was reckoning without that strange quiescent power of authority which Teresa also possessed, in her slight, dark body. And without the black, flashing glances which rested on her from time to time, from Teresa's eyes, full of searching fierceness and fiery misgiving. A fiery soul, in such a demure, slight, dark body. Sometimes a muted word came from her mouth, and a constrained smile moved her lips. But her burning eyes never changed. She did not even look at Ramón.

"How much do you charge per word, Chica?" he asked her, with a sort of soft fondness.

Then her dark eyes flashed at him, and her mouth gave a little smile. It was evident she was hopelessly in love with him, in a sort of trance or muse of love. And she maintained such a cold sort of blankness towards Kate.

"She despises me," thought Kate, "because I can't be in love as she is."

And for one second Kate envied Teresa. The next second, she despised her. "The harem type—"

Well, it was Ramón's nature to be a sort of Sultan. He looked very handsome in his white clothes, very serene and pasha-like in his assurance, yet at the same time, soft, pleasant, something boyish also in his physical well-being. In his soft yet rather pasha-like way, he was mixing a cocktail of gin and vermouth and lime. Teresa watched him from the corner of her eye. And at the same time, she watched Kate, the potential enemy, the woman who talked with men on their own plane.

Kate rose to get spoons. At the same moment, he stepped back from the low table where he was squeezing a lime, so that he came into slight collision with her. And Kate noticed again, how quick and subtle was his physical evasion of her, the soft, almost liquid, hot quickness of sliding out of contact with her. His

natural voluptuousness avoided her as a flame leans away from a draught.

She flushed slightly. And Teresa saw the quick flush under the fair, warm-white skin, the leap of yellow light, almost like anger, into Kate's grey-hazel eyes. The moment of evasion of two different blood-streams.

And Teresa rose and went to Ramón's side, bending over and looking in the tumblers, asking, with that curious affected childishness of dark women:

"What do you put in?"

"Look!" said Ramón. And with the same curious male childishness of dark men, he was explaining the cocktail to her, giving her a little gin in a spoon, to taste.

"It is an impure tequila," she said naïvely.

"At eight pesos a bottle?" he laughed.

"So much! It is much!"

She looked into his eyes for a second, and saw all his face go darker, warmer, as if his flesh were fusing soft towards her. Her small head poised the prouder. She had got him back.

"Harem tricks!" said Kate to herself. And she was somewhat impatient, seeing the big, portentous Ramón enveloped in the toils of this little dark thing. She resented being made so conscious of his physical presence, his full, male body inside his thin white clothes, the strong, yet soft shoulders, the full, rich male thighs. It was as if she herself, also, being in presence of this Sultan, should succumb as part of the harem.

What a curious will the little dark woman had! What a subtle female power inside her rather skinny body! She had the power to make him into a big, golden full glory of a man. Whilst she herself became almost inconspicuous, save for her big black eyes lit with a tigerish power.

Kate watched in wonder. She herself had known men who made her feel a queen, who made her feel as if the sky rested on her bosom and her head was among the stars. She knew what it was to rise grander and grander, till she filled the universe with her womanhood.

Now she saw the opposite taking place. This little bit of a black-eyed woman had an almost uncanny power, to make Ramón great and gorgeous in the flesh, whilst she herself became inconspicuous, almost *invisible,* save for her great black eyes. Like a

sultan, he was, like a full golden fruit in the sun, with a strange and magnificent presence, glamour. And then, by some mysterious power in her dark little body, the skinny Teresa held him most completely.

And this was what Ramòn wanted. And it made Kate angry, angry. The big, fluid male, gleaming, was somewhat repulsive to her. And the tense little female with her pale-dark face, wan under her great, intense, black eyes, having all her female being tense in an effort to exalt this big glistening man, this enraged Kate. She could not bear the glistening smile in Ramón's dark eyes, a sort of pasha satisfaction. And she could not bear the erect, tense little figure of the dark woman, using her power in this way.

This hidden, secretive power of the dark female! Kate called it harem, and self-prostitution. But was it? Yes, surely it was the *slave* approach. Surely she wanted nothing but sex from him, like a prostitute! The ancient mystery of the female power, which consists in glorifying the blood-male.

Was it right? Kate asked herself. Wasn't it degrading for a woman? And didn't it make the man either soft and sensuous, or else hatefully autocratic?

Yet Kate herself had convinced herself of one thing, finally: that the clue to all living and to all moving-on into new living lay in the vivid blood-relation between man and women. A man and a woman in this togetherness were the clue to all present living and future possibility. Out of this clue of togetherness between a man and a woman, the whole of the new life arose. It was the quick of the whole.

And the togetherness needed a balance. Surely it needed a balance! And did not this Teresa throw herself entirely into the male balance, so that all the weight was on the man's side?

Ramón had not wanted Kate. Ramón had got what he wanted —this black little creature, who was so servile to him and so haughty in her own power. Ramón had never wanted Kate: except as a friend, a clever friend. As a woman, no!—He wanted this little viper of a Teresa.

Cipriano wanted Kate. The little general, the strutting little soldier, he wanted Kate: just for moments. He did not really want to marry her. He wanted the moments, no more. She was to give him his moments, and then he was off again, to his army, to his men. It was what he wanted.

It was what she wanted too. Her life was her own! It was not her métier to be fanning the blood in a man, to make him almighty and blood-glamorous. Her life was her own!

She rose and went to her bedroom to look for a book she had promised Ramón. She could not bear the sight of him in love with Teresa any longer. The heavy, mindless smile on his face, the curious glisten of his eyes, and the strange, heavy, lordly *aplomb* of his body affected her like a madness. She wanted to run.

This was what they were, these people! Savages, with the impossible fluid flesh of savages, and that savage way of dissolving into an awful black mass of desire. Emerging with the male conceit and haughtiness swelling his blood and making him feel endless. While his eyes glistened with a haughty blackness.

The trouble was, that the power of the world, which she had known until now only in the eyes of blue-eyed men, who made queens of their women—even if they hated them for it in the end —was now fading in the blue eyes, and dawning in the black. In Ramón's eyes at this moment was a steady, alien gleam of pride, and daring, and power, which she knew was masterly. The same was in Cipriano's quick looks. The power of the world was dying in the blond men, their bravery and their supremacy was leaving them, going into the eyes of the dark men, who were rousing at last.

Joachim, the eager, clever, fierce, sensitive genius, who could look into her soul, and laugh into her soul, with his blue eyes: he had died under her eyes. And her children were not even his children.

If she could have fanned his blood as Teresa now fanned the blood of Ramón, he would never have died.

But it was impossible. Every dog has his day.—And every race.

Teresa came tapping timidly.

"May I come?"

"Do!" said Kate, rising from her knees and leaving little piles of books all round the book-trunk.

It was a fairly large room, with doors opening on to the patio and the sun-hard garden, smooth mango-trees rising like elephant's trunks out of the ground, green grass after the rains, chickens beneath the ragged banana leaves. A red bird splashed in the

basin of water, opening and shutting brown wings above his pure scarlet, vivid.

But Teresa looked at the room, not out of doors. She smelt the smell of cigarettes and saw the many cigarette stumps in the agate tray by the bed. She saw the littered books, the scattered jewellery, the brilliant New-Mexican rugs on the floor, the Persian curtain hung behind the bed, the handsome, coloured bedcover, the dresses of dark silk and bright velvet flung over a trunk, the folded shawls with their long fringe, the scattered shoes, white, grey, pale-brown, dark-brown, black, on the floor, the tall Chinese candlesticks. The room of a woman who lived her own life, for her own self.

Teresa was repelled, uneasy, and fascinated.

"How nice this is!" she said, touching the glowing bedcover.

"A friend made it for me, in England."

Teresa looked with wonder at everything, especially at the tangle of jewellery on the dressing-table.

"Don't you like those red stones!" said Kate, kneeling again to put the books back, and looking at the brown neck bent absorbedly over the jewels. Thin shoulders, with a soft, dark skin, in a bit of a white dress! And loosely folded masses of black hair held by tortoise-shell pins.—An insignificant little thing, humble, Kate thought to herself.

But she knew really that Teresa was neither insignificant nor humble. Under that soft brown skin, and in that stooping female spine was a strange old power to call up the blood in a man, and glorify it, and, in some way, keep it for herself.

On the sewing-table was a length of fine India muslin which Kate had bought in India, and did not know what to do with. It was a sort of yellow-peach colour, beautiful, but it did not suit Kate. Teresa was fingering the gold-thread selvedge.

"It is not organdie?" she said.

"No, muslin. Hand-made muslin from India.—Why don't you take it? It doesn't suit me. It would be perfect on you."

She rose and held the fabric against Teresa's dark neck, pointing to the mirror. Teresa saw the warm-yellow muslin upon herself, and her eyes flashed.

"No!" she said. "I couldn't take it."

"Why not? It doesn't suit me. I've had it lying about for a year now, and was wondering whether to cut it up for curtains. Do have it."

Kate could be imperious, almost cruel in her giving.

"I can't take it from you!"

"Of course you can!"

Ramón appeared in the doorway, glancing round the room, and at the two women.

"Look!" said Teresa, rather confused. "The Señora wants to give me this India muslin."—She turned to him shyly, with the fabric held to her throat.

"You look very well in it," he said, his eyes resting on her.

"The Señora ought not to give it to me."

"The Señora would not give it you unless she wished to."

"Then!" said Teresa to Kate. "Many thanks! But many thanks!"

"It is nothing," said Kate.

"But Ramón says it suits me."

"Yes, doesn't it suit her!" cried Kate to him. "It was made in India for someone as dark as she is. It *does* suit her."

"Very pretty!" said Ramón.

He had glanced round the room, at the different attractive things from different parts of the world, and at the cigarette ends in the agate bowl: the rather weary luxury and disorder, and the touch of barrenness, of a women living her own life.

She did not know what he was thinking. But to herself she thought: This is the man I defended on that roof. This is the man who lay with a hole in his back, naked and unconscious under the lamp. He didn't look like a Sultan then.

Teresa must have divined something of her thought, for she said, looking at Ramón:

"Señora! But for you Ramón would have been killed. Always I think of it."

"Don't think of it," said Kate. "Something else would have happened. Anyhow it wasn't I, it was destiny."

"Ah, but you were the destiny!" said Teresa.

"Now there is a hostess, won't you come and stay some time at Jamiltepec?" said Ramón.

"Oh, do! Do come!" cried Teresa.

"But do you really want me?" said Kate, incredulous.

"Yes! Yes!" cried Teresa.

"She needs a woman-friend," said Ramón gently.

"Yes, I do!" she cried. "I have never had a true, *true* woman-friend: only when I was at school, and we were girls."

Kate doubted very much her own capacity for being a *true,* true woman-friend to Teresa. She wondered what the two of them saw in her. As what did they see her?

"Yes, I should like to come for a few days," she replied.

"Oh, yes!" cried Teresa. "When will you come?"

The day was agreed.

"And we will write the Song of Malintzi," said Ramón.

"Don't do that!" cried Kate quickly.

He looked at her, in his slow, wondering way. He could make her feel, at moments, as if she were a sort of child and as if he were a ghost.

Kate went to Jamiltepec, and before the two women knew it, almost, they were making dresses for Teresa, cutting up the pineapple-coloured muslin. Poor Teresa, for a bride she had a scanty wardrobe: nothing but her rather pathetic black dresses that somehow made her look poor, and a few old white dresses. She had lived for her father—who had a good library of Mexicana and was all his life writing a history of the State of Jalisco— and for the hacienda. And it was her proud boast that Las Yemas was the only hacienda, within a hundred miles range, which had not been smashed at all during the revolutions that followed the flight of Porfirio Diaz.

Teresa had a good deal of the nun in her. But that was because she was deeply passionate, and deep passion tends to hide within itself, rather than expose itself to vulgar contact.

So Kate pinned the muslin over the brown shoulders, wondering again at the strange, uncanny softness of the dark skin, the heaviness of the black hair. Teresa's family, the Romeros, had been in Mexico since the early days of the Conquest.

Teresa wanted long sleeves.

"My arms are so thin!" she murmured, hiding her slender brown arms with a sort of shame. "They are not beautiful like yours."

Kate was a strong, full-developed woman of forty, with round, strong white arms.

"No!" she said to Teresa. "Your arms are not thin: they are exactly right for your figure, and pretty and young and brown."

"But make the sleeves long, to the wrist," pleaded Teresa.

And Kate did so, realising it became the other woman's nature better.

"The men here don't like little thin women," said Teresa, wistfully.

"One doesn't care what *the men* like," said Kate. "Do you think Don Ramón wishes you were a plump partridge?"

Teresa looked at her with a smile in her dark, big bright eyes, that were so quick, and in many ways so unseeing.

"Who knows!" she said. And in her quick, mischievous smile it was evident she would like also, sometimes, to be a plump partridge.

Kate now saw more of the hacienda life than she had done before. When Ramón was at home, he consulted his overseer, or administrator, every morning. But already Teresa was taking this work off his hands. She would see to the estate.

Ramón was a good deal absent, either in Mexico or in Guadalajara, or even away in Sonora. He was already famous and notorious throughout the country, his name was a name to conjure with. But underneath the rather ready hero-worship of the Mexicans, Kate somehow felt their latent grudging. Perhaps they took more satisfaction in ultimately destroying their heroes, than in temporarily raising them high. The real perfect moment was when the hero was downed.

And to Kate, sceptic as she was, it seemed much more likely that they were sharpening the machete to stick in Ramón's heart, when he got a bit too big for them, than anything else. Though, to be sure, there was Cipriano to reckon with. And Cipriano was a little devil whom they quite rightly feared. And Cipriano, for once, was faithful. He was, to himself, Huitzilopochtli, and to this he would maintain a demonish faith. He was Huitzilopochtli, Ramón was Quetzalcoatl. To Cipriano this was a plain and living fact. And he kept his army keen as a knife. Even the President would not care to run counter to Cipriano. And the President was a brave man too.

"One day," he said, "we will put Quetzalcoatl in Puebla Cathedral, and Huitzilopochtli in Mexico Cathedral, and Malintzi in Guadalupe. The day will come, Ramón."

"We will see that it comes," Ramón replied.

But Ramón and Montes suffered alike from the deep, devilish animosity the country sent out in silence against them. It was the same, whoever was in power: the Mexicans seemed to steam with invisible, grudging hate, the hate of demons foiled in their

own souls, whose only motive is to foil everything, everybody, in the everlasting hell of cramped frustration.

This was the dragon of Mexico, that Ramón had to fight. Montes, the President, had it to fight the same. And it shattered his health. Cipriano also had it up against him. But he succeeded best. With his drums, with his dances round the fire, with his soldiers kept keen as knives he drew real support from his men. He grew stronger and more brilliant.

Ramón also, at home in his own district, felt the power flow into him from his people. He was their chief, and by his effort and his power he had almost overcome their ancient, fathomless resistance. Almost he had *awed* them back into the soft mystery of living, awed them until the tension of their resistant, malevolent wills relaxed. At home, he would feel his strength upon him.

But away from home, and particularly in the city of Mexico, he felt himself bled, bled, bled by the subtle, hidden malevolence of the Mexicans, and the ugly negation of the greedy, mechanical foreigners, birds of prey forever alighting in the cosmopolitan capital.

While Ramón was away, Kate stayed with Teresa. The two women had this in common, that they felt it was better to stand faithfully behind a really brave man, than to push forward into the ranks of cheap and obtrusive women. And this united them. A certain deep, ultimate faithfulness in each woman, to her own man who needed her fidelity, kept Kate and Teresa kindred to one another.

The rainy season had almost passed, though throughout September and even in October occasional heavy downpours fell. But the wonderful Mexican autumn, like a strange, inverted spring, was upon the land. The waste places bloomed with pink and white cosmos, the strange wild trees flowered in a ghostly way, forests of small sunflowers shone in the sun, the sky was a pure, pure blue, the floods of sunshine lay tempered on the land, that in part was flooded with water, from the heavy rains.

The lake was very full, strange and uneasy, and it had washed up a bank of the wicked water-hyacinths along all its shores. The wild-fowl were coming from the north, clouds of wild ducks like dust in the high air, sprinkling the water like weeds. Many, many wild fowl, grebe, cranes, and white gulls of the inland seas, so that the northern mystery seemed to have blown so far south. There was a smell of water in the land, and a sense of soothing.

For Kate firmly believed that part of the horror of the Mexican people came from the unsoothed dryness of the land and the untempered crudity of the flat-edged sunshine. If only there could be a softening of water in the air, and a haze above trees, the unspoken and unspeakable malevolence would die out of the human hearts.

Kate rode out often with Teresa to see the fields. The sugar-cane in the inner valley was vivid green, and rising tall, tall. The peons were beginning to cut it with their sword-like machetes, filling the bullock-wagons, to haul the cane to the factory in Sayula. On the dry hill-slopes the spiky tequila plant—a sort of maguey—flourished in its iron wickedness. Low wild cactuses put forth rose-like blossoms, wonderful and beautiful for such sinister plants. The beans were gathered from the bean-fields, some gourds and squashes still sprawled their uncanny weight across the land. Red chilies hung on withering plants, red tomatoes sank to the earth. Some maize still reared its flags, there was still young corn to eat on the cob. The banana crop was small, the children came in with the little wild yellow tejocote apples, for making preserves. Teresa was making preserves, even with the late figs and peaches. On the trees, the ponderous mango trees, some fruit was again orange-yellow and ripe, but the most still hung in strings, heavy and greenish and dropping like the testes of bulls.

It was autumn in Mexico, with wild duck on the waters, and hunters with guns, and small wild doves in the trees. Autumn in Mexico, and the coming of the dry season, with the sky going higher and higher, pure pale blue, the sunset arriving with a strange flare of crystal yellow light. With the coffee berries turning red on the struggling bushes under the trees, and bougainvillea in the strong light glowing with a glow of magenta colour so deep you could plunge your arms deep in it. With a few hummingbirds in the sunshine, and the fish in the waters gone wild, the flies, that steamed black in the first rains, now passing away again.

Teresa attended to everything, and Kate helped. Whether it was a sick peon in one of the little houses, or the hosts of bees from the hives under the mangoes, or the yellow, yellow bees-wax to be made into little bowlfuls, or the preserves, or the garden, or the calves, or the bit of butter and the little fresh cheeses made of strands of curd, or the turkeys to be overlooked: she saw to it

along with Teresa. And she wondered at the steady, urgent, efficient *will* which had to be exerted all the time. Everything was kept going by a heavy exertion of will. If once the will of the master broke, everything would break, and ruin would overtake the place almost at once. No real relaxation, ever. Always the sombre, insistent will.

Ramón arrived home one evening in November, from a long journey to Sonora. He had come overland from Tepic, and twice had been stopped by floods. The rains, so late, were very unusual. He was tired and remote-seeming. Kate's heart stood still a moment as she thought: He goes so remote, as if he might go away altogether into death.

It was cloudy again, with lightning beating about on the horizons. But all was very still. She said good-night early, and wandered down her own side of the terrace, to the look-out at the end, which looked on to the lake. Everything was dark, save for the intermittent pallor of lightning.

And she was startled to see, in a gleam of lightning, Teresa sitting with her back to the wall of the open terrace, Ramón lying with his head in her lap, while she slowly pushed her fingers through his thick black hair. They were as silent as the night.

Kate gave a startled murmur and said:

"I'm so sorry! I didn't know you were here."

"I wanted to be under the sky!" said Ramón, heaving himself to rise.

"Oh, *don't* move!" said Kate. "It was stupid of me to come here. You are tired."

"Yes," he said, sinking again. "I am tired. These people make me feel I have a hole in the middle of me. So I have come back to Teresa."

"Yes!" said Kate. "One isn't the Living Quetzalcoatl for nothing. Of course they eat holes in you.—Really, is it worth it?—To give yourself to be eaten away by them."

"It must be so," he said. "The change has to be made. And some man has to make it. I sometimes wish it wasn't I."

"So do I wish it. So does Teresa. One wonders if it isn't better to be just a man," said Kate.

But Teresa said nothing.

"One does what one must. And after all, one is always just a man," he said. "And if one has wounds—à la guerre comme à la guerre!"

His voice came out of the darkness like a ghost.

"Ah!" sighed Kate. "It makes one wonder what a man is, that he must needs expose himself to the horrors of all the other people."

There was silence for a moment.

"Man is a column of blood, with a voice in it," he said. "And when the voice is still, and he is only a column of blood, he is better."

She went away to her room sadly, hearing the sound of infinite exhaustion in his voice. As if he had a hole, a wound in the middle of him. She could almost feel it, in her own bowels.

And if, with his efforts, he killed himself?— Then, she said, Cipriano would come apart, and it would be all finished.

Ah, why should a man have to make these efforts on behalf of a beastly, malevolent people who weren't worth it! Better let the world come to an end, if that was what it wanted.

She thought of Teresa soothing him, soothing him and saying nothing. And him like a great helpless, wounded thing! It was rather horrible, really. Herself, she would have to expostulate, she would have to try to prevent him. Why should men damage themselves with this useless struggling and fighting, and then come home to their women to be restored!

To Kate, the fight simply wasn't worth one wound. Let the beastly world of man come to an end, if that was its destiny, as soon as possible. Without lifting a finger to prevent it.—Live one's own precious life, that was given but once, and let the rest go its own hellish way.

She would have *had* to try to prevent Ramón from giving himself to destruction this way. She was willing for him to be ten Living Quetzalcoatls. But not to expose himself to the devilish malevolence of people.

Yet he would do it. Even as Joachim had done. And Teresa, with her silence and her infinitely soft administering, she would heal him far better than Kate, with her expostulation and her opposition.

"Ah!" said Kate to herself. "I'm glad Cipriano is a soldier, and doesn't get wounds in his *soul*."

At the same time, she knew that without Ramón, Cipriano was just an instrument, and not ultimately interesting to her.

In the morning, Teresa appeared alone to breakfast. She

Eemed very calm, hiding her emotions in her odd, brown, proud
little way.

"How is Ramón?" said Kate.

"He is sleeping," said Teresa.

"Good! He seemed to me almost done up, last night."

"Yes."—The black eyes looked at Kate, wide with unshed tears
and courage, and a beautiful deep, remote light.

"I *don't* believe in a man's sacrificing himself in this way,"
said Kate. "And I *don't*."

Teresa still looked her full in the eyes.

"Ah!" she said. "He doesn't sacrifice himself. He feels he
must do as he does. And if he must, I must help him."

"But then you are sacrificing yourself to *him,* and I don't believe in that either," said Kate.

"Oh, no!" replied Teresa quickly, and a little flush burned in
her cheek, and her dark eyes flashed. "I am not sacrificing myself
to Ramón. If I can give him—sleep—when he needs it—that is
not sacrifice. It is—" She did not finish, but her eyes flashed,
and the flush burned darker.

"It is love, I know," said Kate. "But it exhausts you too."

"It is not simply love," flashed Teresa proudly. "I might have
loved more than one man: many men are lovable. But Ramón!
—My soul is with Ramón."—The tears rose to her eyes. "I do
not want to talk about it," she said, rising. "But you must not
touch me there, and judge me."

She hurried out of the room, leaving Kate somewhat dismayed.
Kate sighed, thinking of going home.

But in an hour Teresa appeared again, putting her cool, soft,
snake-like little hand on Kate's arm.

"I am sorry if I was rude," she said.

"No," said Kate. "Apparently it is I who am wrong."

"Yes, I think you are," said Teresa. "You think there is only
love. Love is only such a little bit."

"And what is the rest?"

"How can I tell you if you do not know?—But do you think
Ramón is no more to me than a lover?"

"A husband!" said Kate.

"Ah!" Teresa put her head aside with an odd impatience.
"Those little words! Those little words! Nor either a husband.
—He is my life."

"Surely it is better for one to live one's own life!"

"No! It is like seed. It is no good till it is given. I know. I kept my own life for a long time. As you keep it longer, it dies. And I tried to give it to God. But I couldn't, quite. Then they told me, if I married Ramón and had any part in the Quetzalcoatl heresy, my soul would. be damned.—But something made me know it was not true. I even knew he needed my soul.—Ah, Señora—" a subtle smile came on Teresa's pale face—"I have lost my soul to Ramón.—What more can I say!"

"And what about his soul?"

"It comes home to me—*here!*" She put her hand over her womb.

Kate was silent for a time.

"And if he betrays you?" she said.

"Ah, Señora!" said Teresa. "Ramón is not just a lover. He is a brave man, and he doesn't betray his own blood. And it is his soul that comes home to me.—And I would struggle to my last breath to give him sleep, when he came home to me with his soul, and needed it," she flashed. Then she added, murmuring to herself: "No, thank God! I have not got a life of my own! I have been able to give it to a man who is more than a man, as they say in their Quetzalcoatl language. And now it needn't die inside me, like a bird in a cage.—Oh, yes, Señora! If he goes to Sinaloa and the west coast, my soul goes with him and takes part in it all. It does not let him go alone. And he does not forget that he has my soul with him. I know it.—No, Señora! You must not criticise me or pity me."

"Still!" said Kate. "It still seems to me it would be better for each one to keep her own soul, and be responsible for it."

"If it were possible!" said Teresa. "But you can no more keep your own soul inside you for yourself, without its dying, than you can keep the seed of your womb. Until a man gives you his seed, the seed of your womb is nothing. And the man's seed is nothing to him.—And until you give your soul to a man, and he takes it, your soul is nothing to you.—And when a man has taken your whole soul— Ah, do not talk to me about betraying. A man only betrays because he has been given *a part*, and not the whole. And a woman only betrays because only the part has been taken from her, and not the whole. That is all about betrayal. I know. —But when the whole is given, and taken, betrayal can't exist. What I am to Ramón, I am. And what he is to me, he is. I do not care what he does. If he is away from me, he does as he

wishes. So long as he will always keep safe what I am to him."

Kate did not like having to learn lessons from this little waif of a Teresa. Kate was a woman of the world, handsome and experienced. She was accustomed to homage. Other women usually had a slight fear of her, for she was powerful and ruthless in her own way.

Teresa also feared her a little, as a woman of the world. But as an intrinsic woman, not at all. Trenched inside her own fierce and proud little soul, Teresa looked on Kate as on one of those women of the outside world, who make a very splendid show, but who are not so sure of the real secret of womanhood, and the innermost power. All Kate's handsome, ruthless female power was second-rate to Teresa, compared with her own quiet, deep passion of connection with Ramón.

Yes, Kate was accustomed to looking on other women as inferiors. But the tables were suddenly turned. Even as, in her soul, she knew Ramón to be a greater man than Cipriano, suddenly she had to question herself, whether Teresa was not a greater woman than she.

Teresa! A greater woman than Kate? What a blow! Surely it was impossible!

Yet there it was. Ramón had wanted to marry Teresa, not Kate. And the flame of his marriage with Teresa she saw both in his eyes and in Teresa's. A flame that was not in Kate's eyes.

Kate's marriage with Cipriano was curious and momentary. When Cipriano was away, Kate was her old individual self. Only when Cipriano was present, and then only sometimes, did the connection overwhelm her.

When Teresa turned and looked at her with this certain flame, touched with indignation, Kate quailed. Perhaps for the first time in her life she quailed and felt abashed: repentant.

Kate even knew that Teresa felt a little repugnance for her: for the foreign white woman who talked as cleverly as a man and who never gave her soul: who did not believe in giving her soul. All these well-dressed, beautiful women from America or England, Europe, they all kept their souls for themselves, in a sort of purse, as it were.

Teresa was determined that Kate should leave off treating her, very, very indefinably, as an inferior. It was how all the foreign women treated the Mexican women. Because the foreign women

were their own mistresses! They even tried to be condescending to Ramón.

But Ramón! He could look at them and make them feel small, feel really nothing, in spite of all their money and their experience and their air of belonging to the ruling races. The ruling races! Wait! Ramón was a challenge to all that. Let those rule who can.

"You did not sleep?" Teresa said to Kate.

"Not very well," said Kate.

"No, you look as if you had not slept very well.—Under your eyes."

Kate smoothed the skin under her eyes, querulously.

"One gets that look in Mexico," she said. "It's not an easy country to keep your youth in.—You are looking well."

"Yes, I am very well."

Teresa had a new, soft bloom on her dark skin, something frail and tender, which she did not want to have to defend against another woman.

"I think I will go home now Ramón has come," said Kate.

"Oh, why? Do you wish to?"

"I think I'd better."

"Then I will go with you to Sayula. In the boat, no?"

Kate put her few things together. She had slept badly. The night had been black, black with something of horror in it. As when the bandits had attacked Ramón. She could see the scar in his back, in the night. And the drumming crash of falling water, menacing and horrible, seemed to keep up for hours.

In her soul, Kate felt Teresa's contempt for her way of wifehood.

"I have been married too," Kate had said. "To a very exceptional man, whom I *loved*."

"Ah, yes!" said Teresa. "And he died."

"He wanted to die."

"Ah, yes! He wanted to die."

"I did my level best to prevent him from wearing himself out."

"Ah, yes, to prevent him."

"What else could I have done?" flashed Kate in anger.

"If you could have given him your life, he would not even have wanted to die."

"I *did* give him my life. I loved him—oh, you will never

know.—But he didn't *want* my soul.   He believed I should keep
a soul of my own."

"Ah, yes, men are like that, when they are merely men.   When
a man is *warm* and brave—then he wants the woman to give him
her soul, and he keeps it in *his* womb, so he is more than a mere
man, a single man.   I know it.   I know where my soul is.   It is
in Ramón's womb, the womb of a man, just as his seed is in my
womb, the womb of a woman.   He is a man, and a column of
blood.   I am a woman, and a valley of blood.   I shall not contra-
dict him.   How can I?   My soul is inside him, and I am far
from contradicting him when he is trying with all his might to
do something that *he* knows about.   He won't die, and they won't
kill him.   No!   The stream flows into him from the heart of the
world : and from me.—I tell you, because you saved his life, and
therefore we belong to the same thing, you and I and he—and
Cipriano.   But you should not misjudge me.   That other way of
women, where a woman keeps her own soul—ah, what is it but
weariness !"

"And the men ?"

"Ah! if there are men whose souls are warm and brave, how
they comfort one's womb, Caterina !"

Kate hung her head, stubborn and angry at being put down from
her eminence.—The slave morale! she said to herself.   The miserable old trick of a woman living just for the sake of a man.
Only living to send her soul with him, inside his precious body.
And to carry his precious seed in her womb!   Herself, apart
from this, nothing.

Kate wanted to make her indignation thorough, but she did
not quite succeed.   Somewhere, secretly and angrily, she envied
Teresa her dark eyes with the flame in them and their savage
assurance.   She envied her her serpent-delicate fingers.   And
above all, she envied her, with repining, the comfort of a living
man permanent in her womb.   And the secret, savage indomitable
pride in her own womanhood, that rose from this.

In the warm morning after the rain, the frogs were whirring
frantically.   Across the lake, the mountains were blue black, and
little pieces of white, fluffy vapour wandered low across the trees.
Clouds were along the mountain-tops, making a level sky-line of
whitish softness the whole length of the range.   On the lonely,
fawn-coloured water, one sail was blowing.

"It is like Europe—like the Tyrol to-day," said Kate wistfully.

"Do you love Europe very much?" asked Teresa.

"Yes, I think I love it."

"And must you go back to it?"

"I think so. Soon! To my mother and my children."

"Do they want you very much?"

"Yes!" said Kate, rather hesitant. Then she added: "Not *very* much, really. But I want them."

"What for?—I mean," Teresa added, "do you long for them?"

"Sometimes," said Kate, the tears coming to her eyes.

The boat rowed on in silence.

"And Cipriano?" Teresa asked timidly.

"Ah!" said Kate shortly. "He is such a stranger to me."

Teresa was silent for some moments.

"I think a man is always a stranger to a woman," said Teresa. "Why should it not be so?"

"But you," said Kate, "haven't any children."

"Ramón has.—And he says: 'I cast my bread upon the waters. It is my children too. And if they return to me after many days, I shall be glad.'—Is it not the same for you?"

"Not quite!" said Kate. "I am a woman, I am not a man."

"I, if I have children," said Teresa, "I shall try to cast my bread upon the waters, so my children come to me that way. I hope I shall. I hope I shall not try to fish them out of life for myself, with a net. I have a very great fear of love. It is so personal. Let each bird fly with its own wings, and each fish swim its own course.—Morning brings more than love. And I want to be true to the morning."

CHAPTER XXVI

KATE IS A WIFE

KATE was glad to get back to her own house, and to be more or less alone. She felt a great change was being worked in her, and if it worked too violently, she would die. It was the end of something, and the beginning of something, far, far inside her: in her soul and womb. The men, Ramón and Cipriano, caused the change, and Mexico. Because the time had come.—Nevertheless if what was happening happened too rapidly, or violently, she felt she would die. So, from time to time she had to withdraw from contact, to be alone.

She would sit alone for hours on the shore, under a green willow tree that hung its curtains of pale-green fronds, on the beach. The lake was much fuller and higher up the shore, softer, more mysterious. There was a smell of the piles of water-hyacinth decaying at the water's edges. Distance seemed farther away. The near conical hills were dotted with green bushes, like a Japanese drawing. Bullock-wagons with solid wheels came rolling to the village, high with sugar cane, drawn by eight oxen with ponderous heads and slowly swinging horns, while a peon walked in front, with the guiding-stick on the cross-beam of the yoke. So slow, so massive, yet with such slight control!

She had a strange feeling, in Mexico, of the old prehistoric humanity, the dark-eyed humanity of the days, perhaps, before the glacial period. When the world was colder, and the seas emptier, and all the land-formation was different. When the waters of the world were piled in stupendous glaciers on the high places, and high, high upon the poles. When great plains stretched away to the oceans, like Atlantis and the lost continents of Polynesia, so that seas were only great lakes, and the soft, dark-eyed people of that world could walk around the globe. Then there was a mysterious, hot-blooded, soft-footed humanity with a strange civilization of its own.

Till the glaciers melted, and drove the peoples to the high places,

like the lofty plateaux of Mexico, separated them into cut-off nations.

Sometimes, in America, the shadow of that old pre-Flood world was so strong, that the day of historic humanity would melt out of Kate's consciousness; and she would begin to approximate to the old mode of consciousness, the old, dark will, the unconcern for death, the subtle, dark consciouness, non-cerebral, but vertebrate. When the mind and the power of man was in his blood and his back-bone, and there was the strange, dark inter-communication between man and man, and man and beast, from the powerful spine.

The Mexicans were still this. That which is aboriginal in America still belongs to the way of the world before the Flood, before the mental-spiritual world came into being. In America, therefore, the mental-spiritual life of white people suddenly flourishes like a great weed let loose in virgin soil. Probably it will as quickly wither. A great death come. And after that, the living result will be a new germ, a new conception of human life, that will arise from the fusion of the old blood-and-vertebrate consciousness with the white man's present mental-spiritual consciousness. The sinking of both beings, into a new being.

Kate was more Irish than anything, and the almost deathly mysticism of the aboriginal Celtic or Iberian people lay at the bottom of her soul. It was a residue of memory, something that lives on from the pre-Flood world, and cannot be killed. Something older, and more everlastingly potent, than our would-be fair-and-square world.

She knew more or less what Ramón was trying to effect: this fusion! She knew what it was that made Cipriano more significant to her than all her past, her husbands and her children. It was the leap of the old, antediluvian blood-male into unison with her. And for this, without her knowing, her innermost blood had been thudding all the time.

Ireland would not and could not forget that other old, dark, sumptuous living. The Tuatha De Danaan might be under the western sea. But they are under the living blood, too, never quite to be silenced. Now they have to come furth again, to a new connection. And the scientific, fair-and-square Europe has to mate once more with the old giants.

But the change, Kate felt, must not come on her too soon and too suddenly, or it would rupture her and she would die. The old

way has its horror.   The heavy-footed *à terre* spirit of aboriginal
Mexico could be so horrible to her, as to make her wicked.   The
slow, indomitable kind of existing and persisting, without hope
or élan, which is in the aboriginal American, sometimes made her
feel she would go mad.   The sullen will persisting over the slow,
dark centuries, counting the individual existence a trifle !   A
tenacity of demons, less than human.   And a sudden ferocity, a
sudden lust of death rousing incalculable and terrible.

People who never really changed.   Men who were not faithful
to life, to the living actuality.   Faithful to some dark necessity
out of the past.   The actual present suddenly collapsing in the
souls of the men and the women, and the old, black, volcanic lava
bursting up in violence, followed by a lava-rock indifference.

The hope !   The hope !   Would it ever be possible to revive the
hope in these black souls, and achieve the marriage which is the
only step to the new world of man ?

But meanwhile, a strange, almost torn nausea would come over
Kate, and she felt she must go away, to spare herself.   The
strange, reptilian insistence of her very servants.   *Blood is one
blood.   We are all of one blood-stream.*   Something aboriginal
and tribal, and almost worse than death to the white individual.
Out of the dark eyes and the powerful spines of these people,
all the time the unknown assertion : *The blood is one blood.*   It
was a strange, overbearing insistence, a claim of blood-unison.

Kate was of a proud old family.   She had been brought up
with the English-Germanic idea of the *intrinsic* superiority of
the hereditary aristocrat.   Her blood was different from the common blood, another, finer fluid.

But in Mexico, none of this.   Her criada Juana, the aguador
who carried the water, the boatman who rowed her on the lake,
all looked at her with one look in their eyes.   *The blood is one
blood.   In the blood, you and I are undifferentiated.*   She saw
it in their eyes, she heard it in their words, it tinged their deference
and their mockery.   And sometimes it made her feel physically
sick : this overbearing blood-familiarity.

And sometimes, when she tried to hold herself up, in the proud
old assertion : *My blood is my own.   Noli me tangere,* she would
see the terrible ancient hatred in their eyes, the hatred which
leads them to atrocities and fearful maimings.

They would defer to her spirit, her knowledge, her under-

standing. They would give her deference, and a sort of grudging reverence for this. She belonged to the ruling races, the clever ones. But back again they demanded her acquiescence to the primeval assertion: *The blood is one blood. We are one blood.* It was the assertion that swept away all individualism, and left her immersed, drowned in the grand sea of the living blood, in immediate contact with all these men and all these women.

To this she must submit. Or they would persist in the slow revenge.

And she could not submit, off-hand. It had to be a slow, organic process. Anything sudden or violent would destroy her.

Now she understood Ramón's assertion: Man is a column of blood: Woman is a valley of blood. It was the primeval oneness of mankind, the opposite of the oneness of the spirit.

But Kate had always looked upon her blood as absolutely her own, her individual own. Her spirit she shared, in the spirit she communed. But her blood stayed by her in individuality.

Now she was confronted by the other great assertion: The blood is one blood.—It meant a strange, marginless death of her individual self.

Now she understood why Ramón and Cipriano wore the white clothes and the sandals, and were naked, or half-naked, as living gods. It was the acquiescence in the primitive assertion. It was the renewal of the old, terrible bond of the blood-unison of man, which made blood-sacrifice so potent a factor of life. The blood of the individual is given back to the great blood-being, the god, the nation, the tribe.

Now she understood the strange unison she could always feel between Ramón and his men, and Cipriano and his men. It was the soft, quaking, deep communion of blood-oneness. Sometimes it made her feel sick. Sometimes it made her revolt. But it was the power she could not get beyond.

Because, admitting his blood-unison, Ramón at the same time claimed a supremacy, even a godliness. He was a man, as the lowest of his peons was a man. At the same time, rising from the same pool of blood, from the same roots of manhood as they, and being, as they were, a man of the pulsing blood, he was still something more. Not in the blood nor in the spirit lay his individuality and his supremacy, his godhead. But in a star within him, an inexplicable star which rose out of the dark sea and shone

between the flood and the great sky. The mysterious star which unites the vast universal blood with the universal breath of the spirit, and shines between them both.

Not the rider on the white horse: nor the rider on the red. That which is beyond the riders and the horses, the inexplicable mystery of the star whence no horseman comes and to which no horseman can arrive. The star which is a man's innermost clue, which rules the power of the blood on the one hand, and the power of the spirit on the other.

For this, the only thing which is supreme above all power in a man, and at the same time, is power; which far transcends knowledge; the strange star between the sky and the waters of the first cosmos: this is man's divinity.

And some men are not divine at all. They have only faculties. They are slaves, or they should be slaves.

But many a man has his own spark of divinity, and has it quenched, blown out by the winds of force or ground out of him by machines.

And when the spirit and the blood in man begin to go asunder, bringing the great death, most stars die out.

Only the man of a great star, a great divinity, can bring the opposites together again, in a new unison.

And this was Ramón, and this was his great effort: to bring the great opposites into contact and into unison again. And this is the god-power in man. By this power you shall know the god in man. By none other.

Ramón was a man as the least of his peons was a man, with the beating heart and the secret loins and the lips closed on the same secret of manhood. And he was human as Kate was human, with the same yearning of the spirit, for pure knowledge and communion, the soul in the greatness of its comprehending.

But only he had that starry power for bringing together the two great human impulses to a point of fusion, for being the bird between the vast wings of the dual-created power to which man has access and in which man has his being. The Morning Star, between the breath of dawn and the deeps of the dark.

Men had tried to murder him with knives. Carlota would have murdered him with her spirit. Each half separately wanted to commit the murder of him.

But he kept himself beyond. He was the living Quetzalcoatl, and the tiny sparkle of a star was rising in his own men, in his own woman.

The star between the two wings of power: that alone was divinity in a man, and final manhood.

Kate had a message from Cipriano to say he was coming out to stay in the Villa Aragon. The Villa Aragon was the chief house on the lake, in small but rather beautiful grounds with tufts of palm-trees and heavy hedges of jasmine, a garden kept always green by constant watering. The house was built rather like a little castle, absurd, yet its deep, spacious verandahs opening on to the slopes and knolls of the tree-clustered garden, above the lake, were pleasant.

Cipriano arrived very pleased, his black eyes shining with the boyish look. He wanted Kate to marry him, go through the Mexican civil marriage, and instal herself in the Villa Aragon. She hesitated. She knew she must go back to Europe, to England and Ireland, very soon. The necessity was imperative. The sense of menace that Mexico put over her, and the feeling of inner nausea, was becoming too much to bear. She felt she could not stand it, unless she went away to relax for a time.

This she told to Cipriano. And his face fell.

"It doesn't matter to me very much whether I marry or not, before I go," she said. "But I must go soon—soon."

"How soon?"

"By January."

His face lightened again.

"Then marry me before you go," he said. "Next week."

She agreed, with curious indifference, and he, his eyes flashing again like a boy's moved quickly, to make the necessary legal preparations.

She did not care whether she married or not. In one essential sense, she had married Cipriano already. He was first and foremost a soldier, swift to come to her, and swift to go. She would always be a good deal alone.

And him alone, just as a man and a soldier, she could marry easily enough. It was this terrible Mexico that frightened her with a sense of doom.

The Quetzalcoatl movement had spread in the country, but sinisterly. The Archbishop had declared against it, Ramón and

Cipriano and their adherents were excommunicated.   An attempt had been made to assassinate Montes.

The adherents of Quetzalcoatl in the capital had made the Church of San Juan Bautista, which was called the Church of the Black Saviour, their Metropolitan House of Quetzalcoatl. The Archbishop, a choleric man, had summoned his fervent followers to march in procession to this Church of San Juan, now called the House of Quetzalcoatl, and seize it and restore it to the Catholic Church.   The government, knowing it would have to fight sooner or later, arrested the Archbishop and broke up the procession after some bloodshed.

Then a kind of war began.   The Knights of Cortes brought out their famous hidden stores of arms, not very impressive, after all, and a clerical mob headed by a fanatical priest, surged into the Zócalo.   Montes had the guns turned on them.   But it looked like the beginnings of a religious war.   In the streets the white and blue serapes of Quetzalcoatl and the scarlet and black serapes of Huitzilopochtli were seen in bands, marching to the sound of tom-toms, and holding up the curious round banners, made of feather-work, of Quetzalcoatl, and the tall scarlet signs of Huitzilopochtli, long poles with the soft club of scarlet feathers at the top, tufted with a black point.—In the churches, the priests were still inflaming the orthodox to a holy war.   In the streets, priests who had gone over to Quetzalcoatl were haranguing the crowd.

It was a wild moment.   In Zacatecas General Narciso Beltran had declared against Montes and for the Church.   But Cipriano with his Huitzilopochtli soldiers had attacked with such swiftness and ferocity, Beltran was taken and shot, his army disappeared.

Then Montes declared the old Church illegal in Mexico, and caused a law to be passed, making the religion of Quetzalcoatl the national religion of the Republic.   All churches were closed.   All priests were compelled to take an oath of allegiance to the Republic, or condemned to exile.   The armies of Huitzilopochtli and the white and blue serapes of Quetzalcoatl appeared in all the towns and villages of the Republic.   Ramón laboured ceaselessly. Cipriano appeared in unexpected flashes, in unexpected places. He managed to rouse the most discontented States, Vera Cruz, Tamaulipas, Yucatan, to a sort of religious frenzy.   Strange baptisms took place in the sea, and a scarlet and black tower of Huitzilopochtli rose along the shores.

The whole country was thrilling with a new thing, with a re-

lease of new energy. But there was a sense of violence and crudity in it all, a touch of horror.

The Archbishop was deported, no more priests were seen in the streets. Only the white and blue and earth-coloured serapes of Quetzalcoatl, and the scarlet and black of Huitzalopochtli, were seen among the crowds. There was a great sense of release, almost of exuberance.

This is why Cipriano came to Kate with those black, flashing, boyish eyes. He was in a strange state of triumph. Kate was frightened, and she felt curiously hollow. Even the queer, new, flashing triumph and the sense of a new thing on the face of the earth could not quite save her. She belonged too much to the old world of Europe, she could not, could not make herself over so quickly. But she felt that if she could go back to Ireland, and let her life and her body *pause* for a time, then she could come back and take her share.

For it was not her spirit alone which was changing, it was her body, and the constitution of her very blood. She could feel it, the terrible katabolism and metabolism in her blood, changing her even as a creature, changing her to another creature.

And if it went too fast, she would die.

So, she was legally married to Cipriano, and she went to live with him in the Villa Aragon, for a month. After a month, she would sail away, alone, to Ireland. He agreed too.

It was strange, to be married to him. He made her go all vague and quiet, as if she sank away heavy and still, away from the surface of life, and lay deep in the underlife.

The strange, heavy, *positive* passivity. For the first time in her life she felt absolutely at rest. And talk, and thought, had become trivial, superficial to her: as the ripples on the surface of the lake are as nothing, to the creatures that live away below in the unwavering deeps.

In her soul, she was still and proud. If only the body had not suffered the unbearable nausea of change. She had sunk to a final rest, within a great, opened-out cosmos. The universe had opened out to her new and vast, and she had sunk to the deep bed of pure rest. She had become almost like Teresa in sureness.

Yet the process of change within her blood was terrible to her.

Cipriano was happy, in his curious Indian way. His eyes kept that flashing, black, dilated look of a boy looking newly on a strange, almost uncanny wonder of life. He did not look very

definitely at Kate, or even take much definite notice of her.   He did not like talking to her, in any serious way.   When she wanted to talk seriously, he flashed a cautious, dark look at her, and went away.

He was aware of things that she herself was hardly conscious of.   Chiefly, of the curious irritant quality of talk.   And this he avoided.   Curious as it may seem, he made her aware of her own old desire for frictional, irritant sensation.   She realised how all her old love had been frictional, charged with the fire of irritation and the spasms of frictional voluptuousness.

Cipriano, curiously, by refusing to share any of this with her, made it become external to her.   Her strange seething feminine will and desire subsided in her and swept away, leaving her soft and powerfully potent, like the hot springs of water that gushed up so noiseless, so soft, yet so powerful, with a sort of secret potency.

She realised, almost with wonder, the death in her of the Aphrodite of the foam: the seething, frictional, ecstatic Aphrodite. By a swift dark instinct, Cipriano drew away from this in her. When, in their love, it came back on her, the seething electric female ecstasy, which knows such spasms of delirium, he recoiled from her.   It was what she used to call her "satisfaction."   She had loved Joachim for this, that again, and again, and again he could give her this orgiastic "satisfaction," in spasms that made her cry aloud.

But Cipriano would not.   By a dark and powerful instinct he drew away from her as soon as this desire rose again in her, for the white ecstasy of frictional satisfaction, the throes of Aphrodite of the foam.   She could see that to him, it was repulsive.   He just removed himself, dark and unchangeable, away from her.

And she, as she lay, would realise the worthlessness of this foam-effervescence, its strange externality to her.   It seemed to come upon her from without, not from within.   And succeeding the first moment of disappointment, when this sort of "satisfaction" was denied her, came the knowledge that she did not really want it, that it was really nauseous to her.

And he, in his dark, hot silence would bring her back to the new, soft, heavy, hot flow, when she was like a fountain gushing noiseless and with urgent softness from the volcanic deeps.   Then she was open to him soft and hot, yet gushing with a noiseless soft power.   And there was no such thing as conscious "satisfaction."   What happened was dark and untellable.   So different

from the beak-like friction of Aphrodite of the foam, the friction which flares out in circles of phosphorescent ecstasy, to the last wild spasm which utters the involuntary cry, like a death-cry, the final love-cry. This she had known, and known to the end, with Joachim. And now this too was removed from her. What she had with Cipriano was curiously beyond her knowing: so deep and hot and flowing, as it were subterranean. She had to yield before it. She could not grip it into one final spasm of white ecstasy which was like sheer knowing.

And as it was in the love-act, so it was with him. She could not *know* him. When she tried to know him, something went slack in her, and she had to leave off. She had to let be. She had to leave him, dark and hot and potent, along with the things that *are,* but are not known. The presence. And the stranger. This he was always to her.

There was hardly anything to say to him. And there was no personal intimacy. He kept his privacy round him like a cloak, and left her immune within her own privacy. He was a stranger to her, she to him. He accepted the fact absolutely, as if nothing else were possible. She, sometimes, felt it strange. She had so craved for intimacy, *insisted* on intimacy.

Now she found herself accepting him finally and forever as the stranger in whose presence she lived. It was his impersonal presence which enveloped her. She lived in his aura, and he, she knew, lived in hers, with nothing said, and no personal or spiritual intimacy whatever. A mindless communion of the blood.

Therefore, when he had to go away, it did not matter so very much. His presence was something he left with her, and he took her presence along with him. And somehow, there was no need for emotions.

He had to leave early one morning, for Mexico. The dawn came perfect and clear. The sun was not yet on the lake, but it caught the mountains beyond Tuliapan, and they shone magically distinct, as if some magic light were focussed on them. The green furrows of the mountain sides were as if in her own hand. Two white gulls, flying, suddenly got the light, and glittered. But the full, soft, noiseless dun lake was pallid, unlit.

She thought of the sea. The Pacific was not very far away. The sea seemed to have retreated entirely out of her consciousness. Yet she knew she needed its breath again.

Cipriano was going down to bathe. She saw him walk out on

the masonry of the square basin which was their own tiny harbour. He threw off his wrap and stood dark in silhouette against the pale, unlit water. How dark he was! Dark as a Malay. Curious that his body was as dark, almost, as his face. And with that strange archaic fulness of physique, with the full chest and the full, yet beautiful buttocks of men on old Greek coins.

He dropped off the edge of masonry and waded out in the dim, soft, uncanny water. And at that moment the light tipped over the edge of the mountain and spilled gold upon the surface of the lake. And instantly he was red as fire. The sunshine was not red, the sun was too high for that. It was golden with morning. But as it flushed along the surface of the lake it caught the body of Cipriano and he was red as fire, as a piece of pure fire.

The Sons of the Morning! The column of blood! A Red Indian. She looked at him in wonder, as he moved pure red and luminous further into the lake, unconscious. As if on fire!

The Sons of the Morning! She let her effort at knowing slip away from her once more, and remained without effort, within the communion.

It was his race, too. She had noticed before how the natives shone pure red when morning or evening light caught them, rather level. As fires they stood in the water. The Red Indian.

He went away, with his man, on horseback. And she watched him ride over the brow of the road, sitting dark and still on his silky, roan horse. He loved a red horse. And there was a curious motionlessness about him as he rode horseback, and old, male pride, and at the same time the half-ghostly, dark invisibility of the Indian, sitting close upon the horse as if he and it belonged to one birth.

He was gone, and for a while she felt the old nostalgia for his presence. Not for him, exactly. Not even to see him or touch him or speak to him. Only to feel him about.

Then quickly she recovered. She adjusted herself to the presence he left behind with her. As soon as he had *really* gone, and the act of going was over, his presence came back to her.

She walked a little while by the shore, beyond the breakwater wall. She loved to be alone: a great deal alone, with a garden and the lake and the morning. "I am like Teresa, really," she said to herself.

Suddenly before her she saw a long, dark soft rope, lying over a pale boulder. But her soul was softly alert, at once. It was a

snake, with a subtle pattern along its soft dark back, lying there over a big stone, with its head sunk down to earth.

It felt her presence, too, for suddenly, with incredible soft quickness, it contracted itself down the boulder, and she saw it entering a little gap in the bottom of the wall.

The hole was not very big. And as it entered it quickly looked back, poising its little, dark, wicked, pointed head, and flickering a dark tongue. Then it passed on, slowly easing its dark length into the hole.

When it had all gone in, Kate could see the last fold still, and the flat little head resting on the fold, like the devil with his chin on his arms, looking out of a loop-hole. So the wicked sparks of the eyes looked out at her, from within the recess. Watching out of its own invisibility.

So she wondered over it, as it lay in its hidden places. At all the unseen things in the hidden places of the earth. And she wondered if it was disappointed at not being able to rise higher in creation: to be able to run on four feet, and not keep its belly on the ground.

Perhaps not! Perhaps it had its own peace. She felt a certain reconciliation between herself and it.

CHAPTER XXVII

HERE!

SHE and Teresa visited one another along the lake. There was a kinship and a gentleness between them, especially now Kate was going away for a while.

There was a certain autumnal purity and lull on the lake. The moisture still lingered, the bushes on the wild hills were green in puffs. Sunlight lay in a rich gleam on the mountains, and shadows were deep and velvety. The green almost covered the rocks and the pinkish land. Bright green the sugar cane, red the ploughed earth, dark the trees with white specks of villages here and there. And over the wild places, a sprinkle of bushes, then stark grey rock still coming out.

The sky was very high and pure. In the morning came the sound of drums, and on the motionless, crystal air the cry for the pauses of the day. And always the day seemed to be pausing and unfolding again to the greater mystery. The universe seemed to have opened vast and soft and delicate with life.

There was something curiously soothing even in the full, pale, dove-brown water of the lake. A boat was coming over, with its sail hollowed out like a shell, pearly white, and its sharp black canoe-beak slipping past the water. It looked like the boat of Dionysos coming with a message, and the vine sprouting.

Kate could hardly remember now the dry rigid pallor of the heat, when the whole earth seemed to crepitate viciously with dry malevolence: like memory gone dry and sterile, hellish.

Ramón and Teresa came along the lake, and rowed into the basin. It was a morning when the shadows on the mountains were almost corn-flower blue.

"Yet you must go away?" Ramón said to her.

"For a little while. You don't think I am Lot's wife, do you?"

"No!" laughed Ramón. "I think you're Cipriano's."

"I am really. But I want to go back for a little while."

"Ah yes! Better go, and then come again. Tell them in your Ireland to do as we have done here."

"But how?"

"Let them find themselves again, and their own universe, and their own gods. Let them substantiate their own mysteries. The Irish have been so wordy about their far-off heroes and green days of the heroic gods. Now tell them to substantiate them, as we have tried to substantiate Quetzalcoatl and Huitzilopochtli."

"I will tell them," she said. "If there is anybody to listen."

"Yes!" he said.

He watched the white sail blowing nearer.

"But why do you go away?" he asked her, after a silence.

"You don't care, do you?" she said.

There was a dead pause.

"Yes, I care," he said.

"But why?"

Again it was some time before he answered.

"You are one of us, we need you," he said.

"Even when I don't do anything?—and when I get a bit bored with living Quetzalcoatls—and the rest, and wish for a simple Don Ramón?" she replied.

He laughed suddenly.

"What is a simple Don Ramón?" he said. "A simple Don Ramón has a living Quetzalcoatl inside him. But you help all the same."

"You go ahead so grandly, one would not think you needed help: especially from a mere woman who—who after all is only the wife of your friend."

They were sitting on a bench under a red-flowering poinsettia whose huge scarlet petal-leaves spread out like sharp plumes.

"The wife of my friend!" he said. "What could you be better?"

"Of course," she said, more than equivocal.

He was leaning his arms on his knees, and looking out to the lake, abstract, and remote. There was a certain worn look on his face, and the vulnerability which always caught at Kate's heart. She realised again the isolation and the deadly strain his effort towards a new way of life put upon him. Yet he had to do it.

This again gave her a feeling of helplessness, a woman's utter helplessness with a man who goes out to the beyond. She had to stifle her resentment, and her dislike of his "abstract" efforts.

"Do you feel awfully sure of yourself?" she said.

"Sure of myself?" he re-echoed. "No! Any day I may die

and disappear from the face of the earth. I not only know it, I *feel* it. So why should I be sure of *myself?*"

"Why should you die?" she said.

"Why should anybody ever die?—even Carlota!"

"Ah!—her hour had come!"

"Can you set one's hour as one sets an alarm clock?" Kate paused.

"And if you're not sure of yourself, what are you sure of?" she challenged.

He looked at her with dark eyes which she could not understand.

"I am sure—sure—" his voice tailed off into vagueness, his face seemed to go grey and peaked, as a dead man's, only his eyes watched her blackly, like a ghost's. Again she was confronted with the suffering ghost of the man. And she was a woman, powerless before this suffering ghost which was still in the flesh.

"You don't think you are wrong, do you?" she asked, in cold distress.

"No! I am not wrong. Only maybe I can't hold out," he said.

"And then what?" she said, coldly.

"I shall go my way, alone." There seemed to be nothing left of him but the black, ghostly eyes that gazed on her. He began to speak Spanish.

"It hurts me in my soul, as if I were dying," he said.

"But why?" she cried. "You are not ill?"

"I feel as if my soul were coming undone."

"Then don't let it," she cried, in fear and repulsion.

But he only gazed with those fixed, blank eyes. A sudden deep stillness came over her; a sense of power in herself.

"You should forget for a time," she said gently, compassionately laying her hand on his. What was the good of trying to understand him or wrestle with him? She was a woman. He was a man, and—and—and therefore not quite real. Not true to life.

He roused himself suddenly from her touch, as if he had come awake, and he looked at her with keen, proud eyes. Her motherly touch had roused him like a sting.

"Yes!" he said. "It is true!"

"Of course it is!" she replied. "If you want to be so—so abstract and Quetzalcoatlian, then bury your head sometimes like an ostrich in the sand, and forget.

"So!" he said, smiling. "You are angry again!"

"It's not so simple," she said. "There is a conflict in me. And you won't let me go away for a time."

"We can't even prevent you," he said.

"Yes, but are against my going—you don't let me go in peace."

"Why must you go?" he said.

"I must," she said. "I must go back to my children, and my mother."

"It is a necessity in you?" he said.

"Yes!"

The moment she had admitted the necessity, she realised it was a certain duplicity in herself. It was as if she had two selves, one, a new one, which belonged to Cipriano and to Ramón, and which was her sensitive, desirous self : the other hard and finished, accomplished, belonging to her mother, her children, England, her whole past. This old accomplished self was curiously invulnerable and insentient, curiously hard and "free." In it, she was an individual and her own mistress. The other self was vulnerable, and organically connected with Cipriano, even with Ramón and Teresa, and so was not "free" at all.

She was aware of a duality in herself, and she suffered from it. She could not definitely commit herself, either to the old way of life, or to the new. She reacted from both. The old was a prison, and she loathed it. But in the new way she was not her own mistress at all, and her egostic will recoiled.

"That's just it!" she said. "It *is* a necessity in me, and you want to prevent me."

"No! No!" said Ramón. "I hope not."

"Yes! You put a weight on me, and paralyse me, to prevent me from going," she said.

"We must not do that," he said. "We must leave you, and not come near you for a time, if you feel it is so."

"Why! Why can't you be friendly? Why can't you be *with* me in my going? Why can't you *want* me to go, since I must go?"

He looked at her with dispassionate eyes.

"I can't do that," he said. "I don't believe in your going. It is a turning back : there is something renegade in it.—But we are all complicated. And if you *feel* you must go back for a time, go! It isn't terribly important. You have chosen, really. I am not afraid for you."

It was a great relief to her to hear this : because she was terribly afraid for herself. She could never be sure, never be *whole* in

her connection with Cipriano and Ramón.   Yet she said, mocking
slightly:

"Why *should* you be afraid for me?"

"Aren't you sometimes afraid for yourself?" he asked.

"Never!" she said.   "I'm absolutely sure about myself."

They had been sitting in the garden of the Villa Aragon, under
the poinsettia tree with the huge scarlet petal-leaves, like soft red
quill feathers.   The morning was becoming hot.   The lake had
gone still, with the fallen wind.   Everything was still.   Save the
long scarlet of the poinsettia.

Christmas was coming!   The poinsettia reminded Kate of it.

Christmas!   Holly-berries!   England!   Presents!   Food—If she
hurried, she could be in England for Christmas.   It felt so safe,
so familiar, so normal, the thought of Christmas at home, in
England, with her mother.   And all the exciting things she could
tell to the people at home!   And all the exciting gossip she could
hear!   In the distance, it looked very attractive.—She still had a
qualm as to what the actual return would be like.

"One can have too much of a good thing," she said to Ramón.

"What good thing in particular?" he asked her.

"Oh—Quetzalcoatl and all that!" she said.   "One can have
too much of it."

"It may be," he said, rising and going quietly away; so quietly,
he was gone before she knew.   And when she realised he had
gone like that, she flushed with anger.   But she sat on under the
poinsettia tree, in the hot, still November sun, looking with anger
at the hedge of jasmine, with its pure white flowers, and its sere,
withered flowers, and its pinkish buds among the dark leaves.
Where had she heard something about jasmine?   "And the jasmine flowers between us!"

Oh! how tired she was of all that!

Teresa came down the garden slope.

"You are still sitting here?" she exclaimed.

"Where else should I be?" Kate answered.

"I don't know.—Ramón has gone to Sayula, to see the Jefe.
He wouldn't wait for us, to come with us in the boat."

"I suppose he was in a hurry," said Kate.

"How fine these Noche Buenas are!" said Teresa looking at
the brilliant spread of red poinsettias.

"They are your Christmas flower, aren't they?" said Kate.

"Yes—the flowers of the Noche Buena—"

"How awful, Christmas with hibiscus and poinsettia! It makes me long to see mistletoe among the oranges, in a fruiterer's shop in Hampstead."

"Why that?" laughed Teresa.

"Oh!" Kate sighed petulantly. "To get back to simple life. To see the 'buses rolling on the mud in Piccadilly, on Christmas Eve, and the wet pavements crowded with people under the brilliant shops."

"Is that life, to you?" asked Teresa.

"Yes! Without all this abstraction, and *will*. Life is good enough for me if I am allowed to live and be myself."

"It is time Cipriano should come home," said Teresa.

But this made Kate rise from her seat, with sudden impatience. She would not have this thing put over her! She would break free, and show them!

She went with Teresa to the village. The air seemed mysteriously alive, with a new Breath. But Kate felt out of it. The two women sat under a tree on the beach at Sayula, talking a little, and watching the full expanse of the dove-pale lake.

A black boat with a red-painted roof and a tall mast was moored to the low breakwater-wall, which rose about a yard high, from the shallow water. On the wall stood loose little groups of white-clad men, looking into the black belly of the ship. And perched immobile in silhouette against the lake, was a black-and-white cow, and a huge monolithic black-and-white bull. The whole silhouette frieze motionless, against the far water that was coloured brown like turtle doves.

It was near, yet seemed strange and remote. Two peons fixed a plank gangway up to the side of the boat. Then they began to shove the cow towards it. She pawed the new broad planks tentatively, then, with that slow Mexican indifference, she lumbered unwillingly on to the gangway. They edged her slowly to the end, where she looked down into the boat. And at last, she dropped neatly into the hold.

Now the group of men broke into motion, for the huge and spangled bull. A tall old Mexican, in fawn, skin-tight trousers and little leather jacket, and a huge felt hat heavily embroidered with silver, gently took the ring in the bull's nose, gently lifted the wedge of the bull's head, so the great soft throat was uplifted. A peon behind put his head down, and with all his might began shoving the mighty, living flanks of the bull. The slim-legged,

high hatted old Mexican pulled evenly at the nose-ring. And with a calm and weighty poise, the bull stepped along the crest of the wall, delicately and impassively, to the plank gangway. There he stopped.

The peons began to re-group. The one behind, with his red sash tied so determinedly over his white hips, ceased to shove, the slim-legged Mexican let go the ring.

Then two peons passed a rope loosely round the haunches of the bull. The high-hatted farmer stepped on to the planks, and took the nose-ring again, very gently. He pulled softly. The bull lifted its head, but held back. It struck the planks with an unwilling foot. Then it stood, spangled with black on its whiteness, like a piece of the sky, immobile.

The farmer pulled once more at the ring. Two men were pulling the rope, pressing in the flanks of the immovable, passive, spangled monster. Two peons, at the back, with their heads down and their red-sashed, flexible loins thrust out behind, shoved with all their strength in the soft flanks of the mighty creature.

And all was utterly noiseless and changeless; against the fullness of the pale lake, this silent, monumental group of life.

Then the bull stepped slowly, imperturbably, yet against its will, on to the loose planks, and was edged slowly along, to the brink of the boat. There he waited.

He stood huge and silvery, dappled like the sky, with black snake markings down his haunches, looming massive above the red roof of the *canoa*. How would he ever duck to that roof, and drop under, into the darkness of the ship?

He lowered his head, and looked into the hold. The men behind shoved his living flanks. He took no heed, but lowered his head and looked again. The men pushed with all their might, in the dense Mexican silence.

Slowly, carefully, the bull crouched himself, made himself small, and with a quick, massive little movement dropped his forefeet down into the body of the boat, leaving his huge hind-quarters heaved up behind. There was a shuffle and a little stagger down below, then the soft thud as his hind-feet leaped down. He had gone.

The planks were taken away. A peon ran to unfasten the mooring rope from the stones of the shore. There was a strange thudding of soft feet within the belly of the boat. Men in the water were pushing the ship's black stern, to push her off. But she was

heavy. Slowly, casually they pulled the stones from under her flat bottom, and flung them aside. Slowly she edged, swayed, moved a little, and was afloat.

The men climbed in. The two peons on the ship's rims were poling her out, pressing their poles and walking heavily till they reached the stern, then lifting their poles and running to the high prow. She slid slowly out, on to the lake.

Then quickly they hoisted the wide white sail. The sail thrust up her horn and curved in a whorl to the wind. The ship was going across the waters, with her massive, sky-spangled cargo of life invisible.

All so still and soft and remote.

"And will Ramón want you to sit beside him in the church as the bride of Quetzalcoatl—with some strange name?" Kate asked of Teresa.

"I don't know," said Teresa. "Later, he says, when the time comes for them to have a goddess."

"And will you mind?"

"For myself, I am afraid of it. But I understand that Ramón wants it. He says it is accepting the greater responsibility of one's existence. And I think that is true. If there is God in me, and God as woman, then I must accept this part of myself also, and put on the green dress, and be for the time the God-woman, since it is true of me also. I think it is true. Ramón says we must make it manifest. When I think of my brothers, I know we must. So I shall think of the God that beats invisible, like the heart of all the world. So when I have to wear the green dress, and sit before all the people in the church, I shall look away to the heart of all the world, and try to be my sacred self because it is necessary, and the right thing to do. I would not do it if I thought it was not right."

"But I thought the green dress was for the Bride of Huit-zilopochtli!" said Kate.

"Ah yes!" Teresa caught herself up. "Mine is the black dress with the white edges, and the red clouds."

"Would you rather have the green?" Kate asked. "Have it if you would. I am going away."

Teresa glanced up at her quickly.

"The green is for the wife of Huitzilopochtli," she said, as if numbed.

"I can't see that it matters," said Kate.

Teresa looked at her with quick, dark eyes.

"Different men must have different wives," she said. "Cipriano would never want a wife like me."

"And different women must have different husbands," said Kate. "Ramón would always be too abstract and overbearing for me."

Teresa flushed slowly, looking down at the ground.

"Ramón needs far too much submission from a woman, to please me," Kate added. "He takes too much upon himself."

Teresa looked up quickly, and raised her head proudly, showing her brownish throat like a rearing, crested snake.

"How do you know that Ramón needs submission from a woman?" she said. "How do you know? He has not asked any submission from you.—And you are wrong. He does not ask submission from me. He wants me to give myself gently to him. And then he gives himself back to me far more gently than I give myself to him. Because a man like that is more gentle than a woman. He is not like Cipriano. Cipriano is a soldier. But Ramón is gentle. You are mistaken in what you say."

Kate laughed a little.

"And you are a soldier among women, fighting all the time," Teresa continued. "I am not such. But some women must be soldiers in their spirit, and they need soldier husbands. That is why you are Malintzi, and your dress is green. You would always fight. You would fight with yourself, if you were alone in the world."

It was very still by the lake. They were waiting for Ramón.

A man was stripping palm-stalks, squatting in silence under a tree, in his white clothes, his black head bent forward. Then he went to wet his long strips in the lake, returning with them dangling.

Then he sat down again, and deftly, silently, with the dark, childlike absorption of the people took up his work. He was mending a chair bottom. When Kate watched him, he glanced up with a flash of black eyes, saluting her. And she felt a strange power surge in her limbs, from the flash of living recognition and deference in his eyes. As if his deference were a sort of flame of life, rich in him when he saw her.

A roan horse speckled with white was racing prancing along the shore, neighing frantically. His mame flowed in the wind, his feet struck the pebbles as he ran, and again he opened his long

nose and neighed anxiously. Away up the shore he ran. What had he lost?

A peon had driven a high-wheeled wagon, drawn by four mules, deep into the lake, till the water was above the high axles of the wheels, almost touching the bed of the cart. It looked like a dark square boat drawn by four soft, dark sea-horses which slowly waved their long dark ears like leaves, while the peon, in white with his big hat proudly balanced, stood erect. The mules deep in the water stepped gently, curving to the shore.

It was winter, but like spring by the lake. White and yellow calves, new and silky, were skipping, butting up their rear ends, lifting their tails, trotting side by side down to the water, to sniff at it suspiciously.

In the shadow of a great tree a mother-ass was tethered, and her foal lay in the shadow, a little thing black as ink, curled up, with fluffy head erect and great black ears spreading up, like some jet-black hare full of witch-craft.

"How many days?" called Kate to the peon, who had come out of the straw hut.

He gave her the flash of his dark eyes, in a sort of joy of deference. And she felt her breast surge with living pride.

"Last night, *Patrona!*" he smiled in answer.

"So new! So new! He doesn't get up, can't he?"

The peon went round, put his arm under the foal and lifted it to its feet. There it straddled on high, in amaze, upon its black legs like bent hair-pins.

"How nice it is!" cried Kate in delight, and the peon laughed at her with a soft, grateful flame, touched with reverence.

The ink-black ass-foal did not understand standing up. It rocked on its four loose legs, and wondered. Then it hobbled a few steps, to smell at some green, growing maize. It smelled and smelled and smelled, as if all the dark aeons were stirring awake in its nostrils.

Then it turned, and looked with its bushy-velvet face straight at Kate, and put out a pink tongue at her. She laughed aloud. It stood wondering, dazed. Then it put out its tongue again. She laughed at it. It gave an awkward little skip, which surprised its own self very much. Then it ventured forward again, and all unexpectedly even to itself, exploded into another little skip.

"Already it dances!" cried Kate. "And it came into the world only last night."

"Yes, already it dances!" reiterated the peon.

After bethinking itself for a time, the ass-foal walked uncertainly towards the mother. She was a well-liking grey-and-brown she-ass, rather glossy and self-assured. The ass-foal straight found the udder, and was drinking.

Glancing up, Kate met again the peon's eyes, with their black, full flame of life heavy with knowledge and with a curious reassurance. The black foal, the mother, the drinking, the new life, the mystery of the shadowy battle-field of creation; and the adoration of the full-breasted, glorious woman beyond him: all this seemed in the primitive black eyes of the man.

"Adios!" said Kate to him, lingeringly.

"Adios Patrona!" he replied, suddenly lifting his hand high, in the Quetzalcoatl salute.

She walked across the beach to the jetty, feeling the life surging vivid and resistant within her. "It is sex," she said to herself. "How wonderful sex can be, when men keep it powerful and sacred, and it fills the world! like sunshine through and through one!—But I'm not going to submit, even there. Why should one give in, to anything!

Ramón was coming down towards the boat, the blue symbol of Quetzalcoatl in his hat. And at that moment the drums began to sound for mid-day, and there came the mid-day call, clear and distinct, from the tower. All the men on the shore stood erect, and shot up their right hands to the sky. The women spread both palms to the light. Everything was motionless, save the moving animals.

Then Ramón went on to the boat, the men saluting him with the Quetzalcoatl salute as he came near.

"It is wonderful, really," said Kate, as they rowed over the water, "how—how splendid one can feel in this country! As if one were still genuinely of the nobility."

"Aren't you?" he said.

"Yes, I am. But everywhere else it is denied. Only here one feels the full force of one's nobility. The natives still worship it."

"At moments," said Ramón. "Later, they will murder you and violate you, for having worshipped you."

"Is it inevitable?" she said flippantly.

"I think so," he replied. "If you lived here alone in Sayula, and queened it for a time, you would get yourself murdered—or worse—by the people who had worshipped you."

"I don't think so," she said.

"I know," he replied.

"Why?" she said, obstinate.

"Unless one gets one's nobility from the gods, and turns to the middle of the sky for one's power, one will be murdered at last."

"I do get my nobility that way," she said.

But she did not quite believe it. And she made up her mind still more definitely, to go away.

She wrote to Mexico City, and engaged a berth from Vera Cruz to Southampton: she would sail on the last day of November. Cipriano came home on the seventeenth, and she told him what she had done. He looked at her with his head a little on one side, with a queer boyish judiciousness, but she could not tell at all what he felt.

"You are going already?" he said in Spanish.

And then she knew, at last, that he was offended. When he was offended, he never spoke English at all, but spoke Spanish just as if he were addressing another Mexican.

"Yes," she said. "On the 30th."

"And when do you came back?" he asked.

"Quien sabe!—Who knows!" she retorted.

He let his black eyes rest on her face for some minutes, watching her, unchanging and incomprehensible. He was thinking, superficially, that if he liked, he could use the law and have her prevented from leaving the country—or even from leaving Sayula —since she was legally married to him. There was the old fixity of Indian anger, glinting fixed and relentless in the depths of his eyes. And then the almost invisible change in his face, as the hidden emotion sank down and the stoic indifference, the emotionlessness of centuries, and the stoic kind of tolerance came over him. She could almost feel the waves of successive shadow and coldness go through his blood, his mind hardly aware at all. And again a fear of losing his contact melted her heart.

It was somehow, to her, beautiful, to feel shadows, and cold gleams, and a hardness like stone, then the strange heavy inertia of the tropical mid-day, the stupor of the Sun, moving upon him while he stood motionless, watching her. In the end it was that weird, sultry, tropical stupor of the hot hours, a heat-swoon of sheer indifference.

"Como quieres tu!" he said. "As you wish."

And she knew he had already released her, in the dark, sultry

stupor of his blood.   He would make no further effort after her.
This also was the doom of his race.

He took a boat and went down to Jamiltepec, to Ramón : as she
knew he would.

She was alone, as usual.   It occurred to her, that she herself
willed this aloneness.   She could not relax and be with these
people.   She could not relax and be with anybody.   She always
had to recoil upon her own individuality, as a cat does.

Sex, sexual correspondence, did it matter so very much to her?
It might have mattered more, if she had not had it.   But she had
had it—and very finally and consummately, with Cipriano.   So she
knew all about it.   It was as if she had conquered another territory, another field of life.   The conqueress!   And now she would
retire to the lair of her own individuality, with the prey.

Suddenly, she saw herself as men often saw her : the great cat,
with its spasms of voluptuousness and its lifelong lustful enjoyment of its own isolated, isolated individuality.   Voluptuously to
enjoy a contact.   Then with a lustful feline gratification, to
break the contact, and roam alone in a sense of power.   Each
time, to seize a sort of power, purring upon her own isolated individuality.

She knew so many women like that.   They played with love
and intimacy as a cat with a mouse.   In the end, they quickly ate
up the love mouse, then trotted off into a full belly and a voluptuous sense of power.

Only sometimes the love-mouse refused to be digested, and
there was lifelong dyspepsia.   Or, like Cipriano, turned into a
sort of serpent, that reared and looked at her with glittering eyes,
then slid away into the void, leaving her blank, the sense of power
gone out of her.

Another thing, she had observed, with a touch of horror.   One
after the other, her women "friends," the powerful love-women, at
the age of forty, forty-five, fifty, they lost all their charm and
allure, and turned into real grimalkins, greyish, avid, and horrify-
ing, prowling around looking for prey that became scarcer and
scarcer.   As human beings they went to pieces.   And they remained these grey-ribbed grimalkins, dressed in elegant clothes,
the grimalkin howl even passing into their smart chatter.

Kate was a wise woman, wise enough to take a lesson.

It is all very well for a woman to cultivate her ego, her individuality.   It is all very well for her to despise love, or to love

love as a cat loves a mouse, that it plays with as long as possible, before devouring it to vivify her own individuality and voluptuously fill the belly of her own ego.

"Woman has suffered far more from the suppression of her ego than from sex suppression," says a woman writer, and it may well be true. But look, only look at the modern woman of fifty and fifty-five, those who have cultivated their ego to the top of their bent! Usually, they are grimalkins to fill one with pity or with repulsion.

Kate knew all this. And as she sat alone in her villa, she remembered it again. She had had her fling, even here in Mexico. And these men would let her go again. She was no prisoner. She could carry off any spoil she had captured.

And then what! To sit in a London drawing-room, and add another to all the grimalkins? To let the peculiar grimalkin-grimace come on her face, the most weird grimalkin-twang come into her voice? Horror! Of all the horrors, perhaps the grimalkin women, her contemporaries, were the most repellent to her. Even the horrid old tom-cat men of the civilised roof gutters, did not fill her with such sickly dread.

"No!" she said to herself. "My ego and my individuality are not worth *that* ghastly price. I'd better abandon some of my ego, and sink some of my individuality, rather than go like that."

After all, when Cipriano touched her caressively, all her body flowered. That was the greater sex, that could fill all the world with lustre and which she dared not think about, its power was so much greater than her own will. But on the other hand, when she spread the wings of her own ego, and sent forth her own spirit, the world could look very wonderful to her, when she was alone. But after a while, the wonder faded, and a sort of jealous emptiness set in.

"I must have both," she said to herself. "I must not recoil against Cipriano and Ramón, they make my blood blossom in my body. I say they are limited. But then one must be limited. If one tries to be unlimited, one becomes horrible. Without Cipriano to touch me and limit me and submerge my will, I shall become a horrible, elderly female. I ought to *want* to be limited. I ought to be *glad* if a man will limit me with a strong will and a warm touch. Because what I call my greatness, and the vastness of the Lord behind me, lets me fall through a hollow floor of nothingness, once there is no man's hand there, to hold me warm

and limited. Ah yes! Rather than become elderly and a bit grisly, I will make my submission; as far as I need, and no further."

She called a man-servant, and set off down the lake in a row-boat. It was a very lovely November morning, the world had not yet gone dry again. In the sharp folds of the steep mountain slopes to the north-east, the shadows were pure corn-flower blue. Below was the lingering delicacy of green, already drying. The lake was full still, but subsided, and the water-hyacinth had drifted away. Birds flew low in the stillness. It was very full and still in the strong, hot light. Some maize-fields showed sere stubble, but the palo-blanco flowers were out, and the mesquite bushes were frail green, and there were wafts of perfume from the little yellow flower-balls, like cassia.

"Why should I go away!" said Kate. "Why should I see the 'buses on the mud of Piccadilly, on Christmas Eve, and the crowds of people on the wet pavements, under the big shops like great caves of light? I may as well stay here, where my soul is less dreary. I shall have to tell Ramón I am sorry for the things I said. I won't carp at them. After all, there is another kind of vastness here, with the sound of drums, and the cry of Quetzal-coatl."

Already she could see the yellow and reddish, tower-like upper story of Jamiltepec, and the rich, deep fall of magenta bougain-villea, from the high wall, with the pale spraying of plumbago flowers, and many loose creamy-coloured roses.

"Estan tocando!" said her boatman quietly, looking up at her with dark, pregnant eyes.

He had already heard the sound of the light drum, at Jamil-tepec. The boat rowed softly: and there came a sound of a man's voice singing in the morning.

Her boatman lifted an oar, as a signal to the house. And as the boat rounded the curve into the basin, a man-servant in white clothes came running down to the little jetty. In the changeless sunshine was a scent, perhaps of datura and of roses, and an eter-nal Mexican silence, which the noise of the drum, and the voice of singing, did not disturb.

"Is Don Cipriano here?" asked Kate.

"Está!" murmured the man, with a slight motion towards

Ramón's balcony, whence the singing came. "Shall I say you have come?"

He did not lift his voice above the murmur.

"No!" said Kate. "I shall sit here in the garden a while, before I come up."

"Then I will leave open the door," said the man, "and you can come up when you will."

Kate sat on a seat under a big tree. A creeping plant, with great snake-like cords and big sulphur-and-brown trumpet flowers, hung above. She listened to the singing. It was Ramón, teaching one of the singers.

Ramón had not a very good voice. He sang quietly, as if to the inner air, with very beautiful, simple expression. But Kate could not catch the words.

"Ya?" said Ramón, when he had finished.

"Ya, Patrón!" said the man, the singer.

And he began, in his strong, pure voice that caught at the very bowels, to sing another of the Hymns.

My way is not thy way, and thine is not mine.
But come, before we part
Let us separately go to the Morning Star,
And meet there.

I do not point you to my road, nor yet
Call: "Oh come!"
But the Star is the same for both of us,
Winsome.

The good ghost of me goes down the distance
To the Holy Ghost.
Oh you, in the tent of the cloven flame
Meet me, you I like most.

Each man his own way forever, but towards
The hoverer between;
Who opens his flame like a tent-flap,
As we slip in unseen.

A man cannot tread like a woman,
Nor a woman step out like a man.
The ghost of each through the leaves of shadow
Moves as it can.

But the Morning Star and the Evening Star
Pitch tents of flame
Where we foregather like gypsies, none knowing
How the other came.

I ask for nothing except to slip
In the tent of the Holy Ghost
And be there in the house of the cloven flame,
Guest of the Host.

Be with me there, my woman,
Be bodily there.
Then let the flame wrap round us
Like a snare.

Be there along with me, oh men!
Reach across the hearth,
And laugh with me, while the woman rests,
For all we are worth.

The man had sung this hymn over several times, halting and forgetting, his pure, burning voice faltering out; then the low, rather husky voice of Ramón, with a subtler intensity, coming in, as if heard from the centre of a shell; then again the sudden ripping sound of the true singer's tenor, going like a flame through the blood.

Her mozo, a man-servant, had followed her into the garden, and sat at a distance on his heels, under a tree, with his back to the trunk, like a crouching shadow clothed in white. His toes spread dark and hard, in his open huaraches, and the black braid of his hat-string hung against his dark cheek. For the rest he was pure white, the white cotton tight on his thighs.

When the singing had finished above, and the drum was silent, and even the voices speaking in low tones, were silent, her mozo looked up at Kate, with his black hat-string dangling at his chin, his black eyes shining, and a timid sort of smile on his face.

"Està muy bien, Patrona?" he said shyly. "It is good, isn't it, Mistress?"

"It is very good," she replied, with the infallible echo. But there were conflicting feelings in her breast, and the man knew it.

He looked so young, when he smiled that gay, shy, excited little smile. Something of the eternal child in him. But a child

that could harden in an instant into a savage man, revengeful and brutal. And a man always fully sex-alive, for the moment innocent in the fulness of sex, not in the absence. And Kate thought to herself, as she had thought before, that there were more ways than one of "becoming again as a little child."

But the man had a sharp, watchful look in the corner of his eye: to see if she were feeling some covert hostility. He wanted her to acquiesce in the hymn, in the drum, in the whole mood. Like a child he wanted her to acquiesce. But if she were going to be hostile, he would be quick to be first in the hostility. Her hostile judgment would make a pure enemy of him.

Ah, all men were alike!

At that moment the man stood up, with soft suddenness, and she heard Cipriano's voice from the balcony above:

"What is it, Lupe?"

"Està la Patrona," answered the servant.

Kate rose to her feet and looked up. She saw the head and the naked shoulders of Cipriano above the parapet of the balcony.

"I will come up," she said.

And slowly she went through the great iron gates into the passage-way. Lupe, following, bolted the doors behind her.

On the terrace above she found Ramón and Cipriano both with their upper bodies naked, waiting for her in silence. She was embarrassed.

"I waited to hear the new hymn," she said.

"And how does it seem to you?" asked Ramón, in Spanish.

"I like it," she said.

"Let us sit down," said Ramón, still in Spanish. He and she sat in the cane rocking-chairs: Cipriano stood by the wall of the terrace.

She had come to make a sort of submission: to say she didn't want to go away. But finding them both in the thick of their Quetzalcoatl mood, with their manly breasts uncovered, she was not very eager to begin. They made her feel like an intruder. She did not pause to realise that she *was* one.

"We don't meet in your Morning Star, apparently, do we!" she said, mocking, but with a slight quaver.

A deeper silence seemed suddenly to hold the two men.

"And I suppose a woman is really *de trop,* even here, when two men are together."

But she faltered a bit in the saying. Cipriano, she knew, was baffled and stung when she taunted him.

Ramón answered her, with the gentleness that could come straight out of his heart: but still in Spanish:

"Why, Cousin, what is it?"

Her lip quivered, as she suddenly said:

"I don't really want to go away from you."

Ramón looked swiftly at Cipriano, then said:

"I know you don't."

But the gentle protective tone of his voice only made Kate rebel again. She brimmed over with sudden tears, crying:

"You don't really want me."

"Yes, I want you!—Verdad! Verdad!" exclaimed Cipriano, in his low, secret, almost muttering voice.

And even amid her tears, Kate was thinking to herself: *What a fraud I am! I know all the time it is I who don't altogether want them. I want myself to myself. But I can fool them so they shan't find out.*

For she heard the hot, phallic passion in Cipriano's voice.

Then came the voice of Ramón, like a chill:

"It is you who don't want," he said, in English this time. "You needn't commit yourself to *us*. Listen to your own best desire."

"And if it tells me to go away?" she flashed, defiant through the end of her tears.

"Then go! Oh, certainly go!"

Suddenly her tears came afresh.

"I knew you didn't really want me," she wept.

Then Cipriano's voice said, with a hot, furtive softness of persuasion:

"You are not his! He would not tell you!"

"That is very true," said Ramón. "Don't listen to me!"

He spoke in Spanish. And Kate glanced up sharply through her tears, to see him going quietly, but swiftly, away.

She wiped her face, suddenly calm. Then she looked with wet eyes at Cipriano. He was standing erect and alert, like a little fighting male, and his eyes glowed black and uncannily as he met her wet, limpid glance.

Yes, she was a bit afraid of him too, with his inhuman black eyes.

"You don't want me to go, do you?" she pleaded.

A slow, almost foolish smile came over his face, and his body was slightly convulsed. Then came his soft-tongued Indian speech, as if all his mouth were soft, saying in Spanish, but with the "r" sound almost lost:

"*Yo! Yo!*"—his eyebrows lifted with queer mock surprise, and a little convulsion went through his body again. "*Te quiero mucho! Mucho te quiero! Mucho! Mucho!* I like you very much! Very much!"

It sounded so soft, so soft-tongued, of the soft, wet, hot blood, that she shivered a little.

"You won't let me go!" she said to him.

A NOTE ON THE TYPE IN WHICH THIS BOOK IS SET

The type in which this book has been set (on the Linotype) is Old Style No. 1. In design, the face is of English origin, by MacKellar, Smith and Jordan, and bears the workmanlike quality and freedom from "frills" characteristic of English old styles in the period prior to the introduction of the "modern" letter. It gives an evenly textured page that may be read with a minimum of fatigue. Old Style No. 1 was one of the first faces designed and cut by the Linotype Company, and it is still one of the most popular.

COMPOSED BY THE VAIL-BALLOU PRESS, INC.,
BINGHAMTON, NEW YORK
PRINTED AND BOUND BY H. WOLFF, NEW YORK

A NOTE ON THE TYPE IN
WHICH THIS BOOK IS SET

The type in which this book has been set (on the
Linotype) is Old Style No. 7. In design, the face
is of English origin, but based on the Scotch and
Jenson, and hence . . . modernized quality . . . the
freedom from . . . fully . . . . . . of the Scotch, a
scale in the printed pages . . . the sharpness of the
"modern" letter. It gives an . . . distinguished page
that may be read with ease at most of . . . Old
Style No. 7 was one of the most faces designed and
cut by the Linotype Company, and it is still one of
the most popular.

COMPOSED BY THE VAIL-BALLOU PRESS, INC.
BINGHAMTON, NEW YORK
PRINTED AND BOUND BY H. WOLFF, NEW YORK